The Palynology and Micropalaeontology of Boundaries

Special Publication reviewing procedures

The Society makes every effort to ensure that the scientific and production quality of its books matches that of its journals. Since 1997, all book proposals have been refereed by specialist reviewers as well as by the Society's Books Editorial Committee. If the referees identify weaknesses in the proposal, these must be addressed before the proposal is accepted.

Once the book is accepted, the Society has a team of Book Editors (listed above) who ensure that the volume editors follow strict guidelines on refereeing and quality control. We insist that individual papers can only be accepted after satisfactory review by two independent referees. The questions on the review forms are similar to those for *Journal of the Geological Society*. The referees' forms and comments must be available to the Society's Book Editors on request.

Although many of the books result from meetings, the editors are expected to commission papers that were not presented at the meeting to ensure that the book provides a balanced coverage of the subject. Being accepted for presentation at the meeting does not guarantee inclusion in the book.

Geological Society Special Publications are included in the ISI Index of Scientific Book Contents, but they do not have an impact factor, the latter being applicable only to journals.

More information about submitting a proposal and producing a Special Publication can be found on the Society's web site: www.geolsoc.org.uk.

It is recommended that reference to all or part of this book should be made in one of the following ways:

BEAUDOIN, A. B. & HEAD, M. J. (eds) 2004. *The Palynology and Micropalaeontology of Boundaries*. Geological Society, London, Special Publications, **230**.

MEI, S., HENDERSON, C. M. & CAO, C. 2004. Conodont sample-population approach to defining the base of the Changhsingian Stage, Lopingian Series, Upper Permian. *In*: BEAUDOIN, A. B. & HEAD, M. J. (eds) 2004. *The Palynology and Micropalaeontology of Boundaries*. Geological Society, London, Special Publications, **230**, 105–121.

GEOLOGICAL SOCIETY SPECIAL PUBLICATION NO. 230

The Palynology and Micropalaeontology of Boundaries

EDITED BY

A. B. BEAUDOIN

Provincial Museum of Alberta, Canada

and

M. J. HEAD

University of Cambridge, UK

2004
Published by
The Geological Society
London

THE GEOLOGICAL SOCIETY

The Geological Society of London (GSL) was founded in 1807. It is the oldest national geological society in the world and the largest in Europe. It was incorporated under Royal Charter in 1825 and is Registered Charity 210161.

The Society is the UK national learned and professional society for geology with a worldwide Fellowship (FGS) of 9000. The Society has the power to confer Chartered status on suitably qualified Fellows, and about 2000 of the Fellowship carry the title (CGeol). Chartered Geologists may also obtain the equivalent European title, European Geologist (EurGeol). One fifth of the Society's fellowship resides outside the UK. To find out more about the Society, log on to www.geolsoc.org.uk.

The Geological Society Publishing House (Bath, UK) produces the Society's international journals and books, and acts as European distributor for selected publications of the American Association of Petroleum Geologists (AAPG), the American Geological Institute (AGI), the Indonesian Petroleum Association (IPA), the Geological Society of America (GSA), the Society for Sedimentary Geology (SEPM) and the Geologists' Association (GA). Joint marketing agreements ensure that GSL Fellows may purchase these societies' publications at a discount. The Society's online bookshop (accessible from www.geolsoc.org.uk) offers secure book purchasing with your credit or debit card.

To find out about joining the Society and benefiting from substantial discounts on publications of GSL and other societies worldwide, consult www.geolsoc.org.uk, or contact the Fellowship Department at: The Geological Society, Burlington House, Piccadilly, London W1J 0BG: Tel. +44 (0)20 7434 9944; Fax +44 (0)20 7439 8975; E-mail: enquiries@geolsoc.org.uk.

For information about the Society's meetings, consult *Events* on www.geolsoc.org.uk. To find out more about the Society's Corporate Affiliates Scheme, write to enquiries@geolsoc.org.uk.

Published by The Geological Society from:
The Geological Society Publishing House
Unit 7, Brassmill Enterprise Centre
Brassmill Lane
Bath BA1 3JN, UK
(*Orders*: Tel. +44 (0)1225 445046
         Fax +44 (0)1225 442836)

Online bookshop: http://bookshop.geolsoc.org.uk

British Library Cataloguing in Publication Data
A catalogue record for this book is available from the British Library.

ISBN 1-86239-160-2

Typeset by Tradespools, Frome, UK

Printed by Antony Rowe Ltd, Chippenham, UK

Distributors
USA
  AAPG Bookstore
  PO Box 979
  Tulsa
  OK 74101-0979
  USA
Orders: Tel. + 1 918 584-2555
        Fax +1 918 560-2652
        E-mail: bookstore@aapg.org

India
  Affiliated East-West Press PVT Ltd
  G-1/16 Ansari Road, Daryaganj,
  New Delhi 110 002
  India
Orders: Tel. +91 11 327-9113
        Fax +91 11 326-0538
        E-mail: affiliat@vsnl.net.com

Japan
  Kanda Book Trading Company
  Cityhouse Tama 204
  Tsurumaki 1-3-10
  Tama-shi, Tokyo 206-0034
  Japan
Orders: Tel. +81 (0)423 57-7650
        Fax +81 (0)423 57-7651
        Email: geokanda@ma.kcom.ne.jp

Contents

Preface   vii

BEAUDOIN, A. B. & HEAD, M. J. Drawing a line in the sand: identifying and characterizing boundaries in the geological record   1

MACLEOD, N. Identifying Phanerozoic extinction controls: statistical considerations and preliminary results   11

DORAN, N. A., ARNOLD, A. J., PARKER, W. C. & HUFFER, F. W. Deviation from Red Queen behaviour at stratigraphic boundaries: evidence for directional recovery   35

ZHANG, S. & BARNES, C. R. Late Cambrian and Early Ordovician conodont communities from platform and slope facies, western Newfoundland: a statistical approach   47

ZHANG, S. & BARNES, C. R. Conodont bio-events, cladistics and response to glacio-eustasy, Ordovician–Silurian boundary through Llandovery, Anticosti Basin, Québec   73

MEI, S., HENDERSON, C. M. & CAO, C. Conodont sample-population approach to defining the base of the Changhsingian Stage, Lopingian Series, Upper Permian   105

MCLEAN, D., OWENS, B. & BODMAN, D. Palynostratigraphy of the Upper Carboniferous Langsettian–Duckmantian Stage boundary in Britain   123

NIKITENKO, B. L. & MICKEY, M. B. Foraminifera and ostracodes across the Pliensbachian–Toarcian boundary in the Arctic Realm (stratigraphy, palaeobiogeography and biofacies)   137

HUNT, C. O. Palynostratigraphy of the classic Portland and Purbeck sequences of Dorset, southern England, and the correlation of Jurassic–Cretaceous boundary beds in the Tethyan and Boreal realms   175

HART, M. B. The mid-Cenomanian non-sequence: a micropalaeontological detective story   187

SIKORA, P. J., HOWE, R. W., GALE, A. S. & STEIN, J. A. Chronostratigraphy of proposed Turonian–Coniacian (Upper Cretaceous) stage boundary stratotypes: Salzgitter-Salder, Germany, and Wagon Mound, New Mexico, USA   207

FERNÁNDEZ-MARRÓN, M. T., LÓPEZ-MARTÍNEZ, N., FONOLLÁ-OCETE, J. F. & VALLE-HERNÁNDEZ, M. F. The palynological record across the Cretaceous–Tertiary boundary in differing palaeogeographical settings from the southern Pyrenees, Spain   243

GEDL, P. Dinoflagellate cyst record of the deep-sea Cretaceous–Tertiary boundary at Uzgruň, Carpathian Mountains, Czech Republic   257

VAN EETVELDE, Y. & DUPUIS, C. Upper Palaeocene and Lower Eocene interval in the Dieppe–Hampshire Basin: biostratigraphic analysis based on pyritized diatoms   275

ELEWA, A. M. T. & MORSI, A.-M. M. Palaeobiotope analysis and palaeoenvironmental reconstruction of the Palaeocene–Early Eocene ostracodes from east-central Sinai, Egypt   293

GEDL, P. Dinoflagellate cyst record of the Eocene–Oligocene boundary succession in flysch deposits at Leluchów, Carpathian Mountains, Poland   309

GUERSTEIN, G. R., GULER, M. V. & CASADÍO, S. Palynostratigraphy and palaeoenvironments across the Oligocene–Miocene boundary within the Centinela Formation, southwestern Argentina   325

Index   345

Caption for cover

This is one of the most spectacular and well-known views in the Canadian Rockies: Cirrus Mountain and the Weeping Wall seen from the Big Bend viewpoint in northern Banff National Park, Alberta.

Several important boundaries, both geological and ecological, are evident in this image. The distinct break in slope across the centre, edged by trees, marks the boundary between the Upper Devonian and Lower Mississippian. The steep lower slopes of Cirrus Mountain are formed in grey limestone of the Upper Devonian Palliser Formation. These cliffs are known as the Weeping Wall, so called for the number of waterfalls that cascade down the face. The more gently sloping mid-slopes of Cirrus Mountain are formed by shales of the Banff Formation. The upper slopes are formed from the more resistant dark grey cliff-forming rocks of the Rundle Group. Cirrus Mountain rises to 3215 masl, giving almost 1600 m of relief in this view. To the left of the main peak, in the notch, lies the Mount Coleman normal fault, with the lower peak at the far left capped by rocks of the Palliser Formation. This three-part geological sequence (Palliser–Banff–Rundle) occurs widely in the Front Ranges and in places, as here, the Main Ranges of the Canadian Rockies.

The treeline, an important modern ecological boundary, is also well marked along the slopes of Cirrus Mountain. In this area, the upper subalpine forest is dominated by Engelmann spruce (*Picea engelmannii*) with some Rocky Mountain Sub-alpine Fir (*Abies bifolia*). Whitebark pine (*Pinus albicaulis*) is often a component of the treeline zone. In this view southward, down the North Saskatchewan River valley, the valley floor lies at about 1600 masl. The Icefields Parkway (Hwy 93), a major tourist route, parallels the river.

Photo credits: David Gummer, Provincial Museum of Alberta, June 2002. © 2004 Provincial Museum of Alberta.

Preface

This book arose from a special session sponsored by the Canadian Association of Palynologists, which was held at the Geological Association of Canada–Mineralogical Association of Canada Joint Annual Meeting in Saskatoon in 2002. The session featured seven papers and a poster. It was an interesting and well-attended session, providing a fine opportunity to explore some imaginative and thought-provoking research. The presentations illustrated many approaches to the study of boundaries, and the participants were enthusiastic about the prospects for publication. It was clear from our research that no similarly focused book was available. Given the variety of approaches and applications of boundary problems and the centrality of boundary issues in many geoscience projects, a compilation volume seemed particularly timely. As conveners of the special session, we undertook to steer the project through the publication process.

We also solicited papers from people who were not able to attend the conference, and received a tremendous response. The 16 papers in this volume provide a revealing and extensive survey of the ways in which identification and characterization of boundaries are approached in the many different branches of palynology and micropalaeontology. The papers span geological intervals from the Cambrian to the Miocene, and feature most major micropalaeontological indicators, including conodonts, pollen, spores, diatoms, dinoflagellates, foraminifera and ostracodes. Although the original session had a strong Canadian and North American focus, the papers included here have a much broader geographical range, and include contributions from Poland, Egypt, Belgium, Argentina and the United Kingdom. Boundary problems are evidently not constrained by political boundaries!

The sponsoring organization, the Canadian Association of Palynologists or Association Canadienne des Palynologues (CAP), was founded in 1979. CAP is primarily a newsletter organization, producing two issues a year. The CAP website (*http://www.scirpus.ca/cap/cap.shtml*) also promotes communication among the widely scattered membership and serves as an archive for palynology-related articles and items from the Newsletter. CAP fosters interest in palynology through many activities, including participation in geoscience meetings and encouraging publications, such as this volume.

Although numbers fluctuate, CAP has a core of around 50 members. Participants are drawn from all branches of palynology and work in all geological eras. CAP counts among its members many distinguished Canadian geoscientists. Recently, the Association has also attracted members from other micropalaeontological fields. In common with all science in Canada, CAP has been affected by recent economic downturns. Nevertheless, CAP remains a vibrant and active geoscience association, as the successful compilation of this volume illustrates.

The production of this book has involved many people from different organizations. The Provincial Museum of Alberta supported the assembly of the volume by covering mailing and courier costs. We thank the authors for their patience and co-operation during the assembly process, and the many reviewers for their insightful and authoritative comments on the manuscripts. We are most grateful to the Geological Society for its support and encouragement throughout this project, and in particular John Gregory and Angharad Hills, for their advice and patience.

On a personal level, ABB thanks Yves Beaudoin for tolerating semi-permanent piles of manuscripts on the dining-room table and for cheerfully 'ticking off' reference lists during winter evenings. MJH is indebted, as ever, to his family for their support.

Finally, we hope this volume will promote discussion and stimulate additional research on the fascinating practical problems and theoretical issues posed by boundary identification and characterization. If, 10 years hence, we can contemplate convening another session with new research built on the solid foundation of the work described here, we and the authors will have done our jobs.

Drawing a line in the sand: identifying and characterizing boundaries in the geological record

ALWYNNE B. BEAUDOIN[1] & MARTIN J. HEAD[2]

[1] Quaternary Environments, Provincial Museum of Alberta, 12845-102nd Avenue, Edmonton, Alberta, T5N 0M6, Canada (e-mail: Alwynne.Beaudoin@gov.ab.ca)
[2] Department of Geography, University of Cambridge, Downing Place, Cambridge, CB2 3EN, UK (e-mail: mh300@cam.ac.uk)

Abstract: The identification and characterization of boundaries is a fundamental activity in geoscience. Spatial and temporal boundaries are rarely sharp but are more usually zones of transition, which may have variable characteristics. The examination of palynological and micropalaeontological data is often crucial for the delineation of geological boundaries, especially for the definition of Global Boundary Stratotype Sections and Points (GSSPs). The sixteen papers in this volume highlight many productive methodological approaches to boundary identification. This essay reviews the theoretical background to boundary identification in geology, and provides the contextual perspective for the subsequent papers.

Much of geoscience has to do with classification, of organisms, of rocks, or of processes. Inevitably, classification devolves into an exercise in drawing boundaries: putting a limit on what is included and what is not. In the geological record, this exercise takes place in three dimensions, with space and time interacting to produce a plethora of boundaries and boundary definitions. Although conventionally, on stratigraphic charts, for example, temporal boundaries are often shown as sharp lines, in reality they are rarely so. Similarly, spatial boundaries on maps are seldom as abrupt as they are drawn. Process boundaries are yet more subtle and usually less clear. Indeed, even to speak of 'a boundary' is contentious, since boundaries come in many forms and types. Boundaries are more often intervals or spaces of transition, leaving plenty of room for argument over their placement. Perhaps for this reason, some of the more truculent and long-lasting debates in geology have been over the positioning and identification of boundaries. Drawing a line in the sand may seem a simple exercise but turns out to be fraught with complexities!

Boundary definitions

In geoscience, the criteria for identifying chronostratigraphic, biostratigraphic and lithostratigraphic units are outlined in rules set up by international agreement, such as the International Stratigraphic Guide (Salvador 1994), or

guidelines such as the North American Stratigraphic Code (North American Commission on Stratigraphic Nomenclature 1983), or the Stratigraphic Procedure (Rawson et al. 2002). The demarcation of boundaries is generally a consequence of the identification of units, rather than the other way round. Historically, the identification of boundaries has often arisen from the practical exigencies of geological mapping: the need to produce visual representations of geology, primarily based on sections or surface exposures. Boundaries, therefore, were often synonymous with the limits of mappable units, that were generally field-identified on the basis of lithology. This approach gave rise to the designation of 'body stratotypes', a methodology that proved limiting for the subdivision of geological time because of gaps in the rock record (Harland et al. 1990).

Modern geochronology emphasizes boundaries, especially lower stage boundaries, rather than units, as fundamental for subdivision and correlation (Remane 2003). Under the auspices of the International Commission on Stratigraphy (ICS), various subcommissions have been established to examine the placement of particularly critical temporal boundaries in the geological record (see list in Gradstein & Ogg 2003). Considerable effort has been devoted to the establishment of Global Boundary Stratotype Sections and Points (GSSPs), with more than 40 defined so far (Gradstein et al. undated). For each boundary, a type section and a specific

From: BEAUDOIN, A.B. & HEAD, M.J. (eds) 2004. *The Palynology and Micropalaeontology of Boundaries.* Geological Society, London, Special Publications, **230**, 1–10. 0305-8719/04/$15 © The Geological Society of London 2004.

point within that section are chosen by international agreement as a means to define the boundary formally. The type section is therefore a particular section at an identified location (ICS 2004). Although parastratotype sections may be established at considerable convenience to local and regional stratigraphers, ultimately all securely identified boundaries must be correlatable to the GSSP. In practice, almost all GSSPs are defined from shallow-marine sediments. Macrofossil biostratigraphy is used for many GSSP definitions, particularly in the Mesozoic (see list in ICS 2004). However, changes in micropalaeontological indicators – especially conodonts, calcareous nannofossils, and foraminifera – often underpin these definitions. Micropalaeontology is becoming increasingly important, particularly for GSSPs in the Cenozoic and Palaeozoic, due to the more continuous nature of microfossil recovery. Since it acts as an exemplar, the selection of a type section is often a difficult matter, and candidate sections are minutely scrutinised (see **Sikora** *et al.* and **Mei** *et al.*). The establishment of a GSSP rarely ends discussion or extinguishes debate; GSSPs may be challenged, re-examined, and defended (**Zhang & Barnes** *a*).

Boundary types

Surprisingly, despite all the attention paid to boundaries, there is no cohesive theoretical treatment of them in the geological literature, although stratigraphic principles have been widely discussed (e.g. Hedberg 1976; Salvador 1994; Remane 2003; Walsh 2004). This situation differs from ecology, where there is an emerging body of literature dealing with boundary theory (see Gosz 1991, and Cadenasso *et al.* 2003*a*, 2003*b*). Because ecology deals with living organisms and their environment, this theoretical approach is also applicable to palynology and micropalaeontology. Strayer *et al.* (2003) distinguish two major types of boundaries: investigative and tangible boundaries. Investigative boundaries are those that are imposed by practical or administrative considerations and often have no physical expression in the landscape. Investigative boundaries can also occur when language barriers preclude discussion or access to information. **Nikitenko & Mickey**, for example, review an enormous quantity of literature from Russia, which has not hitherto been accessible to people who do not read Russian. Spatially speaking, tangible boundaries are associated with some biotic change, environmental discontinuity, or landscape expression. It is the exploration of tangible boundaries with

which this volume is primarily concerned. However, it is worth noting that some geological boundaries may be a consequence of investigative boundaries, where research or analyses are constrained by jurisdictional or political limits, such as those that confine national geological surveys. Establishing boundaries may be more than an esoteric exercise; boundary definitions may have important management implications, as in the establishment of ecological reserves, or legal consequences, as in the definition of continental margins (e.g. Hedberg 1979).

Spatial boundaries differ in type and degree. Boundaries may be abrupt or gradual, solid or permeable, permanent or ephemeral, constant or fluctuating, stationary or moving, narrow or broad, relatively straight or highly convoluted. Where a boundary is defined by a physical landscape expression or environmental discontinuity, its character may affect the way in which organisms react to it. Moreover, conditions that form a boundary for one type of organism may have no impact on another. Physical boundaries can also act as a filter, only allowing certain organisms to pass through. For these reasons, the identification and characterization of a boundary through biotic indicators may depend on what organism is being examined as a proxy and the sensitivity of that organism to change. Boundaries may also regulate flows of materials or energy (Cadenesso *et al.* 2003*b*). Where a boundary is defined by a perturbation, the magnitude, extent, and duration of that perturbation may influence biotic response. Some biota may show considerable complacency or resiliency until critical threshold values are crossed.

Analogues from modern ecological and environmental boundaries

The identification of boundaries on the modern landscape provides many examples of these different types. Here, we can examine boundaries in the simplest spatial cases, with the complication of geological time removed. However, the identification of boundaries across the landscape, and the characterization of transitions, provides analogies for the 'space for time' substitution which is the foundation of the 'present is the key to the past' approach to geoscience. Some boundaries are obvious, the land–sea transition, for example, and have long been a focus of research. State-change boundaries, such as the water–atmosphere or ice–water interfaces, are also clearly marked. Other boundaries, such as temperature limits, are more subtle and less visible. These boundaries are often formed when the gradient or rate-of-change of a parameter becomes steep (Cadenesso *et al.* 2003*a*). Process boundaries have been a research focus for decades, especially with respect to fluid dynamics in fluvial (Thornes 1979) and aeolian (e.g. Walker & Nickling 2002) systems. The recognition that unique suites of processes occur at boundaries also permeates meteorology and climatology (e.g. Oke 1993, 1997) and soil science (e.g. Belnap *et al.* 2003).

Despite their definition with respect to the present landscape, spatial boundaries are usually dynamic and do often also incorporate a time dimension, albeit short term. Boundaries that are formed by physical discontinuities, such as breaks in slope, tend to have greater longevity and be fixed to a specific landscape position. Other types of boundaries, including process and biotic boundaries, however, are often more mobile and short lived. They may oscillate or fluctuate around a mean position on several scales from diurnal, such as tidal limits, to subseasonal, such as wetland margins (Shay & Shay 1986; Kantrud *et al.* 1989), to seasonal, such as the active layer–permafrost boundary (French 1993). Other ecological boundaries may move at decadal or century scales and can often be directional. These may include, for example, the migration front for plant species, such as the post-glacial expansion of lodgepole pine in western North America (MacDonald & Cwynar 1985). Boundaries which are most likely to have correlates in the geological record are ones where the mean position is relatively fixed for a long time, or where the directional shift is accompanied by distinctive biotic changes.

Of all modern ecological boundaries, perhaps none is as well studied as the treeline, both the alpine (altitudinal) treeline and the northern boreal (latitudinal) treeline (e.g. Frenzel *et al.* 1996; Arno & Hammerly 1984). This boundary exemplifies many of the issues of identification and characterization that pervade ecological and geological boundary definition. Wardle (1974, p. 396) emphasized that 'timberline is the sharpest temperature-dependent boundary in nature', and thus its location is climate-related. But, because of the physiological plasticity and response of trees to environmental stress, the treeline is not, in fact, a sharp line, but rather a zone representing a complex transition between forested and treeless areas. Strictly, the alpine treeline (or tree limit) is the upper elevation limit of krummholz forms of nominally arboreal species, and the timberline is the limit of standing tree growth (Wardle 1974). Between

these limits, in the krummholz zone, trees often occur in isolated 'tree islands' and may be deformed, flagged, or stunted. Where elevational controls are sharp, as on steep slopes, the alpine treeline zone can be quite narrow, in contrast to the northern boreal treeline zone, which is often broad. Here, an expanse of 'forest-tundra' is identified, which in northern Canada may be up to about 200 km wide (Timoney *et al.* 1992). Thus, the boundary between forested and non-forested areas represents the interplay of topographical, latitudinal, biotic, temporal and ecological factors.

Such definitional minutiae may seem picayune, but they have significant implications for interpretation of palynological data. Because altitudinal treeline shows a strong correlation with growing season temperature, many studies have attempted to characterize its modern position through palynological signatures, and then use these signatures to interpret past pollen records as a 'proxy' temperature signal (e.g. Beaudoin 1986; Pellatt *et al.* 2000). There are several problems to this approach, not least being the assumption that the present boundary is in equilibrium with, or controlled by, current conditions and thus is a surrogate measure for contemporary conditions. But because tree response to a perturbation or a temperature change may be lagged, this assumption may be suspect. The response may also vary depending on the floristic composition of the treeline, because not all taxa will necessarily react in the same way. Computational issues may also over-simplify the situation. Usually, some form of regression between modern pollen signatures and growing season temperatures is performed and the results used to interpret signatures from past records. This approach forces a one-to-one correspondence (albeit with some probability attached) with the values from the past record, and does not allow for the fact that the character of the treeline may have varied over time, for example, through floristic change. The inferred record may therefore appear more sharply focused and delineated than it probably was. Modern analogies are always laden with such ambiguities, but nevertheless remain the best approach for ecological or environmental boundary characterization.

Geological boundaries

In the geological past, boundary identification becomes even more complex with the addition of the time dimension. The same dichotomies apply, although we can also add swift or slow, abrupt or gradual, continuous or gapped to the mix. We can also distinguish between abiotic (lithostratigraphic) and biotic (biostratigraphic) boundaries. Biostratigraphic boundaries are analogous to modern ecological boundaries because they are defined by changes in biota. These could, of course, coincide with lithostratigraphic changes, but this need not be the case. These boundaries can be both spatially and temporally transgressive, and may be of local or regional significance. Critical boundaries, such as those that define stages, must be of more than local extent (Remane 2003). This can make their identification in geological records problematic, not least because geological studies often have a very limited spatial view. Often, boundary inferences are made from samples obtained from one or a few cores or boreholes. So the geological or subsurface view of boundaries is often highly patchy and discontinuous and represents only a limited subset of the available environmental variance. Where multiple views are available (e.g. **Zhang & Barnes** *a*, **Nikitenko & Mickey**), it may be important to tease out the ecological variability, such as shallow v. deep water or warm water v. cool water, so that the more substantive regionally or globally significant variation can be clearly identified.

Techniques for boundary identification

Boundaries in the geological record are identified using many techniques, but the examination of palynological and micropalaeontological data is often crucial. Perhaps the easiest boundaries to identify are those where there is an abrupt lithostratigraphic change or where there is a clear temporal break in the record – as at an erosional unconformity. The identification of chronostratigraphic boundaries may be more difficult, and in some cases relies on biotic events. Thus, chronostratigraphic and biostratigraphic boundaries may coincide. Significant biostratigraphic changes are often marked by the appearance or disappearance of important indicator taxa or, more often, assemblage changes.

The reliance on indicator taxa for boundary definition raises questions of consistency, fidelity and reproducibility, especially when these taxa form only a small part of an assemblage. For example, in a multi-core pollen study of a well-defined Holocene temporal level from Lake O'Hara (Beaudoin & Reasoner 1992) showed that minor taxa (present as less than 1% of the assemblage) were unreliable indicators, because their occurrence was highly variable and they did not show high fidelity between contemporaneous samples. Where a boundary is defined by

a discontinuity, it may also act as a filter, adding further complications to the recognition of indicator taxa. The incorporation of biotic remains in sediments may be complicated by taphonomic factors, such as downslope transport (**Zhang & Barnes** *a*), and by post-depositional factors affecting preservation (**Van Eetvelde & Dupuis**).

Sampling factors also influence the potential for boundary identification. First and last appearance of taxa in a stratigraphic record may be influenced by how much of the record has been examined, and are fundamentally statements of probability, associated with confidence limits (Holland 2003). Over millennia, geological processes, primarily erosion, reduce the amount of any exposed stratigraphic unit. Hence, only some of the original sediment, and therefore part of the original variability, is available for examination. Thus, the probability of finding remains of any organism is influenced by how much of the sediment unit is left. Peters & Foote (2002), for example, suggest that the evaluation of extinction rates may be influenced by these sampling factors. Using data from marine sedimentary formations, they conclude that derived extinction rates may be spurious, an artefact of the amount of the stratigraphic record available for examination. It may be more difficult therefore to identify boundaries within intervals for which the sedimentary record is slender or poorly preserved.

Numerical or statistical methods are often useful in distinguishing meaningful and consistent biotic changes. These methods are most applicable where large data-sets are available, and they can help to identify patterns in otherwise overwhelming amounts of data. Numerical methods can be used to answer two important biostratigraphic questions. First, given changing assemblages through time or up a stratigraphic section, where are the significant breaks or most important changes? Such judgements can be made qualitatively, by visual inspection for instance, but numerical methods have the advantage of being reproducible, given the same data-set, and following defined rules. Numerical zonation methods have been widely employed in Quaternary palynology to identify assemblages (e.g. Birks & Gordon 1985), especially when stratigraphic constraints are included (Grimm 1987). Pollen zone boundaries may be ecologically or chronostratigraphically important (e.g. **Fernández-Marrón** *et al.*). Second, given several assemblages and some knowledge of contemporaneous environmental conditions, can we make inferences about assemblage-environment linkages or controls?

Such environmental inferences can then be extended to assemblages where the contemporaneous conditions are not well known. Ordination or classification methods have been used to explore these patterns in palynological or micropalaeontological data, using techniques such as cluster analysis or principal components analysis (see Kovach 1989). These techniques can often highlight environmental shifts, such as sea-level or water temperature changes, in complex data. Several studies in this volume, including **Zhang & Barnes** *a*, **Elewa & Morsi**, and **Nikitenko & Mickey**, use numerical methods for this purpose.

Using palynology and micropalaeontology to identify boundaries in the geological record

From the widest perspective, there are certain biological events in the geological past that stand out as being pivotal: the occurrence of the first fossils, the appearance of the first terrestrial fauna, the rise of flowering plants. However, no events have arguably generated more debate than mass extinctions and their causes. By their very nature, extinctions, reflecting significant changes in biota, are often defining events for boundaries. **MacLeod** takes this 'big picture' approach by examining the pattern and periodicity of extinction events shown by marine invertebrate genera through the sweep of Phanerozoic time. He investigates the association between these and the five most widely invoked explanatory factors – bolide impacts, continental flood-basalt eruptions, eustatic changes, and marine anoxia events. His analysis shows that two factors – marine regression and volcanic eruptions – explain most of the observed events. **MacLeod** observes that terrestrial mechanisms provide sufficient control to account for most extinction events through the Phanerozoic. The popular-culture image of extinction, exemplified by startled dinosaurs staring skywards as a flaming fireball approaches, apparently needs some revision!

MacLeod's analysis of extinction intensity through time also leads to some provocative suggestions. Rather than being a steadily declining trend through the Phanerozoic, **MacLeod** shows that the extinction intensity became marked around the end of the Devonian, with a notable reduction in extreme-intensity events around the end of the Triassic. **MacLeod** links these to changes in the global carbon cycle as a consequence of evolutionary events. He offers two possibilities for the causal mechanism: the diversification of land plants in the Late

Palaeozoic and the diversification of phytoplankton in the Late Triassic. This opens intriguing possibilities of linkages and feedback mechanisms between evolutionary events, climate changes, and extinctions – perhaps pointing the way to a more integrated theoretical perspective.

Doran *et al.* also adopt a 'big picture' approach and also examine evolutionary trends, in this case in post-extinction planktonic foraminifera, concentrating on two boundaries, the Cenomanian–Turonian (C–T) and the Cretaceous–Tertiary (K–T). Their concern is with the rate and pattern of faunal recovery after extinction. If extinction is a boundary, it can be regarded as the quintessential filter, only allowing certain life-forms to pass. What happens to the taxa that make it through extinction? **Doran** *et al.*'s analysis shows rapid evolutionary change in foraminifera following these major extinction events. They suggest that this pattern relates to specific characteristics, which they term 'passport' characteristics, that allowed some taxa to pass through or survive the extinction events. These taxa may not necessarily be best adapted to the post-extinction environment, but they form the foundation for subsequent populations.

After much debate, the GSSP for the Cambrian–Ordovician boundary was located at Green Point, western Newfoundland, Canada, and defined on the basis of conodont biostratigraphy (Cooper *et al.* 2001). This GSSP was contentious because of differing opinions about the conodont record, in particular the degree of transport and mixing. To clarify this issue, **Zhang & Barnes** *a* analyse conodont communities associated with different environmental settings, from shallow platform to distal slope, across this boundary in western Newfoundland. They use multivariate statistical techniques to identify consistent patterns and gradational relationships, and show that conodont communities were partitioning the environment according to slope position and water depth. Therefore, conodont community change may reflect sea-level changes affecting water depth, in particular sea-level rise in the Early Ordovician. Overprinted on this are community changes resulting from rapid evolution and diversification. Both factors are important to an evaluation of the conodont record across this boundary.

The end of the Ordovician is marked by the second-most severe mass extinction in the Phanerozoic, resulting in the estimated loss of some 85% of all marine species (Jablonski 1991; Sheehan 2001). This was brought about by a continental glaciation in North Africa that resulted in cooler oceanic temperatures and more aerated bottom waters: changes that had profound implications for marine organisms (Hallam & Wignall 1999; Sheehan 2001). **Zhang & Barnes** *b* have examined the depletion of conodont taxa at the end of the Ordovician, and particularly the nature and timing of their post-extinction recovery. Their analysis of deposits of Early Llandovery (earliest Silurian) age from the essentially complete succession on Anticosti Island, Quebec, has revealed an unexpectedly complex series of speciation, extinction, immigration and emigration events that can be in part correlated to eustatic and other ocean–climate changes. The Anticosti Basin may indeed have been an important centre of evolutionary radiation for conodont animals during the earliest Silurian.

Taxonomic matters often lie at the heart of boundary definitions, as in the study by **Mei** *et al.* They present the case for establishment of a GSSP for the base of the Changhsingian Stage (Upper Permian) at Meishan, China, based on the analysis of conodonts. They suggest that the boundary should be defined at the first appearance of *Clarkina wangi*. This species was established following the authors' examination of conodonts from the Meishan section, using characteristics of the sample-population rather than individuals to distinguish taxa: focusing on carinal morphology. Taxa are defined when the population as a whole exhibits a predominance of the particular morphology. In this instance, the transition from one carinal configuration to another occurs over a narrow interval, allowing the boundary to be relatively well constrained. Their sample-population analysis is an interesting way of approaching a question that is relevant to many micropalaeontological indicators – how much morphological variation can be allowed before a new taxon is recognized?

The Carboniferous System is internationally defined (by GSSPs) at its top and base, but the inter-regional correlation of stages continues to present challenges. The Duckmantian is a European stage within the lower Upper Carboniferous. It overlies the Langsettian Stage, and its base is defined by the base of the Vanderbeckei Marine Band and in a boundary stratotype in Derbyshire, England, UK. The position of this marine band has been correlated with important changes in macro- and microfloral assemblages across northwestern Europe. **McLean** *et al.* have analysed the Duckmantian stratotype in detail, using miospores to characterize the Vanderbeckei Marine Band and the Langsettian–Duckmantian boundary in particular. By then analysing this same marine band in a borehole in the southern North Sea, **McLean** *et al.* have been able to assess the potential of miospores for recognizing the boundary elsewhere. Results show that although the Vanderbeckei Marine Band and can be recognized palynologically, a clear floristic break does not occur at its base. Indeed, a gradual turnover of taxa occurs across the boundary. **McLean** *et al.* conclude that marine flooding events in the Upper Carboniferous coal measures may not exclusively provide the impetus for evolutionary change in the flora, which apparently continued to evolve throughout transgressive–regressive cycles.

In the Lower Jurassic, the Early Toarcian was characterized by a mass-extinction event, marked by rising sea-levels with widespread anoxia, and consequent deposition of black shales (Hallam & Wignall 1999; Harries & Little 1999). **Nikitenko & Mickey** review studies on a broad regional scale from Russia and Alaska, concentrating especially on foraminifera and ostracodes through the Pliensbachian–Toarcian interval. Numerical analysis allows them to identify biogeographical units of ostracodes and foraminifera within the Arctic and Boreal–Atlantic realms. **Nikitenko & Mickey** distinguish consistent patterns of zonation within ostracode and foraminifera that allow correlation both across this region and with the microfossil sequence from Western Europe. In the Early Toarcian in the Arctic, ostracode genera and families completely changed, and more than 80% of the foraminiferal species were replaced. Interestingly, the authors note that the reduction in species and generic diversity began in the Late Pliensbachian in the Arctic – somewhat earlier than in Western Europe.

The exact placement of the Jurassic–Cretaceous boundary remains contentious, largely owing to difficulties in correlating between Tethyan and Boreal realms. These realms occur at a time of marked provincialism in the marine biota, brought about by low global sea-levels. The lowermost stage of the Cretaceous is the Berriasian, whose stratotype is at Berrias, France. Correlating this stratotype beyond the Tethys has been problematic, owing to the localized nature of the ammonite fauna. **Hunt** has used dinoflagellate cyst stratigraphy at classic sites in Dorset, southern England, UK, as a means of correlating these sites with the type Berriasian. Dorset was within the Tethyan Realm, but close to the northern Boreal Realm. This has allowed **Hunt** to use miospores to correlate the Dorset sections with the Terschelling Basin in the Netherlands, which is within the Boreal Realm. This approach achieves a novel correlation between the Berriasian, including its base (and hence the Jurassic–Cretaceous boundary), and the ammonite biostratigraphy of the Boreal Realm.

Hart's historical account of the recognition of a mid-Cenomanian non-sequence in the chalk succession of southern England and northern France is a salutary reminder of the practical application of boundary problems. The non-sequence was originally identified during geological studies, especially micropalaeontological work on the foraminifera, associated with the development of the Channel Tunnel. Work throughout southern England and northern France during subsequent decades showed that this non-sequence represents a hiatus, in some places an unconformity, of regional extent. Above it, the foraminifera include a greater abundance of planktonic forms, indicating more open-marine conditions. This study raises some fascinating issues with respect to boundary definitions. Should this non-sequence or depositional break be considered a sequence boundary? Can a boundary be formed by an absence? The definition of a GSSP relies on its identification within a conformable sequence (Walsh 2004), but Hart's study shows that other types of boundaries may also be useful in regional correlations.

Macrofossil biostratigraphy provides one line of evidence for **Sikora** et al. as they tackle an aspect of the Jurassic–Cretaceous boundary – the establishment of a GSSP. To be useful as a standard, a stratotype must be continuous across the interval, be widely correlatable, and be accessible to the scientific community. **Sikora** et al. examine and compare the macrofossil and microfossil biostratigraphy of two sections proposed as potential GSSPs: at Wagon Mound, New Mexico, USA, and Salzgitter-Salder, central Germany. **Sikora** et al. are able to show that different indicator types provide different temporal signatures, and that, more significantly, the micropalaeontological indicators show a different temporal pattern to macrofossil remains. Their study suggests that neither of the proposed stratotypes are likely to be good candidates for a GSSP. This example shows the value of using multiple indicators for boundary characterization.

The Cretaceous–Tertiary (K–T) boundary is perhaps the most studied of all geological boundaries, and probably, because of its well-publicized association with dinosaur extinction, the most well-known outside geoscience (see Alvarez et al. 1980; Hildebrand 1993). It represents a profound disruption to terrestrial and marine ecosystems on a global scale,

although the scale and rate of biotic extinctions is debated.

An intriguing aspect of the K–T transition is the contrast between North American (and Pacific) and European pollen records. North American records reveal a pronounced extinction event near the boundary (Nichols 1996), followed at some sites by a brief increase in fern abundance (the 'fern spike') that is thought to relate to short-term environmental disturbance (Tschudy et al. 1984; Fleming & Nichols 1990; Sweet 2001). In contrast, no appreciable changes have been recorded in pollen records from the Old World, including Europe. To test this apparent lack of change, **Fernández-Marrón** et al. have analysed spore and pollen data from two sections that span the K–T transition in Spain. Because these sections represent differing palaeoenvironmental settings, any effects caused by local factors and taphonomy should be detected. While no noticeable extinctions could be linked to the boundary, a statistical analysis reveals significant differences in assemblage composition. These changes, which include an increase in trilete fern spores across the K–T transition and a reduction in the Danian samples, offer a new means to identify the K–T boundary in terrestrial deposits of the region.

Dinoflagellate cysts are relatively unaffected by short-term environmental disruption, owing to their ability to remain dormant for several years. This presumably explains their continuous record across the K–T boundary, which makes them well suited for studying environmental changes through this interval (Brinkhuis et al. 1998). Most sites presently studied represent shelfal facies (e.g. Brinkhuis & Leereveld 1988; Brinkhuis & Schiøler 1996; Brinkhuis et al. 1998). The study by **Gedl** a examines dinoflagellate cysts at a deep-water site in the Czech Republic, thereby offering a new perspective on this critical boundary. **Gedl** a concludes that a warm, stable, marine climate prevailed across the boundary. Although no major changes in assemblages were found, minor changes might relate to gradual sea-level fall or increasing nutrient availability. A peak abundance of heterotrophic dinoflagellate cysts near the boundary appears to indicate upwelling in this part of the Tethys.

The Palaeocene–Eocene transition is marked by significant changes in many Earth systems, including global climate, with a marked carbon isotope anomaly, and ocean circulation, accompanied by palaeogeographical changes (Norris & Röhl 1999; Zachos et al. 2001). Both marine and terrestrial organisms show considerable evolutionary turnover through this interval (Berggren *et al.* 1998; Hallam & Wignall 1999). Despite the abundant evidence for change, the establishment of a GSSP for the Palaeocene–Eocene is currently subject to vigorous debate (see Aubry *et al.* 1999; Walsh 2004). Two studies in this volume shed further light on this interval.

Van Eetvelde & Dupius use diatoms to examine the Upper Palaeocene to Lower Eocene interval in two localities from northern France. Here, examination of the record is complicated by preservation issues because the diatoms are heavily pyritized, requiring specialized extraction techniques. Nevertheless, three distinct diatom assemblages can be recognized, and these offer the prospect of correlation between the sequences of the Dieppe–Hampshire and North Sea basins.

Elewa & Morsi also examine the Palaeocene–Eocene interval, in this case based on ostracodes recovered from sediment sequences in northeast Egypt. Numerical analysis permits the identification of ecozones, distinguished by environmental parameters, including water depth, temperature, turbulence and dissolved oxygen content. **Elewa & Morsi** conclude that changes in ostracode assemblages were mainly the result of changing local environmental conditions, rather than speciation or extinction. However, they do detect faunal changes probably associated with the Palaeocene–Eocene thermal maximum (Kennett & Stott 1991), which elsewhere is associated with extinctions.

The Eocene–Oligocene transition is generally characterized by falling temperatures and a drop in global sea-level. However, the boundary itself is contentious, owing to disagreements in definition (Berggren *et al.* 1995, pp. 197–198; Brinkhuis & Visscher 1995). It is marked either by the highest occurrence of the foraminiferal genus *Hantkenina* or that of the dinoflagellate cyst *Areosphaeridium diktyoplokum*. The latter datum, which is stratigraphically higher than the former, is used by **Gedl** *b* in his study of dinoflagellate cysts from the Carpathian Mountains of Poland. **Gedl**'s study identifies the position of the Eocene–Oligocene boundary in the Leluchów section, and infers a drop in relative sea-level that might correlate with Early Oligocene eustatic lowering. Sea-surface temperatures are found to drop prior to the Eocene–Oligocene boundary at this site.

The Oligocene–Miocene boundary represents one of the most important eustatic rises in the Cenozoic, with high sea-levels continuing throughout the early Early Miocene (Haq *et al.* 1987, 1988; Hardenbol *et al.* 1998). In South America, a major marine transgression in Patagonia is associated with this event, although its precise dating has remained questionable. **Guerstein** *et al.* have used palynology to assign a Late Oligocene and early Early Miocene age to the marine Centinela Formation deposited near the margin of this transgression. A maximum flooding surface is indicated by high ratios of dinoflagellate cysts in the earliest Miocene.

In conclusion, the sixteen papers summarized here highlight many methodological and definitional issues with boundaries in geology. Although not all problems are resolved, the papers point the way to productive investigative and analytical approaches that may prove worthwhile in other situations.

References

ALVAREZ, L. W., ALVAREZ, W., ASARO, F. & MICHEL, H. V. 1980. Extraterrestrial cause for the Cretaceous–Tertiary extinction. *Science*, **208**, 1095–1108.

ARNO, S. F. & HAMMERLY, R. P. 1984. *Timberline: Mountain and Arctic Forest Frontiers*. The Mountaineers, Seattle, Washington, 304 pp.

AUBRY, M. P., BERGGREN, W. A., VAN COUVERING, J. A. & STEININGER, F. 1999. Problems in chronostratigraphy: stages, series, unit and boundary stratotypes, global stratotype section and point and tarnished golden spikes. *Earth-Science Reviews*, **46(1–2)**, 99–148.

BEAUDOIN, A. B. 1986. Using *Picea/Pinus* ratios from the Wilcox Pass core, Jasper National Park, Alberta, to investigate Holocene timberline fluctuations. *Géographie physique et Quaternaire*, **40**, 145–152.

BEAUDOIN, A. B. & REASONER, M. A. 1992. Evaluation of differential pollen deposition and pollen focussing at three Holocene intervals in Lake O'Hara, Yoho National Park, British Columbia, Canada: intra-lake variability in pollen percentages, concentration and influx. *Review of Palaeobotany and Palynology*, **75**, 103–131.

BELNAP, J., HAWKES, C. V. & FIRESTONE, M. K. 2003. Boundaries in miniature: two examples from soil. *BioScience*, **55**, 739–749.

BERGGREN, W. A., KENT, D. V., SWISHER III, C. C. & AUBRY, M.-P. 1995. A revised Cenozoic geochronology and chronostratigraphy. *In*: BERGGREN, W. A., KENT, D. V. & HARDENBOL, J. (eds) *Geochronology, Time Scales and Global Stratigraphic Correlation*. SEPM Special Publications **54**, Tulsa, Oklahoma, 129–212.

BERGGREN, W. A., LUCAS, S. & AUBRY, M.-P. 1998. Late Paleocene-Early Eocene climatic and biotic evolution: an overview. *In*: AUBRY, M.-P., LUCAS, S. & BERGGREN, W. A. (ed.) *Late Paleocene-Early Eocene Climatic and Biotic Events in the Marine and Terrestrial Records*. Columbia University Press, New York, 1–17.

BIRKS, H. J. B. & GORDON, A. D. 1985. *Numerical Methods in Quaternary Pollen Analysis*. Academic Press, New York, 317 pp.

BRINKHUIS, H. & LEEREVELD, H. 1988. Dinoflagellate cysts from the Cretaceous/Tertiary boundary sequence of El Kef, northwest Tunisia. *Review of Palaeobotany and Palynology*, **56**, 5–19.

BRINKHUIS, H. & SCHIØLER, P. 1996. Palynology of the Geulhemmerberg Cretaceous/Tertiary boundary section (Limburg, SE Netherlands). *Geologie en Mijnbouw*, **75**, 193–213.

BRINKHUIS, H. & VISSCHER, H. 1995. The upper boundary of the Eocene Series: a reappraisal based on dinoflagellate cyst biostratigraphy and sequence stratigraphy. *In*: BERGGREN, W. A., KENT, D. V. & HARDENBOL, J. (eds) *Geochronology, Time Scales and Global Stratigraphic Correlation*. SEPM Special Publications, **54**, Tulsa, Oklahoma, 295–304.

BRINKHUIS, H., BUJAK, J. P., SMIT, J., VERSTEEGH, G. J. M. & VISSCHER, H. 1998. Dinoflagellate-based sea surface temperature reconstructions across the Cretaceous–Tertiary boundary. *Palaeogeography, Palaeoclimatology, Palaeoecology*, **141**, 67–84.

CADENESSO, M. L., PICKETT, S. T. A., WEATHERS, K. C., BELL, S. S., BENNING, T. L., CARREIRO, M. M. & DAWSON, T. E. 2003*a*. An interdisciplinary and synthetic approach to ecological boundaries. *BioScience*, **53**, 717–722.

CADENESSO, M. L., PICKETT, S. T. A., WEATHERS, K. C. & JONES, C. G. 2003*b*. A framework for a theory of ecological boundaries. *BioScience*, **53**, 750–758.

COOPER, R. A., NOWLAN, G. S. & WILLIAMS, S. H. 2001. Global Stratotype Section and Point for the base of the Ordovician system. *Episodes*, **24(1)**, 19–28.

FLEMING, R. F. & NICHOLS, D. J. 1990. Fern-spore abundance anomaly at the Cretaceous–Tertiary Boundary: a regional bioevent in western North America. *In*: KAUFFMAN, E. G. & WALLISER, O. H. (eds) *Extinction Events in Earth History*. Springer Verlag, Berlin and New York, 347–349.

FRENCH, H. M. 1993. Cold-climate processes and landforms. *In*: FRENCH, H. M. & SLAYMAKER, O. (eds) *Canada's Cold Environments*. McGill–Queen's University Press, Montreal and Kingston, Canada, 143–167.

FRENZEL, B., BIRKS, H. H., ALM, T. & VORREN, K. D. (eds) 1996. *Holocene Treeline Oscillations, Dendrochronology and Palaeoclimate*. Paläoklimaforschung Band 20/Palaeoclimate Research Volume, **20**, Special Issue: ESF Project 'European Palaeoclimate and Man' 13. Gustav Fischer Verlag, Stuttgart, Germany, x + 303 pp.

GOSZ, J. R. 1991. Fundamental ecological characteristics of landscape boundaries. *In*: HOLLAND, M. M., RISSER, P. G. & NAIMAN, R. J. (eds) *Ecotones: the Role of Landscape Boundaries in the Management and Restoration of Changing Environments*. Chapman and Hall, New York, 8–30.

GRADSTEIN, F. M., FINNEY, S. C. & OGG, J. G. undated. ICS on Stage. 15 pp, PDF manuscript, World Wide Web Address: www.stratigraphy.org/stage.pdf, last accessed 13 March 2004.

GRADSTEIN, F. M. & OGG, J. G. 2003. International Union of Geological Sciences International Commission on Stratigraphy (ICS) Consolidated Annual Report for 2003. 130 pp, PDF manuscript, World Wide Web Address: www.stratigraphy.org, last accessed 7 February 2004.

GRIMM, E. C. 1987. CONISS: a Fortran 77 program for stratigraphically constrained cluster analysis by the method of incremental sum of squares. *Computers & Geosciences*, **13**, 13–35.

HALLAM, A. & WIGNALL, P. B. 1999. Mass extinctions and sea-level changes. *Earth-Science Reviews*, **48**, 217–250.

HAQ, B. U., HARDENBOL, J. & VAIL, P. R. 1987. Chronology of fluctuating sea levels since the Triassic. *Science*, **235**, 1156–1166.

HAQ, B. U., HARDENBOL, J. & VAIL, P. R. 1988. Mesozoic and Cenozoic chronostratigraphy and cycles of sea-level change. *In*: WILGUS, C. K., HASTINGS, B. S., KENDALL, C. G.St. C., POSAMENTIER, H. W., ROSS, C. A. & VAN WAGONER, J. C. (eds) *Sea-Level Changes: an Integrated Approach*. SEPM Special Publication, **42**. Tulsa, Oklahoma, 71–108, plus one separate chart.

HARDENBOL, J., THIERRY, J., FARLEY, M. B., JACQUIN, T., DE GRACIANSKY, P.-C. & VAIL, P. R. 1998. Mesozoic and Cenozoic sequence chronostratigraphic framework of European basins. *In*: DE GRACIANSKY, P. C., HARDENBOL, J., JACQUIN, T. & VAIL, P. R. (eds) *Mesozoic and Cenozoic Sequence Stratigraphy of European Basins*. SEPM Special Publication, **60**, Tulsa, Oklahoma, 3–29, plus 8 separate charts.

HARLAND, W. B., ARMSTRONG, R. L., COX, A. V., CRAIG, L. E., SMITH, A. G. & SMITH, D. G. 1990. *A Geologic Time Scale 1989*. Cambridge University Press, Cambridge, UK, 262 pp.

HARRIES, P. J. & LITTLE, C. R. S. 1999. The early Toarcian (Early Jurassic) and the Cenomanian-Turonian (Late Cretaceous) mass extinctions: similarities and contrasts. *Palaeogeography, Palaeoclimatology, Palaeoecology*, **154**, 39–66.

HEDBERG, H. D. (ed.) 1976. *International Stratigraphic Guide: a Guide to Stratigraphic Classification, Terminology, and Procedure by International Subcommission on Stratigraphic Classification of IUGS Commission on Stratigraphy*. Wiley, New York, 200 pp.

HEDBERG, H. D. 1979. Ocean floor boundaries. *Science*, **204**, 135–144.

HILDEBRAND, A. R. 1993. The Cretaceous/Tertiary boundary impact (or the dinosaurs didn't have a chance). *Journal of the Royal Astronomical Society of Canada*, **87**, 77–118.

HOLLAND, S. M. 2003. Confidence limits on fossil ranges that account for facies changes. *Paleobiology*, **29**, 468–479.

ICS (International Commission on Stratigraphy) 2004. The Global Boundary Stratotype Section and Point (GSSP). World Wide Web Address: www.stratigraphy.org, last accessed 7 February 2004.

JABLONSKI, D. 1991. Extinctions: a paleontological perspective. *Science*, **253**, 754–757.

KANTRUD, H. A., MILLAR, J. B. & VAN DER VALK, A. G. 1989. Vegetation of wetlands of the prairie pothole region. *In:* VAN DER VALK, A. (ed.) *Northern Prairie Wetlands*. Iowa State University Press, Ames, Iowa, 132–187.

KENNETT, J. P. & STOTT, L. D. 1991. Abrupt deep-sea warming, palaeoeoceanographic changes and benthic extinctions at the end of the Palaeocene. *Nature*, **353**, 225–229.

KOVACH, W. L. 1989. Comparisons of multivariate analytical techniques for use in pre-Quaternary plant palaeoecology. *Review of Palaeobotany and Palynology*, **60**, 255–282.

MACDONALD, G. M. & CWYNAR, L. C. 1985. A fossil pollen based reconstruction of the late Quaternary history of lodgepole pine (*Pinus contorta* ssp. *latifolia*) in the western interior of Canada. *Canadian Journal of Forest Research*, **15**, 1039–1044.

NICHOLS, D. 1996. Vegetational history in Western Interior North America during the Cretaceous–Tertiary transition. *In:* JANSONIUS, J. & MCGREGOR, D. C. (eds) *Palynology: Principles and Applications*. American Association of Stratigraphic Palynologists Foundation, Dallas, Texas, **3**, 1189–1195.

NORRIS, R. D. & RÖHL, U. 1999. Carbon cycling and chronology of climate warming during the Palaeocene/Eocene transition. *Nature*, **401**, 775–778.

North American Commission on Stratigraphic Nomenclature 1983. North American Stratigraphic Code. *American Association of Petroleum Geologists Bulletin*, **67**, 841–875.

OKE, T. R. 1993. *Boundary Layer Climates*. 2nd edition. Routledge, London, 436 pp.

OKE, T. R. 1997. Surface climate processes. *In:* BAILEY, W. G., OKE, T. R. & ROUSE, W. R. (eds) *The Surface Climates of Canada*. McGill–Queen's University Press, Montreal and Kingston, Canada, 21–43.

PELLATT, M. G., SMITH, M. J., MATHEWES, R. W., WALKER, I. R. & PALMER, S. L. 2000. Holocene treeline and climate change in the subalpine zone near Stoyoma Mountain, Cascade Mountains, southwestern British Columbia, Canada. *Arctic, Antarctic and Alpine Research*, **32**, 73–83.

PETERS, S. E. & FOOTE, M. 2002. Determinants of extinction in the fossil record. *Nature*, **416**, 420–424.

RAWSON, P. F., ALLEN, P. M. *et al.* 2002. *Stratigraphical Procedure*. Professional Handbook, Geological Society of London, 57 pp.

REMANE, J. 2003. Chronostratigraphic correlations: their importance for definition of geochronologic units. *Palaeogeography, Palaeoclimatology, Palaeoecology*, **196**, 7–18.

SALVADOR, A. (ed.) 1994. *International Stratigraphic Guide, Second Edition. A Guide to Stratigraphic Classification, Terminology, and Procedure*. International Union of Geological Sciences and the Geological Society of America, 214 pp.

SHAY, J. M. & SHAY, C. T. 1986. Prairie marshes in western Canada, with specific reference to the ecology of 5 emergent macrophytes. *Canadian Journal of Botany*, **64**, 443–454.

SHEEHAN, P. M. 2001. The Late Ordovician mass extinction. *Annual Review of Earth and Planetary Sciences*, **29**, 331–364

STRAYER, D. L., POWER, M. E., FAGAN, W. F., PICKETT, S. T. A. & BELNAP, J. 2003. A classification of ecological boundaries. *BioScience*, **53**, 723–729.

SWEET, A. R. 2001. Plants, a yardstick for measuring the environmental consequences of the Cretaceous–Tertiary boundary event. *Geoscience Canada*, **28(3)**, 127–138.

THORNES, J. 1979. Fluvial processes. *In:* EMBLETON, C. & THORNES, J. (eds) *Process in Geomorphology*. Edward Arnold, London, 213–271.

TIMONEY, K. P., LA ROI, G. H., ZOLTAI, S. C. & ROBINSON, A. L. 1992. The high subarctic forest-tundra of northwestern Canada: position, width, and vegetation gradients in relation to climate. *Arctic*, **45**, 1–9.

TSCHUDY, R. H., PILLMORE, C. L., ORTH, C. J., GILMORE, J. S. & KNIGHT, J. D. 1984. Disruption of the terrestrial plant ecosystem at the Cretaceous–Tertiary boundary, Western Interior. *Science*, **225**, 1030–1032.

WALKER, I. J. & NICKLING, W. G. 2002. Dynamics of secondary airflow and sediment transport over and in the lee of transverse dunes. *Progress in Physical Geography*, **26**, 47–75.

WALSH, S. L. 2004. Solutions in chronostratigraphy: the Paleocene/Eocene boundary debate, and Aubry vs. Hedberg on chronostratigraphic principles. *Earth-Science Reviews*, **64(1–2)**, 119–155.

WARDLE, P. 1974. Alpine timberlines. *In:* IVES, J. D. & BARRY, R. G. (eds) *Arctic and Alpine Environments*. Methuen, London, 371–402.

ZACHOS, J. C., PAGANI, M., SLOAN, L. C., THOMAS, E. & BILLUPS, K. 2001. Trends, rhythms, and aberrations in global climate 65 Ma to present. *Science*, **292**, 686–693.

Identifying Phanerozoic extinction controls: statistical considerations and preliminary results

N. MACLEOD

*Department of Palaeontology, The Natural History Museum, Cromwell Road, London,
SW7 5BD, UK (e-mail: N.MacLeod@nhm.ac.uk)*

Abstract: Two prominent patterns have been recognized in Phanerozoic extinction data: (1) a quasi-periodic distribution of extinction-intensity peaks, and (2) a linear, declining background extinction intensity gradient. Characterization and interpretation of both patterns are necessary to understand Phanerozoic extinction controls. The extinction-intensity peak spectrum has been variously interpreted as a reflection of the time-series of major sea-level regressions, continental flood-basalt province (CFBP) eruptions, and bolide impacts. In order to evaluate the level of association between these time-series and the Phanerozoic marine invertebrate extinction record statistically, a new Monte Carlo simulation strategy is presented. Results of simulation-based tests suggest that the time-series of major, eustatic sea-level regressions and CFBP eruption events have a statistically significant ($p \leqslant 0.05$) association with Tatarian–Pliocene, stage-level, extinction intensity peaks. Associations between this peak series and the time-series of crater-producing bolide impacts do not appear significant at this level. A limited multicausal event scenario was also tested using the Monte Carlo method, and recognized the combination of sea-level regression and CFBP volcanism to be significantly associated with the largest extinction intensity peaks of the last 250 Ma. The background extinction-intensity gradient has been interpreted variously as: (1) an indicator of progressive improvement in extinction resistance through selection; (2) the by-product of an invasion of marginal (extinction-resistant) habitats; and (3) as a taxonomic–stratigraphical artefact. Results of subdivided linear trend analyses suggest that the background extinction-intensity gradient is largely confined to the Late Palaeozoic–Cenozoic interval. No statistically significant gradient is present in the most recent compilation of Early–Middle Palaeozoic data on marine, invertebrate extinctions. The timing of gradient initiation and extinction variance analyses suggest that reorganization of global carbon cycles and oceanographical circulation patterns in the Devonian–Early Carboniferous, and the evolutionary appearance of modern phytoplankton groups in the Late Triassic both had dramatic effects on the character of the extinction-intensity gradient.

Over the past 20 years, enquiries into the nature and causes of Phanerozoic extinction events have constituted one of the most active and integrative of all Earth science research programmes. There are many reasons for this activity level within such a quintessentially palaeontological subject. For some, genuine extinction research became possible only after the Alvarez *et al.* (1980) bolide impact hypothesis for the Cretaceous–Tertiary (K–T) extinction was proposed. That study demonstrated how the question of extinction causation could be expressed in the context of reductive, hypothesis-driven science (e.g. Raup 1986, 1991; Glen 1994). For others, the concept of mass extinction provided a way of reintroducing catastrophism into geology (e.g. Berggren & Van Couvering 1984; Ward 1992, 1995, 2000). Others saw the bolide causation hypothesis in particular as providing a mechanism whereby microevolu-

tionary processes might be decoupled from macroevolutionary processes, thus justifying a 'hard' version of punctuated equilibrium (e.g. Gould 1984, 1985, 2002). Still others were swept up in the spotlight of media-driven concerns about the extent to which biodiversity reductions in the modern world represent a harbinger of a modern mass extinction to rival those of the geological past (e.g. Ward 1995, 2000; Leakey & Lewin 1996). For all, the new ideas swirling round the extinction question held out the hope of contributing toward the solution of some of palaeontology's most long-standing mysteries (e.g. the cause of the dinosaur extinction, the cause of the Permo-Triassic extinction), not to mention the promise of funding, often from non-traditional sources (e.g. NASA).

Despite all the work that has gone into palaeontological extinctions-related research programmes during the last two decades, the

From: BEAUDOIN, A.B. & HEAD, M.J. (eds) 2004. *The Palynology and Micropalaeontology of Boundaries.*
Geological Society, London, Special Publications, **230**, 11–33. 0305-8719/04/$15 © The Geological Society of
London 2004.

scientific community seems no closer to a consensus on extinction causes today than it was at the beginning of the modern extinction studies era in 1980. Frequent media reports of the impact-extinction scenario's hegemony notwithstanding, both of the formal, published, opinion surveys carried out over this interval (Hoffman & Nitecki 1985; Galvin 1998), as well as allusions to an, as yet, unpublished survey (Glen 1996, 1998), show that Earth scientists hold a variety of views on Phanerozoic extinction causation. These surveys also identify palaeontologists – those with the greatest in-depth knowledge of Phanerozoic extinction data – as the group most hostile to the idea of a single cause for extinctions in general and mass extinctions in particular. David Raup (1986, 1991), and William Glen (1996, 1998) have suggested that palaeontological intransigence over the bolide impact scenario represents evidence that palaeontologists are: (1) unprofessional in their innate rejection of a hypothesis first advanced by non-palaeontologists and/or (2) ignorant of the facts of the bolide impact case. However, after more than two decades of almost continuous controversy, symposia, seminars, articles and conversations, it would seem that fairness also dictates entertainment of the possibility that palaeontologists have carefully evaluated the both data and interpretations in favour of single-cause extinction scenarios in the fossil record and, for the most part, found those data and interpretations insufficient to warrant their support (e.g. Archibald 1996; MacLeod & Keller 1996; Hallam & Wignall 1997).

At this juncture in the ongoing debate it seems appropriate to review critically the basis on which extinction controls have been identified or evaluated in the past and, if possible, make recommendations for procedural improvements. As has been noted before (e.g. MacLeod 2003), David Raup's (1991) dictum of consistency provides the logical foundation upon which any strategy for recognizing extinction causes must be based.

> There is no way of assessing cause and effect [in historical studies] except to look for patterns of coincidence – and this requires multiple examinations of each cause–effect pair. If all extinction events are different the deciphering of any one of them will be next to impossible (p. 151).

Failure to appreciate the significance of this logical construct has led (literally) to decades of confusion among the proponents of various extinction causal scenarios. For example, the dictum's successful – though unacknowledged – application to the question of distributional patterns in iridium abundance anomalies, shocked quartz occurrences, and glass spherule occurrences is the primary reason why Earth scientists (including the overwhelming majority of palaeontologists, see Hoffman & Nitecki 1985; Galvin 1998; Glen 1998), now accept the reality of a collision between the Earth and a meteor–cometary impactor some 65 Ma ago. Had the coincident occurrence of these three impact indicators not been observed in a (now) large number of stratigraphic successions and at horizons isotopically or biostratigraphically dated to the appropriate time, the case for a K–T bolide impact would be fatally weakened. To paraphrase Raup (1991) in this context, if the K–T impact event had left different local physiochemical signatures in different stratigraphic successions, the deciphering of any one of them would have been next to impossible.

So too with the identification of extinction controls. The study of any one locality – or indeed of any one event – is insufficient to evaluate generalized extinction control or causation hypotheses, irrespective of the detail at which any local study is carried out. Detailed, single-locality or single-event studies are necessary, of course. Without them there would be no hope of collecting the data required for comparative analyses. Taken in isolation, however, these studies cannot be used to identify generalized extinction causes; especially if their data are either collected or presented in a manner that prevents comparison with other such studies either in time or space.

Aside from clarifying the importance of data comparability across events, appreciation of the significance of adopting a comparative approach to the determination of generalized extinction causes has another critical implication: the value of statistical hypothesis testing. Raup's (1991) passage alluding to 'patterns of coincidence' means the observation of repeated instances of stratigraphic (temporal) or geographical (spatial) association. Naturally occurring events or proxy observations can exhibit association – even repeated associations – for any number of reasons. Not all of these reasons support a deterministic or direct, cause–effect interpretation of the relation. Nevertheless, repeated instances of association beyond the point of reasonable expectation under a null statistical model must be judged as favouring such a deterministic relation. This judgement is inherently probabilistic in character and should be referenced explicitly to a probability density distribution for an applicable association statistic.

In large part, the difficulty in evaluating the power of alternative causal scenarios to account for extinction patterns has been the lack of appropriate probability density distributions for stratigraphic or geographical association metrics. The recent proliferation of jack-knifing, bootstrapping, Monte Carlo simulation, and other data-resampling methods in biological statistics (e.g. Manley 1997) in general, and in palaeontological studies in particular (e.g. Kitchell *et al.* 1987; Kitchell & MacLeod 1988; MacLeod 1991, 2003) has largely solved this problem in principle. All that remains, in practice, is to employ the tools already available.

The final concern of this review is one of scope. Various patterns are present in Phanerozoic extinction data, each of which denotes a different phenomenological domain. The most extensively cited of these patterns is the quasi-periodic distribution of extinction intensity peaks, some of which have been described as 'mass extinctions' (e.g. Newell 1967; Jablonski 1986*a*, 1986*b*). Given all the media attention that the concept of mass extinction has garnered over the last two decades, there is some degree of irony in realizing that there remains no precise, scientific definition of this widely used term. Various articles allude to the 'big three' (end-Permian, end-Ordovician, end-Cretaceous) or the 'big five' (end-Permian, end-Ordovician, end-Cretaceous, end-Devonian, end-Triassic) mass extinction events. As alluded to above, statistical analyses of these extinction peak data have been undertaken and these have used various methods to identify these peaks (e.g. Raup & Sepkoski 1982, 1984; Sepkoski & Raup 1986). Nevertheless, no statistical summary has thus far unambiguously identified any of these groupings as being either qualitatively or quantitatively different from other large extinction events (e.g. Middle Cambrian, end-Cambrian; see also Hallam & Wignall 1997).

The second, although much less well-studied, Phanerozoic extinction pattern is the declining background extinction gradient (Raup & Sepkoski 1982; Sepkoski & Raup 1986; Jablonski 1986*a*). For the most part this has been seen as a nuisance factor to be corrected for, so that other analyses may proceed (e.g. Raup & Sepkoski 1984). The widespread recognition of this pattern, however, implies a causal agent, the identification of which might lead to a deeper understanding of evolutionary processes, the history of life, taxonomic practice, or all three.

The point to draw from these introductory observations is that any successful explanation for Phanerozoic extinction causes must seek to account for all consistently expressed patterns within these data – not simply a subset thereof. In this same vein, it must also be appreciated that limitations on the nature of the extinction data themselves will necessarily constrain the approaches used and, ultimately, the conclusions reached.

The data

Any review or data (re)analysis formulated along these lines must be clear about the nature and scope of its data. The extinction data used in this investigation were compiled by the late J. J. Sepkoski Jr and consist of counts of marine invertebrate genera from all Phanerozoic stages. These data were tabulated by Sepkoski to estimate standing diversity along with numbers of genera originating and becoming extinct at some point within each of the time intervals. Various versions of these data have been used in a large number of extinction and diversification studies (e.g. Raup and Sepkoski 1986, 1988; Raup 1986, 1991; Raup & Boyajian 1988; Sepkoski 1990, 1994, 1996; Kirchner & Weil 2000; Kirchner 2002; MacLeod 2003).

Smith (2001) has recently raised the important question of the extent to which taxonomic data compilations such as those of Sepkoski reflect a true record of life's diversity history or a record that has been strongly biased by systematic differences in the amount of fossiliferous strata of different ages available for sampling. In the context of the present study, if Sepkoski's set of extinction-intensity values were found to be strongly correlated with stage-level estimates of the amount of rock available for sampling, the former could be regarded validly as a simple reflection of variation in the latter. In particular, Smith (2001) argued that the Hettangian–Pliocene interval of the Sepkoski extinction data did contain evidence for this type of bias in the form of a 'significant position [cross-]correlation value at a lag of 0 and −1 and a significant negative correlation value at a lag of −5.' (p. 361). Unfortunately, there are several problems with Smith's (2001) use of cross-correlation analysis and his interpretation of those results.

Cross-correlation analysis assumes that both time-series have been sampled identically at discrete and uniform intervals (Davis 1973, 1986, 2002). This basic assumption is badly violated by both of Smith's (2001) data-sets, in which the sampling interval shows a substantial variance (standard deviation = 1.68 Ma). In addition, the statistical interpretation of the cross-correlation calculation is only valid to the extent that both time-series can be concatenated to form a bivariate normal distribution. If the series are not bivariate normal, then the probability estimates may be erroneous. In this light, the marginally significant nature of Smith estimated correlations at lags 0 and –1 should be treated with some scepticism. (Note: the +5 lag is irrelevant to Smith's hypothesis of a close association between the two time-series). Moreover, recall that the null hypothesis for the standard correlation test is $r = 0.0$. Failure to accept the null hypothesis at a marginal – and possibly overestimated – probability value does not constitute compelling evidence of a strong sampling bias in Sepkoski's Hettangian–Pliocene extinction data.

A better test of Smith's data would be to compare the simple parametric or non-parametric correlations, depending on the conformance of the underlying variable distributions to normality assumptions. After appropriate transformations (arcsine in the case of the per cent extinction intensity data; log_{10} in the case of outcrop area data) and detrending the parametric test yields a substantially non-significant correlation of 0.269 ($t = 1.553$, d.f. $= 31$), whereas the non-parametric Kendall's τ test yields a marginally significant correlation of 0.250 ($z = 2.049$, d.f. $= 32$). In either instance – as in Smith's (2001) cross-correlation results – there is no statistical support for a dominant sampling-area bias in the Sepkoski extinction data.

For the present analysis, the standing diversity and total extinction counts for each of Sepkos-

ki's stage-level Phanerozoic subdivisions were used to estimate the marine invertebrate extinction-intensity time-series (Fig. 1). The per cent extinction metric was used as the best available extinction-intensity estimator because it is scaled for the number of genera at risk in each time interval and because it is relatively insensitive to estimation errors in both stage standing diversity and chronology (see Sepkoski & Raup 1986). Moreover, the per cent extinction-intensity time-series:

(1)   quantifies successfully the quasi-periodic character of extinction intensity peaks;
(2)   identifies all widely recognized 'mass extinction' events; and
(3)   illustrates the background extinction-intensity gradient.

Rearrangement of this extinction-intensity spectrum in rank order (Fig. 2) illustrates this spectrum's continuous nature. Such continuity precludes any possibility of recognizing a distinct class of 'mass extinction' events objectively separable from 'background extinction' events on the basis of extinction intensity. Peaks in extinction intensity obviously do occur, but they are a function of the data ordering, not an intrinsic component of the data-set itself. The challenge of extinction-causation analysis, then, is to attempt to account for the ordering or distribution of these events in terms of the ordering and distribution time-series of other events in Earth history.

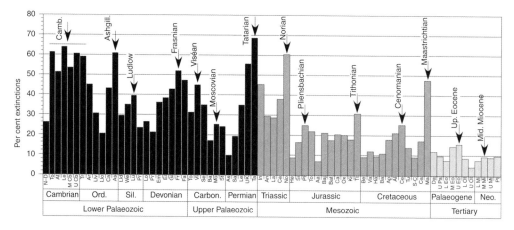

Fig. 1. Genus-level, extinction-intensity record for Phanerozoic stages represented as a histogram of equal-sized bins. Data from Sepkoski (pers. comm. via Kirchner 2002: see Acknowledgements). Black bars, Palaeozoic stages; dark-grey bars, Mesozoic stages; light-grey bars, Cenozoic stages. Arrows identify local extinction-intensity peaks.

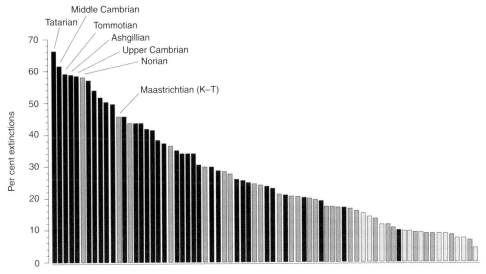

Fig. 2. Rank-ordered, genus-level, Phanerozoic extinction intensities. Bar shading as in Figure 1. Note continuity of the overall extinction-intensity spectrum and predominance of Palaeozoic data at the spectrum's high end. Note also the relatively low rank (12) of the Maastrichtian (= Cretaceous–Tertiary, or K–T) 'mass extinction' event. Continuity of the spectrum as a whole, along with variability of individual extinction event's rank suggests that: (1) a contiguous 'mass extinction' category cannot be recognized objectively, and (2) the same set of causal processes is responsible for events throughout the spectrum.

Methods and models

In practice, the identification of likely controls on Phanerozoic extinction patterns requires that aspects of patterning in the extinction-intensity time-series be described quantitatively and then compared with the time-series of putative causal mechanisms. There are several different candidate causal mechanism series that have already been compared to aspects of these extinction data.

Extinction-intensity peaks

The most prominent extinction-intensity pattern investigated to date has been the temporal distribution of local peaks or extinction intensity maxima. Soon after the revival of interest in mass extinction mechanisms, Raup and Sepkoski claimed to have demonstrated a 26 Ma periodicity in the spacing of extinction-intensity peaks for the last 250 Ma of Earth history (see Raup & Sepkoski 1984, 1986; Sepkoski & Raup 1986; Sepkoski 1990). Extinction-intensity peak periodicity was subsequently challenged on a wide variety of palaeontological and analytial grounds (e.g. see Prothero 1994 and Manley 1997 for reviews). Manley (1997) has recently

reviewed the statistical problems associated with applying randomization methods to unequally spaced time-series (especially those that contain a non-random trend) for the purpose of periodicity testing. His reanalysis of Sepkoski's family-level extinction data concluded that no statistically significant periodic signal was contained therein. MacLeod (2003) applied Manley's methods to Sepkoski's Phanerozoic genus-level data and also found that time-series to contain no significant periodic signal. Whereas failure of the periodic model to account for the distribution of local extinction-intensity peaks all but rules out causal mechanisms based on celestial mechanics (e.g. oscillations in the galactic plane or a previously unknown planet), these results do not rule out extraterrestrial causation *per se*.

Aside from periodicity studies, the most common way of identifying the mechanisms responsible for the extinction-intensity peak distribution has been to tabulate correspondences between the temporal distributions of these peaks and the temporal distributions of putative causal mechanisms (see Table 1). Under this tabulation approach, the mechanism identified as being most likely to be responsible for the peak distribution is the one exhibiting the

Table 1. *Tabulation of extinction events and cause (modified from Hallam & Wignall 1997)*

Extinction interval	Bolide impact	Volcanic eruption	Climatic cooling	Climatic warming	Eustatic regression	Anoxia– transgression	Counts
Late Eocene			●				1
End-Palaeocene		●		●		●	3
End-Cretaceous	●	●	●		●		4
End-Cenomanian						●	1
Early Toarcian						●	1
End-Triassic					●		1
End Permian		●		●		●	3
Late Moakouan					●		1
Devonian–Carboniferous						●	1
Frasnian–Fammenian						●	1
Late Ashgill			●	●	●	●	4
Middle–Late Cambrian						●	1
Late Early Cambrian					●	●	2
Late Precambrian						●	1
Counts	1	3	3	3	5	10	

greatest number of correspondences (e.g. Hallam & Wignall 1997; Wignall 2001). This approach is insufficient for a number of reasons:

(1) because the number of matches between any two time-series is not referenced to a statistical null model, there is no way to evaluate the association's statistical significance;

(2) matches with stages that do not contain a local extinction-intensity peak are not taken into consideration in evaluating the level of association;

(3) variations in the total frequency of event series are not taken into consideration in evaluating the level of association;

(4) mechanisms whose preservational frequency diminishes into the geological past are placed at a disadvantage in any raw tabulation (e.g. the records of bolide impacts and CFBP eruptions is largely confined to the Mesozoic–Cenozoic whereas accurate, stage-level records for global, eustatic transgression/regression phases and marine anoxia events are available for the entire Phanerozoic);

(5) there is no way to evaluate the explanatory power of coincidences between putative causal time-series on the target extinction pattern.

Monte Carlo simulation strategies can be used to address all these problems.

The concept behind the Monte Carlo method for analysing into tabulated co-occurrences was introduced to the palaeontological literature by Raup & Crick (1979). Suppose extinction-intensity peaks and occurrences of an environmental perturbation (e.g. major bolide impacts, sea-level lowstands, CFBP eruptions) were scattered randomly in time with no deterministic relation between their time-series. If the interval used to recognize different time-spans is sufficiently coarse (e.g. see Table 1), a number of co-occurrences between the perturbation and the extinction-intensity peak patterns would be expected purely by chance. In order to build a logical case for a non-random relation between two time-series, however, the number of associations must be greater than that expected by chance alone.

But how does one construct a probability distribution for two unique and non-repeatable historical time-series? Hypothetical random series can be constructed from the observed time-series (Fig. 3). These represent – at least metaphorically – alternative histories in which each event series is known to be independent of the other. If each time-series represents a valid estimate of the event's occurrence frequency, and if a sufficient number of these alternative, random histories are created, the number of observed matches between the two simulated time-series will provide an estimate of the probability density distribution for the match count under a statistical null model of no deterministic relation. Accordingly, the observed number of matches between the extinction record and the time-series of any putative causal mechanism can be compared with the expected match distribution under this null hypothesis and the probability of obtaining the observed

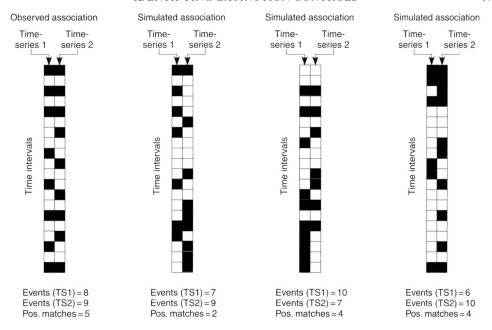

Fig. 3. Diagrams illustrating operation of the Monte Carlo simulation procedure for evaluating the statistical level of matches between discontinuous stratigraphic event time-series. Far left: two series of observations ordered stratigraphically with the time axis subdivided into discrete intervals. Observed numbers of event occurrence and co-occurrences shown below diagram. Each of the three simulated time-series pair (right) represents the results of comparisons between artificially constructed time-series assembled by sampling the corresponding observed time-series randomly and with replacement. Event frequencies and numbers of positive co-occurrences (matches) reflect possible values for these parameters under a randomized, non-deterministic relation model. By creating a large number of such simulations (usually $\geqslant 1000$) and tabulating the co-occurrence results, a probability density distribution can be estimated and used to evaluate the observed co-occurrence value to a specified confidence level.

level of association evaluated. The Monte Carlo approach has the additional advantage of supporting extension to the consideration of interacting causal time-series and – unlike classical 'urn problem' methods (see Raup & Crick 1979) – being fully generalizable to time-series of any composition.

The extinction-intensity gradient

Compared to the extinction-intensity peak pattern, the background extinction-intensity gradient has scarcely received any analytical attention. Indeed, what analysis of this extinction pattern there has been seems largely confined to attempts to remove the 'background' pattern from the extinction-intensity peak pattern so that the heights of the peaks could be estimated more accurately (e.g. Raup & Sepkoski 1984). Because the background extinction-intensity gradient has been regarded as a linear function, its characterization has been approached by Model 1 least-squares, linear

regression analysis, with the significance of the regression determined through a combination of standard, parametric F-tests augmented (in some instances) by bootstrapped significance estimates (see Manley 1997). However, the linear and continuous nature of this pattern has, up to now, always been assumed (e.g. Raup & Sepkoski 1984). Exploration of alternative, non-linear models for characterizing this pattern – along with their implications for causal interpretation – is one of the primary objectives of this investigation.

If a time-series data-set exhibits a consistent trend, then any sufficiently large subset of the data should, upon analysis, also yield values consistent with the overall trend (Fig. 4a). The 'sufficiently large' qualifier in the above statement is necessary because a certain amount of random scatter about the trend line is to be expected. If the specified subset is so small that this scatter obscures the trend, that result cannot be regarded as sufficient to challenge the trend's existence. If a time-series trend is complicated by

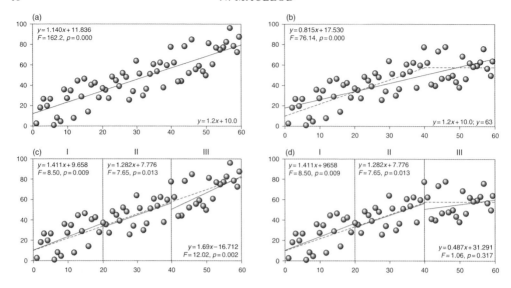

Fig. 4. (**a**) and (**b**): hypothetical trended time-series formed by randomly perturbing data from the line $y = 1.2x + 10$ (dashed line). (**a**) Statistically significant linear trend-line (solid line) estimated by least-squares regression analysis. (**b**) Data perturbed randomly from the line $y = 1.2x + 10$ for the first 40 time units and then randomly perturbed from the line $y = 63$ for the next 20 time units (dashed line) with the resulting statistically significant, linear trend-line (solid line) estimated by least-squares regression analysis. (**c**) Analysis of consistently trended time-series (as in (**a**); dashed line) subdivided into three intervals with trend-lines estimated for each interval (solid lines). In each case, trend-lines are statistically significant, with slopes that are statistically equivalent to one another. (**d**) Analysis of inconsistently trended time-series (as in (**b**); dashed lines) subdivided into three intervals with trend-lines estimated for each interval (solid lines). Note that by subdividing the data and testing for linearity (or equivalence of slope), the non-linear model segment is identified successfully. Data analysis strategies such as these can be used to test complex, process-level extinction and diversification hypotheses.

non-linearities or a loss of trend, however (e.g. multiple trends, increases in the data's variance along the trend, Fig. 4b), application of a linear model may return a result with a superficially high statistical certainty (Davis 1973, 1986; Zar 1974; Sokal & Rohlf 1981, 1995). In the absence of a more specific, non-linear model, the most obvious analytical approach to determination of whether significant non-linearities exist within a large data-set is to subdivide the data into large, contiguous blocks and submit these to trend analysis tests using the least-squares method (Figs 4c & 4d).

Correlates with the distribution of extinction-intensity peaks

Table 2 gives empirical patterns, time-series scopes, and sources for the various comparison time-series considered in this analysis. Owing to limitations in the parsing of Sepkoski's extinction data, the stage level of temporal resolution was chosen for all time-series. This inevitably

degrades some of the biostratigraphic data available in better-studied stratigraphical intervals (e.g. close to the Cretaceous–Tertiary boundary). It also grossly underestimates the precision with which some of the putative causal mechanisms' time-series are known (e.g. Courtillot *et al.* 1996; Grieve *et al.* 1996; Courtillot & Renne in press). This rather coarse binning level is necessary, however, because the stratigraphic ranges of most marine invertebrate taxa are presently not known to substage levels of temporal resolution.

One obvious result of this convention is that extinction horizons cannot be assumed to be concentrated in particular portions of the stage in which they occur (e.g. close to or at the younger stage boundary). Another is that some extinctions attributed to particular stages may be associated with a causal mechanism that is known to predate or post-date those extinctions. An interesting example of the latter is the Manicouagan impact, which Grieve *et al.* (1996) report as having an age of 214 Ma. This age is considered Middle Norian by the Grad-

Table 2. *Stage-level associations between extinction intensity peaks and various putative causal mechanism time-series*

Stage/substage	Extinction peak	Bolide impact (1)	Sea-level regress. (2)	Sea-level transgression (3)	Marine anoxia (4)	CFBP eruption (5)
			Extinction mechanism			
Pliocene		▨	▨			
Upper Miocene		▨	▨			
Middle Miocene	■	▨	▨		▨	■
Lower Miocene				■		
Upper Oligocene			■		▨	
Lower Oligocene			■		▨	■
Upper Eocene	■	▨	▨			
Middle Eocene		▨	▨		▨	
Lower Eocene		▨		■		
Palaeocene	■	▨				■
Maastrictian	■	▨	▨		▨	
Campanian		■	▨		■	
Sant.–Coniacian		▨		■	▨	
Turonian		▨		■	■	
Cenomanian	■	▨	▨	■	▨	
Albian		▨		▨	▨	
Aptian		▨		■	▨	
Barremian			■	■	▨	
Hauterivian		■	▨	■	■	
Valanginian		▨		▨	▨	■
Berriasian		▨	■		▨	
Tithonian	■		▨			
Kimmeridgian						
Oxfordian				■	▨	
Callovian				▨	▨	
Bathonian		■			▨	
Bajocian		▨		▨		
Aalenian	■	▨		▨		
Toarcian		▨	▨		■	■
Pliensbachian		▨			■	
Sinemurian		▨			▨	
Hettangian				▨	▨	
Norian	■	■	■		▨	■
Carnian			▨		▨	
Ladinian				■		
Anisian		▨		▨	▨	
Induan		▨		▨	▨	
Tatarian	■	▨			▨	■

Grey boxes indicate minor bolide impacts (10 km–50 km crater diameter), regression, transgression, and anoxia intervals. Black boxes indicate major bolide impacts (>50 km crater diameter), lowstand, highstand, and anoxia intervals. Data sources as follows: (1) Grieve *et al.* 1996; (2, 3) Haq 1991; Hallam 1992; (4) Parrish & Curtis 1982; Hallam 1987; (5) Wignall 2001.

stein & Ogg (1996) time-scale. Accordingly, the stage-binning convention outlined above would associate this impact with the Norian extinction event, despite the fact that some authors (e.g. Hallam & Wignall 1997) have argued that the Manicouagan impact predates some proportion of the Norian extinction by millions of years. Set against this source of potential error are problems associated with placing too much emphasis on substage levels of resolution, including:

(1)   appeals to substage resolution levels cannot be justified in light of the available stratigraphic resolution for the broad range of marine genera;

(2)   geological time-scales themselves can
       undergo considerable revision year to
       year; and
(3)   the inherent imprecision of using the
       genus level of taxonomic resolution
       argues for caution in making fine-scale
       temporal distinctions.

On balance, the inevitable loss of temporal
resolution imposed on the analysis by the overall
quality of available biostratigraphic data is
offset by the advantage of being able to compare
occurrence patterns across the extinction-intensity peak spectrum.

The time-series distribution of each extinction
mechanism was compared to the stage-level
extinction-intensity peak distribution using the
Monte Carlo resampling method described
above. Each resulting simulation represented
an estimate of the number of mechanism-peak
associations that might be expected under a
statistical null model of no deterministic relation
between the two time-series. For each analysis,
1000 such simulations were performed in order
to estimate the random association frequency
distribution for each putative causal mechanism.
The resulting frequency distributions were then
compared with the actual number of observed
associations for each putative cause–effect pair
in order to obtain valid, non-parametric, statistical estimates of each association's strength.
Results of analyses for nine putative causal
mechanisms are presented in Table 3.

Bolide impacts are thought to influence
marine invertebrate extinction rates through
climate changes that lead to extinctions of
planktonic primary producers at the base of
marine food chains. The Alvarez et al. (1982; see
also Alvarez & Asaro 1990; Alvarez et al. 1994;
Alvarez 1997) scenario of short-term, bolide
impact-induced global climate change being the
primary cause of extinction-intensity peaks over
the past 250 Ma is represented by two simulations. The first of these tests the association

between extinction intensity peaks and impacts
producing craters greater than or equal to 10 km
in diameter. The second tests the association
between extinction intensity peaks and impacts
producing craters between 50 and 150 km in
diameter. Whereas the former would probably
be recognized to include impacts too small to
have produced global environmental effects (but
see Raup 1991), the latter includes many craters
whose associated impact events have repeatedly
been identified as mass extinction causal agents
(e.g. Popagai, Chicxulub, Manicouagan; see
Hallam & Wignall 1997 for a review).

When the distribution of the entire impact
events time-series matching these two intensity-
class criteria is compared statistically with the
extinction-intensity peak distribution, the
observed association levels are identified as
insufficient to refute the null, or non-deterministic hypothesis at traditional confidence levels
($p = 0.05$). If this confidence level was lowered to
0.10 – reflecting a 90% certainty – the deterministic alternative hypothesis could be accepted
for the association between extinction-intensity
peaks and larger impact class. Before rushing to
embrace this result as the sole – or even the most
likely – explanation for the extinction-intensity
peak distribution, however, it is appropriate to
assess the statistical strength of associations
between the extinction peaks and other causal
mechanisms' time-series.

Eustatic sea-level fall has long been suspected
as a cause of elevated extinction intensities
(Newell 1967; Hallam 1989; Archibald 1996;
Hallam & Wignall 1997, 1999). This mechanism
is thought to operate by: (1) reducing the
amount of habitable area on the continental
shelves for marine organisms, and (2) global
climate changes resulting from the relatively
rapid oxidation of organic matter on the
exposed shelves. Eustatic sea-level lowstands
also tend to be associated with the development
of widespread marine anoxia due to reductions
in the intensity of marine circulation. The latter

Table 3. *Estimated association probabilities*

Extinction cause series	No. of occurrences	No. of positive associations	Median assoc probability
Bolide impact (>10 km)	20	6	0.172
Bolide impact (50–150 km)	6	3	0.088
Major eustatic regression	16	6	0.040
Major eustatic lowstand	7	3	0.135
Major eustatic transgression	22	2	0.991
Major eustatic highstand	7	1	0.732
Anoxia (major)	25	5	0.718
Anoxia (major, global)	10	2	0.609
CFBP eruption	9	6	0.000

mechanism could be especially problematic for habitat area-stressed benthic invertebrate populations, since anoxic bottom waters generated during a prolonged sea-level lowstand would surge across shelf habitats during the initial phases of the following eustatic sea-level rise (Wignall & Hallam 1992).

This complex extinction causal mechanism was represented by three different simulation couplets (Table 3). The first of these sets focuses on the effect of progressively lowering sea-level by comparing the extinction-intensity peak distribution with instances of: (1) eustatic sea-level fall, and (2) the stage-level distributions of temporally localized, major sea-level lowstands. The second set seeks confirmation of the sea-level effect through examination of the reciprocal pattern of eustatic sea-level rises and major highstands. The last focuses on the association between extinction-intensity peaks and the development widespread intervals of anoxic conditions on the Earth's continental shelves. Like these mechanisms themselves, the results of these simulations are both complex and revealing.

Based on 1000 random simulations, there appears to be an unusually strong, and statistically significant, correspondence between intervals of declining eustatic sea-level and peaks of extinction intensity (Table 3). Note that this high correspondence does not simply reflect the fact that there are a relatively large number of stages characterized by sea-level fall. The number of associations between these two spectra is much higher than would be expected under the corresponding random model. Nevertheless, this effect seems to be confined strictly to intervals in which eustatic sea-level is declining progressively. The corresponding simulations of the extinction-intensity peak distribution and the distribution of localized sea-level lowstands did not identify the association between these two time-series as statistically significant. These results would seem to imply that marine benthic faunas can be severely stressed by declining sea-levels, but that the effect is continuous over the entire course of the sea-level fall, as opposed to being either localized or inordinately intensified in the temporal vicinity of lowstands.

Interestingly, Hallam & Wignall (1999) have recently reviewed the lithostratigraphy of all major extinction intervals and come to exactly the opposite conclusion; namely, that all major extinction intervals do coincide with pronounced fluctuations in the eustatic sea-level curve (see their fig. 11, p. 239). Hallam & Wignall's (1999) results are not inconsistent with the Monte Carlo simulation results reported above. Hallam & Wignall (1999) are simply discussing a different aspect of the eustatic sea-level curve. Whereas the Monte Carlo study was performed on the smoothed version of the global eustatic sea-level curve reported by Haq (1991) and Hallam (1992), the Hallam & Wignall (1999) study focuses on much smaller scale eustatic sea-level fluctuations that, although present on the level of the outcrop or core, are invisible in the longer-term Phanerozoic sea-level curve. While there is absolutely no doubt that all of the major Phanerozoic extinctions do take place during times of sea-level fluctuation (as Hallam & Wignall 1997, 1999 have shown), there is also absolutely no doubt that such fluctuations occur multiple times in virtually every Phanerozoic stage, *irrespective of the level of extinction intensity*. It is simply not appropriate to emphasize only the positive instances of associations between short-term sea-level fluctuation and elevated extinction intensity and ignore the much larger set of negative associations. Also, by equating genuine major sea-level lowstands (e.g. the end-Permian lowstands) with short-term fluctuations in sea-level that take place in the context of major transgressions (e.g. Cenomanian) and regressions (e.g. Maastrichtian), Hallam & Wignall (1999) have given an accurate, but incomplete, assessment of the level of association between environmental stresses induced by sea-level fluctuation *per se* and marine invertebrate extinctions. The Monte Carlo simulation analysis assumes that the smaller-scale sea-level fluctuations are embedded in the global Phanerozoic sea-level curve, but tests the higher-level hypothesis of whether major Phanerozoic extinctions are associated with large-scale regression, transgression, lowstand, and highstand intervals. (Because of the common occurrence of Phanerozoic short-term sea-level fluctuations, a corresponding Monte Carlo analysis is not needed unless or until it can be demonstrated that such fluctuations can be subdivided unambiguously down into more restrictive groupings.)

These sea-level regression-lowstand results are confirmed by reciprocal analyses of sea-level rises and highstands (Table 3). Indeed, under a random model, a negative association between extinction-intensity peaks and intervals of progressively rising sea-level is even more significant than its positive association with declining sea-levels. As was true of the previous simulation couplet, the effect appears confined to intervals in which sea-level is changing, rather than being focused in stages containing local sea-level maxima or highstands.

Perhaps the most unexpected results of these sea-level effect simulations, however, came from

the analysis of associations between the extinction-intensity peak distribution and intervals of
marine anoxia (Table 3). Irrespective of whether
the environmental data were inclusive (containing all significant instances of continental shelf
anoxia) or restrictive (confined only to very
intense or very widespread anoxia events), the
observed levels of association both fell well
within the range considered consistent with a
non-deterministic relation between the extinction peak and anoxia time-series. This result
contrasts with previous claims that anoxia is
repeatedly associated with peaks of extinction
intensity (e.g. Wignall & Hallam 1992; Hallam &
Wignall 1997; Wignall & Twitchett 2002).

These interpretive contrasts are also reminiscent of the contrasting views of sea-level effects
on extinction-peak distributions discussed previously. Once again, there is no doubt that
localized extinction events are often associated
with marine anoxia (see references above). There
is also no doubt that many stages characterized
by major marine anoxia events do not exhibit
elevated extinction levels. The Monte Carlo
simulation studies undertaken in this investigation have shown that extinction-intensity peaks
are not associated with major, global anoxia
events to a statistically significant degree. In
order to demonstrate a statistical case for the
association between anoxia events (or sea-level
fluctuations) proponents of that mechanism
must specify the time-series of all anoxia (or
sea-level) events comparable to those associated
with extinction peaks – including those that are
not associated with extinction peaks – and test
that time-series in the manner outlined above.
Anything less runs the risk of confusing the
distinction between anecdote and analysis.

The last simulation series compared the
patterns of extinction intensity peaks with the
distribution of CFBP eruptions. This association, first noted by Rampino & Stothers (1988,
see also Courtillot et al. 1996; Wignall 2001), is
thought to be based on severe and repeated
perturbations of the global climate induced by
sustained intervals of temporally localized, but
exceedingly large, subaerial basaltic eruptions.
Comparison of the association frequency
between extinction-intensity peaks and well-
dated Mesozoic–Cenozoic CFPB eruptions
with results obtained from a series of 1000
random simulations based on these two time-
series provides unequivocal statistical support
for the alternative, deterministic model. The
statistical significance of this association is
unquestionable. Out of 1000 random simulations, only one produced an association level as
great as that observed in the actual stage-level

comparison. This is by far the highest level of
significance for any of the association frequencies analysed in this investigation. Accordingly,
the presumption of a likely deterministic, cause–
effect relation between this class of volcanic
eruption, and the temporal distribution of
extinction-intensity peaks, is very strong.

Because the simulation analyses discovered
two statistically significant patterns of association between putative causal mechanisms and
the extinction-intensity peak time-series (eustatic
sea-level falls and CFBP eruptions), the question
of whether a dynamic interaction between these
two time-series can go any way toward explaining additional aspects of the extinction-intensity
peak spectrum is raised. The most obvious
candidate pattern is peak height or extinction-
intensity magnitude. MacLeod (1998) noted that
the three largest extinction-intensity peaks in the
last 250 Ma (Tatarian, Norian, Maastrichtian)
each occurred during stages that also contained
a CFBP eruption event (Siberian Traps, Central
Atlantic Magmatic Event, Deccan Traps) and
the culmination of a eustatic sea-level fall (see
Fig. 1 and Table 2). Two of these peaks are also
associated with a large bolide impact event (the
Norian Manicouagan impact, and the Maastrichtian Chicxulub impact). However, the lack
of a confirmed, large, crater-producing impact
(>50 km diameter crater) associated with the
Tatarian extinction intensity peak – the most
intense marine extinction event of the entire
Phanerozoic – widespread evidence that many
Norian and Maastrichtian extinctions took
place prior to the impact events themselves (see
MacLeod & Keller 1996; Hallam & Wignall
1997 and references therein; MacLeod et al.
1997), and the occurrence of similarly large
impact caters in stages not characterized by
elevated extinction intensities, all suggest that
impacts played, at best, a subordinate role in
contributing to these extinctions.

Using the same Monte Carlo data simulation
strategy outlined above, it is possible to evaluate
the statistical significance of the bicausal
mechanism (CFBP eruptions and eustatic sea-
level fall) scenario. Results of this analysis are
presented in Figure 5. Surprisingly, as many as
four matches between the stage-level extinction
intensity peak, sea-level regression, and CFBP
eruption time-series over the last 250 Ma can be
expected on random grounds alone. In terms of
the relative frequency of these matches, however, the 1000 simulations make it clear that
match patterns of three or more are quite rare.
The estimated median probability of achieving a
pattern of three matches between these time-
series by random coincidence alone is approxi-

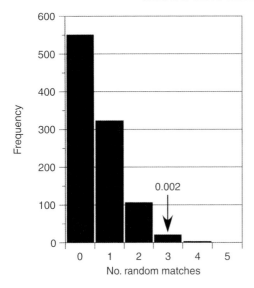

Fig. 5. Estimated probability density distribution for co-occurrences between the CFBP volcanic eruption and the long-term eustatic sea-level regression time-series with the extinction-intensity peak time-series. The observed number of matches between these three time-series (3, see Table 2) was attained by this random simulation ($n = 1000$) 23 times.

mately 0.002 – well above the level traditionally required for identifying statistical confidence. Accordingly, the observation of three stage-level matches between these spectra is taken as statistical support for the interpretation that both eustatic sea-level falls and CFBP eruptions were deterministically involved in causing the Tatarian, Norian, and Maastrichtian extinction events. Given the strength of this result it also seems likely that multiple event associations are principal causes of other instances of elevated extinction-intensity events throughout the Phanerozoic.

Patterns in the extinction-intensity gradient

The so-called background extinction-intensity gradient is quantified typically by performing a least-squares regression (Model 1 regression of Sokal & Rohlf 1981, 1995) of extinction magnitude on time (Raup & Sepkoski 1982; Sepkoski & Raup 1986; see also Davis 2002). In this investigation, extinction magnitude was estimated as per cent stage-level generic extinctions (see justification above), and time as the endpoint of each stage as given in the Gradstein & Ogg (1996) time-scale. Use of the endpoint as the time estimate should not be construed as implying that stage-level extinctions are concen-

trated at the stage ends or inter-stage boundary transitions. Rather, this convention is justified as the only date by which we can be certain that all extinctions assigned to each stage have taken place.

Figure 6 illustrates the intensity–age scatter-plot for these data. Results of the least-squares (extinction intensity on time) regression analysis (also shown in Fig. 6) are statistically significant as assessed by both F-test ($F = 61.77$, d.f. $= 1$, 70) and bootstrap methods (median probability of obtaining a slope as high as 0.0743 under random re-ordering of the data: 0.00). These results mirror prior findings of Raup & Sepkoski (1982; Sepkoski & Raup 1986) regarding the nature of the Tatarian–recent extinction-intensity gradient.

There have been various attempts to interpret this gradient. Some authors have attributed it to successive improvements in species fitness over time (Raup & Sepkoski 1982; Van Valen 1994). Others point to a progressive increase in extinction resistance conferred as a result of: (1) an increase in the number of species per clade with consequent extension of the clades' geographical distribution (Sepkoski 1984; Flessa & Jablonski 1985), or (2) the progressive radiation of clades into marginal environments where extinction resistance is conferred as a result of improved tolerance to environmental fluctuations (Vermeij 1987). Vermeij (1987) has also argued that the gradient might be either a taxonomic or stratigraphic artefact. In each case, the explanatory model assumes the validity of the gradient throughout the entire interval. Expanding the focus of analysis from the Tatarian–recent interval allows this latter assumption to be examined.

Coincidentally, suspicions that the extinction-intensity gradient may contain hitherto unsuspected non-linearities has solid empirical and theoretical justification. Analysis of residuals resulting from linear modelling of the Phanerozoic extinction intensity gradient suggests that Sepkoski's genus-level extinction data do not conform well to a single-factor causal model (Fig. 7). In addition, Martin (1996) pointed to several alternative environmental patterns whose trends also appear to mirror to a greater or lesser extent the extinction-intensity gradient. Thus, elevated SO_4 values in Early–Middle Palaeozoic sediments, along with the contrasting low values in Cenozoic sediments, have been interpreted as evidence that Early–Middle Palaeozoic oceans were characterized by much more sluggish circulation and higher levels of anoxia than their relatively well-mixed and highly oxygenated Mesozoic–Cenozoic counter-

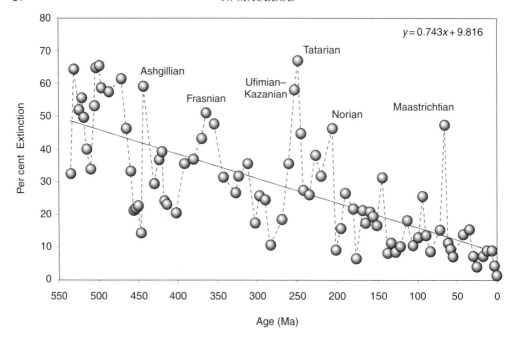

Fig. 6. Genus-level, extinction-intensity record for Phanerozoic stages represented as a scatter-plot superimposed on the linear, least-squares regression of these extinction-intensity magnitudes on time. Data from Sepkoski (pers. comm. via Kirchner 2002). See text for discussion.

parts (see Martin 1996 and references therein). If, as has been suggested by Martin (1996), Early–Middle Palaeozoic marine habitats were less stable than Mesozoic and Cenozoic marine habitats, this might be reflected in a more complex form for the extinction-intensity gradient than has been assumed to-date.

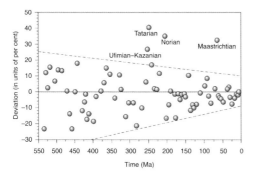

Fig. 7. Scatter-plot of residuals from the regression analysis shown in Figure 6. Note well-structured increase in residual variability with increasing time. This pattern of variation suggests that the extinction-intensity gradient may be difficult to estimate reliably for older subintervals. Labelled points represent residuals for local extinction-intensity peaks that stand well above the data-set's first-order linear trend.

Least-squares regression analysis of these Early and Middle Palaeozoic data (Cambrian–Devonian) confirms this suspicion. Although the estimated gradient value in this interval is similar to that of the succeeding interval, significance tests reveal that, for these data, the null hypothesis of no trend cannot be rejected (Fig. 8). Many interval subdivisions were examined in the course of this investigation in an attempt to locate the most likely initiation point of the background extinction intensity gradient (see Discussion section). In terms of the magnitude of the contrast between associated F-values, the most likely position appears to be coincident with the Frasnian extinction intensity peak. The interval from the Upper Devonian (Famennian) through the Neogene (Pliocene) exhibits a well-constrained and highly significant declining trend in per cent extinction magnitudes (slope: 0.077, F-value: 43.637 with d.f.: 1, 44; see Fig. 8). In contrast, the interval from the Cambrian (Nemakitian–Daldynian) through the Upper Devonian (Frasnian) exhibits a poorly constrained and statistically non-significant trend (slope = 0.109, F-value = 3.960 with d.f.: 1, 20). Since this Lower Palaeozoic interval represents over one-third of the Phanerozoic time-span, it seems inappropriate to conclude that the interval is too short for any linear trend to have

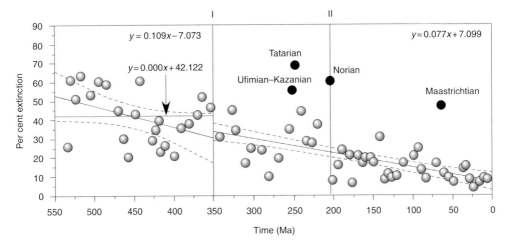

Fig. 8. Genus-level, extinction-intensity record for Phanerozoic stages represented as a scatter-plot with estimated gradients shown as linear trend lines with associated 95 per cent confidence bands (dashed) and 'gradient events' shown as labelled vertical lines. The Late Devonian event (Event I, estimated timing 250 Ma) represents the oldest point at which the extinction-intensity gradient loses coherence. Stages to the left (older) of this line exhibit no statistically significant extinction-intensity gradient. Stages to the right (younger) of this line exhibit a highly significant gradient of linearly decreasing extinction intensities over time. (Note: extinction-intensity peaks that stand well above the overall trend-line (solid black data points) were not used to estimate the gradient. If these points are included in the analysis, however, the result is not qualitatively different). A second event (estimated timing 209 Ma) marks the point where inter-stage variability in the extinction-intensity data collapses. See text for discussion and interpretation.

become noticeable. Consequently, the more likely form of these data can be described as a discontinuous or stepped function with the step between a 'not well-defined' or 'absent' extinction-intensity trend, and a 'well-developed, declining' extinction-intensity trend occurring somewhere in the vicinity of the Late Devonian–Early Carboniferous (Fig. 8).

There is one other consistent pattern in these Phanerozoic extinction-intensity data that bears on their interpretation. As can also be seen clearly in Figure 8, a dramatic decrease in the variance of per cent extinction-intensity values occurs in the Late Triassic, after the Norian extinction-intensity peak. If the confounding effects of the set of extinction-intensity peaks are removed from the data-set, then the magnitude of this variance reduction can be quantified by comparison of standard deviations from sub-intervals identified (provisionally) in Figure 8. These are shown in Figure 9. Note the similarity between the values for the gradient-less Cambrian–Devonian sub-interval and the Devonian–Triassic sub-interval, as well as their dramatic distinction from the post-Triassic sub-interval. These suggest that, in addition to the onset of progressively declining extinction intensity values in the Late Devonian–Early Carboniferous, something occurred in the Late Triassic that

served to buffer the entire marine system from the extreme fluctuations in extinction probabilities that, up to that time, had been characteristic of the marine biotic realm.

Discussion

For both aspects of the Phanerozoic extinction record, the identification of a consistent pattern is required before hypotheses of causal process can be tested rigorously. While efforts directed toward this pattern identification task have a reasonably long history in the case of the extinction-intensity peak distribution (largely as a result of Raup and Sepkoski's early claims for periodicity in these data), mass extinction research since 1980 has nevertheless focused on the description of individual extinction events in ever greater geochemical, sedimentological, and palaeontological detail. This was especially true of attempts to understand the Maastrichtian, or the so-called K–T boundary, extinction event, although, more recently, the Tatarian (or end-Permian) event has become the focus of similar scrutiny. Irrespective of these efforts, to the extent that the purpose of such research is provide insight into generalized extinction causes, the best that isolated, single-event investigations can hope to achieve in terms of

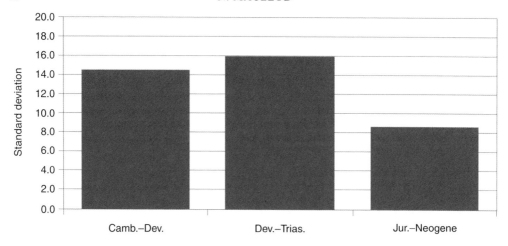

Fig. 9. Aggregate, extinction-peak normalized inter-stage variability in extinction-intensity values. Note the similarity between the two pre-Jurassic subdivisions and their joint difference from the Jurassic–Neogene subdivision.

addressing the problem of generalized cause is to provide data for later comparative analyses.

Aside from a limited amount of truly comparable data on which to found such studies, comparative analysis of the Phanerozoic extinction record has also been hampered by the lack of a reliable procedure whereby quantitative tests of association could be evaluated against a specific null hypothesis. The Monte Carlo simulation procedure outlined above provides a first step toward fashioning analytical tools to accomplish such evaluations. Similarly, the sub-interval sampling strategy provides students of extinction data – as well as other stratigraphic observation series – with a method of testing for nonlinearities in time-series data and identifying the pattern-level discontinuities that might suggest causal relations.

In terms of the extinction-intensity peak data, results of this investigation suggest that the primary factors influencing generalized extinction probabilities in the marine realm are (in order of importance): (1) the occurrence pattern of CFBP eruptions, and (2) the general state of major eustatic sea-level trends. Noticeably heightened extinction intensities (= increased extinction probabilities) are likely to occur whenever a collectively large (>1.5 million cubic kilometres of extrusives) series of volcanic eruptions takes place over a time-span of less than three million years (Courtillot *et al.* 1996; Courtillot & Renne in press). Based on historical data spanning the last 250 Ma, the statistical likelihood of this generalized relation being non-deterministic is effectively 0.0, even though the

observed stage-level association ratio is 0.67 (see Table 3). Heightened extinction intensities will also tend to occur whenever eustatic sea-level goes into a phase of long-term decline spanning (on average) not less than seven million years. Based on similar historical data, the statistical likelihood that this generalized relation is non-deterministic is less than 0.05, even though the observed stage-level association ratio is only 0.38 (see Table 3).

Bolide impacts that leave crater diameters of between 10 and 150 km have a very different statistical association with extinction-intensity peaks than either CFBP eruptions or eustatic sea-level falls. The idea that bolide impacts *per se* are associated deterministically with extinction intensity peaks is clearly unsustainable. There are simply too many records of medium- to large-sized bolide impacts having occurred during extinction quiescent intervals of Earth history. Moreover, the idea that large bolide impacts (e.g. those leaving craters between 50 and 150 km diameter) have determined the distribution of extinction-intensity peaks over-states the statistical strength of the observed association. Over the last 250 Ma there are too few known craters of this size (six) to be able to account for all major extinction peaks (eight). At best, only three such large craters can be regarded as coinciding with extinction-intensity peaks at the stage level of temporal resolution (see Table 2). Because large extinction events often occur in the absence of any evidence for an unusually large bolide impacts, and because large impact events often occur in stages that do not exhibit elevated extinction intensities (see

Fig. 1 and Table 2), other factors must be involved in controlling the generalized extinction-intensity peak distribution.

Jones *et al.* (2002) have recently advanced the interesting scenario of CFBP volcanic fields being themselves the signatures of very large impact events (e.g. collisions between the Earth and iron impactors greater than or equal to 20 km in diameter travelling at 10 km sec^{-1}). This argument is based on:

(1) mechanistic difficulties with the 'super-plume model' currently accepted as the cause of CFBP eruption events;
(2) new calculations estimating the volume of decompression melting that could be expected as a result of this impact type;
(3) results of hydrodynamic simulation experiments; and
(4) new calculations regarding the probability of the Earth encountering objects of this type during the course of the Phanerozoic.

These results indicate that such high-density, high-velocity, and large object impacts would auto-obliterate the associated crater and initiate supersolidus decompression melting of the local mantle, producing as much as 3×10^6 km^3 of melt (30% of which might be delivered to the surface). These simulations also suggest that the resultant eruptions would continue episodically for at least one million years.

This 'super-impact' scenario might explain a variety of problems with current geomorphological and volcanological observations from CFBP eruption fields. These include the absence of any craters of a size corresponding to this large-impact class, and the lack of a normal, volcanogenic mechanism for moving such a large volume of melt material out of the mantle in the relatively short time indicated by chronometric studies of CFBP events. Nevertheless, the super-impact scenario remains a purely theoretical construct for the time being. Jones *et al.* (2002) attempted to apply the super-impact scenario to the Siberian and Deccan traps, but this was unconvincing because they failed to adequately report critical data (e.g. lack of synchrony between the onset of eruption and Ir anomaly emplacements). Nonetheless, this failure does not detract from the plausibility of the model itself. Empirical confirmation of the super-impact scenario will only come when – conforming to Raup's (1991) dictum – a set of physiochemical attributes unique to this class of impact are proposed, accepted by the relevant scientific communities, and observed at the sites of CFBP eruption fields.

The ultimate fate of this super-impact scenario, however, in no way alters the analyses, results, or conclusions of this investigation. As shown above, the class of impacts responsible for the terrestrial impact cratering record does not exhibit a stage-level pattern of association with extinction-intensity peaks adequate for identification as a generalized cause of the latter's distribution. If a separate and larger class of impacts is found to be responsible for the creation of CFBP eruptions, this in no way changes the fact that the distribution of such events – irrespective of their cause – does show the sort of tight and, for the most part, mutually exclusive association pattern with extinction-intensity peaks that strongly supports a deterministic link between these event classes. Indeed, one of the most attractive aspects of the super-impact scenario is that it provides a more specific mechanism than any other available to date for generating a source of environmental perturbation that might extend over a sufficiently long time interval to match the best palaeontological estimates for the durations of major extinction events.

Irrespective of whether the Jones *et al.* (2002) super-impact scenario is ultimately confirmed, coincidences between causal mechanism classes undoubtedly occur, especially at the rather coarse levels of time resolution afforded by current synoptic palaeontological data. Although coarse relative to some forms of physical data, available biotic data easily demonstrate that extinction-peak killing mechanisms do not depend on the overwhelming of formidable biotic and ecological homeostatic processes through massive, but short-term, environmental perturbation. Rather, these data indicate clearly that the disruption of local ecosystems occurs by quasi-continuous and unpredictably timed perturbations of variable magnitude over time intervals that – while short in geological terms – are long in ecological and population biological terms. Much empirical data of contemporary conservation biology confirms that this sort of continuous environmental disturbance is an effective killing mechanism for local populations over relatively short time periods (see Scheffer *et al.* 2001 for a review). The coincidence scenario simply scales this effect up to global magnitudes.

In terms of direct empirical support, the coincidence scenario is much more consistent with the extended temporal signatures of many large extinction events (see Erwin 1993; Archibald 1996; MacLeod & Keller 1996; and Hallam & Wignall 1997 for examples) than the 'bad weekend' scenarios offered by supporters of an impact–extinction link (e.g. Alvarez 1997). Moreover, the more pluralistic coincidence hypothesis allows each mechanism to play its own role in the precipitation of major extinction events, rather than arbitrarily denying that geological events and processes known to produce severe environmental perturbations throughout Earth history have any deterministic link to extinction probabilities (e.g. Ryder 1996).

Although this investigation has found evidence for at least substantial links between the distribution of extinction peaks and all three major extinction mechanisms, it is interesting to note that statistical significance at the standard $p = 0.05$ level was met exclusively for associations between extinction peaks and the time-series of terrestrial CFBP eruptions and major, eustatic, sea-level regression trends. Given current data, the effect of crater-leaving bolide impacts appears to be one of inducing variations – albeit a rather large variation in the case of the Chicxulub bolide – on the themes set by interactions between these two extinction-mechanism classes.

The other general theme evident from acceptance of CFBP eruption and sea-level regression as the pace-setting extinction-peak mechanisms, with bolide impacts playing a largely subsidiary role, is the strong apparent link that each mechanism implies between events in the terrestrial and marine realms. The Phanerozoic extinction record is predominantly a record of what is happening to life in the oceans. Yet, the manner of operation for all three leading extinction casual mechanisms is through climate change that, for the most part, appears to be amplified by terrestrial processes. The large, subaqueous CFBP eruptions that formed the submarine Ontong-Java and Kerguelen plateaus (that were emplaced during the Barremian and Aptian stages, respectively) are not associated with peaks in extinction intensity. The primary mechanism by which CFBP eruptions and bolide impacts is thought to perturb the environment is through injection of particulate material into the stratosphere (but see Pope 2002). Such injections would be minimal for deep-ocean impact events (Croft 1982). As for sea-level regressions, although the traditional killing mechanism associated with this event class is loss of habitat area to neritic marine biotas (Hallam 1989), exposure of formerly submarine continental shelves during a rapid eustatic sea-level fall would also elicit severe climatic effects (e.g. intensification of climatic gradients, increased seasonality, global cooling; see MacLeod 1998 and references therein) through alterations of atmospheric chemistry.

This terrestrial–marine linkage is also suspected to have played a role in controlling patterns of background extinction intensity. As stated above, initiation of the declining extinction gradient appears to occur within the Late Devonian through Early Carboniferous interval. Accurate estimation of this threshold is complicated by the presence of the very large Late Permian–Triassic extinction intensity levels. These were preceded by much lower extinction intensity values in the Late Carboniferous and Early Permian whose magnitudes appear consistent with post-Norian 'background' extinction values (Figs 1 & 8). If the Late Permian–Triassic is regarded as an anomalous interval of relatively high extinction intensities embedded within a 'groundmass' of lower extinction values, initiation of the background extinction gradient began in the Late Devonian–Early Carboniferous. Alternatively, if the Late Carboniferous through Early Permian is regarded as an anomalous interval of low extinction intensities embedded within a groundmass of higher extinction values, initiation of the background extinction-intensity gradient might be brought forward as far as the Early Jurassic. At present, the former interpretation is preferred: because the significance contrast between the two intervals' F-values is greatest for the Cambrian–Devonian/Carboniferous–Palaeogene subdivision scheme, and for mechanistic reasons.

The Late Devonian–Early Carboniferous interval was a watershed, not only for the history of life, but also for the organization of global geochemical cycles. Indeed, the latter occurred largely because of the former. For example, this interval follows a major extinction event for the acritarchs – the only well-known Early–Middle Palaeozoic marine planktonic primary-producer group – as well as the appearance of the first abundant land plants, first forests, and first deep soils. These contingent evolutionary–ecological events would have radically altered the Palaeozoic carbon cycle, the effect of which can be seen in shifts toward lower $^{87}Sr/^{86}Sr$ ratios (Burke et al. 1982) and heavier $\delta^{13}C$ values (see Hallam 1992). These shifts have generally been thought to reflect lower levels of terrestrial runoff to marine environments (implying lower nutrient input to nearshore marine settings), and increased rates of photosynthesis–carbon recycling in the upper parts of the water column, respectively. This transition also records a shift toward lighter $\delta^{34}S$ values (Hallam 1992) suggesting a general intensification of marine circulation patterns at this time, probably in response to the initial stages of Pangaea assembly. Overall, these trends suggest that the marine biosphere underwent a change from relatively stagnant conditions characterized by the geologically frequent occurrence of shifting patches of poorly oxygenated waters and relatively high rates of terrestrial runoff, to a better-mixed, less-anoxic post-Devonian condition with lower levels of terrestrial runoff. This switch would favour a decline in overall extinction-intensity values as marine biotas became adapted to more stable conditions with rising nutrient levels as a by-product of selection for physiological and ecological mechanisms designed to maximize rates of marine primary production and nutrient recycling (Hallock 1987; Martin 1996).

Although numerous kill mechanisms have been proposed for the Permo-Triassic extinction (see Erwin 1993 and Wignall 2001 for reviews), based on the results of this investigation – as well as others – it seems likely that climatic effects brought on as a result of lowered sea-level, the Siberian Trap CFBP eruptions, and the tectonic amalgamation of Pangaea played deterministic roles (as well as perhaps being accentuated by a short-term, global anoxia event, see Wignall & Hallam 1992; Wignall & Twitchett 2002). It is interesting to speculate that these extinctions might also have been exacerbated by the possible lack of a diversified marine phytoplankton flora in the Late Permian oceans. The identities of Late Palaeozoic phytoplankton groups have long been enigmatic. As mentioned above, acritarchs suffered a major diversity decline at the close of the Devonian (Tappan & Loeblich 1973). While most plant protist classes extant in the Devonian continued throughout the remainder of the Phanerozoic (Tappan 1980), the numerical dominance enjoyed by the Early Palaeozoic acritarch flora did not re-establish itself until the diversification of modern phytoplankton groups in the Early Jurassic (Tappan & Loeblich 1973). The Late Palaeozoic interval is particularly interesting in that a decline in marine primary productivity caused by the extinction or near extinction of phytoplankton clades has been implicated consistently in studies of several Mesozoic and Cenozoic marine extinction-intensity peaks. Reviewing this literature suggests that enough circumstantial evidence is available to sketch an outline of this flora's diversity history even in the absence of a direct fossil record.

Following the Late Devonian extinction event, overall extinction intensities remained relatively high in the enigmatic Early Carboniferous (see Fig. 1). During the Late Carboniferous and Early Permian, however, these estimates plummet to the lowest values that had been recorded up to that time. The magnitude of these low extinction-intensity values – which are comparable to those characteristic of post-Triassic stages in which a diversified phytoplankton flora was a quasi-permanent fixture – provides circumstantial evidence for the existence of a diversified phytoplankton flora during (at least) the Late Carboniferous–Early Permian. Consistent with this inference is the diversity of the benthic, filter-feeding, marine fauna that characterizes this interval.

Throughout the Late Permian, however, extinction-intensity magnitudes mount to the Tatarian high. Given the decimation of filter-feeding faunas across the Permo-Triassic boundary (Erwin 1993), and the post-Permian association between phytoplankton diversity lows and elevated extinction-intensity peaks, it strains credulity to believe that Late Permian phytoplankton floras were unaffected by this event. Owing to the relatively high levels of marine invertebrate extinction that characterize the Triassic, a continued phytoplankton diversity low may also have characterized this immediate post-Palaeozoic interval, perhaps lengthening the extinction-recovery phase. With the diversification of dinoflagellates and calcareous nannoplankton in the Late Triassic–Early Jurassic, however, extinction-intensity magnitudes underwent a dramatic reduction, to values only slightly higher than those characteristic of Palaeogene and Neogene intervals (see Figs 1 & 8). The subsequent macroevolutionary importance of the Late Triassic–Early Jurassic phytoplankton diversification is not only seen in the Jurassic–recent extinction record (where it may have played a role in controlling rates during background- and peak-intensity intervals, Wignall 2001), but is also beginning be appreciated as a major control in Mesozoic–Cenozoic diversification patterns (e.g. Valentine & Jablonski 1986 (molluscs); Smith 1984, and MacLeod 2003 (echinoderms)).

Summary

Progress toward understanding the major controls on marine Phanerozoic extinction patterns is necessary for a variety of palaeontological and conservation biological reasons. Up to now such progress has been impeded by:

(1)   an undue focus on the collection of information about individual events;
(2)   lack of appropriate analytical strategies for comparing patterns of stratigraphic coincidence against predictions from reasonable null models; and

(3)   failure to investigate analytically all pro-
       minent patterns exhibited by the Phaner-
       ozoic extinction record.

By correcting these oversights, comprehensive
explanations for this important aspect of life's
history on this planet can begin to be developed
in light of the necessary integration between
palaeontological and physical data.

Preliminary Monte Carlo simulation studies
of stratigraphical association patterns –
described herein and applied for the first time
in the context of extinction studies – suggest that
the extinction-intensity peak distribution most
closely matches the distributions of CFBP
volcanic events and long-term eustatic sea-level
regressions. Based on the statistical significance
of these associations, both mechanisms are
identified as the most likely candidates for
generalized control of Phanerozoic marine
extinction probabilities. Monte Carlo association analysis of coincidental interactions
between CFBP volcanism and sea-level regression also identify the coincidence of these
mechanisms as providing first-order, generalized
controls on the distribution of large extinction-
intensity peaks, at least for the last 250 Ma.
Bolide impacts leaving craters of between 50 and
150 kilometres have a much lower, and non-
significant ($p = 0.05$), level of statistical association with the extinction-intensity peak record.
Accordingly, this class of bolide impact is not
regarded as fulfilling the requirements of a
generalized control mechanism, although, of
course, individual bolide impacts may have
played a role in accentuating global extinction
intensities on a coincidental basis. These results
imply that Earth-based tectonic factors have
played a much larger role in controlling Phanerozoic extinction history than extraterrestrial
bombardments (although the recent theoretical
proposition of CFBP volcanic events being the
signatures of very large bolide impacts events is
noted with interest).

New analyses of the background extinction-
intensity gradient also reveal previously unsuspected associations. Subdivided time-series trend
analyses indicate that this gradient is not a
general feature of the Phanerozoic extinction
record, but is restricted to the Jurassic–Neogene
interval at least and Late Palaeozoic–Neogene
interval at most. The previous interval (Cambrian–Devonian at least, Cambrian–Triassic at
most) is not characterized by a statistically
significant, linear, extinction-intensity trend.
These results suggest that onset of a linear
'background extinction' gradient coincided
either with the Late Palaeozoic reorganization

of the global carbon cycle (driven by the
evolutionary diversification of land plants) or
the Late Triassic reorganization of the global
carbon cycle (driven by the evolutionary diversification of modern phytoplankton groups).
Both these evolutionary events had substantial
effects on marine invertebrate diversification –
as well as extinction – patterns.

Combining the results of these two analyses, it
would appear as though the primary controls on
the Phanerozoic pattern of marine extinction
intensity are: (1) tecto-eustatic and (2) evolutionary. Both process classes effect extinction
probabilities primarily by inducing global climate changes with small-to-medium, long-term
perturbations being implicated as more danger-
ous than large, short-term perturbations.
Although all aspects of the extinction record
require continued investigation to facilitate the
evaluation of more detailed hypotheses, the
primary *terra incognita* of this research pro-
gramme is the Late Palaeozoic–Triassic interval.
In particular, the identity and evolutionary fates
of Late Palaeozoic–Triassic phytoplankton
floras need to be much better understood in
order to evaluate their likely generalized role in
influencing generalized extinction dynamics.

I would like to thank M. Head for originally inviting
me to participate in the GAC/MAC 2002 Symposium,
the keynote talk for which served as a basis for this
article. J. W. Kirchner graciously supplied a copy of J.
Sepkoski's genus-level data with updates through 1997
for use in this study. A. B. Beaudoin served as editor
for this chapter and did a great job both chivvying me
along and understanding my abject failure to meet
several deadlines. I also thank A. Smith, D. Price, and
V. Courtillot for discussions on aspects of the
arguments presented herein. The entire manuscript
was ably reviewed by D. Archibald, W. Clemens, T.
Hallam, J. Lipps, and A. B. Beaudoin, all of whose
comments resulted in many clarifications and other
improvements.

References

ALVAREZ, W. 1997. T. rex *and the Crater of Doom.*
    Princeton University Press, Princeton, NJ, 185 pp.
ALVAREZ, W. & ASARO, F. 1990. An extraterrestrial
    impact. *Scientific American*, **263**, 78–84.
ALVAREZ, L. W., ALVAREZ, F., ASARO, F. &
    MICHEL, H. V. 1980. Extraterrestrial cause for
    the Cretaceous–Tertiary extinction. *Science*, **208**,
    1095–1108.
ALVAREZ, W., ALVAREZ, L. W., ASARO, F. and
    MICHEL, H. 1982. Current status of the impact
    theory for the terminal Cretaceous extinction.
    Geological implications of impacts of large
    asteroids and comets on Earth. *Geological Society
    of America Special Papers*, **190**, 305–315.

ALVAREZ, W., ASARO, F., CLAEYS, P., GRAJALES-N., J. M., MONTANARI, A. & SMIT, J. 1994. Developments in the K/T impact theory since Snowbird II, New developments regarding the K/T event and other catastrophes in earth history. *Lunar and Planetary Institute Contribution*, **825**, 3–5.

ARCHIBALD, J. D. 1996. *Dinosaur Extinction and the End of an Era: What the Fossils Say. Critical Moments in Paleobiology and Earth History*. Columbia University Press, New York, 237 pp.

BERGGREN, W. A. & VAN COUVERING, J. A. 1984. *Catastrophes and Earth History*. Princeton University Press, Princeton, NJ, 464 pp.

BURKE, W. H., DENISON, R. E., HETHERINGTON, E. A., KOEPNICK, R. B., NELSON, H. F. & OTTO, J. B. 1982. Variation in $^{87}Sr/^{86}Sr$ throughout Phanerozoic time. *Geology*, **10**, 516–519.

COURTILLOT, V. E. & RENNE, P. R. in press. On the ages of flood basalt events. *Comptes Rendus de l' Académie des Sciences*.

COURTILLOT, V., JAEGER, J.-J., YANG, Z., FÉRAUD, G. & HOFMANN, C. 1996. The influence of continental flood basalts on mass extinctions: where do we stand? *In*: RYDER, G., FASTOVSKY, D. & GARTNER, S. (eds) *The Cretaceous–Tertiary Event and Other Catastrophes in Earth History*. Geological Society of America, Special Paper, 307, 513–525.

CROFT, S. K. 1982. A first-order estimate of shock heating and vaporization in oceanic impacts. *In*: SILVER, L. T. & SCHULTZ, P. H. (eds) *Geological Implications of Impacts of Large Asteroids and Comets on the Earth*. Geological Society of America Special Papers, **190**, 143–152.

DAVIS, J. C. 1973. *Statistics and Data Analysis in Geology*. John Wiley, New York, 550 pp.

DAVIS, J. C. 1986. *Statistics and Data Analysis in Geology (second edition)*. John Wiley, New York, USA, 646 pp.

DAVIS, J. C. 2002. *Statistics and Data Analysis in Geology (third edition)*. John Wiley, New York, 638 pp.

ERWIN, D. H. 1993. The great Paleozoic crisis: life and death in the Permian. *Critical Moments in Paleobiology and Earth History Series*. Columbia University Press, New York, USA, 327 pp.

FLESSA, K. W. & JABLONSKI, D. 1985. Declining Phanerozoic background extinction rates: effect of taxonomic structure? *Nature*, **313**, 216–218.

GALVIN, C. 1998. The great dinosaur extinction controversy and the K–T research program in the late 20th century. *Earth Sciences History*, **17**, 41–55.

GLEN, W. 1994. *Mass-Extinction Debates: How Science Works in a Crisis*. Stanford University Press, Stanford, California, USA, 370 pp.

GLEN, W. 1996. Observations on mass-extinction debates. *In*: RYDER, G., FASTOVSKY, D. & GARTNER, S. (eds) *The Cretaceous–Tertiary Event and Other Catastrophes in Earth History*, Geological Society of America Special Paper, **307**, 39–54.

GLEN, W. 1998. A manifold current upheaval in science. *Earth Sciences History*, **17(2)**, 190–209.

GOULD, S. J. 1984. The cosmic dance of Siva. *Natural History*, **93**, p. 8.

GOULD, S. J. 1985. The paradox of the first tier: an agenda for paleobiology. *Paleobiology*, **11**, 2–12.

GOULD, S. J. 2002. *The Structure of Evolutionary Theory*. Belknap/Harvard University Press, Cambridge, Massachusetts, 1433 pp.

GRADSTEIN, F. M. & OGG, J. 1996. A Phanerozoic time scale. *Episodes*, **19**, 3–5.

GRIEVE, R., RUPERT, J., SMITH, J. & THERRIAULT, A. 1996. The record of terrestrial impact cratering. *GSA Today*, **5**, 193–195.

HALLAM, A. 1987. Mesozoic marine organic-rich shales. *In*: BROOKS, J. & FLEET, A. (eds), *Marine Petroleum Source Rocks*, Geological Society, London, Special Publications, **26**, 251–261.

HALLAM, A. 1989. The case for sea-level change as a dominant causal factor in mass extinctions of marine invertebrates. *Philosophical Transactions of the Royal Society of London, Series B*, **325**, 437–455.

HALLAM, A. 1992. *Phanerozoic Sea-Level Changes*. Columbia University Press, New York, USA, 266 pp.

HALLAM, A. & WIGNALL, P. B. 1997. *Mass Extinctions and their Aftermath*. Oxford Science Publications, Oxford, 328 pp.

HALLAM, A. & WIGNALL, P. B. 1999. Mass extinctions and sea-level changes. *Earth-Science Reviews*, **48**, 217–250.

HALLOCK, P. 1987. Fluctuations in the trophic resource continuum: a factor in global diversity cycles? *Paleoceanography*, **83**, 49–64.

HAQ, B. 1991. Sequence stratigraphy, sea-level change and significance for the deep sea. *International Association of Sedimentologists, Special Publication*, **12**, 3–39.

HOFFMAN, A. & NITECKI, M. A. 1985. Reception of the asteroid hypothesis of terminal Cretaceous extinctions. *Geology*, **13**, 884–887.

JABLONSKI, D. 1986a. Background and mass extinctions. The alteration of macroevolutionary regimes. *Science*, 231, 129–133.

JABLONSKI, D. 1986b. Evolutionary consequences of mass extinctions. *In*: RAUP, D. M. & JABLONSKI, D. (eds) *Patterns and Processes in the History of Life*. Springer-Verlag, Berlin, 313–329.

JONES, A. P., PRICE, G. D., PRICE, N. J., DeCARLI, P. S. & CLEGG, R. A. 2002. Impact induced melting and the development of large igneous provinces. *Earth and Planetary Science Letters*, **202**, 551–561.

KIRCHNER, J. W. 2002. Evolutionary speed limits inferred from the fossil record. *Nature*, **415**, 65–68.

KIRCHNER, J. W. & WEIL, A. 2000. Delayed biological recovery throughout the fossil record. *Nature*, **404**, 177–180.

KITCHELL, J. A., ESTABROOK, G. & MacLEOD, N. 1987. Testing for equality of rates of evolution. *Paleobiology*, **13**, 272–285.

KITCHELL, J. A. & MACLEOD, N. 1988. Testing macroevolutionary interpretations of symmetry and synchroneity in the fossil record. *Science*, **240**, 1190–1193.

LEAKEY, R. & LEWIN, R. 1996. *The Sixth Extinction*. Weidenfield, London, 271 pp.

MACLEOD, N. 1991. Punctuated anagenesis and the importance of stratigraphy to paleobiology. *Paleobiology*, **17**, 167–188.

MACLEOD, N. 1998. Impacts and marine invertebrate extinctions. *In*: GRADY, M. M., HUTCHINSON, R., MCCALL, G. J. H. & ROTHERBY, D. A. (eds) *Meteorites: Flux with Time and Impact Effects*. Geological Society of London, London, pp. 217–246.

MACLEOD, N. 2003. The causes of Phanerozoic extinctions. *In*: ROTHSCHILD, L. & LISTER, A. (eds) *Evolution of the Earth*. Academic Press, London.

MACLEOD, N. & KELLER, G. 1996. *The Cretaceous–Tertiary Mass Extinction: Biotic and Environmental Changes*. W. W. Norton, New York, 595 pp.

MACLEOD, N., RAWSON, P. F. ET AL. 1997. The Cretaceous–Tertiary biotic transition. *Journal of the Geological Society of London*, **154**, 265–292.

MANLEY, B. F. J. 1997. *Randomization, Bootstrap and Monte Carlo Methods in Biology*. Chapman and Hall, London, 399 pp.

MARTIN, R. E. 1996. Secular increase in nutrient levels through the Phanerozoic: implications for productivity, biomass, and diversity of the marine biosphere. *Palaios*, **11**, 209–219.

NEWELL, N. D. 1967. Revolutions in the history of life. *In*: ALBRITTON, C. C., HUBBERT, M. K., WILSON, L. G. & NEWELL N. D. (eds) *Uniformity and Simplicity: a Symposium on the Principle of the Uniformity of Nature*. Geological Society of America Special Papers, **89**, Boulder, Colorado, 63–91.

PARRISH, J. T. & CURTIS, R. L. 1982. Atmospheric circulation, upwelling, and organic-rich rocks in the Mesozoic and Cenozoic eras. *Palaeogeography, Palaeoclimatology, Palaeoecology*, **40**, 31–66.

POPE, K. O. 2002. Impact dust not the cause of the Cretaceous–Tertiary mass extinction. *Geology*, **30**, 99–102.

PROTHERO, D. R. 1994. *The Eocene–Oligocene Transition: Paradise Lost*. Columbia University Press, New York, 291 pp.

RAMPINO, M. R. & STOTHERS, R. B. 1988. Flood basalt volcanism during the past 250 million years. *Science*, **241**, 663–668.

RAUP, D. M. 1986. *The Nemesis Affair: A Story of the Death of the Dinosaurs and the Ways of Science*. W. W. Norton, New York, 220 pp.

RAUP, D. M. 1991. *Extinction: Bad Genes or Bad Luck*. W. W. Norton, New York, 210 pp.

RAUP, D. M. & BOYAJIAN, G. E. 1988. Patterns of generic extinction in the fossil record. *Paleobiology*, **14**, 109–125.

RAUP, D. M. & CRICK, R. 1979. Measurement of faunal similarity in paleontology. *Journal of Paleontology*, **53**, 1213–1227.

RAUP, D. M. & SEPKOSKI, J. J., Jr 1982. Mass extinctions in the marine fossil record. *Science*, **215**, 1501–1503.

RAUP, D. M. & SEPKOSKI, J. J., Jr 1984. Periodicity of extinctions in the geologic past. *Proceedings of the Natural Academy of Sciences*, **81**, 801–805.

RAUP, D. M. & SEPKOSKI, J. J., Jr 1986. Periodic extinction of families and genera. *Science*, **231**, 833–836.

RAUP, D. M. & SEPKOSKI, J. J., Jr 1988. Testing for periodicity in extinction. *Science*, **241**, 94–96.

RYDER, G. 1996. K/T boundary: historical context, counter-revolutions, and burdens of proof. *In*: RYDER, G., FASTOVSKY, D. & GARTNER, S. (eds) *The Cretaceous–Tertiary Event and Other Catastrophes in Earth History*. Geological Society of America Special Paper, *307*, Boulder, Colorado, *31–38*.

SCHEFFER, M., CARPENTER, S., FOLEY, J. A., FOLKES, C. & WALKER, B. 2001. Catastrophic shifts in ecosystems. *Nature*, **413**, 591–596.

SEPKOSKI, J. J., Jr 1984. A kinetic model of Phanerozoic taxonomic diversity III. Post-Paleozoic families and mass extinctions. *Paleobiology*, **10**, 246–267.

SEPKOSKI, J. J., Jr 1990. The taxonomic structure of periodic extinction. *In*: SHARPTON, V. L. & WARD, P. D. (eds) *Global Catastrophes in Earth History: an Interdisciplinary Conference on Impacts, Volcanism, and Mass Mortality*. Geological Society of America Special Paper, **247**, Boulder, Colorado, 33–44.

SEPKOSKI, J. J., Jr 1994. Extinction and the fossil record. *Geotimes*, **March 1994**, 15–17.

SEPKOSKI, J. J., Jr 1996. Patterns of Phanerozoic extinction: a perspective from global databases. *In*: WALLISER, O. H. (ed.) *Global Events and Event Stratigraphy*. Springer-Verlag, Berlin, 35–52.

SEPKOSKI, J. J., Jr & RAUP, D. M. 1986. Periodicity in marine extinction events. *In*: ELLIOTT, D. K. (ed.) *Dynamics of Extinction*. Wiley-Interscience, New York, 3–36.

SMITH, A. 1984. *Echinoid Paleobiology*. George Allen & Unwin, London, 190 pp.

SMITH, A. B. 2001. Large-scale heterogeneity of the fossil record: implications for Phanerozoic biodiversity studies. *Philosophical Transactions of the Royal Society of London, Series B*, **356**, 351–367.

SOKAL, R. R. & ROHLF, F. J. 1981. *Biometry: the Principles and Practice of Statistics in Biological Research (second edition)*. W. H. Freeman, San Francisco, California, USA, 859 pp.

SOKAL, R. R. & ROHLF, F. J. 1995. *Biometry: the Principles and Practice of Statistics in Biological Research (third edition)*. W. H. Freeman, New York, 887 pp.

TAPPAN, H. 1980. *The Paleobiology of Plant Protists*. W. H. Freeman, San Francisco, California, 1028 pp.

TAPPAN, H. & LOEBLICH, A. R. 1973. Evolution of the oceanic plankton. *Earth Science Reviews*, **9**, 207–240.

VALENTINE, J. W. & JABLONSKI, D. 1986. Mass extinctions: selectivity of marine larval types. *Proceedings of the National Academy of Sciences*, **83**, 6912–6914.

VAN VALEN, L. M. 1994. Concepts and the nature of selection by extinction: is generalization possible? *In*: GLEN, W. (ed.) *The Mass Extinction Debates: How Science Works in a Crisis.* Stanford University Press, Stanford, California, 200–216.

VERMEIJ, G. J. 1987. *Evolution and Escalation: an Ecological History of Life.* Princeton University Press, Princeton, New Jersey, 527 pp.

WARD, P. D. 1992. *On Methusalah's Trail: Living Fossils and the Great Extinctions.* Freeman, New York, 212 pp.

WARD, P. D. 1995. *The End of Evolution: Dinosaurs, Mass Extinction and Biodiversity.* Weidenfeld and Nicolson, London, 302 pp.

WARD, P. D. 2000. *Rivers in Time: the Search for Clues to Earth's Mass Extinctions.* Columbia University Press, New York, 315 pp.

WIGNALL, P. B. 2001. Large igneous provinces and mass extinctions. *Earth-Science Reviews*, **53**, 1–33.

WIGNALL, P. B. & HALLAM, A. 1992. Anoxia as a cause of the Permian/Triassic extinction: facies as evidence from northern Italy and the western United States. *Palaeogeography, Palaeoclimatology, Palaeoecology*, **93**, 21–46.

WIGNALL, P. B. & TWITCHETT, R. J., 2002. Extent, duration, and nature of the Permian–Triassic superanoxic event. *In*: KOEBERL, C. & MACLEOD, K. C. (eds) *Catastrophic Events and Mass Extinctions: Impacts and Beyond, Special Paper*, **356**. The Geological Society of America, Boulder, Colorado, 395–413.

ZAR, J. H. 1974. *Biostatistical Analysis.* Prentice Hall, Englewood Cliffs, New Jersey, USA, 620 pp.

Deviation from Red Queen behaviour at stratigraphic boundaries: evidence for directional recovery

N. A. DORAN[1], A. J. ARNOLD[1], W. C. PARKER[1] & F. W. HUFFER[2]

[1]*Department of Geology, 108 Carraway Building, Florida State University, Tallahassee, FL 32306-4100, USA*

[2]*Department of Statistics, 214 OSB, Florida State University, Tallahassee, FL 32306-4330, USA (e-mail: Doran@gly.fsu.edu)*

Abstract: Boundary-defining events influence the evolutionary behaviour of post-extinction survivors. The Cox proportional hazards model takes into account the varying background extinction rates characteristic of boundaries and enables survivorship analysis of post-boundary behaviour. Survivorship results from the Middle Cretaceous to recent planktonic foraminifera reveal two intriguing observations. First, they indicate significantly age-dependent extinction probabilities in populations of species following two boundaries: Cenomanian–Turonian (C–T) and Cretaceous–Tertiary (K–T); the survivors are short lived and show rapid turnover. Characteristics that might mediate this macroevolutionary behaviour are clearly distinct from those that precede the extinction. We hypothesize that the rapid taxonomic turnover during post-extinction macroevolutionary recovery is driven by the lingering expression of 'passport' characteristics, where the primary adaptive value was during the preceding extinction. Second, age-dependency of extinction oscillates through time. Many survivorship curves averaging long-term data have exponential or near-exponential form: suggesting a lack of age-dependence consistent with the Red Queen hypothesis. The boundary events discussed here, analysed in higher-resolution 15 Ma subsets, demonstrate perturbation of some post-extinction populations toward positive age-dependence, and are followed by long intervals suggestive of recovery. Red Queen behaviour, when measured over very long time-spans, appears to be the time-averaged result of these boundary-generated oscillations between short-term positive age-dependence and longer-term return to nearly age-independent Red Queen behaviour.

It is unavoidable that the characteristics which survivor species carry with them through a mass extinction must necessarily be the same characteristics that mediate recovery – a fact so simple as to be a truism were its implications not so far-reaching. The implications for our understanding of adaptation are particularly compelling. Adaptation is such an integral aspect of the evolutionary process that its role often goes unquestioned – so much so that it can be tempting to begin an evolutionary study with the *a priori* assumption that organisms' adaptations reflect a harmonious relationship with the environment in which we find them. However, the survivors of an extinction, although they may (fortuitously or otherwise) have 'passport' (the 'passport' concept was developed from earlier work of A. J. Arnold, but is named here for the first time) characteristics that allowed them to pass through an event, may not necessarily reflect optimal adaptation to the post-extinction setting in which these survivors find themselves. These survivor species may even be less well adapted to the post-extinction world than their recently extinct relatives would have been had they survived. In this sense, a passport characteristic, like a true passport, may lose its utility once the boundary has been passed.

Extinctions and their causes have received a great deal of attention – far out of proportion to the brevity of the events that they record. Conversely, biotic recovery from extinction, although it can span tens of millions of years (Arnold *et al.* 1995*b*; Erwin 2001), receives far less attention than such long recovery times would invite. We might speculate that this is because the post-extinction biota is viewed as depauperate and therefore of diminished interest; but, whatever the reasons, it is important to remember that it is not the victims of extinction but the survivors that shape subsequent diversification.

It is sometimes held that opportunists pass through boundaries and eventually dominate the recovery biota. Studies on the K–T and E–O

From: BEAUDOIN, A.B. & HEAD, M.J. (eds) 2004. *The Palynology and Micropalaeontology of Boundaries.* Geological Society, London, Special Publications, **230**, 35–46. 0305-8719/04/$15 © The Geological Society of London 2004.

events have suggested that recovery is a much more complicated issue. Extinction survivors may include a range of survival characteristics, including residence in protected habitats, broad adaptive ranges, dormancy, larval stages, and many others (Kauffman 1984; Keller 1986*a*, *b*, 1988, 1989*a*, *b*; Hansen *et al.* 1987; Hansen 1988; Kauffman & Walliser 1988; Harries *et al.* 1996; Jablonski 2002). One mechanism of survival involves intrinsic biological factors, such as a proclivity for rapid speciation based on factors related to population structure or generation time. Lineages that show rapid speciation may leave distinctive patterns of survivorship during their recovery.

A lingering question also relates to the magnitude of extinctions. Are mass extinctions distinct departures from normal background levels of diversity fluctuation, or are they simply the most extreme end members of a continuous distribution of diversity fluctuations, different in degree but not in kind? In other words, is there anything special about mass extinctions other than the fact that we notice them because of their magnitude? In spite of a great deal of discussion, the issue is still unresolved (e.g. Boyajian 1986, 1991; Jablonski 1986, 1989, 2001; Thackery 1990; Hubbard & Gilinsky 1992; Raup 1994; Kirchner & Weil 2000). Our results suggest that some boundary extinction events can be distinguished from background diversity fluctuations, but that the distinction is expressed most clearly by the nature of recovery rather than by the magnitude of the extinction itself.

The Red Queen Hypothesis is based on Van Valen's (1973) Law of Constant Extinction – a counterintuitive but widespread observation that species within ecologically homogeneous taxa tend not to increase (or decrease) their immunity to extinction through time; instead, taxonomic survivorship curves show a constant probability of extinction regardless of species longevity. This observation is judged to be counterintuitive because longer-lived species might be expected to have more time to adapt to the abiotic environment, thereby acquiring a resistance to extinction that their shorter-lived relatives cannot. To explain this observation, Van Valen advanced the Red Queen Hypothesis, which holds that ever-changing biotic interaction between species requires that they continually evolve to avoid extinction, and that species do not develop increased immunity from extinction, because the remainder of the biota is continually evolving in response. Thus, later members of a lineage may be adaptively superior to their ancestors, but their fitness (and species

survivorship) remains unchanged as they evolve to keep pace with an ever-shifting biotic setting. Hence, the Red Queen's comment about life on the other side of the looking glass: 'Now here, you see, it takes all the running you can do, to keep in the same place.' (Carroll 1872).

Unfortunately, to the extent that mass extinctions exert an anomalous influence on extinction patterns and later recovery, they also make survivorship analysis of extinctions more complex. The great variation in extinction rates through boundaries creates inhomogeneous populations that are difficult to compare through the analysis of simple survivorship curves. The simple exponential survivorship predicted under the Red Queen Hypothesis assumed populations undergoing stochastically similar rates of extinction (Van Valen 1973), an assumption that is not met in the vicinity of most extinction boundaries. More complex techniques of survivorship analysis are thus required to account for the temporal variation caused by perturbations associated with mass extinctions, and time-dependent variation in general (Pearson 1992).

Extinction events may also create even longer-term bias in survivorship analysis. Indeed, the lingering effects of extinction may characterize much of the interval between boundaries. Initially, the intent of this research was to model the survivorship of planktonic foraminifera over the last 145 Ma in order to explore patterns of age-dependence. Our results show that stratigraphic boundaries can play a central role in shaping patterns of macroevolutionary survivorship as well as recovery during the intervals between. We show this by applying the assumptions of the Red Queen Hypothesis across major extinction boundaries.

The data

To test boundary survivorship patterns, we will examine the fossil record of planktonic foraminifera. Planktonic foraminifera have an excellent fossil record, yet were nearly eliminated by the K–T boundary event. This distinctive history gives their recovery pattern particular clarity. Their precisely constrained stratigraphic ranges make them ideal candidates for survivorship analysis. Foraminiferal ranges are known to the level of morphospecies; in addition, much of their phylogeny is known from direct observation of transitions in the fossil record.

Longevity data for the Cenozoic Globigerinida were derived primarily from integration of works by Blow (1979), Kennett & Srinivasan (1983) and Bolli & Saunders (1985). The

Palaeogene foraminiferal history was further refined and developed from the Palaeogene Working Group: Berggren (1977), Boersma & Premoli Silva (1983), Toumarkine & Luterbacher (1985), Fordham (1986), Boersma et al. (1987), Premoli Silva & Boersma (1988), and Olsson et al. (1999). Species origination and extinction times are calibrated to the time scale of Berggren et al. (1995). Cretaceous data are derived from Postuma (1971), Robaszynski et al. (1984), Bolli et al. (1989), Hart (1990), Berggren and Norris (1997), BouDagher-Fadel et al. (1997) and Olsson et al. (1999). The stratigraphic resolution of the Cenozoic provides an excellent background for the study of planktonic foraminiferal survivorship. These data are expanded from the version used by Parker & Arnold (1997). In addition to the longevity data, the data also contain morphological information on all Cenozoic species, including landmark-based distance measures, angles, and parameters derived from measurements (e.g. Raupian parameters, principal component analysis).

The phylogenetic relationships were taken from the literature and are based primarily on the reports of stratigraphically preserved ancestor–descendant transitions and phylogenetic analyses. Because the survivorship study is based on individual species' longevities and is not dependent upon branching topology, phylogenetic relationships will not affect the analyses. However, because branching relationships among Palaeogene foraminifera have been thought to affect species ranges (Pearson 1998b), the authors are also working on a follow-up to this study to account for branching topologies.

Only the planktonic foraminifera currently provide the taxonomic and stratigraphic resolution necessary for a study such as this; nonetheless, some concerns must be addressed. One is that it is possible that specialists have divided lineages into operational taxonomic units that only approximate biological reality (Pearson 1992; Parker & Arnold 1997). This may result from 'pseudoextinction' and 'pseudospeciation' (Pearson 1998a); Pearson discussed this problem at length in the context of survivorship analysis (Pearson 1995, 1996, 1998b; McGowan et al. 1999). Since then, an additional problem has arisen regarding the classification of true biological species (in the sense of Mayr's Biological Species Concept). Classification of two or more true biological species under a single name can be the result of so-called 'cryptic' speciation. Cryptic speciation has become an increasingly common observation for many taxa, including planktonic foraminifera (de Vargas et al. 1999,

2001). Recent studies indicate that pelagic biodiversity in general may be greatly underestimated due to cryptic speciation (Norris 2000). For these reasons, and others, it should be stressed that we define all species in terms of the morphological species concept. These problems do not invalidate survivorship analysis, although some refinement of the analyses and their interpretation may become appropriate as issues such as cryptic speciation and pseudo-extinction are clarified over time. This issue is further discussed below.

Cox survivorship analysis

Survivorship analysis has produced valuable palaeontological insights since the time of Simpson (1944), but has also been the subject of controversy. Application of the Epstein test to planktonic foraminifera indicated that they showed exponential patterns consistent with the Red Queen Hypothesis (Arnold 1982). The Total Life Method of Epstein verified the log linearity of survivorship and therefore lack of age-dependence (Epstein 1960a, b). Pearson (1992, 1995) later observed that temporally heterogeneous extinction rates affected survivorship analysis and ought to be taken into account. Taxa existing at different times could experience vastly different rates of extinction (e.g. those present at the K–T boundary v. an assemblage in the Middle Miocene). Thus, extinction rates in real time, or time-dependency of extinction, had to be separated from the issue of the longevity of the taxon, or age-dependency. Pearson proposed his Corrected Survivorship Score (CSS) to account for this distinction (Pearson 1992, 1995; McGowan et al. 1999). Analysis of survivorship near important geological boundaries is particularly problematic, because it is precisely at these boundaries that temporal variation in extinction becomes most pronounced.

Approaches to survivorship that account for time-dependency can also be found among the models used in failure time analysis (Kalbfleisch & Prentice 1980). Data that have an end point at the time an event occurs are called failure time data. Failure may be broadly defined to include any response pertinent to the field of study in question. Failure time data are distinguished by the presence of censoring; that is, for some individuals we only have partial information about the failure time. The most common type of censoring is right censoring; we know only that the survival time of an individual exceeds some given value, c. This happens in medical situations if a patient drops out of the study before the event of interest (e.g. death) is observed, or if a patient survives beyond the end of the study period. For the purpose of this analysis, the taxon range is analogous to the survival of a patient, and extant species in the data-set are considered to be censored.

An alternative to the CSS for addressing survivorship across boundaries and eliminating the problem of time-dependence is the use of a proportional hazards model. Regression models of survivorship often assume a proportional hazard function. The non-parametric version of this model is the Cox proportional hazards model (Cox 1972; Lee 1980). The essence of the Cox model consists of a hazard rate calculated as a product of an arbitrary baseline hazard with an exponential function of the covariate. It takes the form:

$$h(t, z) = h_o(t) \ e^{\beta z}$$

where t represents geological time, $h_o(t)$ is the baseline hazard rate, β a regression parameter, and z a covariate of interest; in palaeontological analyses of species, z might be a morphological character (e.g. chamber number). This model might be applied to an entire population – say, all the planktonic foraminifera – with variations in the background extinction rate handled by the function of $h_o(t)$. The model is called a *proportional* hazards model because the ratio of the hazard functions for two individuals with different values, z_1 and z_2, of the covariate, turns out to be:

$$\frac{h(t, z_1)}{h(t, z_2)} = \frac{h_0(t) \ e^{\beta z_1}}{h_0(t) \ e^{\beta z_2}}$$
$$= e^{\beta(z_1 - z_2)}$$

which does not depend on time, that is, the hazard functions are proportional.

In order to examine age-dependence, our model must include species age as a covariate. Since the species age varies with time, we must slightly reformulate the Cox model as follows:

$$h(t, z(t)) = h_o(t) \ e^{\beta z(t)}$$

where t again represents geological time, $z(t)$ the species age at time t; for a species originating at time t_0, we have $z(t) = t - t_0$ for $t < t_0$. The arbitrary baseline hazard rate is again $h_o(t)$. The coefficient is now multiplied by $z(t)$, where species age is a function of time. With this form of the model we may ask questions about temporal variation in survivorship. This alteration of the model preserves and takes into account information about origination and extinction of foraminiferal species at their respective first appearance datums (FADs) and last appearance datums (LADs) within the context of geological time.

For the Cox model, when $z(t)$ is taken to be the species age, a non-zero value of the regression coefficient, β, indicates a relationship between species age and extinction rates. For positive β values, there is an increase in probability of extinction with increasing species range, or 'age'. Negative coefficients show the converse relationship. Naturally, a time-frame must be defined within which to examine survivorship behaviour. Examining short-term variation in survivorship requires that we balance the competing needs for stratigraphic resolution and statistical certainty. For this study, after experimenting with larger and smaller temporal windows, p-values and β coefficients were calculated for 15 Ma windows of time. Shorter and longer time-frames reflect a similar pattern (the authors are pursuing separate work optimizing this balance). The p-value is the probability of obtaining as large or larger a value of $|\hat{\beta}|$, the absolute value of the estimated coefficient, given that the true value β is 0. The β value and p-value plotted for that interval was considered to lie at the midpoint (or 7.5 Ma into the frame; Figs 1 & 2). The window was moved forward in time at 1 Ma intervals and recalculated.

Results

Sequential calculations of age-dependency for species which originate within 15 Ma time frames from the Middle Cretaceous to the present gives a continuously varying pattern punctuated by sudden shifts at critical boundaries. Figure 1 shows a significant shift in β values following the C–T and K–T events. The E–O event does not show the same pattern. Interestingly, p-values for the coefficient are highly significant following both the C–T and K–T events. The age-dependence in extinction lasts approximately 25 Ma after the K–T boundary. Following these extinctions, the β values appear to drop at a nearly constant rate; the drop takes place over a large portion of the Cenozoic, even sometimes dropping into negative values (Fig. 1). Also noticeable are smaller positive shifts in β at about 108, 72 and 27 million years that interrupt the steady declines from earlier high values.

It is known from previous work that age-dependence in planktonic foraminiferal survivorship is statistically significant for the Cen-

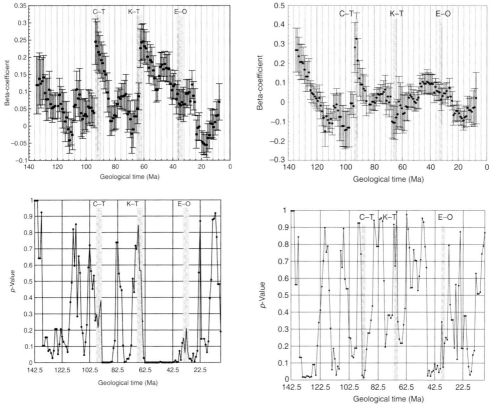

Fig. 1. Beta-coefficient (with standard error bars) and *p*-values for *β* by geological time for all species in the data-set. Positive *β* (top) indicates extinction probability increases as species age increases; negative coefficient indicates the reverse. The *p*-values (below) show strong significance following the C–T and K–T boundaries, although not the E–O.

Fig. 2. Beta-coefficient (with standard error bars) and *p*-values for *β* by geological time for all species in the data-set with ranges greater than 4 Ma. Eliminating shorter-ranged species removes much of the significance of the C–T and K–T events. In both figures, note the somewhat periodic nature of the coefficients and *p*-values.

ozoic planktonic foraminifera as a whole, and that the elimination of short-ranged species (less than 4 Ma duration) from the analysis causes the survivorship curve to revert to exponential form (Parker & Arnold 1997). Because of this, in Figure 2, only the age-dependence of species lasting 4 Ma or longer was assessed. Removal of the short-ranging species reduced the age-dependence effect following the C–T and K–T boundaries. However, the population immediately following the Jurassic–Cretaceous boundary shows significant age-dependence. The *p*-values in both analyses appear to exhibit a quasi-periodic spacing.

Discussion

Age-dependent extinction is indicated by non-zero *β* values, and means the probability of extinction increases (or decreases) as a function of species age. Through the Late Mesozoic and Cenozoic, age-dependence of extinction exhibits fluctuations through time; most of this fluctuation is in the direction of positive *β* indicating that the likelihood of extinction generally tends to increase (rather than decrease) with increasing age; however, we can only speak with confidence about time intervals in which the *p*-values are significant. The pronounced positive departures immediately following the C–T and K–T events (as demonstrated by simultaneously highly significant *p*-values and strongly positive *β* values) suggest that events at these boundaries increase the age-dependence effect. Moreover, the data indicate that short-ranged species are the cause of the age-dependence effect (Fig. 2). Because we cannot test the idea with our data, we have been cautious in giving consideration to the possibility of species senescence; at the same time, our results do not rule it out. Overall, we believe that our data favour the alternative that we expand upon below.

Our initial hypothesis was that this distinctive pattern of significant age-dependent extinction might reflect a taxonomic artefact rather than the biological reality: if rapid anagenesis is the dominant evolutionary pattern during these two post-boundary times, then taxonomists may have arbitrarily subdivided rapidly evolving chronospecies into artificial short-ranged morphospecies (Pearson 1998*a*). Phylogenetic trees of Palaeogene planktonic foraminifera, not only morphospecies' ranges, show strong biases (Pearson 1998*b*). However, if this is the case, then we are still left trying to explain why the anagenesis that generates this distinctive pattern dominates only during recovery times immediately after the C–T and K–T boundaries. We proceed on the assumption that taxonomic decisions are likely to be based on an underlying reality; misinterpretation of that reality as cladogenesis or true extinction rather than anagenesis does not invalidate the observation of age-dependence, it merely changes its interpretation. Thus, appeal to taxonomic artefact merely frames the same questions in a new context. These questions are as follows.

Does extinction leave an imprint that characterizes subsequent recovery? Yes. Post-extinction age-dependence, now verified by two survivorship models (Parker & Arnold 1997 and herein) and an analysis of mean longevity (Arnold *et al.* 1995*b*) strongly suggest this. The change in species age structure is a signature that lingers for at least 15 Ma after the C–T boundary. Significant age-dependence lingers for about 25 Ma in the case of the K–T. Interestingly, molluscan gamma diversity took 25 Ma before this group showed full recovery after the K–T boundary (Hansen 1988). As with foraminifera, it appears that molluscan faunas spend much, if not most, of their time recovering from extinctions. A contrasting interpretation is that age-dependence is a taxonomic artefact. Pearson removed the age-dependence in post-K–T morphospecies longevities by analysing lineages (Pearson 1996); removal of pseudoextinction and pseudospeciation eliminated the effect. However, we must now ask why age-dependence arises after two extinction boundaries. If it is a result of taxonomic artefact in both instances, then why is this taxonomic artefact concentrated so significantly after extinction events?

Can mass extinctions be distinguished from background extinction? Our data suggest that some can, again, by their lingering age-dependence signature. The K–T extinction is both a profound extinction and a sharp stratigraphic boundary, and its age-dependent signature lingers for at least 20 Ma after the event. However, the Cenomanian–Turonian extinction is a second-order extinction, perhaps less distinctive than the Eocene–Oligocene (E–O), and yet it carries a post-boundary signature of age-dependence (and equivalent significance levels) for nearly half as long as the K–T, while the E–O boundary shows no age-dependent signal at all. This suggests to us that some feature other than the magnitude of the extinction is responsible for the observed age-dependency.

What can passport characters tell us about macroevolutionary recovery after boundaries? The results lend themselves to two immediate explanations. One is simply that the recovery intervals are characterized by rapid expansion into ecospace; the other is that a more complicated biological scenario is being played out. The first choice is the traditional understanding of mass extinction recovery and cannot be discounted. However, subtle clues indicate a more complicated macroevolutionary picture that reflects juvenilization of surviving lineages, resulting in what we here designate as 'passport characters'.

Arnold *et al.* (1995*a*) analysed the dynamics of how small planktonic foraminifera tend to survive extinction events. Size increase appears to reflect asymmetrical drift from small beginning size with asymmetry being introduced by a biological absorbing boundary at zero or very small size. Arnold *et al.* posit that this is the underlying cause of Cope's Rule. Cope's Rule holds that lineages tend to increase in mean size over time, making the size of the later descendants noticeably greater than that of the earlier species (such as those following mass extinctions). But this proposal simply frames the question in a new perspective: why are post-extinction survivors small? Arnold *et al.* (1995*a*) suggest that it is not because the Early Palaeocene world favours small size, rather because it was small-bodied species that preferentially survived the K–T and Eocene–Oligocene events and necessarily carried that character with them when they began the post-extinction recoveries. The authors suggest that small-bodied species, by virtue of their generally shorter generation times, should have a more rapid evolutionary response to selective pressure than their large-bodied relatives, a factor that not only explains the tendency of small-bodied species to weather mass extinctions, but is a possible explanation for Cope's Rule that is general enough to apply across the full taxonomic and ecological spectrum. They indirectly supported this hypothesis with the observation that species destined to leave descendants form a significantly greater proportion of the small-bodied foraminiferal biota (as compared with the large-bodied biota) during times of crisis (Fig. 3). After the K–T and E–O extinctions the survivor species, in addition to their smaller mean size, show a globose morphology, an apparent preferential tendency toward pseudoextinction or cladogenesis (rather than true lineage termination) (Arnold et al. 1995a), and in the case of the post-K–T population, rapid turnover and significantly shorter mean species durations (Arnold et al. 1995b).

These interrelated features, although characterized as both microevolutionary (small size, globose morphology) and macroevolutionary (rapid turnover, preferential tendency toward cladogenesis/pseudoextinction among small-bodied species, and shorter durations), have one thing in common: the survivors of the K–T and their immediate descendants share them. We hypothesize that the rapid turnover (or the propensity for it) seen during the Early Palaeocene and after the C–T is, like small size at the organism level, a 'passport character' at the macroevolutionary level. That is, it is the continued expression of rapid turnover that one might expect in species that either:

(1) retain the evolutionary responsiveness to evolve through the rapidly changing conditions of a mass extinction; or

(2) share a propensity for such responsiveness (e.g. through paedomorphosis that emerges during extinctions).

The present finding of significant post-boundary age-dependent survivorship is consistent with this hypothesis.

A second insight that can be gained is in regard to the organismal and ecological characters that might drive rapid post-boundary turnover. Throughout most of the time that we cover, age-dependency is usually asymmetrical in the positive direction; that is, with increasing age species tend to show increasing probability of extinction rather than increasing immunity to extinction. Further, it is the short-lived species that explain (in a statistical, rather than a causal, sense) the age-dependency, and it is therefore these species that bear closer examination. Indeed, as noted by Arnold et al. (1995b; fig. 4) and in temporally expanded form in Figure 4 (herein), there are quasi-periodic windows during which short-lived species (those less than 4 Ma duration) apparently do not originate. Cox & Weibull's (Parker & Arnold 1997) model allows for removal of short-duration cases from the statistical population without compromising the results. When this is done, no age-dependent effect is observed in either Cox or Weibull analysis. Since trophic ecology and population structure have been strongly related to longevity for Palaeogene species (Norris 1992), its influence on speciation rates may point to the causal underpinnings of the post-boundary rapid turn-

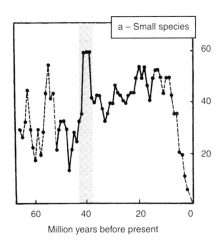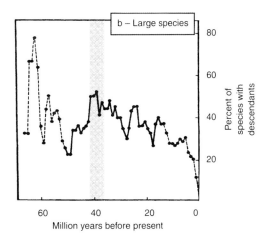

Fig. 3. Differential macroevolutionary characteristics of small (< 300 μm) versus large-bodied species during the E–O event. At the 38 Ma peak, note the significantly greater proportion of small species that leave descendants, as compared with that of large-bodied species. Dashed lines indicate where data are untrustworthy due to edge effects. Reproduced with permission of the *Journal of Paleontology*.

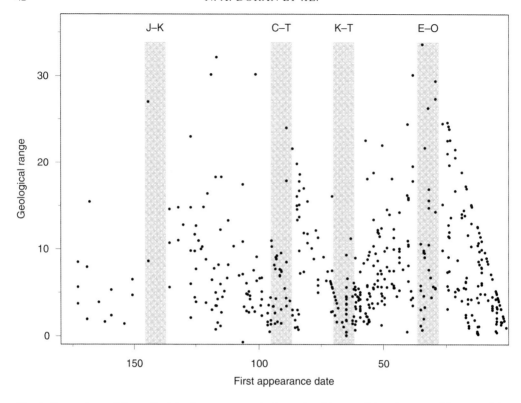

Fig. 4. Comparison of times of origination versus species longevity. Absence of data in upper right part of the graph is an artefact of censorship at the recent (a similar effect is seen at the K–T). 'Gaps' in the origination distribution of short-ranged species (e.g. 18–36 and 45–52 Ma) indicate variations in age-dependent extinction. Cenozoic and Cretaceous short-ranged foraminifera species have had quasi-periodic absences. Note the absence of short-ranged species immediately prior to the K–T boundary and the large number immediately following. The major extinction boundaries, including the Jurassic–Cretaceous boundary (J–K), are marked in grey.

over and age-dependence. Shorter-ranged populations also display a number of morphological differences from their longer-ranged counterparts. The explanatory role of these characters is the subject of ongoing investigation by the present authors.

What does age-dependency imply with respect to the Red Queen Hypothesis? The Red Queen was initially invoked to explain the surprising failure of taxonomic survivorship curves to deviate from exponentiality in the negative direction, as would be predicted if long-lived species tended to develop extinction immunity by adaptation over their durations. The Red Queen Hypothesis holds that species are, in effect, constantly evolving to keep up with adaptive peaks that shift at random with respect to their ability to adapt.

Due to the changing hazard rates experienced by any taxon during its existence, a few preconditions should be added to the application of the Red Queen Hypothesis. These preconditions must address whether hazard rates show significant temporal variation for the population in question. The original Red Queen concept assumed a stochastically constant underlying hazard rate; this assumption may be valid over shorter time-scales, with species populations experiencing identical extinction rates. However, over longer time-scales – with strongly variable extinction rates – background hazard rates must be taken into account (McGowan *et al.* 1999). Unfortunately, the Red Queen Hypothesis is usually envisioned in relation to an exponential survivorship curve. For periods that comprise homogeneous populations (with regard to extinction rates) this is appropriate. Therefore, with constant background hazard rates, the exponential model applies. But when discussing survivorship in the context of fluctuating background hazards, a more complex model needs to be employed, because species undergoing varying extinction rates would not yield a straightforward survivorship curve. For this reason, in the context of changing background rates, it is better to think of the Red Queen Hypothesis as the *absence* of age-dependence in extinction, and the macro-evolutionary consequences devolving therefrom. This absence of age-dependence must be measured in the context of a survivorship model that accounts for temporal inhomogeneities of extinction.

The early expectation of the Red Queen Hypothesis was that extinction probability would decrease with increasing species age. This study shows that planktonic foraminifera, in fact, show preferential deviation in the opposite direction, primarily after mass extinction boundaries, followed by a gradational return to age independence consistent with the Red Queen Hypothesis. In a sense, one might suggest that immediately after the K–T the survivor species are still 'running' – not because they have momentum, but because it was the 'runners' that got through the K–T event. Their ability to speciate rapidly (or their anagenetic responsiveness) explains the post-event pattern of rapid turnover, shortened durations, and age-dependency, and is consistent with their small size.

'Step' v. 'spike' perturbations and extinction

We might envision the abiotic environmental changes that drive extinction as varying from 'spike perturbation' (in which abiotic conditions return to the pre-extinction state after the event) to 'step perturbation' (in which conditions remain changed; steps might vary in height and abruptness. The concept of step perturbation should be distinguished from that of stepwise extinction, which describes multiple steps in extinction response). There is evidence that the K–T extinctions were caused by an impact event (Alvarez *et al.* 1980 *inter alia*); this would be an excellent example of a spike perturbation in which conditions were altered dramatically for a short period, and then recovered. The C–T event was of a lower magnitude than the K–T, with only 27% of marine genera disappearing. Since deep-water foraminifera disappear first, an ocean anoxic event (OAE) has been a strong candidate for the extinction (Jarvis *et al.* 1988; Tur 1996). Interestingly, fluctuations in β values are reminiscent of Raup–Sepkoski periodicities recently affirmed in planktonic foraminifera through time-series analysis (Prokoph *et al.* 2000). In either scenario – an impact or a transient OAE – these extinctions might be characterized as 'spike' perturbations. We stress that although the mechanics of these extinctions

may have been vastly different, the recoveries appear similar and are the basis of our distinction.

In contrast to the K–T and C–T, the most generally accepted explanations for the E–O extinctions are related to the (step) development of the modern mode of thermohaline circulation, driven primarily by colder bottom-water masses. Of course there is a body of evidence suggesting that other factors might have influenced these events. The E–O boundary has a variety of additional scenarios, including several micro-tektite horizons, global deepening of the calcium carbonate compensation depth (CCD), and volcanism, in addition to long-term climatic changes (Kennett *et al.* 1985; Keller 1986*b*). It would be premature to suggest that the step/spike distinction explains our observed differing patterns in age-dependency, but its consistency leads us to draw attention to the possibility.

Conclusion

Cox survivorship analysis of the planktonic foraminifera indicates that events at the C–T and K–T boundaries caused significant age-dependent effects. This is in contrast to the expectations of the Red Queen Hypothesis, where extinction is postulated to occur randomly with respect to species age. Boundaries may therefore complicate our expectations under the Red Queen Hypothesis. Post-boundary populations show an increased probability of extinction with age, and this deviation remains significant for nearly 25 Ma in the case of the K–T boundary, and nearly half that time in the case of the C–T. During the post-boundary period of significant age-dependence, there appears to be a pattern of gradational return toward Red Queen survivorship behaviour (i.e. absence of age-dependence). Ironically, our results, in demonstrating significant but transient deviation from Red Queen behaviour, lend support to the Red Queen Hypothesis, because they suggest that Red Queen behaviour may express the 'normal' conditions to which the biota return after the perturbation of an extinction event. Coefficient values even appear to trend toward negative values – indicating greater resistance to extinction with increasing age. Interestingly, this perturbation and gradational return is not seen after the E–O extinction events.

These results imply that some mass extinctions may exhibit an age-dependency signature that distinguishes them from background diversity fluctuation. It has been unclear whether mass extinctions and background extinctions are end members of a continuous distribution of extinction intensities. According to the Cox model, age-dependency fluctuates through time but appears strongly altered at some boundaries; it may be that post-extinction recovery behaviour provides an important, yet overlooked, signature that distinguishes mass from background extinction.

Since the Red Queen Hypothesis implies that on balance, biotic interaction dominates over abiotic factors in controlling species survivorship, it may follow that the extinction-driven departures from exponential Red Queen behaviour reported herein may signal a shift in the balance from biotic interaction to transient abiotic control of survivorship patterns immediately after some extinctions.

Our results further suggest that Jablonski (1986) may be right in his suggestion that extinction is the most important factor in evolution. The planktonic foraminifera appear to have spent a significant part of their history recovering from the effects of extinction, and much of their macroevolutionary behaviour during recovery seems to be influenced as much by the characteristics that survivors carry through extinction events as by the environments that they encounter during post-extinction times.

We would like to thank P. N. Pearson and P. J. Harries for their insightful comments and suggestions in improving this manuscript.

References

ALVAREZ, L. W., ALVAREZ, W., ASARO, F. & MICHEL, H. V. 1980. Extra-terrestrial cause for the Cretaceous–Tertiary extinction. *Science*, **208**, 1095–1108.

ARNOLD, A. J. 1982. Species survivorship in the Cenozoic Globigerinida. *In*: MAMET, B. & COPELAND, M. J. (eds) *Proceedings of the Third North American Paleontological Convention*, Montreal, Quebec, pp. 9–12.

ARNOLD, A. J., KELLY, D. C. & PARKER, W. C. 1995a. Causality and Cope's rule; evidence from the planktonic foraminifera. *Journal of Paleontology*, **69**, 203–210.

ARNOLD, A. J., PARKER, W. C. & HANSARD, S. P. 1995b. Aspects of the post-Cretaceous recovery of the Cenozoic planktic foraminifera. *In*: LANGER, M. R., LIPPS, J. H., INGLE, J. C. & SLITER, W. V. (eds) *Forams' 94; Selected Papers from the Fifth International Symposium of Foraminifera*. Elsevier, Amsterdam, The Netherlands, pp. 319–327.

BERGGREN, W. A. 1977. Atlas of Paleogene planktonic foraminifera. *In*: RAMSAY, A. T. S. (ed.) *Oceanic Micropaleontology*. Academic Press, London, pp. 205–299.

BERGGREN, W. A., KENT, D. V., SWISHER, C. C. I. & AUBRY, M. 1995. A revised Cenozoic geochronology and chronostratigraphy. Geochronology time scales and global stratigraphic correlation. *SEPM Special Publications*, **54**, 129–212.

BERGGREN, W. A. & NORRIS, R. D. 1997. Biostratigraphy, phylogeny and systematics of Paleocene trochospiral planktic foraminifera. *Micropaleontology*, **43**, 1–116.

BLOW, W. H. 1979. *The Cainozoic Globigerinida*. E. J. Brill, Leiden, The Netherlands, 1413 pp.

BOERSMA, A. & PREMOLI SILVA, I. 1983. Paleocene planktonic foraminiferal biogeography and the paleoceanography of the Atlantic Ocean. *Micropaleontology*, **29**, 355–381.

BOERSMA, A., PREMOLI SILVA, I. & SHACKLETON, N. J. 1987. Atlantic Eocene planktonic foraminiferal paleohydrographic indicators and stable isotope paleoceanography. *Paleoceanography*, **2**, 287–331.

BOLLI, H. M. & SAUNDERS, J. B. 1985. Oligocene to Holocene low-latitude planktic foraminifera. *In*: BOLLI, H. M., SAUNDERS, J. B. & PERCH-NIELSEN, K. (eds) *Plankton Stratigraphy*. Cambridge University Press, Cambridge, pp. 155–262.

BOLLI, H. M., SAUNDERS, J. B. & PERCH-NIELSEN, K. 1989. *Plankton Stratigraphy, Volume 1*. Cambridge University Press, Cambridge, 599 pp.

BOUDAGHER-FADEL, M. K., BANNER, F. T. & WHITTAKER, J. E. 1997. *The Early Evolutionary History of Planktonic Foraminifera*. British Micropaleontological Society Publication Series. Chapman & Hall, London, 269 pp.

BOYAJIAN, G. E. 1986. Phanerozoic trends in background extinction: consequences of aging fauna. *Geology*, **14**, 955–958.

BOYAJIAN, G. E. 1991. Taxon age and selectivity of extinction. *Paleobiology*, **17**, 49–57.

CARROLL, L. 1872. *Through the Looking-Glass and What Alice Found There* (as cited in Van Valen, 1973).

COX, D. R. 1972. Regression models and life tables. *Journal of the Royal Statistical Society*, **34**, 187–220.

DE VARGAS, C., NORRIS, R., ZANINETTI, L., GIBB, S. W. & PAWLOWSKI, J. 1999. Molecular evidence of cryptic speciation in planktonic foraminifers and their relation to oceanic provinces. *Proceedings of the National Academy of Sciences of the United States of America*, **96**, 2864–2868.

DE VARGAS, C., RENAUD, S., HILBRECHT, H. & PAWLOWSKI, J. 2001. Pleistocene adaptive radiation in *Globorotalia truncatulinoides*: genetic, morphologic, and environmental evidence. *Paleobiology*, **27**, 104–125.

EPSTEIN, B. 1960a. Tests for the validity of the assumption that the underlying distribution of life is exponential. Part I. *Technometrics*, **2**, 83–101.

EPSTEIN, B. 1960b. Tests for the validity of the assumption that the underlying distribution of life is exponential. Part II. *Technometrics*, **2**, 167–183.

ERWIN, D. H. 2001. Lessons from the past: biotic recoveries from mass extinctions. *Proceedings of* the *National Academy of Sciences of the United States of America*, **98**, 5933–5403.

FORDHAM, B. G. 1986. *Miocene–Pliocene Planktonic Foraminifers from D.S.D.P. Sites 208 and 77, and Phylogeny and Classification of Cenozoic Species.* Evolutionary Monographs, No. 6. University of Chicago, Chicago, 200 pp.

HANSEN, T. A. 1988. Early Tertiary radiation of marine molluscs and the long-term effects of the Cretaceous–Tertiary extinction. *Paleobiology*, **14**, 37–51.

HANSEN, T. A., FARRAND, R., MONTGOMERY, H., BILLMAN, H. & BLECHSCHMIDT, G. 1987. Sedimentology and extinction patterns across the Cretaceous–Tertiary boundary interval in East Texas. *Cretaceous Research*, **8**, 229–252.

HARRIES, P. J., KAUFFMAN, E. G. & HANSEN, T. A. 1996. Models for biotic survival following mass extinction. *In:* HART, M. B. (ed.) *Biotic Recovery from Mass Extinction Events*. Geological Society of London, London, pp. 41–60.

HART, M. B. 1990. Major evolutionary radiations of the planktonic foraminiferida. *Systematics Association Special Volume*, 42, 59–72.

HUBBARD, A. E. & GILINSKY, N. L. 1992. Mass extinctions as statistical phenomena; an examination of the evidence using chi^2 tests and bootstrapping. *Paleobiology*, **18**, 148–160.

JABLONSKI, D. 1986. Evolutionary consequences of mass extinctions. *In:* RAUP, D. M. & JABLONSKI, D. (eds) *Patterns and Processes in the History of Life*. Springer, Berlin, pp. 313–329.

JABLONSKI, D. 1989. The biology of mass extinction; a palaeontological view. *In:* CHALONER, W. G. & HALLAM, A. (eds) *Evolution and Extinction*. Royal Society of London, London, pp. 357–368.

JABLONSKI, D. 2001. Lessons from the past: evolutionary impacts of mass extinctions. *Proceedings of the National Academy of Sciences of the United States of America*, **98**, 5393–5398.

JABLONSKI, D. 2002. Survival without recovery after mass extinctions. *Proceedings of the National Academy of Sciences of the United States of America*, **99**, 8139–8144.

JARVIS, I., CARSON, G., HART, M., LEARY, P. & TOCHER, B. 1988. Microfossil assemblages and the Cenomanian–Turonian (late Cretaceous) Oceanic Anoxic Event. *Cretaceous Research*, **9**, 3–103.

KALBFLEISCH, J. D. & PRENTICE, R. L. 1980. *The Statistical Analysis of Failure Time Data*. John Wiley & Sons, New York, 321 pp.

KAUFFMAN, E. G. 1984. Dynamics of Cretaceous epicontinental seas. *American Association of Petroleum Geologists Bulletin*, **68**, 1837–1837.

KAUFFMAN, E. G. & WALLISER, O. H. 1988. Global bioevents – abrupt changes in the global biota. *Episodes*, **11**, 289–292.

KELLER, G. 1986a. Eocene–Oligocene boundary reference sections in the Pacific. Developments in paleontology and stratigraphy. *In:* POMEROL, C. & PREMOLI SILVA, I. (eds) *Terminal Eocene Events*. Elsevier, Amsterdam, pp. 209–212.

KELLER, G. 1986b. Stepwise mass extinctions and impact events; late Eocene to early Oligocene. *Marine Micropaleontology*, **10**, 267–293.

KELLER, G. 1988. Extinction, survivorship and evolution of planktic foraminifera across the Cretaceous/Tertiary boundary at El Kef, Tunisia. *Marine Micropaleontology*, **13**, 239–263.

KELLER, G. 1989a. Extended Cretaceous/Tertiary boundary extinctions and delayed population change in planktonic foraminifera from Brazos River, Texas. *Paleoceanography*, **4**, 287–332.

KELLER, G. 1989b. Extended period of extinctions across the Cretaceous/Tertiary boundary in planktonic foraminifera of continental-shelf sections; implications for impact and volcanism theories. *Geological Society of America Bulletin*, **101**, 1048–1419.

KENNETT, J. P. & SRINIVASAN, M. S. 1983. *Neogene Planktonic Foraminifera: a Phylogenetic Atlas.* Hutchinson Ross Publishing, Stroudsburg, PA, 265 pp.

KENNETT, J. P. & VON DER BORCH, C. *ET AL.* 1985. Palaeotectonic implications of increased late Eocene–early Oligocene volcanism from South Pacific DSDP sites. *Nature*, **316**, 507–511.

KIRCHNER, J. W. & WEIL, A. 2000. Delayed biological recovery from extinctions throughout the fossil record. *Nature*, **404**, 177–180.

LEE, E. T. 1980. *Statistical Methods for Survival Data Analysis*. Lifetime Learning Publications, Belmont, CA, 557 pp.

MCGOWAN, A. J., PEARSON, P. N., STEARN, C. W. & PATTERSON, R. T. 1999. ADAPTS (analysis of diversity, asymmetry of phylogenetic trees, and survivorship); a new software tool for analysing stratigraphic range data. *Paleontological Databases; Taxonomic Decisions; Conference Proceedings Derived from Paleontological Society Theme Session T-39.* Unpublished.

NORRIS, R. D. 1992. Extinction selectivity and ecology in planktonic-foraminifera. *Palaeogeography, Palaeoclimatology, Palaeoecology*, **95**, 1–17.

NORRIS, R. D. 2000. Pelagic species diversity, biogeography, and evolution. *Paleobiology*, **26**, 236–258.

OLSSON, R. K., HEMLEBEN, C., BERGGREN, W. A. & HUBER, B. T. 1999. *Atlas of Paleocene Planktonic Foraminifera.* Smithsonian Contributions to Paleobiology, **85**. Smithsonian Institution Press, Washington, DC, 252 pp.

PARKER, W. C. & ARNOLD, A. J. 1997. Species survivorship in the Cenozoic planktonic foraminifera: a test of exponential and Weibull Models. *Palaios*, **12**, 3–11.

PEARSON, P. N. 1992. Survivorship analysis of fossil taxa when real-time extinction rates vary; the Paleogene planktonic foraminifera. *Paleobiology*, **18**, 115–131.

PEARSON, P. N. 1995. Investigating age-dependence of species extinction rates using dynamic survivorship analysis. *Historical Biology*, **10**, 119–136.

PEARSON, P. N. 1996. Cladogenetic, extinction and survivorship patterns from a lineage phylogeny; the Paleogene planktonic foraminifera. *Micropaleontology*, **42**, 179–188.

PEARSON, P. N. 1998a. Evolutionary concepts in biostratigraphy. *In*: DOYLE, P. & BENNETT, M. R. (eds) *Unlocking the Stratigraphical Record: Advances in Modern Stratigraphy*. John Wiley, Chichester, pp. 123–144.

PEARSON, P. N. 1998b. Speciation and extinction asymmetries in paleontological phylogenies; evidence for evolutionary progress? *Paleobiology*, **24**, 305–335.

POSTUMA, J. A. 1971. *Manual of Planktonic Foraminifera*. Elsevier, New York, 397 pp.

PREMOLI SILVA, I. & BOERSMA, A. 1988. Atlantic Eocene planktonic foraminiferal historical biogeography, and paleohydrographic indices. *Palaeogeography, Palaeoclimatology, Palaeoecology*, **67**, 315–356.

PROKOPH, A., FOWLER, A. D. & PATTERSON, R. T. 2000. Evidence for periodicity and nonlinearity in a high-resolution fossil record of long-term evolution. *Geology*, **28**, 867–870.

RAUP, D. M. 1994. The role of extinction in evolution. *Proceedings of the National Academy of Sciences of the United States of America*, **91**, 6758–6763.

ROBASZYNSKI, F., CARON, M., GONZALEZ DONOSO, J. M., WONDERS, A. A. H. & Exxon Planktonic Foraminifera Working Group. 1984. Atlas of Late Cretaceous Globotruncanids. *Revue de Micropaleontologie*, **26**, 145–305.

SIMPSON, G. G. 1944. *Tempo and Mode in Evolution*. Columbia University Press, New York, 237 pp.

THACKERY, F. J. 1990. Rates of extinction in marine invertebrates: further comparisons between background and mass extinctions. *Paleobiology*, **16**, 22–24.

TOUMARKINE, M. & LUTERBACHER, H. 1985. Paleocene and Eocene planktic foraminifera. *In*: BOLLI, H. M., SAUNDERS, J. B. & PERCH-NIELSEN, K. D. (eds) *Planktonic Stratigraphy*. Cambridge University Press, Cambridge, pp. 87–154.

TUR, N. A. 1996. Planktonic foraminifera recovery from the Cenomanian–Turonian mass extinction event, northeastern Caucasus. *In*: HART, M. B. (ed.) *Biotic Recovery from Mass Extinction Events*. Geological Society of London, London, pp. 259–264.

VAN VALEN, L. 1973. A new evolutionary law. *Evolutionary Theory*, **1**, 1–30.

Late Cambrian and Early Ordovician conodont communities from platform and slope facies, western Newfoundland: a statistical approach

SHUNXIN ZHANG & CHRISTOPHER R. BARNES

School of Earth and Ocean Sciences, University of Victoria, PO Box 3055, Victoria, B.C. V8W 3P6, Canada (e-mail:crbarnes@uvic.ca)

Abstract: Twelve conodont communities and assemblages in the Cambrian–Ordovician interval of western Newfoundland are recognized by four cluster analyses, which include 18 468 identifiable conodont specimens recovered from 230 conodont-bearing samples from four stratigraphic sections. Each section represents a different facies: platform, upper proximal slope, lower proximal slope, and distal slope. The 12 conodont communities and assemblages were differentiated into pelagic and nektobenthic communities as well as both the assemblages with a mixture of pelagic and nektobenthic communities and transported assemblage. The distribution of conodont communities along the platform-to-slope environmental gradient shows some gradational relationships. Relative sea-level curves derived in part from the distribution pattern of conodont communities reveal a major sea-level drop in the latest *Cordylodus proavus* Zone time, and two major sea-level rises in the early *Iapetognathus fluctivagus* Zone time and early *Cordylodus angulatus* Zone time, respectively.

The Cambrian–Ordovician boundary has proven to be one of the most contentious and difficult to define of all the Phanerozoic systemic boundaries. It took two separate Boundary Working Groups of the International Union of Geological Sciences over 20 years to approve a GSSP (Global Stratotype Section and Point). Some Cambrian–Ordovician sections have been documented in summary volumes (e.g. Bassett & Dean 1982; Special issue on the Cambrian–Ordovician Boundary, *Geological Magazine*, 1988, Vol. **125(4)**) with the final decision outlined in Cooper *et al.* (2001). Despite examining many sections, the final short-list was reduced to Green Point in western Newfoundland, Canada, Dayangcha in Jilin Province, NE China, and Lava Dam, Utah, United States. The main difficulties in deciding the Cambrian–Ordovician boundary questions revolved mainly around the issues of the exact level, the taxon (and taxonomy) to define that level, and the quality of the section. It was decided by the Cambrian–Ordovician Boundary Working Group early in the debates to use a conodont species that marked a level close to but below the first appearance of planktonic graptolites. Eventually, it was agreed to use the first appearance of the species *Iapetognathus fluctivagus* Nicoll, Miller, Nowlan, Repetski & Ethington. After further re-examination of the data from the three short-listed sections, an agreement was made to have the GSSP at Green Point, western Newfoundland. Earlier, Fortey *et al.* (1982) had documented the faunal distributions for the mid-lower proximal slope Broom Point sections, with later conodont studies by Bagnoli *et al.* (1986). After sampling all the key sections in the Cow Head Group in western Newfoundland, Barnes (1988) proposed that the best section to meet the criteria of a GSSP was at Green Point and provided detailed conodont data for the section, with correlations to the other sections. The final proposal for the GSSP at that locality was made by Cooper *et al.* (2001) and approved by IUGS.

A major criticism by some workers (e.g. Miller 1984; Miller & Flokstra 1999; Dubinina 1991) during the debate was that the Cow Head slope sequence not only contained some breccias (two in the Green Point boundary interval), but that many or most of the limestones were transported downslope from the shallow-water platform. Likewise, they argued that many or most of the contained conodonts could have been similarly derived. However, it was clear from several other detailed studies that the composition of the Late Cambrian–Early Ordovician deep-water conodont faunas (Fåhraeus & Nowlan 1978; Bagnoli *et al.* 1986; Barnes 1988; Stouge & Bagnoli 1988) was significantly different from the lateral equivalents that occupied the shallow-water platform facies (Barnes & Tuke 1970; Stouge 1982; Ji & Barnes 1996). In

From: BEAUDOIN, A.B. & HEAD, M.J. (eds) 2004. *The Palynology and Micropalaeontology of Boundaries*. Geological Society, London, Special Publications, **230**, 47–72. 0305-8719/04/$15 © The Geological Society of London 2004.

fact, the two regions represented different faunal realms (Atlantic Realm and Midcontinent Realm; Pohler & Barnes 1990). The tectono-stratigraphic setting in western Newfoundland remained relatively constant during Middle Cambrian to Early Ordovician times. Thus, this present study of Tremadocian conodont faunas can be used to interpret the evolving conodont community patterns and can be compared to the Arenigian studies of Pohler *et al.* (1987) and Pohler (1994), which demon-strated the different composition and commu-nity structure of the shelf-break conodont faunas. Despite these obvious differences in conodont faunas along the environmental gra-dient of the platform–shelf-break–proximal to distal slope facies, the critics argued that many of the faunas were transported downslope. The purpose of this paper is to re-evaluate the conodont faunas across the Cambrian–Ordovi-cian boundary; to apply multivariate statistical methods to establish the pattern of conodont communities over this interval; and to draw quantitative comparisons between the commu-nity patterns on the platform and those on the proximal to distal slope.

In western Newfoundland, Upper Cambrian and Lower Ordovician strata are represented by the para-autochthonous Port au Port and St George groups and the allochthonous Cow Head Group. These units belong to the Humber Zone of the Appalachian Orogen (Williams 1979). The Port au Port and the St George groups have been interpreted by most workers as representing deposition on a carbonate plat-form, and the Cow Head Group as representing deposition on an adjacent continental slope from Mid-Cambrian to Mid-Ordovician times (Hiscott & James 1985; James & Stevens 1986; James *et al.* 1989; Knight *et al.* 1991) (Fig. 1).

The Upper Cambrian and Lower Ordovician shelf-break and upper slope deposits are nowhere exposed, but their nature has been determined from studies of the numerous large clasts in sediment gravity flows redeposited on the lower slope (James & Stevens 1986; Pohler *et al.* 1987; Pohler & James 1989; Pohler 1994).

In the para-autochthonous sequence, the Port au Port Group is divided into the March Point, Petite Jardin and Berry Head formations (upper-most Middle and Upper Cambrian), and the overlying St George Group is divided into the Watt's Bight, Boat Harbour, Catoche and Aguathuna formations (Lower Ordovician; Ibexian, Tremadocian–Arenigian) (Fig. 2).

In the Upper Cambrian and Lower Ordovi-cian allochthonous sequence, the Cow Head Group is divided into proximal and distal facies,

the former being the Shallow Bay Formation, and the latter being the Green Point Formation. The Shallow Bay Formation includes the Downes Point, Tucker's Cove, Stearing Island, and Factory Cove members, and the Green Point Formation is divided into the Martin Point, Broom Point and St Paul's members (Fig. 2).

This paper covers the interval of: (1) the Berry Head Formation, Port au Port Group and lower Watt's Bight Formation (St George Group) for the para-autochthonous sequence; and (2) the upper Tuckers Cove and the lower Stearing Island members, Shallow Bay Formation, and the upper Martin Point and lower Broom Point members, Green Point Formation (Cow Head Group) for the proximal and distal facies of the allochthonous sequence. These intervals cross the Cambrian–Ordovician boundary (Fig. 2), and mark a period of rapid initial diversification of the euconodonts (Sweet 1988).

The conodont faunas across the Cambrian–Ordovician boundary interval within the Cow Head Group were described by Bagnoli *et al.* (1986) and Barnes (1988), and those within the upper Port au Port and St George groups by Ji & Barnes (1994*a*). Studies on conodont ecology for this interval in western Newfoundland have been made by Ji & Barnes (1994*b*) for the platform facies, based on presence–absence statistical analysis. This present study will analyse the data of Bagnoli *et al.* (1986) and Barnes (1988), and re-analyses part of the data of Ji & Barnes (1994*a*) to document the development and replacement of conodont communities along the environment gradient from shallow platform, across the shelf-break and upper slope, to proximal and distal slope, based on a new statistical analysis using the absolute abundance of the conodont elements.

Review of earlier work and the concepts of community and assemblage

Barnes *et al.* (1973), Barnes & Fåhraeus (1975) and Fåhraeus & Barnes (1975) proposed a model for conodont palaeoecology based on the studies of Ordovician conodonts. Midconti-nent and North Atlantic Provinces were recog-nized (Sweet & Bergström 1974, 1984), which were later termed Realms (Pohler & Barnes 1990). Lindström (1976) argued for a large number of provinces. The Midcontinent con-odont fauna was interpreted as representing raised temperatures and salinities in shallow, low-latitude seas, and the North Atlantic con-odont fauna as a more cosmopolitan normal-marine fauna occupying cool and/or deep waters

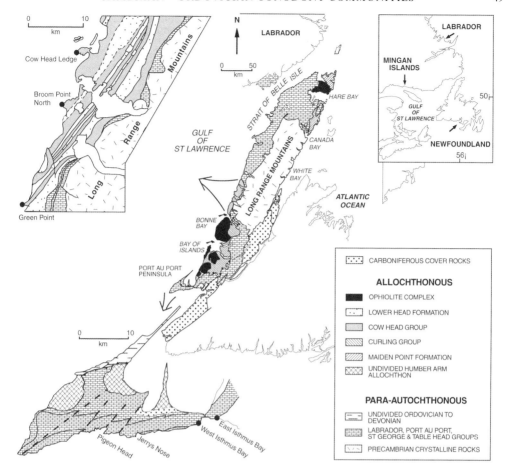

Fig. 1. Geological map of the Humber Zone in western Newfoundland, with inset maps showing sections and location of Mingan Islands, Québec (modified from James & Stevens 1986; Ji & Barnes 1994*a*; Johnston & Barnes 1999). The locations of sections included in this study are represented by black dots.

(Barnes & Fåhraeus 1975; Pohler & Barnes 1990). In both provinces, conodont communities (or biofacies) can be recognized that show a lateral segregation along an onshore–offshore environmental gradient, which implies that the conodonts were benthic or nektobenthic in habit, with relatively few pelagic taxa. The term 'community' is used herein to denote an ecological association of taxa usually related to particular environmental parameters, and the term 'assemblage' to denote a non-ecological association (mixture) of taxa that reflect different environmental parameters.

Based on Barnes & Fåhraeus' (1975) model and detailed studies on the Arenigian (Early Ordovician) conodonts from western Newfoundland, a sequence of conodont communities has been established, which extended from the shelf platform (Ji & Barnes 1994*b*) to the shelf-

break and upper slope (Pohler 1994), and on to the proximal and distal slope (Johnston & Barnes 1999). The conodont community distribution is summarized in Figure 3a. In this model, each assemblage is a mixture of both the post-mortem elements of the *in situ* nektobenthic community and elements from the pelagic community from the overlying water column. Figure 3b postulates more extreme conditions that involved some downslope transport of the elements. During intervals of lowered sea-level, the platform and parts of the shelf-break were exposed and some material was transported on to the slope. Some elements of the shelf-break and upper-slope conodont fauna could then be preserved in the slope facies sediments. Pohler *et al.* (1987) and Pohler (1994) recognized the shelf-break and upper slope communities within transported clasts in the megabreccias. However,

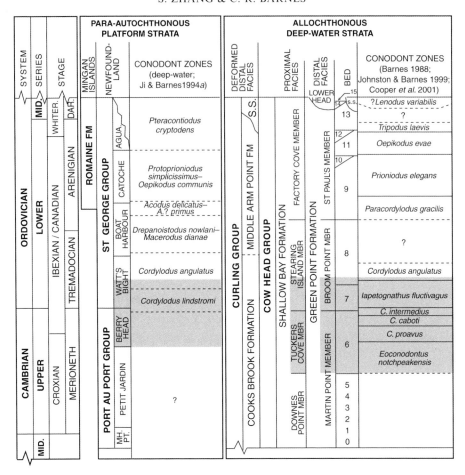

Fig. 2. Summary of the chronostratigraphy and biostratigraphy of different para-autochthonous and allochthonous sequences in western Newfoundland and the Mingan Islands, Québec (extracted and modified from James *et al.* 1989). The shaded area covers the interval of this study.

this work was primarily based on field and petrographic observations of the Arenigian transported breccias (Beds 10, 12 and 14), and on the conodont samples collected from different breccia clast lithologies. This present study will test the hypothesis shown in Figure 3b based on bedded deep-water sediments, but for an earlier time interval.

Conodont communities can be differentiated at different taxonomic levels (e.g. Merrill & von Bitter 1984). The Ordovician conodont communities recognized previously in western Newfoundland are basically generic-level communities, named after one or two dominant genera. The reconstruction of most of those conodont communities was based largely on the relative abundance of distinct conodont assemblages. The distribution pattern of the different conodont communities through time shows their

rapid introduction followed by a period of stasis (Ji & Barnes 1994*b*; Johnston & Barnes 1999).

Late Croixian (Late Cambrian) and Tremadocian (Early Ordovician) conodont communities from western Newfoundland have not been well established, except for those from the carbonate platform (Ji & Barnes 1994*b*). This paper selects this interval to differentiate the conodont communities at the species level; to apply a more rigorous statistical analysis than that of Ji & Barnes (1994*b*); and to test the hypotheses summarized in Figure 3.

Database and statistical approach

Statistical reconstructions of conodont communities based on cluster analysis have been widely used (e.g. von Bitter 1972; McCracken & Barnes 1981; Nowlan & Barnes 1981; Sweet & Berg-

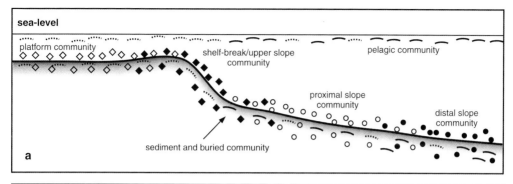

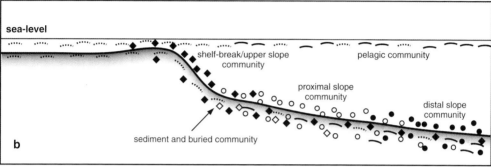

Fig. 3. (**a**) Model of conodont nektobenthic and pelagic modes of life modified from Barnes & Fåhraeus (1975) and Pohler & Barnes (1990), also showing the buried conodont community as a combination of nektobenthic and pelagic communities in Cambrian–Ordovician strata of western Newfoundland; (**b**) a model of conodont nektobenthic and pelagic modes of life during lower sea-levels: the platform community was not developed; the buried community in deep-water deposits may be mixed with transported shallow-water (shelf-break/upper slope) nektobenthic communities in western Newfoundland. Dashed curved lines and solid curved lines represent pelagic communities in relatively shallow water with aerobic conditions and relatively deep water with anaerobic conditions, respectively; white diamonds, black diamonds, white dots and black dots represent platform, shelf-break/upper slope, proximal slope and distal slope communities, respectively.

ström 1984; Ji & Barnes 1994*b*; Zhang & Barnes 2002*a*, 2002*b*). With the increased conodont data from western Newfoundland, it is now possible to refine the pattern of conodont communities along an environmental gradient from platform to distal slope, and to understand how the replacement of conodont communities responded to sea-level changes. Although Pohler (1994) and Johnston & Barnes (1999) demonstrated the general pattern of Arenigian conodont communities from shelf-break and slope, it was not supported by statistical analysis. Ji & Barnes (1994*b*) used cluster analysis to determine conodont community structure; however, they only attempted Q-type analysis of presence–absence data. In this present paper, both R- and Q-type cluster analysis of absolute abundance data are employed to recognize the conodont communities. This provides a means of visualizing the conodont community patterns.

Database

The database for this study is built mainly on three previous studies from western Newfoundland: the Late Croixian (= Sunwaptan) and Early Tremadocian conodonts from the platform facies (Ji & Barnes 1994*a*), and those from upper and lower proximal slope to distal slope facies (Bagnoli *et al.* 1986; Barnes 1988). The lateral lithofacies reconstruction of James *et al.* (1989, fig. 16) is followed herein. The database includes 18 468 identifiable conodont specimens recovered from 230 conodont-bearing samples (av. 3 kg; barren samples are excluded) from five upper Croixian (= Sunwaptan) and Lower Tremadocian sections spanning the *Eoconodontus notchpeakensis* Zone to the lower *Cordylodus angulatus* Zone, and representing inner platform to distal slope facies, with only the outer platform and shelf-break facies being absent.

(1) The shallow platform facies includes part of two sections:

    (a) East Isthmus Bay section (Z1), seven samples from the uppermost Cambrian Berry Head Formation which contained 24 disjunct conodont elements representing four multi-element species (Ji & Barnes 1994a, appendix B on p. 81);

    (b) West Isthmus Bay section (Z2), six samples from the lowest Ordovician lower Watt's Bight Formation which produced 179 disjunct conodont elements representing 13 multielement species (Ji & Barnes 1994a, appendix B on p. 82).

(2) Upper proximal slope facies: Cow Head Ledge section, 13 samples from the uppermost Cambrian Tucker's Cove Member and lowest Ordovician Stearing Island Member, Shallow Bay Formation (Barnes 1988, table 1), which yield 290 disjunct conodont elements representing 18 multielement species.

(3) Lower proximal slope facies: Broom Point North section, 77 samples from the uppermost Cambrian Tuckers Cove Member, Shallow Bay Formation and lowest Ordovician Broom Point Member, Green Point Formation, which contained 4119 disjunct conodont elements representing 49 multielement species. Of the 77 samples, 16 in the upper part of the section are from the collection of Bagnoli et al. (1986, table 1) and 61 in the lower and middle part of the section are from that of Barnes (1988, table 2, but in which the numbers of elements given for Cambrooistodus cambricus Miller to Eoconodontus notchpeakensis Miller on page 391, all need to be dropped down one line due to an editorial error).

(4) Distal slope facies: Green Point section, 55 samples from the uppermost Cambrian Martin Point Member and lowest Ordovician Broom Point Member, Green Point Formation, which yield 9356 disjunct conodont elements representing 39 species (Barnes 1988, table 6). For clarity, some systematic notes are made as follows:

    (a) Barnes 1988, table 6: samples 17 and 18 contained five and 24 specimens assigned earlier to Cordylodus primitivus sp. nov. by Bagnoli et al. (1986), but referred to C. hastatus sp. nov. by Barnes (1988, synonymy) and likewise included as C. hastatus Barnes herein.

    (b) The specimens identified as *Iapetognathus preaengensis* Landing by Barnes (1988, figs 13y, z, aa–ee) were revised systematically as *I. fluctivagus* new species, *I. aengensis* (Lindström) and *Cordylodus* sp. by Nicoll et al. (1999). Herein, Barnes' (1988) usage is followed, including using the name for the community, since that database is being incorporated.

    (c) *Cordylodus andresi* Barnes (defined by Barnes 1988) is a junior homonym of *C. andresi* Viira & Sergeeva (in Viira et al. 1987).

Conodont community/assemblage analysis: statistical methodology

In analysing the data to establish conodont communities, cluster analysis of the species abundance data is adopted (number of conodont elements for each species per kilogram), using SPSS version 6.1 for the Macintosh (SPSS 1994). Both Q- and R-mode hierarchical cluster analyses were performed for both cases (samples) and variables (species). The recorded species abundance for each sample was divided into seven intervals (<1, 1–4, 5–9, 10–24, 25–49, 50–99, and ≥100). Pearson's correlation coefficient was used as an index of similarity, which indicates the strength of the linear relationship between the variables, with larger values indicating stronger relationships, and clusters were created using the within-groups linkage method. These intervals of absolute element abundance are expressed as a graded series of dots that are plotted at the intersection of certain species and samples. The pattern of community partitioning is determined from the assemblages of dots representing distinctive groupings of samples and specimens. This methodology was adopted recently by Westrop & Cuggy (1999) in a study of Late Cambrian trilobites, and later by Zhang & Barnes (2002a, 2002b) in studies of Late Ordovician and Early Silurian conodont palaeoecology.

Four R- and Q-type cluster analyses were designed and performed for East and West Isthmus Bay (Fig. 4), Cow Head Ledge (Fig. 5), Broom Point North (Fig. 6), and Green Point (Fig. 7) sections. Cluster analysis tends to divide an ecological gradient into discrete units, whereas the gradational nature of the conodont community groups is evident in the abundance data shown in the Q- and R-mode dendrograms.

Overall, over the Late Cambrian and Early Ordovician interval along the environment

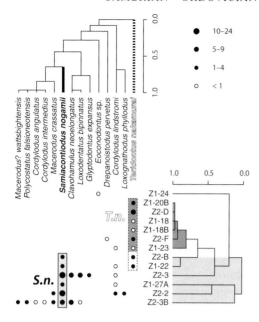

Fig. 4. Results of Q- and R-mode cluster analysis of 13 selected conodont-bearing samples from the platform facies (Berry Head and lower Watt's Bight formations) (sample data of Berry Head Formation from East Isthmus Bay section labelled as Z1, and sample data of lower Watt's Bight from West Isthmus Bay section labelled as Z2). Samples are in Q-mode clustering order, taxa are in R-mode clustering order and relative abundance of taxa is expressed as a graded series of dots. Intersections of Q- and R-clusters define two conodont communities, indicated by the abbreviations: *T.n., Teridontus nakamurai; S.n., Semiacontiodus nogamii*. The database is extracted from appendix B of Ji & Barnes (1994*a*, pp. 81–82). Pelagic and nekto-benthic communities are differentiated by dashed dark grey boxes with hollow letters and solid light grey boxes with bold letters, respectively. The dashed box without shading indicates a pelagic community not discussed as a separate community in the text.

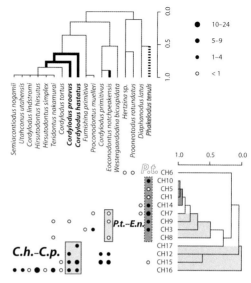

Fig. 5. Results of Q- and R-mode cluster analysis of 13 conodont-bearing samples from the upper proximal slope facies Stearing Island Member, Shallow Bay Formation, in the Cow Head Ledge section. Samples are in Q-mode clustering order, taxa are in R-mode clustering order and relative abundance of taxa is expressed as a graded series of dots. Intersections of Q- and R-clusters define three conodont communities and assemblages, indicated by the abbreviations: *P.t., Phakelodus tenuis; P.t.–E.n., P. tenuis–Eoconodontus notchpeakensis; C.h.–C.p., Cordylodus hastatus–C. proavus*. The database is from table 1 of Barnes (1988). Pelagic and nektobenthic communities are differentiated by a dashed dark-grey box with hollow letters and solid light-grey boxes with bold letters, respectively.

gradient from platform to distal slope in western Newfoundland, 12 different conodont communities and assemblages are recognized herein by cluster analysis. Some of the communities are common in a variety of facies, which suggests a pelagic mode of life. However, most of communities are unique to certain facies, which suggests a nektobenthic mode of life with insignificant downslope transportation or mixing. In contrast, the assemblages recognized by the analysis are caused either by significant downslope transportation, or by the mixing of components of both pelagic and nektobenthic communities. The pelagic communities are discussed in detail in the following section, together with the different assemblages comprising pelagic species, followed by sections dealing with transported assemblages and nektobenthic communities.

Pelagic communities

The Phakelodus tenuis *community and the* P. tenuis–Eoconodont notchpeakensis *assemblage*

Phakelodus tenuis (Müller) is a coniform proto-conodont, and is locally preserved as fused clusters of elements. It is one of the most common species in the samples used herein. *Phakelodus tenuis* has not been reported from the platform facies of both uppermost Cambrian Berry Head Formation at East Isthmus Bay section and lowest Ordovician Watt's Bight Formation at West Isthmus Bay section (Fig. 4). However, this species is common in all

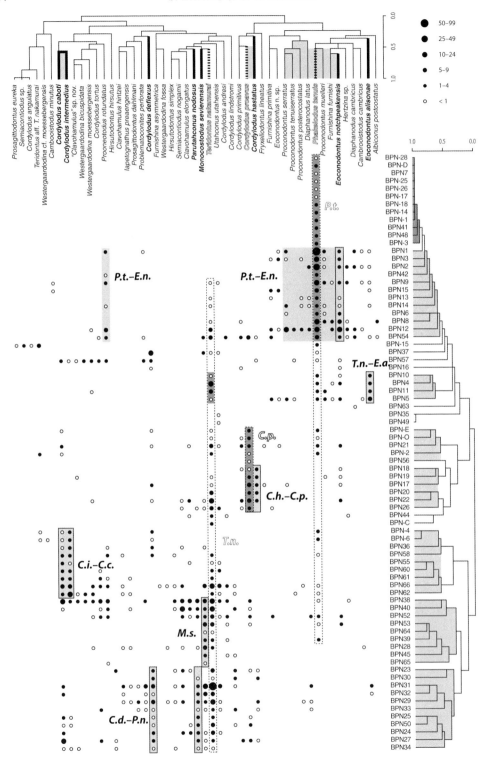

correlative sections from upper proximal slope to distal slope (Figs 5–7).

Cluster analysis for the Cow Head Ledge, Broom Point North, and Green Point samples (Figs 5–7) produced two main groups in Q-mode clustering order. One group contains *Phakelodus tenuis*, and another group yields very few *P. tenuis*, but abundant *Teridontus nakamuria*.

The conodont community and assemblage related to *Phakelodus tenuis* are recognized: (1) a *P. tenuis* community distributed in both the Upper Cambrian and Lower Ordovician in each section along the environment gradient from upper proximal slope to distal slope; (2) a *P. tenuis–Eoconodontus notchpeakensis* assemblage in the Upper Cambrian at the Cow Head Ledge and Broom Point North sections (Fig. 8).

Phakelodus tenuis *community*. Unlike the other conodont communities recognized in this study, the *Phakelodus tenuis* community is made up mainly by the eponymous species. The community can be recognized at Cow Head Ledge, Broom Point North, and Green Point sections, but it always has a low species abundance (Figs 5–7). Figure 8 shows that this community occurs discontinuously throughout these three sections, alternating with other communities. In the Lower Ordovician Broom Point Member, Green Point Formation at

Broom Point North section (Fig. 8), the community alternates with conodont-barren intervals in units 95 and 96 (James & Stevens 1986; Barnes 1988), which are dominated by parted lime mudstone containing layers about 2 cm thick, separated by paper-thin argillaceous limestone.

Miller (1984) concluded that *Phakelodus* Miller was cosmopolitan, based on its wide occurrence in North America, Europe, Asia, India and Australia. He considered that it was pelagic, based on its presence in various facies ranging from shallow, normal-marine, to possibly restricted platform-margin and shelf palaeoenvironments, to deep continental-slope deposits in Nevada; and especially in black, organic and pyrite-rich alum shales in Sweden (Müller 1959). These latter sediments were deposited under anoxic bottom conditions (Henningsmoen 1957; Schovsbo 2001), and the only faunas preserved were pelagic. Miller (1984) also noted that *Phakelodus* did not tolerate algal or peritidal facies that represented shallow water and raised salinity. This genus has not been reported from Upper Cambrian and Lower Ordovician platform facies in western Newfoundland, including the Port au Port Peninsula, where the characteristic lithofacies range from dolostone to limestone with massive thrombolite mounds (Knight & James 1988; Ji & Barnes 1994*a*, 1994*b*), and the *Teridontus nakamurai* and *Semiacontiodus nogamii* communities are prevalent (Figs 4 & 8).

The distribution pattern of the *Phakelodus tenuis* community in western Newfoundland

Fig. 6. Results of Q- and R-mode cluster analysis of 77 conodont-bearing samples from the lower proximal slope facies of the Tucker's Cove Member, Shallow Bay Formation and Broom Point Member, Green Point Formation at Broom Point North section. Samples are in Q-mode clustering order; taxa are in R-mode clustering order; and relative abundance of taxa is expressed as a graded series of dots. Intersections of Q- and R-clusters defined nine conodont communities and assemblages, indicated by the abbreviations: *P.t.*, *Phakelodus tenuis*; *T.n.*, *Teridontus nakamurai*; *P.t.–E.n.*, *P. tenuis–Eoconodontus notchpeakensis*; *T.n.–E.a.*, *Teridontus nakamurai–E. alisonae*; *C.p.*, *Cordylodus proavus*; *C.h.–C.p.*, *C. hastatus–C. proavus*; *C.i–C.c*, *C. intermedius–C. caboti*; *M.s.*, *Monocostodus sevierensis*; *C.d.–P.n.*, *C. deflexus–Parutahconus nodosus*. The database is the combination of table 2 of Barnes (1988) and the Broom Point part of table 1 of Bagnoli *et al.* (1986). Pelagic and nektobenthic communities are differentiated by dashed dark-grey boxes with hollow letters and solid light-grey boxes with bold letters, respectively. The dashed boxes without shading indicate the pelagic communities not discussed as separate communities in the text. The nominate species and the main component of the nektobenthic community are differentiated by shaded boxes with solid outlines and shaded box without outlines, respectively.

Fig. 7. (overleaf) Results of Q- and R-mode cluster analysis of 55 conodont-bearing samples from Martin Point and Broom Point members, Green Point Formation at the Green Point section. Samples are in Q-mode clustering order; taxa are in R-mode clustering order; and relative abundance of taxa is expressed as a graded series of dots. Intersections of Q- and R-clusters defined six conodont communities and assemblages, indicated by the abbreviations: *P.t.*, *Phakelodus tenuis*; *T.n.*, *Teridontus nakamurai*; *U.u.–I.p.*, *Utahconus utahensis–Iapetognathus preaengensis*; *C.c–C.i*, *Cordylodus caboti–C. intermedius*; *C.c.*, *C. caboti*; *C.h.–C.p.*, *C. hastatus–C. proavus*. The database is from table 6 of Barnes (1988). Pelagic and nektobenthic communities are differentiated by a dashed dark-grey boxes with hollow letters and solid light-grey boxes with bold letters, respectively. The dashed boxes without shading indicate the pelagic communities not discussed as separate communities in the text. The nominate species and the main component of the nektobenthic community are differentiated by shaded boxes with solid outlines and shaded boxes without outlines, respectively.

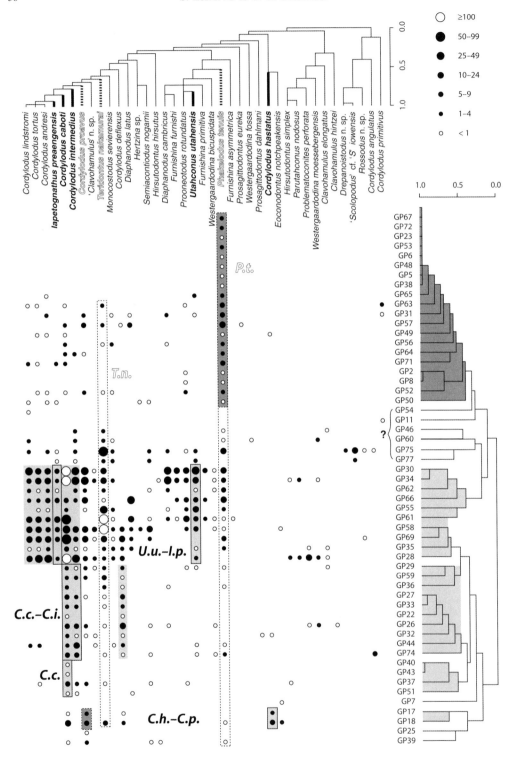

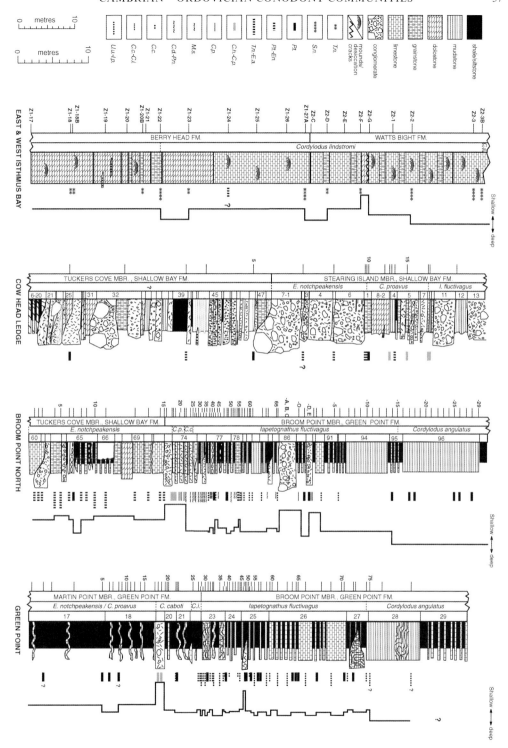

supports its pelagic habit, where it is usually the sole component of the community. It is always related to green, grey and black shale and ribbons lime of mudstone with graptolites, which represent the greatest water depth and anaerobic conditions (James & Stevens 1986) that other conodonts could not tolerate. The low species abundance suggests that this species could tolerate some degree of anoxia, but not extreme anoxia.

The nature of the *Phakelodus tenuis* community and its environmental preference coincided with House's (1985) observation that phases of low biological diversity and/or extinction are often correlated with the spread of euxinic conditions. Further, McGhee *et al.* (1991) noted that such a biological phenomenon and euxinic conditions are commonly associated with global transgressive phases.

Additionally, 12 samples from the Green Point section yielded the *Phakelodus tenuis* community, but included a few specimens of the other species. They form a doorstep pattern in Q-type output, and are characterized by a relatively high abundance of *P. tenuis* (<1–24 specimens per kilogram), but with the co-occurrence of 16 other species distributed among the different samples (Fig. 7). Among the 16 species, *Cordylodus caboti* Bagnoli, Barnes & Stevens is relatively common, occurring in seven samples at low abundance (<1–4 specimens per kilogram). These samples occur through the whole section, but are concentrated in units 25 and 26 (James & Stevens 1986; Barnes 1988), which comprise shale and ribbon limestone with graptolites. The presence of *C. caboti* in these samples may indicate

Fig. 8. The distribution of the conodont communities and assemblages identified by cluster analysis over four different sections of Upper Cambrian and Lower Ordovician strata. The platform section (East and West Isthmus Bay) is from Ji & Barnes (1994*a*); upper proximal slope (Cow Head Ledge), lower proximal slope (Broom Point North) and distal slope (Green Point) sections are from Barnes (1988) and Bagnoli *et al.* (1986). Inferred sea-level curves are based on the distribution of the conodont communities and assemblages, except for the upper proximal slope section that has fewer samples than other sections. The left-hand scale bar is for the two sections on the left; the right-hand scale bar is for other two sections on the right. The abbreviations in legend: *T.n., Teridontus; S.n., Semiacontiodus nogamii; P.t., Phakelodus tenuis; P.t.– E.n., P. tenuis–Eoconodontus notchpeakensis; T.n.– E.a., Teridontus nakamurai–E. alisonae; C.h.–C.p., Cordylodus hastatus–C. proavus; C.p., C. proavus; M.s., Monocostodus sevierensis; C.d.–P.n., C. deflexus– Parutahconus nodosus; C.c., C. caboti; C.p., C.c–C.i, Cordylodus caboti–C. intermedius; U.u.–I.p., Utahconus utahensis–Iapetognathus preaengensis.*

dysaerobic conditions, as *C. caboti* is interpreted as nektobenthic (see later discussion).

Phakelodus tenuis–Eoconodontus notchpeakensis assemblage. The *Phakelodus tenuis– Eoconodontus notchpeakensis* assemblage can be recognized in the Cow Head Ledge and Broom Point North sections, but is best developed in the Broom Point North section (Figs 5, 6 & 8). At this latter locality, it is characterized by abundant *P. tenuis* (being 60% on average, with 1–99 specimens per kilogram), and *E. notchpeakensis* (being 10% on average, with <1–24 specimens per kilogram). Another striking characteristic of the assemblage at Broom Point North is that out of all the sections it shows the most diverse proconodontid species. Within this assemblage, except for the eponymous species, the common representatives are species of *Proconodontus* Miller. Out of 12 samples, samples 7, 5, and 4 yielded: *Proconodontus muelleri* Miller, *P. serratus* Miller, and *P. posterocostatus* Miller respectively – comprising 9% of the assemblage overall (Fig. 9b). Six of the 12 samples produced *Prooneotodus rotundatus* Druce & Jones, which is a paraconodontid that forms 11% of the assemblage with six other paraconodontid species belonging to five genera (Fig. 9b). The composition of the assemblage is different from the interpretations made by Dubinina (1991, fig. 7).

However, at Cow Head Ledge, the recognition of the assemblage is based on the rare occurrence of *Eoconodontus notchpeakensis* and *Proconodontus muelleri* (<1–4 specimens per kg). *Eoconodontus notchpeakensis* has only been recovered from three out of 55 samples at the Green Point section, which are not clustered together and do not have a close relationship to any communities recognized by the cluster analysis.

At Broom Point North, the *Phakelodus tenuis–Eoconodontus notchpeakensis* assemblage is mainly preserved in units 60, 61, 65 and 69–72 (Fig. 8), which are parted limestone, ribbon limestone, ribbon to parted grainstone, and parted grainstone. These lithologies are generally related to deep, quiet, and locally high-energy environments (James & Stevens 1986). At Cow Head Ledge, the community is mainly found in units 7.5 and 8.1 (Fig. 8), which are dominated by grainstone and ribbon limestone. Compared with units 60, 61, 65, 69–72 at Broom Point North, these lithologies represent a higher-energy environment, or gravity-driven downslope transportation. The high species

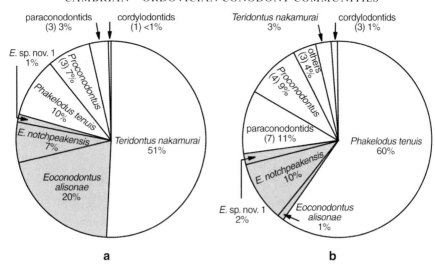

Fig. 9. Relative abundance pie diagram for conodont taxa of *Teridontus nakamurai–E. alisonae* (**a**) and *Phakelodus tenuis–Eoconodontus notchpeakensis* (**b**) assemblages. Samples from the lower proximal slope facies of the Tucker's Cove Member, Shallow Bay at Broom Point North section (Barnes 1988). Shaded areas show the main components of the nektobenthic communities; the numbers in brackets after certain taxa represent the number of species.

diversity of proconodontids and the high species abundance of *E. notchpeakensis* at Broom Point North, together with their rarity at Cow Head Ledge and Green Point, suggest that these conodonts had a narrow environmental preference – for the lower proximal slope.

Dubinina (1991, fig. 7, p. 115) observed only 1–2% of *Proconodontus* sp. from the total assemblage during *Eoconodontus notchpeakensis* times, and argued that rare occurrences of *Proconodontus* elements in western Newfoundland were probably transported. However, if these elements were transported from shallow water, they should be more abundant in the more proximal Cow Head Ledge than in Broom Point North, but this is not the case: elements of *Proconodontus* being rare in the Cow Head Ledge section.

The more narrowly and more widely distributed species that are grouped together suggest a mixture of pelagic *P. tenuis* and nektobenthic *Eoconodontus notchpeakensis* communities (Fig. 6). Only the earliest *Cordylodus* species, *C. primitivus* Bagnoli, Barnes & Stevens, occurs in the interval in which this assemblage is preserved, and only two of 12 samples yield <1–4 specimens (per kilogram) of *C. primitivus* at Broom Point North. This does not support Miller's (1984) observation that both *Cordylodus* and *Eoconodontus* occur in stinkstones – one of Klapper & Barrick's (1978) criteria of a pelagic mode of life.

Teridontus nakamurai *community and* T. nakamurai–Eoconodontus alisonae *assemblage*

Teridontus nakamurai community. *Teridontus nakamurai* (Nogami) is the oldest protopanderodontid (Sweet 1988) conodont: ranging from Late Cambrian to Early Ordovician, and is another of the most common species in the samples used herein. The *Teridontus nakamurai* community is one of the communities composed mainly of the nominate species (Figs 4 & 8). The pelagic mode of life of this species was suggested by Miller (1984), but its rareness in anaerobic environments was not explained.

As mentioned above, the cluster analysis for the Broom Point North and Green Point sections provides two dominant groups: one rich in *Phakelodus tenuis*, and the other in *Teridontus nakamurai*.

These two species show a strong antipathetic relationship in many samples from Cow Head Ledge, Broom Point North, and Green Point sections (Figs 10a–10c). *Phakelodus tenuis* does not occur in the platform facies, but *Teridontus nakamurai* occurs anywhere from platform to distal slope, but not in the anoxic shale and ribbon limestone. The two species from Upper Cambrian and Lower Ordovician continental slope deposits in Highgate Gorge, Northwestern Vermont (Landing 1983) show a similar pattern

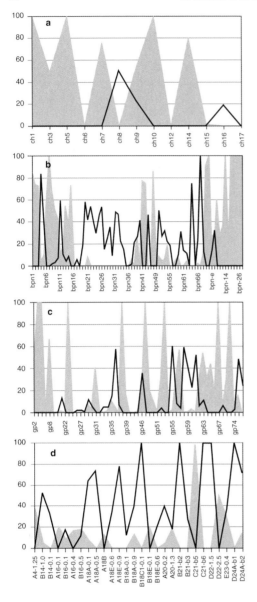

Fig. 10. *Teridontus nakamurai* and *Phakelodus tenuis* show a strong antipathetic relationship – even displaying a mutually exclusive pattern among the samples from Cow Head Ledge (**a**); Broom Point North (**b**); Green Point (**c**); and NW Vermont (**d**) sections. The database of (**a**)–(**c**) is from tables 1, 2 and 6 of Barnes (1988) and table 1 of Bagnoli *et al.* (1986); (**d**) is from figs 5 and 6 of Landing (1983; samples are rearranged based on stratigraphic order, and samples from section F are not included). The solid and shaded curves represent percentage of *T. nakamurai* and *P. tenuis* in total fauna in each sample, respectively.

(Fig. 10d) to that of western Newfoundland, but with *T. nakamurai* being more abundant. This is probably related to the shallower-water depth of the Highgate Gorge section. Such a pattern reflects a pelagic mode of life.

The *Teridontus nakamurai* community is restricted to the upper part of the Berry Head Formation at East Isthmus Bay and the lower part of the Watt's Bight Formation at West Isthmus Bay (Figs 4 & 8). This interval of the section is dominated by dolostone, dolomitized limestone, and oolitic limestone – and minor erosion surfaces and desiccation cracks occur in the upper part (Ji & Barnes 1994*a*, appendix A). The community obviously preferred a very shallow-water environment with raised salinity and locally high energy, but did extend into deeper water, although it is not found in lithologies deposited in anaerobic conditions, unlike *Phakelodus tenuis* (Fig. 8).

Thus, the species *Teridontus nakamurai* and *Phakelodus tenuis* can exist within aerobic and anaerobic conditions respectively, but their sole nominate communities may represent the shallowest and deepest water that conodonts could reach during the Late Cambrian and Early Ordovician.

Teridontus nakamurai–Econodontus alisonae assemblage. The *Teridontus nakamurai–Eoconodontus alisonae* assemblage is only recognized in the Broom Point North section, where it alternates with the *Phakelodus tenuis–E. notchpeakensis* assemblage in the Tucker's Cove Member (Figs. 6 & 8). Compared with the latter assemblage, the *T. nakamurai–E. alisonae* assemblage contains more abundant *T. nakamurai*, with 51% on average and <1–24 specimens per kilogram, compared with *E. alisonae* Landing, with 20% on average and 1–9 specimens per kilogram (Fig. 9a). Both *Proconodontus* and paraconodontid species are less abundant than in the *P. tenuis–E. notchpeakensis* assemblage. The observations on the composition of the assemblage do not support the interpretation by Dubinina (1991, fig 8) that the conodont fauna in western Newfoundland during *E. alisonae* times, of about 40% *E. alisonae* and 20% *E. notchpeakensis*, *Proconodontus* and *T. nakamurai*, made by Dubinina (1991, fig. 8).

The *Teridontus nakamurai–Eoconodontus alisonae* assemblage is preserved in units 63 and 66 at Broom Point North section (Fig. 8), which are parted grainstone and ribbon-to-parted grainstone. These lithologies represent a higher-energy and probably shallower environment than that of *Phakelodus tenuis–E. notchpeakensis* community. If downslope transportation of *Proconodontus* species was a significant factor, as advocated by Dubinina (1991, fig. 8), then the *Proconodontus* species should be more abundant in the *T. nakamurai–E. alisonae* assemblage than in the *P. tenuis–E. notchpeakensis* assemblage, instead of the opposite (Fig. 9a & b).

Like to the *Phakelodus tenuis–Eoconodontus notchpeakensis* assemblage, the *Teridontus nakamurai–E. alisonae* assemblage also represents a mixture of both the pelagic *T. nakamurai* community and the nektobenthic *E. alisonae* community.

The two species of *Eoconodontus: E. notchpeakensis* and *E. alisonae*, formed a mixed assemblage with different pelagic species, *Phakelodus tenuis* and *Teridontus nakamurai*, respectively (Figs 6 & 9a, b), which suggests that *E. notchpeakensis* and *P. tenuis* may have preferred a deeper-water environment than *E. alisonae* and *T. nakamurai*.

Cordylodus proavus *community*

Cordylodus proavus Müller is widespread in the western Newfoundland slope facies; as a community, it is only recognized in the lower proximal slope section at Broom Point North (Figs 6 & 8).

The community is preserved in either ribbon and parted limestone with argillaceous interbeds, or in conglomerate. The former lithology represents the *in situ* deposit in the lower proximal slope, and the latter represents debris flows from the shelf-break or upper slope. The wide distribution of the species and the wide range of the lithofacies suggest a more pelagic mode of life for *C. proavus* than the other species of the genus. However, as a pelagic species, its relationship with *Teridontus nakamurai* and *Phakelodus tenuis* is unclear.

Transported assemblage: Cordylodus hastatus–C. proavus *assemblage*

Cordylodus hastatus is distinguished by its robust to massive elements. Together with *C. proavus*, it forms the *C. hastatus–C. proavus* assemblage, which has a wide environmental distribution from the upper proximal to the distal slope, recognized at the Cow Head Ledge, Broom Point North, and Green Point sections, and with a short stratigraphic range in the *C. proavus* Zone/*C. caboti* Zone of the Upper Cambrian (Figs 5–8).

The Cow Head Ledge samples used herein extend up to the lower part of *Cordylodus lindstromi* Zone (= *Iapetognathus fluctivagus* Zone of Cooper *et al.* 2001). The three successive samples from the Cow Head Ledge section yield *C. hastatus*, a species which is the main component of one of the three conodont community and assemblages recognized in that section (Figs 5 & 8).

At the Cow Head Ledge section, the *Cordylodus hastatus–C. proavus* assemblage occurs in the lenticular grainstone and lenticular intraclast grainstone of units 8-5 and 8-8 (James & Stevens 1986; Barnes 1988). At the Broom Point North section, most of the samples yielding the *C. hastatus–C. proavus* assemblage are from the conglomerate and parted limestone in unit 74 (Figs 6 & 8) (James & Stevens 1986; Barnes 1988). At the Green Point section (Figs 7 & 8), samples GP17 and GP18 contained five and 24 specimens of *Cordylodus primitivus* (Barnes 1988, table 6; Bagnoli *et al.* 1986, table 1; samples GP1A and GP1B = GP17 and GP18 of Barnes 1988). However, based on Barnes (1988), these specimens should be referred to *C. hastatus*. The assemblage is preserved in unit 19 (James & Stevens 1986; Barnes 1988) in Green Point, which is a conglomerate bed that consists of 90% clasts (three-quarters tabular, average size 5 cm, largest size 20 cm). Thus, the assemblage tended to be preserved in the bedded rocks in the relative shallow environment of the upper proximal slope facies, and in the conglomerate in the relative deep environment of the distal slope. Undoubtedly, these conglomerate samples were transported from a shallower-water location.

When *Cordylodus hastatus* was established, several specimens illustrated as other *Cordylodus* species by earlier workers were considered as synonyms (Barnes 1988), including:

(1) one specimen of *Cordylodus prion* Lindström of Druce & Jones (1971, pl. 2, fig. 4);
(2) one specimen of *Cordylodus prion* of Landing (1983, fig. 8B);
(3) two specimens of *Cordylodus proavus* of Apollonov *et al.* (1984, pl. 30, figs 3, 14);
(4) two specimens of *Cordylodus proavus* of Chen & Gong (1986, pl. 36, fig. 13, 17); and
(5) three specimens of *Cordylodus primitivus* of Bagnoli *et al.* (1986, pl. 1, fig. 9).

These specimens were from both relatively shallow-water (Druce & Jones 1971; Chen & Gong 1986) and relatively deep-water deposits (Landing 1983; Apollonov *et al.* 1984; Bagnoli *et al.* 1986). Recently, *Cordylodus hastatus* was

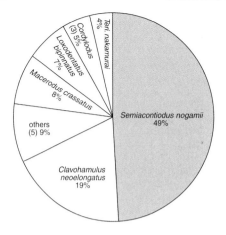

Fig. 11. Relative abundance pie diagram for conodont taxa of the *Semiacontiodus nogamii* community. Samples from platform facies of the uppermost Berry Head and lower Watt's Bight formations (Ji & Barnes 1994*a*). Shadowed area shows the main component of the community; the numbers in brackets after certain taxa represent the number of species.

reported from the Lloyd George Member, Kechika Formation, NE British Columbia, distinguished by intraformational conglomerate, lime mudstone, and wackestone (Pyle & Barnes 2000, 2002). *Cordylodus hastatus* makes up 6% of the conodont fauna from sample GP-94-6-6 from a conglomerate from the Grey Peak section of a carbonate ramp facies (Pyle & Barnes 2002).

Thus, given the robust elements of *Cordylodus hastatus* and its associated lithofacies, and as the *C. hastatus–C. proavus* assemblage is recognized in the upper proximal slope, lower proximal slope, and distal slope facies, elements of this assemblage were probably transported from the shelf-break or upper slope. This is a good example to test the hypothesis in Fig. 3b. Comparing the narrow environmental distribution of *Cordylodus hastatus* to that of *C. proavus* may suggest that these two species had a nektobenthic and a pelagic mode of life, respectively.

Nektobenthic communities

Most of the communities discussed in the following sections contain abundant *Teridontus nakamurai* (considered as a pelagic species in the earlier discussion). Hence, most of the communities discussed in this section are a mixture of both pelagic and nektobenthic faunal components. Therefore, the following section will avoid a duplicate discussion of pelagic communities.

Platform community: Semiacontiodus nogamii community

The *Semiacontiodus nogamii* community (Fig. 4) is the only Early Ordovician nektobenthic community recognized in the platform facies, East and West Isthmus Bay sections, instead of the *Semiacontiodus–Teridontus* community recognized by Ji & Barnes (1994*b*). Although the Berry Head and Watt's Bight formations include much dolostone and dolomitized limestone, samples in Q-mode-cluster forming the community are mainly from limestone. Thus, this community should represent a shallow-water environment with normal to slightly raised salinity. The *S. nogamii* community occurs in the uppermost Berry Head (Upper Cambrian–Lower Ordovician) and lower Watt's Bight (Lower Ordovician) formations (Fig. 8), and is composed of 49% *S. nogamii* Miller, but with only 4% *Teridontus nakamurai* (Fig. 11). In the East and West Bay sections, the *S. nogamii* community replaced the *T. nakamurai* community in the upper Berry Head Formation, together with the initial introduction of *Cordylodus lindstromi* Druce & Jones on to the platform in western Newfoundland during a flooding event.

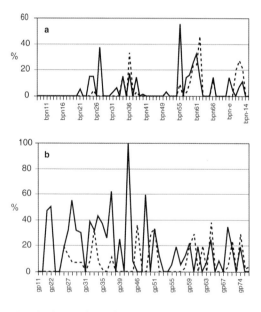

Fig. 12. Comparison of the relative abundance of *Cordylodus caboti* and *C. intermedius* between two different facies: (**a**) lower proximal slope (Broom Point section); (**b**) distal slope (Green Point section) (Barnes 1988). The solid and dashed curves represent the percentage of *Cordylodus caboti* and *C. intermedius* in total fauna in each sample, respectively.

Table 1. Relative abundance of Cordylodus species in sections from the platform (East and West Isthmus Bay), upper proximal slope (Cow Head Ledge), lower proximal slope (Broom Point North), and distal slope (Green Point) facies

	East & West Isthmus Bay	Cow Head Ledge	Broom Point North	Green Point
angulatus	1 sample (2%)*	?		2 samples [<1–34% (17%)]*
andresi	–	–	9/24 (38%); 3–20% (10%)	15/42 (36%); 1–12% (7%)
tortus	–	2/7 (28%); 1–3% (2%)*	10/35 (29%); 1–24 (8%)	15/38 (39%); 2–8% (4%)
lindstromi	2/20 (10%); 2–6% (4%)*	one sample; 3%*	9/39 (23%); 1–25% (10%)	16/42 (38%); 1–100% (7%)
intermedius	6/20 (30%); 1–11% (5%)	–	15/46 (33%); 3–46% (17%)	25/46 (54%); 2–61% (17%)
caboti	–	–	22/50 (44%); 1–55% (15%)	33/48 (69%); 6–100% (30%)
hastatus	–	3/3 (100%); 6–100% (37%)	12/37 (35%); 1–36% (15%)	4/25 (16%); 8–31% (19%)
proavus	–	4/7 (57%); 8–27% (15%)	21/52 (40%); 1–100% (21%)	23/44 (52%); 1–100% (11%)
deflexus	–	–	21/55 (38%); 2–19% (18%)	17/48 (35%); 1–50% (12%)
primitivus	–	2/7 (28%); 24–27% (26%)*	10/57 (18%); 1–33% 10%	1 sample; 17%*

The species are listed in the left column in stratigraphic order from bottom to top. Dashes represent the absence of that species; four pieces of data in each cell from left to right represent: (1) the ratio of sample numbers containing the species to the total sample number of the interval in which the species occurs; (2) percentage of samples in the interval in which the species occurs; (3) range of relative abundance of the species; (4) average abundance of the species. *indicates data based only on one or two samples.

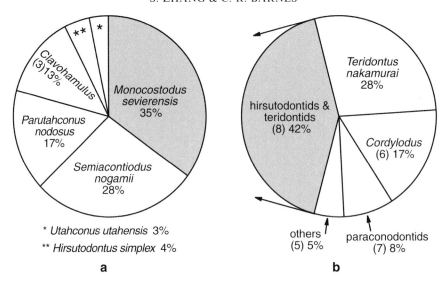

Fig. 13. Relative abundance pie diagram for conodont taxa of the *Monocostodus sevierensis* community. Samples from the lower proximal slope facies Broom Point Member, Green Point Formation at the Broom Point North section (Barnes 1988). Shadowed areas show the main components of the communities; the numbers in brackets after certain taxa represent the number of species. (**a**) Relative abundance of *Teridontus* and *Hirsutodontus* lineages except for the pelagic *T. nakamurai*; (**b**) relative abundance of all taxa.

Semiacontiodus nogamii can be also found in upper and lower proximal slope and distal slope environments at low abundance, which is considered as either being due to transportation or to an unfavourable environment (see later discussion).

Lower proximal slope communities

Three communities can be recognized on the lower proximal slope (Figs 6 & 8): the *Cordylodus caboti–C. intermedius,* the *C. deflexus–Parutahconus nodosus,* and the *Monocostodus sevierensis* communities. Both species diversity and species abundance are higher when compared with the platform community.

Cordylodus caboti–C. intermedius *community.* Both *Cordylodus caboti* and *C. intermedius* Furnish are more abundant at Green Point than at Broom Point North (Table 1, Fig. 12). The *C. caboti–C. intermedius* community is present in both sections. In Broom Point North (Figs 6 & 8), nine samples are closely grouped together under these two species in the Q-mode clustering. The community recognized at Broom Point North is not related to either the *Monocostodus sevierensis* community or to the *C. deflexus–Parutahconus nodosus* communities that are considered as the nektobenthic

representatives (see discussion below). Such a partitioning pattern suggests that *C. caboti–C. intermedius* community was nektobenthic.

Cordylodus deflexus–Parutahconus nodosus *community*

The *Cordylodus deflexus–Parutahconus nodosus* community can be recognized among eleven samples in the Broom Point North section (Figs 6 & 8). The species *Parutahconus nodosus* Landing was established by Landing (*in* Fortey *et al.* 1982), based on material from the Broom Point North and South sections. It has not been reported elsewhere, and it may be endemic. The community containing this species is mainly preserved in upper unit 74 and unit 75 (James & Stevens 1986; Barnes 1988). The former is conglomerate and parted limestone, but the samples were collected from bedded grainstone; the latter is composed of parted limestone, alternating grainstone and mudstone separated by green-grey argillaceous limestone, with the samples being taken from the grainstone beds.

In the Cow Head Group, over 80% of the grainstone particles are peloids, which originated from shelf-break calcified algae (Coniglio & James 1985). The question is whether, like the peloids, the components of the *Cordylodus deflexus–Parutahconus nodosus* community were transported downslope.

Within this community, three species of *Clavohamulus* Furnish, with low abundance (<1–4 specimens per kilogram), were found in a few samples in the Q-mode cluster. Miller (1984) noted that the species of this genus occur in various shallow-water lithologies, including stromatolitic limestone, and stromatolitic and non-stromatolitic dolostone, all of which probably represent a warm, shallow, high-salinity environment. Three samples out of 11 in the community contain *Clavohamulus hintzei* Miller, which was considered to tolerate a variety of shallow, high-energy, and possibly high-salinity conditions, but also lived in more normal-marine environments found on cratonic and miogeoclinal carbonate platforms (Lehnert *et al.* 1997). This species was found in the Watts Bight Formation at Pigeon Head and Lower Cove sections and lower Boat Harbour Formation at Jerry's Nose and Pigeon Head sections in the adjacent platform facies, western Newfoundland (Ji & Barnes 1994*a*). A shallow-water representative, *Semiacontiodus nogamii*, a species characteristic of the Late Cambrian to Early Ordovician conodont community in the East and West Isthmus Bay sections, is found in four samples of the *Cordylodus deflexus–Parutahconus nodosus* community. The rare elements of the shallow-water conodonts found in the lower proximal slope facies may have been transported by turbidites and/or debris flows.

However, *Parutahconus nodosus*, one of the characteristic nominate species of the community, is a common species within the community, although at low abundance (<1–4 specimens per kilogram), and is hardly found beyond the lower proximal slope facies, which may suggest a nektobenthic mode of life, and an *in situ* fauna. In both the Broom Point North and Green Point sections, *Cordylodus deflexus* Bagnoli, Barnes & Stevens displays a more stable distribution than do any of the other *Cordylodus* species (Table 1). *Cordylodus deflexus* is slightly more abundant in the Broom Point North than in Green Point section. This may indicate that *C. deflexus* had the widest tolerance to the slope environments among several species of the genus.

Monocostodus sevierensis community. The *Monocostodus sevierensis* community can be recognized among nine samples in the Broom Point North section (Figs 6 & 8). The obvious feature of this community is that the species diversity within the *Teridontus* and *Hirsutodontus* lineages is increased. Except for *T. nakamurai*, eight species of the lineages (*Clavohamulus elongatus* Miller, *C. hintzei*, 'C.'

sp. nov. Barnes, *H. simplex* (Druce & Jones), *Parutahconus nodosus, Monocostodus sevierensis* (Miller), *Semiacontiodus nogamii* and *Utahconus utahensis* (Miller)) form 42% of the community (Fig. 13b), and every sample in the Q-mode cluster forming the community yields the nominate species, with 35% belonging to the two lineages (Fig. 13a). There are no specimens of *Cordylodus deflexus*, although *M. sevierensis* can be found in the *C. deflexus–Parutahconus nodosus* community.

Except for the data of Landing (1983), almost all the earlier reported occurrences of *Monocostodus sevierensis* were from shallow-water deposits in North America (Miller 1969; Miller *et al.* 1981; Nowlan 1985) and Australia (Druce *et al.* 1982).

Landing (1983), however, reported *Monocostodus sevierensis* from the Gorge Formation, Vermont, USA, which is a continental slope deposit. In western Newfoundland, the community dominated by this species is scattered among units 75, 77, 78, 83, and 85 of the Broom Point North section (Fig. 8) (James & Stevens 1986; Barnes 1988), which are bedded parted limestone, parted to ribbon limestone, parted to ribbon grainstone, shale, and parted lime mudstone respectively. Unit 77 produced numerous trilobites. These units are not influenced by major transportation, but rare elements of *Clavohamulus* and *Semiacontiodus* species may have been transported by turbidites and/or debris flows, as discussed earlier.

Distal slope communities

Distal slope communities are those recognized in the Green Point section (Figs 7 & 8). Their principal feature is that they have the greatest number of *Cordylodus* species among all the different facies (Table 1). Globally, *Cordylodus* species are a major component of most slope and platform communities, and they play an important role in Late Cambrian and Early Ordovician biostratigraphy.

Abundant elements of *Cordylodus* were found in lagerstätten stinkstones in Sweden, which was cited by Miller (1984) as evidence of the pelagic mode of life of *Cordylodus*. Barnes & Fåhraeus (1975) concluded that *Cordylodus proavus* was pelagic, but that younger species such as *C. angulatus* Pander became adapted to a more nektobenthic mode of life. Western Newfoundland material (Barnes 1988, used herein) does not provide enough data to prove the habit for *C. angulatus*, because the sampled sections only extend into the basal part of the *C. angulatus* Zone, except for the West Isthmus Bay section.

The analysis of the mode of life of *Cordylodus* species is based on the interval from the first appearance of *C. primitivus* (within the *Eoconodontus notchpeakensis* Zone) to the first appearance of *C. angulatus* (the base of *C. angulatus* Zone) in western Newfoundland (Fig. 2; Table 1). The sections are chosen from platform facies, through proximal slope facies, to distal slope facies.

The platform facies, represented by the sections at East and West Isthmus Bay (Ji & Barnes 1994*a*), has the lowest number of *Cordylodus* species. Although the Cow Head Ledge section, representing the upper proximal slope facies, only extends into lower *C. lindstromi* Zone (= *Iapetognathus fluctivagus* Zone of Cooper *et al.* 2001), it does not yield several species that occur in *C. proavus* and *C. caboti* zones in lower proximal and distal slope facies, such as *C. andresi* Viira & Sergeeva, *C. deflexus*, *C. caboti* Bagnoli, Barnes & Stevens, and *C. intermedius* Furnish. This overall distribution pattern shows that most *Cordylodus* species preferred a deeper-water environment. The question is whether all *Cordylodus* species had an even distribution in deeper facies beyond the upper proximal slope.

Table 1 summarizes the percentage of samples containing a particular species through the interval in which the species occurs within each section, and also the relative abundance of the

species in those samples. The *Cordylodus* species in the platform facies, taking West Isthmus Bay section (Z2) as a example and using the interval from base of Watt's Bight Formation to the sample containing the last appearance of *C. intermedius* (in total 20 conodont-bearing samples), only two and six samples produce *C. lindstromi* and *C. intermedius*, with 4% and 5% relative abundance, respectively (Table 1). Comparing the relative abundance of these two species in platform facies to those in the slope facies (Broom Point and Green Point), the former is much lower than the latter. Hence, although these two species do appear in the platform facies, the slope may be their preferred environment.

Three communities can be recognized in the distal slope (Figs 7 & 8): the *Cordylodus caboti*, *C. caboti–C. intermedius* and *Utahconus utahensis–Iapetognathus preaengensis* communities.

Cordylodus caboti community. Cordylodus caboti only occurs on the slope (Broom Point North and Green Point sections) (Figs 6, 7 & 12; Table 1). It is the nominate species of the *C. caboti* Zone that succeeds the *C. proavus* Zone (Barnes 1988). Based on its occurrence in the stratigraphic sequence, it should be found in the intervals of the Isthmus and Cow Head Ledge sections that are selected for this study – but it is absent in both

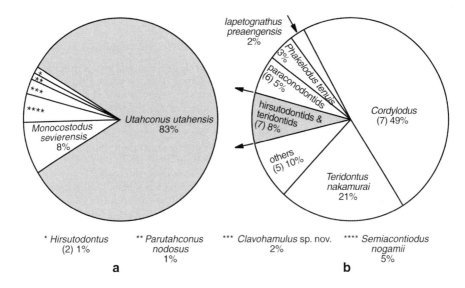

Fig. 14. Relative abundance pie diagram for conodont taxa of the *Utahconus utahensis–Iapetognathus preaengensis* community. Samples from the distal slope facies of the Broom Point Member, Green Point Formation at Green Point section (Barnes 1988). Shadowed areas show the main components of the communities; the numbers in brackets followed taxa represents the number of species. (**a**) relative abundance of *Teridontus* and *Hirsutodontus* lineages except for the pelagic *T. nakamurai*, (**b**) relative abundance of all taxa.

sections. This is presumed to relate to its palaeoecological preferences, i.e. environments deeper than the upper proximal slope.

The conodont community dominated by *Cordylodus caboti* is only recognized by cluster analysis in the Green Point section (Figs 7 & 8), where it occurs in the *C. lindstromi* Zone (= *Iapetognathus fluctivagus* Zone of Cooper *et al.* 2001). The *C. caboti* community has both low species abundance and low species diversity, with the latter only ranging from one to eight (Fig. 7).

Furthermore, comparing the relative abundance of *Cordylodus caboti* in the distal slope facies to that in the lower proximal slope facies (Fig. 12, Table 1), the former ranges from 6% to 100%, with an average of 30% among 33 out of 48 samples (69%); and the latter ranges between 1% and 55%, with an average of 15% among 22 out of 50 samples (44%). The relative abundance data suggest that *C. caboti* preferred a deep-water environment and aerobic conditions, which is supported by the absence of both *Phakelodus tenuis* and *Teridontus nakamurai*.

Cordylodus caboti–C. intermedius community. As discussed earlier, the *Cordylodus caboti–C. intermedius* community is also recognized in the lower proximal slope (Figs 6 & 8). The difference is that the community recognized in the distal slope contains common *C. deflexus*. But it rarely contains *Utahconus utahensis*, which is characteristic of the *U. utahensis–Iapetognathus preaengensis* community in the Green Point section. The *Cordylodus caboti–C. intermedius* community also differs from the *Utahconus utahensis–Iapetognathus preaengensis* community in having a lower species diversity, ranging from two to 11 (Fig. 7) (see discussion below).

Utahconus utahensis–Iapetognathus preaengensis community. The *Utahconus utahensis–Iapetognathus preaengensis* community is only recognized in the Green Point section (Figs 7 & 8). This community has a high species diversity, with 10–20 species. Besides the nominate species, the community has *Cordylodus lindstromi, C. tortus* Barnes, *C. andresi, C. caboti, C. intermedius*, and *C. proavus*, that are common to abundant.

Comparing Figure 14 with Figure 13, the relative abundance of *Cordylodus* is much higher in the distal slope *Utahconus utahensis–Iapetognathus preaengensis* community (49%) (Fig. 14b) than that in the lower proximal slope *Monocostodus sevierensis* community (17%) (Fig. 13b).

The rapid increase in the relative abundance of *Cordylodus* corresponds to the decrease in the relative abundance of *Teridontus* and *Hirsutodontus* lineages in the distal slope facies. Although the relative abundance of the *Teridontus* and *Hirsutodontus* lineages in the *Utahconus utahensis–Iapetognathus preaengensis* community is lower (seven species form 8% of the community: Fig. 14) than that in the *Monocostodus sevierensis* community (42%, Fig. 13) in the proximal slope facies, *U. utahensis* itself occupies 83% of the *Teridontus* and *Hirsutodontus* lineages in the distal slope. However, *U. utahensis* in the *M. sevierensis* community in the lower proximal slope comprises only 3% of the two lineages (Fig. 13). If the appearance of *U. utahensis* in the distal slope was due to transportation, as concluded by Miller (1984) and Dubinina (1991), logically this species would be more abundant in the proximal slope. If downslope transport involved this species, it should be traceable back to its platform source area, but it has not been reported from the adjacent carbonate platform area (Ji & Barnes 1994*a*).

Iapetognathus preaengensis Landing, another characteristic species of the community, forms 2% among 20 species of the community. It only occurs in a few samples outside of the community in the distal slope facies and the different communities in lower proximal slope with low species abundance (<1 specimen per kilogram). Its distribution pattern is similar to that of *Utahconus utahensis*.

Interpretation of the eustatic signal for the latest Cambrian and earliest Ordovician

Downslope conodont transport during sea-level drop in latest *Cordylodus proavus* Zone times

In the uppermost Cambrian, conglomerates were widespread in the slope environment, represented by the lowest Stearing Island Member (within the shallow Bay Formation in the Cow Head Ledge section), by the lowest Broom Point Member (within the Green Point Formation in the Broom Point North section), and by the uppermost Martin Point Member (within the Green Point Formation at the Green Point section). The conglomerates were derived through downslope slumps or flows carrying carbonate blocks from the shelf margin (James 1981). It has been proposed that the conglomerates were generated during regressive phases, when the carbonate platform margin was exposed and brecciated, with the formation of a karst surface (James *et al.* 1989).

As noted above, among the 12 conodont communities and assemblages (distributed from platform to distal slope) recognized by the cluster analysis, only the *Cordylodus hastatus–C. proavus* assemblage has a wide environmental distribution (from the upper proximal to the distal slope), recognized at the Cow Head Ledge, Broom Point North, and Green Point sections. The assemblage tended to be preserved in the

bedded rocks in the Cow Head Ledge section (representing a relatively shallow environment), and in the conglomerate in the Broom Point North and Green Point sections (representing a relatively deep distal environment). Such a distribution pattern was probably created by a regressive event.

In western Newfoundland, the base of the *Cordylodus proavus* Zone is not accurately constrained. In the Green Point section, the *C. hastatus–C. proavus* assemblage contains *C.*

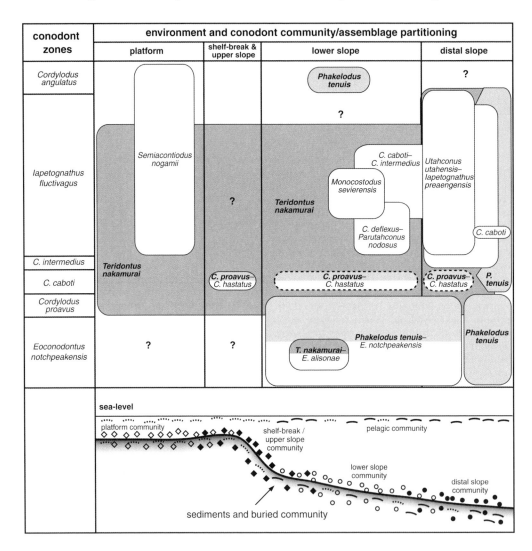

Fig. 15. Summary of conodont community distribution through space and time during the Late Cambrian and Early Ordovician in western Newfoundland. Shaded solid boxes, white solid boxes, and dashed boxes represent pelagic, nektobenthic, and transported communities, respectively. Dark and light shaded boxes represent two trends of shallow/aerobic and deep/anaerobic conditions. The environmental profile shows an ideal condition with the buried conodont fauna as a combination of nektobenthic and pelagic communities without the influence of downslope transport. See Figure 3 for details.

caboti, indicating the *C. caboti* Zone. One sample (BPN22), representing the *C. hastatus–C. proavus* assemblage at the Broom Point North section, contains *Clavohamulus elongatus*, which indicates that the sea-level drop was within or later than the age of the *C. elongatus* Subzone. This regression is probably related to the 'event 1' recognized by Miller (1992).

Sea-level rise and aerobic conditions leading to community diversity in early Iapetognathus fluctivagus *Zone time*

The base of the *Cordylodus lindstromi* Zone was taken earlier as the base of the Tremadocian, which marks the conodont turnover after the latest Cambrian sea-level drop (Barnes *et al.* 1995). Recently, the base of *Iapetognathus fluctivagus* Zone was suggested to mark such a boundary (Cooper *et al.* 2001). In western Newfoundland, the first appearances of *C. lindstromi* and *I. preaengensis* were coupled with a major increase in both conodont diversity and abundance. The *Semiacontiodus nogamii, C. deflexus–Parutahconus nodosus*, and *Utahconus utahensis–I. preaengensis* communities suddenly appeared in the platform, lower proximal slope, and distal slope facies, respectively. The species diversity of the conodont communities increases along the environment gradient, with 2–8, 5–15, and 10–20 species in the East and West Isthmus Bay, Broom Point North, and Green Point sections, respectively. The three communities are preserved mainly in the oolitic limestone at East and West Isthmus Bay, grainstone or parted limestone at Broom Point North, and lime mudstone at Green Point, respectively, which indicate aerobic conditions. Comparing the lithofacies in which the *Cordylodus hastatus–C. proavus* assemblage was preserved, these lithofacies apparently represent *in situ* deposits, and the products of the transgression succeeding a major regression. Combining the lithofacies, the distribution and diversity of the conodont communities, the sea-level rise in the earliest Ordovician was probably coupled with aerobic conditions.

Sea-level rise and anaerobic conditions causing severe changes among communities in early Cordylodus angulatus *Zone time*

During the time interval between the first appearance of *Cordylodus lindstromi/Iapetognathus fluctivagus* and the first appearance of *C. angulatus*, several different communities repeatedly replaced each other, being associated with lithofacies changes between limestones and shales, which may reflect frequent secondary sea-level changes. However, the conodont communities underwent a major change during the first appearance of *C. angulatus*. In the Broom Point North section, the community is dominated by *Phakelodus tenuis*, with low species diversity and species abundance, and preserved in units 95 (ribbon lime grainstone separated by shale) and 96 (lime mudstone; Fig. 8) (James & Stevens 1986; Barnes 1988). In the Green Point section the two samples (GP75 and GP77) collected from unit 28 (lime mudstone) (James & Stevens 1986; Barnes 1988) contain conodonts that are less abundant and diverse than the *Utahconus utahensis–Iapetognathus preaengensis* community compared to the samples grouped under the community, although the two samples show a close relationship to the *U. utahensis–I. preaengensis* community (Fig. 7). One possible explanation is that the disappearance of the older communities is not only a reflection of an eustatic event but possibly of a critical threshold in ocean ventilation (oxygenation) (Barnes *et al.* 1995). However, in the East and West Isthmus Bay section, the *Semiacontiodus nogamii* community reappeared with a higher species diversity than in the earlier interval, which is 7.5 m above a bed containing desiccation cracks and 12.5 m below the first appearance of *C. angulatus*. The reappearance of this community in the shallow platform facies is probably the result of well-oxygenated conditions.

Conclusions

Western Newfoundland provides several complete stratigraphic sections along the environment gradient, from the platform to the distal slope, for the Upper Cambrian and Lower Ordovician boundary interval. This was a critical interval, with initial rapid evolution, diversification, and ecological partitioning of euconodonts. These sections have been sampled in detail for conodonts, and detailed taxonomic and biostratigraphic studies have been published (Bagnoli *et al.* 1986; Barnes 1988). The resulting databases contain 18 468 identifiable conodont specimens processed from 230 conodont-bearing samples, which has allowed a series of statistical palaeoecological analyses (Q- and R-mode cluster analyses) to be carried out. As a result, a complex pattern of evolving conodont communities has been defined.

Some distinct patterns emerged from the analysis and the interpretations, namely:

- The distribution of conodont communities along the platform to slope environment gradient in western Newfoundland shows some gradational relationships (Fig. 15).

- The *Phakelodus tenuis* and *Teridontus nakamurai* communities were the two major pelagic conodont communities, but showed an antipathetic relationship. The former was related to a deep-water environment and anaerobic conditions, whereas the latter preferred shallow to deep water and aerobic conditions. Such a relationship can be used as an indicator of sea-level change.
- The earlier *Cordylodus* species, such as *C. proavus*, probably had a pelagic mode of life, but most of *Cordylodus* species are interpreted to have had a nektobenthic mode of life, and to have favoured deeper water and aerobic conditions, except for *C. hastatus*, which tended to live in shallower, high-energy marine environments.
- The presence of the *Cordylodus hastatus–C. proavus* assemblage in each section, from the upper proximal slope to the distal slope, reflects a downslope transportation event.
- The conodont communities maintained a relatively stable development during pre-*Cordylodus proavus* Zone times (latest Cambrian) both in platform and in slope settings, with the former dominated by *Teridontus nakamurai*, and the latter by *Phakelodus tenuis* and the two species of *Eoconodontus*.
- The data from the slope facies show that the earliest conodont communities evolved and were replaced rapidly during the *Cordylodus proavus–C. angulatus* zonal interval, which reflects a rapid sea-level change during this time interval.
- The main sea-level drop occurred in the latest *Cordylodus proavus* Zone time and is recognized by the downslope transportation of the *C. hastatus* community. The main periods of sea-level rise occurred in early *C. lindstromi* Zone (= *Iapetognathus fluctivagus* Zone of Cooper *et al.* 2001) and early *C. angulatus* Zone times, which are characterized by high community diversity under aerobic conditions, and the major changes within the communities under anaerobic conditions in the slope environment, respectively.

CRB is indebted to N. James and R. Stevens for their assistance in the field and for discussions. Financial support by a Pan-LITHOPROBE grant (LITHO-PROBE Contribution No. 1335) and ongoing support from both the Natural Sciences and Engineering Research Council of Canada (NSERC) and the Earth System Evolution Program of the Canadian Institute for Advanced Research are appreciated.

References

APOLLONOV, M. K., CHUGAEVA, M. N. & DUBININA, S. V. 1984. *Trilobites and Conodonts for the Batybay Section (Uppermost Cambrian–Lower Ordovician) in Malyi Karatau Range (Atlas of the Paleontological Plates)*. Alma-Ata: Academy of Sciences of the Kazakh SSR Nauka, Kazakh SSR Publishing House, 48 pp.

BAGNOLI, G., BARNES, C. R. & STEVENS, R. K. 1986. Lower Ordovician (Tremadocian) conodonts from Broom Point and Green Point, Western Newfoundland. *Bollettino della Società Paleontologica Italiana*, **25(2)**, 145–158 (printed in 1987).

BARNES, C. R. 1988. The proposed Cambrian–Ordovician global boundary stratotype and point (GSSP) in Western Newfoundland, Canada. *Geological Magazine*, **125(4)**, 381–414.

BARNES, C. R. & FÅHRAEUS, L. E. 1975. Provinces, communities, and the proposed nektobenthic habit of Ordovician conodontophoroids. *Lethaia*, **8**, 133–149.

BARNES, C. R. & TUKE, M. F. 1970. Conodonts from the St. George Formation (Ordovician), northern Newfoundland. *Geological Survey of Canada, Bulletin*, **187**, 79–97.

BARNES, C. R., FORTEY, R. A. & WILLIAMS, S. H. 1995. The pattern of global bio-events during the Ordovician Period. *In*: WALLISER, O. T. (ed.) *Global Events and Event Stratigraphy in the Phanerozoic*. Springer-Verlag, Berlin, pp. 139–172.

BARNES, C. R., REXROAD, C. B. & MILLER, J. F. 1973. Lower Paleozoic conodont provincialism. *In*: RHODES, F. T. H. (ed.) *Conodont Paleozoology*. Geological Society of America, Special Paper, **141**, 157–190.

BASSETT, M. G. & DEAN, W. T. (eds) 1982. *The Cambrian–Ordovician Boundary: Sections, Fossil Distributions, and Correlations*. National Museum of Wales, Geological Series, No. **3**, 227 pp.

CHEN, J. & GONG, W. 1986. Conodonts. *In*: CHEN, J. (ed.) *Aspects of Cambrian–Ordovician Boundary in Dayangcha, China*. Contribution to Dayangcha International Conference on Cambrian–Ordovician Boundary, Beijing. China Prospect Publishing House, pp. 93–223.

CONIGLIO, M. & JAMES, N. P. 1985. Calcified algae as sediment contributors to Early Paleozoic limestones: evidence from deep-water sediments of the Cow Head Group, western Newfoundland. *Journal of Sedimentary Petrology*, **55(5)**, 746–754.

COOPER, R. A., NOWLAN, G. S. & WILLIAMS, S. H. 2001. Global Stratotype Section and Point for base of the Ordovician System. *Episodes*, **24(1)**, 19–28.

DRUCE, E. C. & JONES, P. J. 1971. *Cambro-Ordovician Conodonts for the Burke River Structural Belt, Queensland*. Bureau of Mineral Resources of Australia, Bulletin, **110**, 158 pp.

DRUCE, E. C., SHERGOLD, J. H. & RADKE, B. M. 1982. A reassessment of the Cambrian–Ordovician boundary section at Black Mountain, western Queensland, Australia. *In*: BASSETT, M. G. & DEAN, W. T. (eds) *The Cambrian–Ordovician Boundary: Sections, Fossil Distributions, and Correlations*. National Museum of Wales, Geological Series, **3**, 193–209.

DUBININA, S. V. 1991. Upper Cambrian and Lower Ordovician conodont associations from open ocean paleoenvironments, illustrated by Batyrbay and Sarykum sections in Kazakhstan. *In*: BARNES, C. R. & WILLIAMS, S. H. (eds) *Advances in Ordovician Geology*. Geological Survey of Canada, Papers, **90–9**, 107–124.

FÅHRAEUS, L. E. & BARNES, C. R. 1975. Conodonts as indicators of paleogeographic regimes. *Nature*, **258**, 515–518.

FÅHRAEUS, L. E. & NOWLAN, G. S. 1978. Franconian (Late Cambrian) to early Champlainian (Middle Ordovician) conodonts from the Cow Head Group, western Newfoundland. *Journal of Paleontology*, **52**, 444–471.

FORTEY, R. A., LANDING, E. & SKEVINGTON, D. 1982. Cambrian–Ordovician boundary sections in the Cow Head Group, western Newfoundland. *In*: BASSETT, M. G. & DEAN, W. T. (eds) *The Cambrian–Ordovician Boundary: Sections, Fossil Distributions, and Correlations*. Natural Museum of Wales, Geological Series, **3**, 95–129.

HENNINGSMOEN, G. 1957. *The Trilobite Family Olenidae*. Skrifter utgitt av Det Norske Videnskaps-Akademi i Oslo, Mathematisk-naturvidenskapelig Klasse, no. **1**, 303 pp.

HISCOTT, R. N. & JAMES, N. P. 1985. Carbonate debris flows, Cow Head Group, western Newfoundland. *Journal of Sedimentary Petrology*, **55**, 735–745.

HOUSE, M. R. 1985. Correlation of mid-Paleozoic ammonoid evolutionary events with global sedimentary perturbations. *Nature*, **313**, 17–22.

JAMES, N. P. 1981. Megablocks of calcified algae in the Cow Head Breccia, western Newfoundland; vestiges of a Lower Paleozoic continental margin. *Geological Society of America, Bulletin*, **92**, 799–811.

JAMES, N. P. & STEVENS, R. K. 1986. *Stratigraphy and Correlation of the Cambro-Ordovician Cow Head Group, Western Newfoundland*. Geological Survey of Canada, Bulletin, **366**, 143 pp.

JAMES, N. P., STEVENS, R. K., BARNES, C. R. & KNIGHT, I. 1989. A lower Paleozoic continental margin carbonate platform, northern Canadian Appalachians. *In*: CREVELLO, P. D., WILSON, J. L., SARG, J. F. & READ, J. F. (eds) *Controls on Carbonate Platform and Basin Development*. Society of Economic Paleontologists and Mineralogists, Special Publications, **44**, 123–146.

JI, Z. & BARNES, C. R. 1994a. *Lower Ordovician Conodonts of the St. George Group, Port au Port Peninsula, Western Newfoundland, Canada*. Palaeontographica Canadiana, **11**, 149 pp.

JI, Z. & BARNES, C. R. 1994b. Conodont paleoecology of the Lower Ordovician St. George Group, Port au Port Peninsula, western Newfoundland. *Journal of Paleontology*, **68(6)**, 1368–1383.

JI, Z. & BARNES, C. R. 1996. Uppermost Cambrian and Lower Ordovician conodont biostratigraphy of the Survey Peak Formation (Ibexian/Tremadoc), Wilcox Pass, Alberta, Canada. *Journal of Paleontology*, **70**, 871–890.

JOHNSTON, D. I. & BARNES, C. R. 1999. Early and Middle Ordovician (Arenigian) conodonts from St. Pauls Inlet and Martin Point, Cow Head Group, Western Newfoundland, Canada; 1. Biostratigraphy and paleoecology. *Geologica et Palaeontologica*, **33**, 21–70.

KLAPPER, G. & BARRICK, J. E. 1978. Conodont ecology: pelagic versus benthic. *Lethaia*, **11**, 15–23.

KNIGHT, I. & JAMES, N. P. 1988. *Stratigraphy of the Lower to Lower Middle Ordovician St. George Group, Western Newfoundland*. Newfoundland Department of Mines, Mineral Development Division, Report, **88**-4, 48 pp.

KNIGHT, I., JAMES, N. P. & LANE, T. E. 1991. The Ordovician St. George unconformity, Northern Appalachians; the relationship of plate convergence as the St. Lawrence Promontory to the Sauk/Tippecanoe Sequence boundary. *Geological Society of America, Bulletin*, **103(9)**, 1200–1225.

LANDING, E. 1983. Highgate Gorge: Upper Cambrian and Lower Ordovician continental slope deposition and biostratigraphy, northwestern Vermont. *Journal of Paleontology*, **57(6)**, 1149–1187.

LEHNERT, O., MILLER, J. F. & REPETSKI, J. E. 1997. Paleogeographic significance of *Clavohamulus hintzei* Miller (Conodonta) and other Ibexian conodonts in an early Paleozoic carbonate platform facies of the Argentine Precordillera. *Geological Society of America, Bulletin*, **109**(4), 429–443.

LINDSTRÖM, M. 1976. Conodont paleogeography of the Ordovician. *In*: BASSETT, M. G. (ed.) *The Ordovician System*. University of Wales Press, National Museum of Wales, Cardiff, pp. 501–522.

MCCRACKEN, A. D. & BARNES, C. R. 1981. Conodont biostratigraphy and paleoecology of the Ellis Bay Formation, Anticosti Island, Québec, with special reference to Late Ordovician–Early Silurian chronostratigraphy and the systemic boundary. *Geological Survey of Canada, Bulletin*, **329**, 51–134.

MCGHEE, G. R. Jr, BAYER, U. & SEILACHER, A. 1991. Biological and evolutionary responses to transgressive–regressive cycles. *In*: EINSELE, G., RICKEN, W. & SEILACHER A. (eds) *Cycles and Events in Stratigraphy*, Springer-Verlag, Berlin, pp. 697–708.

MERRILL, G. K. & VON BITTER, P. H. 1984. Facies and frequencies among Pennsylvanian conodonts: apparatuses and abundances. *Geological Society of America, Special Paper*, **196**, 251–262.

MILLER, J. F. 1969. Conodont fauna of the Notch Peak Limestone (Cambro-Ordovician), House Range, Utah. *Journal of Paleontology*, **43**(2), 413–439.

MILLER, J. F. 1984. Cambrian and earliest Ordovician conodont evolution, biofacies, and provincialism. *Geological Society of America, Special Paper*, **196**, 43–68.

MILLER, J. F. 1992. The Lang Ranch Eustatic Event: a regressive–transgressive couplet near the base of the Ordovician System. *In*: WEBBY, B. D. & LAURIE, J. R. (eds) *Global Perspectives on Ordovician Geology*. Balkema, Rotterdam, The Netherlands, pp. 395–407.

MILLER, J. F. & FLOKSTRA, R. 1999. Graphic correlation of important Cambrian–Ordovician boundary section. *Acta Universitatis Carolinae – Geologica*, **43**(1/2), 81–84.

MILLER, R. H., COOPER, J. D. & SUNDBERG, F. A. 1981. Upper Cambrian faunal distribution in southeastern California and southern Nevada. *In*: TAYLOR, M. E. (ed.) *Short Papers for the 2nd International Symposium on the Cambrian System*. US Geological Survey Open-File Report, **81–743**, 138–142.

MÜLLER, K. J. 1959. Kambrische Conodonten. *Deutsche Geologische Gesellschaft, Zeitschrift*, **111**, 434–485.

NICOLL, R. S., MILLER, J. F., NOWLAN, G. S., REPETSKI, J. E. & ETHINGTON, R. L. 1999. *Iapetonudus* (n. gen.) and *Iapetognahus* Landing, unusual earliest Ordovician multielement conodont taxa and their utility for biostratigraphy. *Brigham Young University Geology Studies*, **44**, 27–101.

NOWLAN, G. S. 1985. Late Cambrian and Early Ordovician conodonts from the Franklinian miogeosyncline, Canadian Arctic Islands. *Journal of Paleontology*, **59**(1), 96–122.

NOWLAN, G. S. & BARNES, C. R. 1981. Late Ordovician conodonts from the Vauréal Formation, Anticosti Island, Québec. *Geological Survey of Canada, Bulletin*, **329**, 1–49.

POHLER, S. M. L. 1994. *Conodont Biofacies of Lower to Lower Middle Ordovician Megaconglomerates, Cow Head Group, Western Newfoundland*. Geological Survey of Canada, Bulletin, **459**, 71 pp.

POHLER, S. M. L. & BARNES, C. R. 1990. Conceptual models in conodont paleoecology. *Courier Forschungsinstitut Senckenberg*, **118**, 409–440.

POHLER, S. M. L. & JAMES, N. P. 1989. Reconstruction of a Lower/Middle Ordovician carbonate shelf margin: Cow Head Group, western Newfoundland. *Facies*, **21**, 189–262.

POHLER, S. M. L., BARNES, C. R. & JAMES, N. P. 1987. Reconstructing a lost faunal realm; conodonts from the megaconglomerates of the Ordovician Cow Head Group, western Newfoundland. *In*: AUSTIN, R. L. (ed.) *Conodonts: Investigative Techniques and Applications*. Ellis Horwood, Chichester, pp. 341–362.

PYLE, L. J. & BARNES, C. R. 2000. Upper Cambrian to Lower Silurian stratigraphic framework of platform-to-basin facies, northeastern British Columbia. *Bulletin of Canadian Petroleum Geology*, **48**(2), 123–149.

PYLE, L. J. & BARNES, C. R. 2002. *Taxonomy, Evolution and Biostratigraphy of Conodonts from the Kechika Formation, Skoki Formation and Road River Group (Upper Cambrian to Lower Silurian), Northeastern British Columbia*. NRC Research Press, Ottawa, 227 pp.

SCHOVSBO, N. H. 2001. Why barren intervals? A taphonomic case study of the Scandinavian Alum Shale and its faunas. *Lethaia*, **34**(4), 271–285.

SPSS. 1994. SPSS version 6.1 for the Macintosh. SPSS, Chicago, Illinois.

STOUGE, S. 1982. *Preliminary Conodont Biostratigraphy and Correlation of Lower to Middle Ordovician Carbonates of St. George Group, Great Northern Peninsula, Newfoundland*. Mineral Department Division, Department of Mines and Energy of Newfoundland and Labrador Report, **82**-3, 59 pp.

STOUGE, S. & BAGNOLI, B. 1988. Early Ordovician conodonts from Cow Head Ledge Peninsula, western Newfoundland. *Palaeontographia Italica*, **75**, 89–179.

SWEET, W. C. 1988. *The Conodonta: Morphology, Taxonomy, Paleoecology, and Evolutionary History of a Long-extinct Animal Phylum*. Oxford Monographs on Geology and Geophysics, **10**, 212 pp.

SWEET, W. C. & BERGSTRÖM, S. M. 1974. Provincialism exhibited by Ordovician conodont faunas. *Society of Economic Paleontologists and Mineralogists, Special Publications*, **21**, 189–202.

SWEET, W. C. & BERGSTRÖM, S. M. 1984. Conodont provinces and biofacies of the Late Ordovician. *Geological Society of America, Special Paper*, **196**, 69–88.

VIIRA, V., SERGEEVA, S. & POPOV, L. 1987. Earliest representatives of the genus *Cordylodus* (Conodonta) from Cambro-Ordovician boundary beds of North Estonia and Leningrad Region. *Proceedings of the Academy of Sciences of the Estonian SSR. Geology*, **36**(4), 145–154.

VON BITTER, P. H. 1972. Environmental control of conodont distribution in the Shawnee Group (Upper Pennsylvanian), eastern Kansas. *University of Kansas Paleontological Publication, Article*, **59**, 1–105.

WESTROP, S. R. & CUGGY, W. B. 1999. Comparative paleoecology of Cambrian trilobite extinctions. *Journal of Paleontology*, **73**, 337–354.

WILLIAMS, S. H. 1979. Appalachian Orogen in Canada. *Canadian Journal of Earth Sciences*, **16**, 792–807.

ZHANG, S. & BARNES, C. R. 2002a. Late Ordovician–Early Silurian (Ashgillian–Llandovery) sea level curve derived from conodont community analysis, Anticosti Island, Québec. *Palaeogeography, Palaeoclimatology, Palaeoecology*, **180**(1–3), 5–32.

ZHANG, S. & BARNES, C. R. 2002b. Paleoecology of Llandovery conodonts, Anticosti Island, Québec. *Palaeogeography, Palaeoclimatology, Palaeoecology*, **180**(1–3), 33–35.

Conodont bio-events, cladistics and response to glacio-eustasy, Ordovician–Silurian boundary through Llandovery, Anticosti Basin, Québec

SHUNXIN ZHANG & CHRISTOPHER R. BARNES

School of Earth and Ocean Sciences, University of Victoria, PO Box 3055 Victoria, B.C. V8W 3P6, Canada (e-mail:crbarnes@uvic.ca)

Abstract: Conodont diversity was severely reduced during the terminal Ordovician mass extinction. Few species, mainly conform taxa, survived across the Ordovician–Silurian boundary. The nature and timing of the post-extinction recovery and diversification have previously been difficult to assess, due to limited knowledge and preservation of the earliest Silurian faunas. Recent documentation of early Llandovery conodont faunas from a complete stratigraphic succession on Anticosti Island, Québec, along with the data re-examined from earlier detailed studies, provides the basis for a new analysis. Five evolutionary cycles are recognized through the Llandovery, together with a distinct set of bio-events that are interpreted as immigration, emigration, origination, and extinction events through consideration of global occurrence data for Llandovery conodonts. These events are supported by the detailed sampling and stratigraphic range data, as well as the first cladistic analysis of the four key genera: *Oulodus, Ozarkodina, Pterospathodus*, and *Rexroadus*. The Anticosti Basin may have been an important centre of evolutionary radiation, given that several genera and species have first appearances in this region and that initial evolutionary lineages can be established for many taxa. Many faunal variations appear to be correlated to eustatic events as well as the changing ocean-climate state through this boundary interval.

The Ordovician–Silurian boundary has proven to be one of the most intriguing both in defining formally and in documenting and explaining the cause, timing and scale of the mass extinction and the nature of the subsequent Early Silurian faunal recovery. The terminal Ordovician glaciation (e.g. Sheehan 2001) is now known to have been the principal cause of the second most severe mass extinction in the entire Phanerozoic. It resulted in the loss of about 28% of the families and 50% of the genera of known marine taxa (Sepkoski 1995). The duration of the mass extinction was brief, with two main phases (Brenchley *et al.* 1994; 2003). The major regression associated with the peak Hirnantian glacial phase resulted in there being relatively few sections spanning the Ordovician–Silurian boundary that are relatively undeformed and fossiliferous. The IUGS eventually approved a GSSP (Global Stratotype Section and Point) at Dob's Linn, Scotland, based on the first appearance of the graptolite *Parakidograptus acuminatus* (Cocks 1985). Strong criticism was directed at the deformed nature and low faunal diversity of the stratotype section (e.g. Lespérance *et al.* 1987). The precise level of the Ordovician–Silurian boundary is presently under re-examination by the Subcommission

on Silurian Stratigraphy because of an improved understanding of the *acuminatus* lineage; a minor redefinition is expected.

A problem in defining the Ordovician–Silurian boundary was that all but about three graptolite species in a single genus (*Normalograptus*) survived the mass extinction. The base of the Silurian was defined at a level a little higher than initially anticipated, in order to use species within the radiation event. Consequently, the glaciation and the mass extinction became, by definition, terminal Ordovician events. The only other serious contender as a GSSP for the base of the Silurian was on Anticosti Island, Québec, with the Point definition based on conodonts (Barnes & McCracken 1981; McCracken & Barnes 1981; Barnes 1989). This section was well exposed, undeformed, and had abundant and diverse faunas, except for zonal graptolites, in the boundary interval.

A period of about a decade of intense sampling and stratigraphic and biostratigraphic studies on many sections around the world provided a large database. It revealed not only the pattern of mass extinction in the terminal Ordovician, but also the nature of evolutionary radiation and ecological adaptation in the subsequent recovery phase in the Early Silurian (Llandovery). With

From: BEAUDOIN, A.B. & HEAD, M.J. (eds) 2004. *The Palynology and Micropalaeontology of Boundaries.* Geological Society, London, Special Publications, **230**, 73–104. 0305-8719/04/$15 © The Geological Society of London 2004.

the recent publication of the final monographic treatment of the Early Silurian conodonts from Anticosti Island (Zhang & Barnes 2002a), it is now possible to re-examine quantitatively the abundant conodont data for the entire Anticosti sequence (Upper Ordovician–Lower Silurian). Zhang & Barnes (2002b) applied statistical techniques to define a pattern of evolving conodont communities through this broad boundary interval, and related such changes, in part, to the significant eustatic changes associated with the various glacial–interglacial phases. New cladistic analyses for four key genera are employed here to help clarify the evolutionary relationships and responses.

Anticosti Island, located in the Gulf of St Lawrence, is underlain by undeformed Upper Ordovician (Ashgillian; Gamachian) and Lower Silurian (Llandovery) strata that are divided into the Vauréal, Ellis Bay, Becscie, Merrimack, Gun River, Jupiter and Chicotte formations (Fig. 1). The whole sequence is represented by excellent coastal and river exposures of richly fossiliferous limestones and minor shales and siliciclastic sediments (Petryk 1981a), totalling about 800–1100 m in thickness. During this time interval, the Anticosti Basin was a slowly subsiding basin on the southern margin of Laurentia, situated at a palaeolatitude of about 15–20° south of the equator, and facing the NW margin of the Iapetus Ocean (Mac Niocall et al. 1997; van Staal et al. 1998). The Anticosti Island succession is virtually complete (although see the contrary opinion of Brenchley et al. 2003) and represents shallow to deep subtidal environ-

ments oscillating between about 10 and 20 m water depth (Copper & Long 1998; Jin & Copper 1999; Zhang & Barnes, 2002b).

The sequence is of particular interest, because it includes the world's thickest and most complete carbonate section for the time spanning the Ordovician and Silurian boundary. The sequence lies at or near the boundary between the Ellis Bay and Becscie formations. Further, the uppermost Ellis Bay, Becscie, Merrimack, Gun River, Jupiter and Chicotte formations together provide the most complete Llandovery conodont sequence. The entire succession has been sampled intensively for conodonts (479 3–4 kg samples taken at 2–3 m intervals with some duplicate sampling: Vauréal-102, Ellis Bay-122, Becscie, Merrimack and Gun River-202, and Jupiter and Chicotte-53 samples). This has resulted in a series of major taxonomic, biostratigraphic, and palaeoecological publications: Vauréal Formation (Nowlan & Barnes 1981), Ellis Bay Formation (McCracken & Barnes 1981; Barnes 1988), Becscie, Merrimack and Gun River formations (Fåhraeus & Barnes 1981; Barnes 1989; Zhang & Barnes 2000, 2002a), and Jupiter and Chicotte formations (Uyeno & Barnes 1983). Additional Anticosti conodont studies have addressed the relationship between palaeoecology and the pattern of eustasy (Zhang & Barnes 2002b, 2002c; Zhang et al. 2002).

The Silurian, especially the Early Silurian, has long been known to have low conodont diversity compared to the Ordovician. Sweet (1985) noted the decrease in conodont species diversity through time beyond the Early Ordovician,

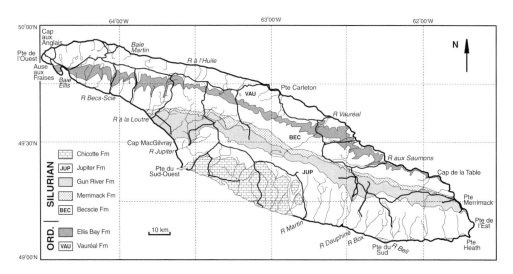

Fig. 1. Geological map of Anticosti Island (after Jin & Copper 1999).

and Sepkoski (1995) provided a diversity curve for conodont genera through the Early Palaeozoic. Sweet (1988) documented the cyclic diversity changes and established four long-term and 20 shorter second-order cycles. The Silurian history of conodonts corresponds with Sweet's IV and V second-order cycles, which shows a high-diversity episode in the late Llandovery and a smaller one in the early Ludlow. Barnes and Bergström (1988) and Armstrong (1995) detailed the conodont faunal changes and extinction across the Ordovician–Silurian boundary. The terminal Ordovician mass extinction was the second most severe in the Phanerozoic history of life and resulted in a reduction of conodont genera from over 50 to 10 (Sepkoski 1995, fig. 5). This profound effect on the Ordovician biota was caused by the continental glaciation in North Africa that generated both cool high-latitude oceanic temperatures and lowered CO_2 levels (Brenchley et al. 1994, 2003; Barnes et al. 1996; Poussart et al. 1999; Sheehan 2001) neither of which had been experienced previously in the Early Palaeozoic. It is in the context of this mass extinction, that the nature and timing of the conodont evolutionary recovery can be examined. Armstrong (1995) considered this earlier, but the earliest Silurian conodont faunas were poorly known. This is partly due to the hiatus that occurs in most Ordovician–Silurian boundary sections; to the post-glacial transgressive phases that are not extensive until the mid-Llandovery; and to the common clastic or dolomitic facies of many lower Llandovery sections that inhibit the collection of abundant conodont faunas. Consequently, the excellent Anticosti conodont faunas, from a limestone sequence that is continuous through the systemic boundary interval and through the Llandovery, allow an analysis of the nature of the recovery phase. This present study documents several distinct conodont speciation, immigration, migration and extinction events through the Llandovery, which are supported by new cladistic analyses of four key genera.

Aldridge (1988) argued for a single generic origination event in the late Llandovery, characterized by the appearance of some new genera with new characteristics or apparatuses (e.g. Pterospathodus Walliser, Apsidognathus Walliser). The early Llandovery was considered to be a period of relatively slow innovation for conodonts. A similar diversity pattern is apparent in Estonian sections, with three high-diversity intervals: top Rhuddanian–early Aeronian, Telychian until earliest Wenlock, and early Ludlow (Männik & Viira 1993).

A model for Silurian ocean-climate change was developed by Jeppsson (1988, 1990, 1997) and Aldridge et al. (1993) that tested such changes with particular reference to sedimentology and conodont faunas. Aldridge et al. (1993) and Jeppsson (1997) identified two cycles in the Llandovery to earliest Wenlock interval: each cycle started with a Secundo episode, then went through a Primo episode, and terminated with an extinction event (Fig. 2). This pattern was based mainly on the lithostratigraphic succession and conodont faunas in the Oslo–Asker district, Norway, where the stratigraphy is well known, sedimentation was fairly continuous, and exposures are good. Based on their interpretations, the Secundo episodes were periods of evolutionary stasis for conodonts. The Spirodden Secundo episode spans the Rhuddanian and early Aeronian, with limited conodont speciation following the Late Ordovician extinction, and with a relatively constant speciation for the whole interval. The Malmoykalven Secundo episode spans most of the late Aeronian, with conodonts also maintaining a very low diversity.

All these studies suggest strongly that after the terminal Ordovician extinction, the notable increase in conodont faunal diversity was delayed until the late Llandovery. Although earlier studies on Early Silurian conodonts (e.g. Aldridge et al. 1993; Jeppsson 1997) tried to include all well-documented sequences, including Anticosti Island, they were limited by the incompletely documented faunas commonly from discontinuous sections. In particular, conodonts from the Becscie, Merrimack and Gun River formations had not then been studied in detail. This work has now been completed (Zhang & Barnes 2000, 2002a, 2002b, 2002c; Zhang et al. 2002).

The conodont database

This study incorporates the earlier results of McCracken & Barnes (1981) and Uyeno & Barnes (1983), but it has been necessary to update and standardize some earlier taxonomic interpretations. Zhang & Barnes (2000, 2002a) recently documented the lower Llandovery conodont taxonomy, and therefore only a brief summary of the revisions is presented here.

(1) Ozarkodina sp. nov. A s.f. of McCracken & Barnes, 1981, p. 84, pl. 7, fig. 21 is placed in multi-element synonymy with Ozarkodina strena Zhang & Barnes.
(2) Walliserodus cf. W. curvatus (Branson & Branson) of McCracken & Barnes, 1981, p. 91, pl. 1, figs 22–25 and Walliserodus

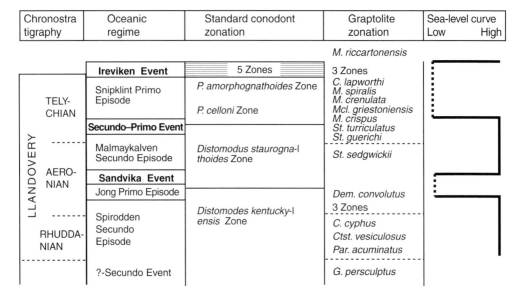

Chronostratigraphy	Oceanic regime	Standard conodont zonation		Graptolite zonation	Sea-level curve Low High

Fig. 2. Early Silurian oceanic changes (after Jeppsson 1998).

sancticlairi Cooper of Uyeno & Barnes, 1983, p. 26, pl. 7, figs 1–3, 5, 6 are included in *Walliserodus curvatus* (Branson & Branson).

(3) *Panderodus gracilis* (Branson & Mehl) of McCracken & Barnes, 1981, pp. 85–86, pl. 1, figs 1–12, 15 and *P. gibber* Nowlan and Barnes of McCracken & Barnes, 1981, p. 85, pl. 2, figs 7–10 are combined within *P. unicostatus* (Branson & Mehl).

(4) *Oulodus* sp. A of Uyeno & Barnes, 1983, p. 19, pl. 1, figs. 14, 15, 18–20 is assigned to *Ou. panuarensis* Bischoff.

(5) *Oulodus* sp. of Uyeno & Barnes, 1983, p. 20, pl. 8, fig. 21 is included in *Ou. sigmoideus* Zhang & Barnes.

(6) *Oulodus*? *fluegeli* subsp. A of Uyeno & Barnes, 1983, p. 18, pl. 7, figs. 11–22 is considered a synonym of *Ou.*? *expansus* (Armstrong).

(7) *Distomodus* cf. *D. kentuckyensis* Branson & Branson of Cooper (1975) adopted by Uyeno & Barnes, 1983, p. 17, pl. 9, figs. 27, 28 is referred to drepanodontiform elements (formerly referred by many authors to '*Drepanodus suberectus*' (Branson & Branson)).

(8) Most of member 6 of the Ellis Bay Formation as used in McCracken & Barnes (1981) has been reassigned to the lower Becscie Formation (Petryk 1981*a*). Hence, the conodont distribution data from member 6, Ellis Bay Formation (McCracken & Barnes 1981) is herein combined with other collections from the lower Becscie Formation used by Zhang & Barnes (2000, 2002*a*, 2002*b*, 2002*c*).

Thus, on the conodont distribution chart (Fig. 3), the lower Becscie Formation is equivalent to the uppermost part (member 6) of the Ellis Bay Formation (McCracken & Barnes 1981). We adopt the Merrimack Formation (of Copper & Long 1989), which is the argillaceous unit referred earlier to the uppermost member of the Becscie Formation. The stratigraphic subdivisions in the Jupiter and Chicotte formations are adjusted slightly from those used by Uyeno & Barnes (1983) following stratigraphic revisions by Copper & Long (1990).

Bio-events and biostratigraphic events

The term 'bio-event' long used by palaeontologists was defined recently by Sageman *et al.* (1997, p. 524) as 'short-term (hours or days to kys) locally, regionally, or interregionally pervasive changes in the ecological, biogeographical, and/or evolutionary character of biotas that are isochronous or nearly so throughout their range'. They divided bio-events into diversification bio-events and reduction bio-events. Both can be classified into three main categories, the former including ecological, biogeographical and evolutionary diversification bio-events, and the latter including ecological, biogeographical and evolutionary reduction bio-events. Evolutionary diversification and reduction bio-events

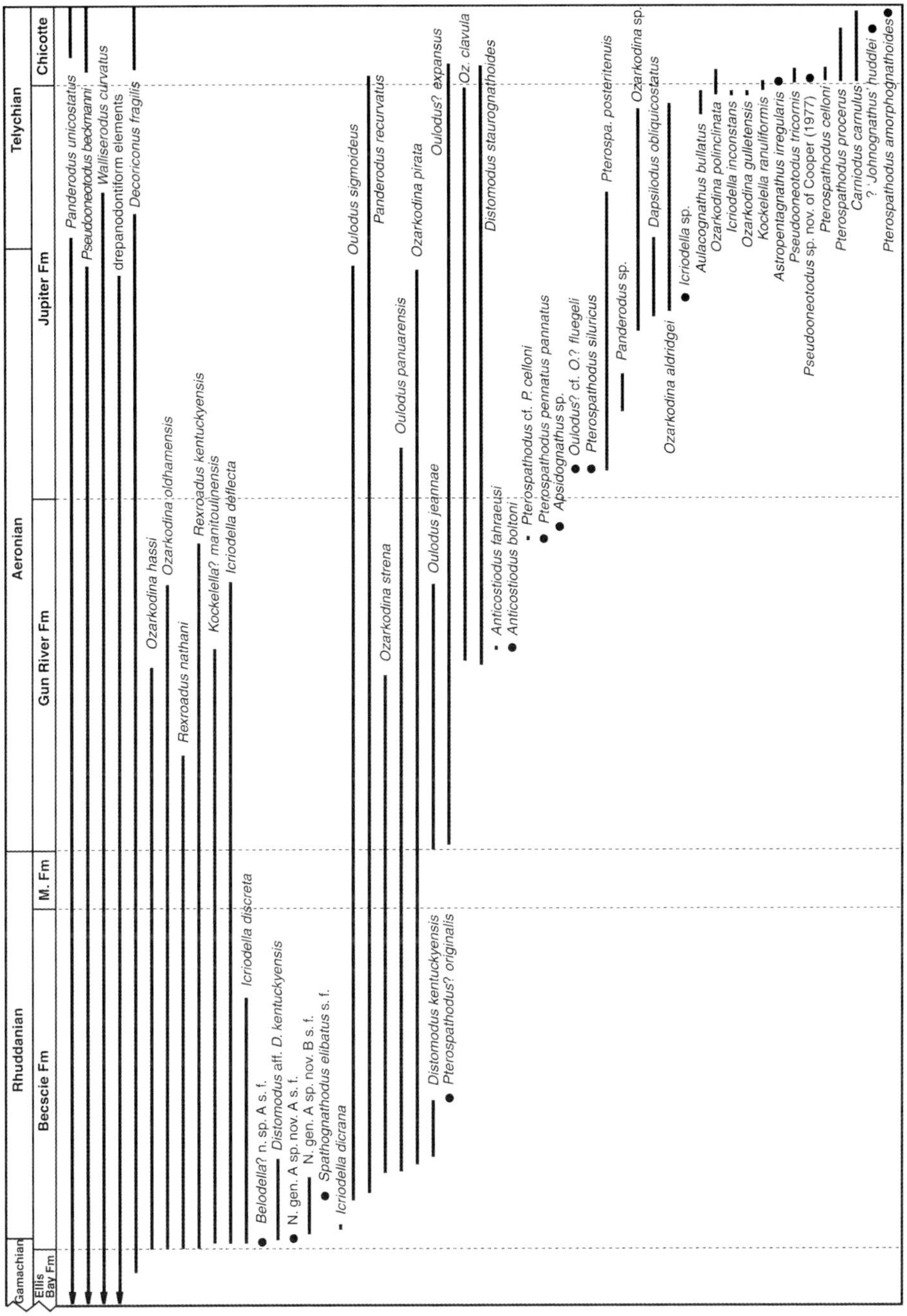

Fig. 3. Summary range chart of conodonts from the Early Silurian Becscie, Merrimack, Gun River, Jupiter and Chicotte formations, Anticosti Island (after Zhang & Barnes 2002*a*).

are equivalent to *in situ* speciation and extinction events, respectively; the other two categories that are related to diversification and reduction bio-events represent migration events.

The appearance and disappearance of species in a particular section can only define biostratigraphic events, not bio-events. After establishing the first and last appearance of certain taxa in several sections, the statistical pattern of appearances and disappearances of these taxa may discriminate between speciation, immigration and extinction events. Understanding the relationships between local bio-events and regional to global trends in speciation and extinction depends upon detailed regional faunal databases. Another important challenge in defining local bio-events is to differentiate speciation from immigration, and extinction from emigration.

The pattern of conodont turnover during the Llandovery is well documented (e.g. Sweet 1985, 1988; Jeppsson 1988, 1990, 1997; Aldridge *et al.* 1993; Männik & Virra 1993; Zhang & Barnes, 2002*a*). Less clear is the role that changing sea-level plays in influencing conodont turnover, and how that turnover is accomplished: through faunal immigration, speciation, extinction, or all three. Similarly, it is unclear how that disappearance occurs: through faunal emigration, extinction, or both. Differentiating between the processes of *in situ* speciation and immigration on the one hand, or extinction and emigration on the other, requires some method of evaluating whether the local first and last appearance horizons of individual taxa are reasonable approximations of their actual (biotic) time of origination and extinction. This goal also requires determination of whether the ancestor for each species, or at least closest known sister species, is also present in the region at the time of species origin (Goldman *et al.* 1999).

Construction of evolutionary trees for Llandovery conodonts from Anticosti Island

In many previous studies, determining both speciation and extinction events in the fossil record has depended greatly on documenting the precise species appearances and disappearances within particular stratigraphic sections, which is the taxonomic approach. One of the essential assumptions of this method, as pointed out by Smith (1994), is that the taxa used are real, not some arbitrary convention of taxonomists, and their appearances and disappearances represent real biological events. Another important factor has been ignored in most previous studies: the difference between immigration and origination

has been obscured because of the uncertainty of phylogenetic relationships. The evolution and extinction patterns of Llandovery conodonts, based on the construction of evolutionary trees, have not yet been examined. Using cladistics to construct evolutionary trees for Llandovery conodonts substantially improves the understanding of evolutionary patterns and processes.

Smith (1994) described the use of cladistic methodology in the construction of an evolutionary tree, beginning with studying the distribution of morphological characters within the taxa. From this, a character–taxon matrix is assembled and a cladistic analysis performed. The resulting cladogram provides a hypothesis of relationships that is independent of biostratigraphic information. If this is tested and branches are found to be well supported by the stratigraphic data, then the cladogram can be converted into an evolutionary tree.

A primary goal of this study is to determine the evolutionary pattern of Llandovery conodonts on the basis of phylogenetic hypotheses, with character analysis providing the detailed support for the phylogenetic hypotheses. However, as none of the reconstructions of conodont apparatuses employed here are based on the preserved animals or bedding-plane assemblages, and as some of the apparatuses are not well reconstructed, in this case, we have selected the key element (usually the diagnostic 'Pa' element) on which to perform the analysis. The essential prerequisite of character analysis is that all the reconstructions of apparatuses are correct, and if the evolution of the key element represents that of the whole apparatus, then character analysis will elucidate the objective pattern of character evolution.

Conodont samples were collected on average every 2–3 m through the Anticosti succession. For some sections the collections were duplicated. Hence, the position of the appearance and disappearance of each species is typically within ±2 m. The Llandovery ramiform–pectiniform conodonts are from three major lineages: ozarkodinid (*Ozarkodina* Branson & Mehl, *Pterospathodus, Kockelella?* Walliser), prioniodinid (*Oulodus* Branson & Mehl, and *Rexroadus* Zhang & Barnes), and prioniodontid (*Distomodus* Branson & Branson and *Icriodella* Rhodes). It has been widely accepted that these three major lineages had evolved independently since the Ordovician (Sweet 1988). Thus the analyses are designed basically for the different lineages, rather than including all species in a single analysis.

The most abundant genera are *Ozarkodina*, *Oulodus* and *Rexroadus*, and many of their species co-occur. The former two genera have been used to establish a revised conodont biozonation (Zhang & Barnes 2002*a*), and the latter genus was newly established to include *Oulodus*? *kentuckyensis* (Branson & Branson) and *Ou.*? *nathani* McCracken & Barnes (Zhang & Barnes 2002*a*). One analysis is designed for all *Ozarkodina* species, and another for prioniodinid species (of *Oulodus* and *Rexroadus*). *Pterospathodus* also played an important role in Llandovery conodont evolution, although its abundance is much lower than for *Ozarkodina, Oulodus* and *Rexroadus*. Overall, *Pterospathodus* is included as an ozarkodinid; however, it evolved in a different family from *Ozarkodina*. To investigate the relationship between *Ozarkodina* and *Pterospathodus* is beyond the scope of this paper, so a separate analysis was designed for the *Pterospathodus* species. The relationships among several species within different lineages and the origination pattern based on the phylogenetic method are investigated. Prioniodontid genera such as *Distomodus* and *Icriodella* are much less abundant and diverse, and, consequently, no analysis of these taxa was made, although the appearance and disappearance of their species will be discussed together with those of *Ozarkodina, Oulodus, Rexroadus* and *Pterospathodus*.

Recently, a new scheme of terminology for conodont element orientation and anatomical notation was proposed (Purnell *et al.* 2000), based on the biological information from natural assemblages. Although this scheme was adopted to describe the conodont characters in a recent cladistics study (Donoghue 2001), it has not been widely used by conodont workers. In order to avoid confusion and to be more widely understood at this point, the traditional terminology (Sweet 1981, 1988) is employed to describe characters and character states.

In this study, both MacClade version 3.0 (Maddison & Maddison 1992) and Paup version 3.1 (Swofford 1993) were employed together. MacClade was used to edit files, and then Paup was used to do automatic searches for parsimonious trees. Finally, MacClade was used to explore the trees further and analyse character evolution. The techniques adopted are as follows: contingent coding strategy (Hawkins *et al.* 1997) is employed; all of the characters are unordered; no weighting is employed *a priori*; heuristics is used as a searching method; *a posteriori* reweighting was employed for choosing one among multiple most-parsimonious trees (Carpenter 1988; Donoghue 2001), when an initial unweighted analysis of the database

produces more than one tree; out-group taxa are used to root the trees.

The in-group taxa include all species within the lineages occurring in the Anticosti Llandovery under consideration. For cladistic analysis, the choice of an out-group taxon can be important for the success of out-group rooting. The best out-group taxon should be the most closely related taxon to the in-group, and could be its possible ancestor. However, with the absence of previous detailed phylogenetic studies, choosing out-group taxa in this study is based on the assumptions that:

(1) the out-group taxa are closely related to the in-group taxa;
(2) the out-group taxa appeared earlier than the interval under consideration.

Analysis I for species of Ozarkodina

The data matrix (Fig. 5) includes eight species of *Ozarkodina* as in-group taxa: *Oz. aldridgei* Uyeno, *Oz. clavula* (Uyeno), *Oz. gulletensis* (Aldridge), *Oz. hassi* (Pollock, Rexroad & Nicoll), *Oz. oldhamensis* (Rexroad), *Oz. pirata* (Uyeno), *Oz. polinclinata* (Nicoll & Rexroad), and *Oz. strena* Zhang & Barnes. The apparatus reconstructions of *Oz. hassi, Oz. oldhamensis, Oz. pirata*, and *Oz. sterna* are based on Zhang & Barnes (2002*a*), those of *Oz. aldridgei, Oz. gulletensis* and *Oz. polinclinata* on Uyeno & Barnes (1983), and that of *Oz. clavula* mostly on Zhang & Barnes (2002*a*), except for the Sa element that is based on Uyeno & Barnes (1983).

The ancestral stocks of the Silurian ozarkodinids are uncertain. The Ordovician genera *Aphelognathus* Branson, Mehl & Branson and '*Plectodina*' Sweet are the most widespread and characteristic of the Ordovician ozarkodinids, and *Ozarkodina hassi* and *Oz. oldhamensis* were considered as the youngest species of '*Plectodina*' (Sweet 1988). *Yaoxianognathus* An also shows considerable similarity to *Ozarkodina* (Zhen *et al.* 1998). However, the ideal out-group candidates for Llandovery *Ozarkodina* species should be those generally recognized Ordovician *Ozarkodina* species. Thus, choosing the out-group taxa for Llandovery *Ozarkodina* species is narrowed. Three options are:

(1) *Ozarkodina* sp. s.f. Nowlan & Barnes from the Upper Ordovician Vauréal Formation, Anticosti Island, Québec (Nowlan & Barnes 1981), this form resembles the Pa element of the Silurian species *Oz. hassi*, but its denticles are more slender and more laterally compressed;

(2) *Ozarkodina sesquipedalis* Nowlan & McCracken from the Upper Ordovician Whittaker Formation, Mackenzie Mountains, Northwest Territories (about 60 m below the Ordovician–Silurian boundary) (Nowlan *et al.* 1988), this species was described as an apparatus, and is similar to some Silurian ozarkodinid species, such as *Oz. hassi* and *Oz. pirata*;

(3) *Ozarkodina alpina* s.f. Serpagli from the Upper Ordovician, Carnic Alps (Serpagli 1967), which is similar to the Pa element of *Ozarkodina sesquipedalis* in overall shape.

Considering the apparatus reconstruction and geographical distribution, the former two species are chosen as the out-group taxa.

25 multistate characters of the apparatus were incorporated in the *Ozarkodina* analysis (Fig. 5).

(1) Pa basal shape: carminate (0); angulate (1); carminate–angulate (2).

(2) Pa cusp: present (0); absent (1).

(3) Pa denticles above basal cavity: cusp (0); fused without apices (1); fused with discrete apices (2).

(4) Pa basal cavity position: about one-third of the blade distance from the posterior tip (0); about the mid-length of the blade (1); near posterior end (2); beneath the cusp (3).

(5) Pa basal cavity shape: without flare (0); symmetrical flare (1); asymmetrical flare (2).

(6) Pa denticulation 1: two processes with equal robustness (0); anterior process more robust than posterior one (1); two ends more robust than middle (2); middle more robust than two ends (3).

(7) Pa denticulation 2: compressed (0); rounded (1).

(8) Pb basal shape: angulate (0); extensive digyrate (1); bipennate (2).

(9) Pb denticulation: discrete (0); partly discrete (1).

(10) Pb processes: anterior shorter than posterior (0); anterior longer than posterior (1); anterior equal to posterior (2).

(11) Pb orientation: arched and bowed (0); slightly arched (1); slightly arched and bowed (2).

(12) Pb basal cavity: small flare on one side (0); small flares on two sides (1); open along processes (2); without flare (3).

(13) Pb cusp 1: within anterior–posterior plane (0); away from anterior–posterior plane (1).

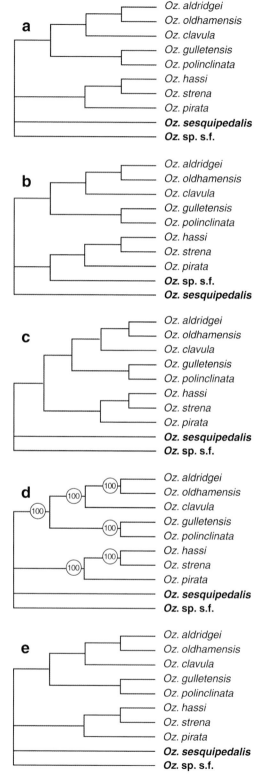

(14) Pb cusp 2: erect (0); posterior (1); lateral (2); proclined (3).

(15) S denticulation: discrete (0); partly discrete (1).

(16) S denticles flanking cusp: shorter than other (0); equal to others (1).

(17) S cusp cross-section: lanceolate (0); convex (1); compressed with sharp edges (2); subround with edges (3).

(18) S basal cavity: with flare on one side (0); without flare (1); recessive basal margin (2).

(19) M basal shape: makellate (0); dolabrate with erect cusp (1); breviform digyrate (2); dolabrate with posterior cusp (3).

(20) M denticulation: discrete (0); partly discrete (1).

(21) M basal cavity: with flare on one side (0); without flare (1); open along process (2); with recessive basal margin (3).

(22) Sa lateral processes: curved down laterally (0); straight down laterally (1).

(23) Sa posterior process: present (0); absent (1).

(24) Sb basal shape: slightly asymmetrical (0); breviform digyrate (1).

(25) Sc anterior process: bent down and inward (0); bent down (1); no anterior process (2).

In analysis I, three most parsimonious clado-grams, with a consistency index (CI) of 0.767 and a retention index (RI) of 0.460, were obtained with a length of 60 steps. *A posteriori* reweighting had an effect on neither the number of cladograms nor the tree topology (Fig. 4a–c). Figure 4c is chosen to trace characters (Fig. 5) and construct the evolutionary tree based on biostratigraphic distribution of the species (Fig. 6). Both 50% majority rule and strict consensus trees are calculated, which sums up the parts in all the rival cladograms that are in agreement (Figs 4d–e).

Two groups can be recognized (Fig. 5). Group I is composed of *Ozarkodina hassi*, *Oz. strena* and *Oz. pirata*, and group II consists of *Oz. oldhamensis*, *Oz. aldridgei*, *Oz. gulletensis*, *Oz. clavula* and *Oz. polinclinata*. When the characters are traced, several character states are recognized as synapomorphies. Two character states related to the Pa element are the synapomorphies of group II: carminate basal shape (0 of 1) (it will be abbreviated as 0 of 1 in the later similar discussion) and cusp absent (1

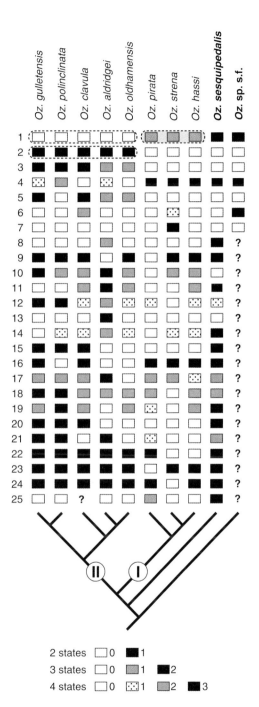

Fig. 5. Data box and one possible maximally parsi-monious reconstruction from one of the most parsi-monious trees (Fig. 4c: branches are rotated) for species of *Ozarkodina* in analysis I. Dashed boxes and dashed box with shading indicate synapomorphies for group II and group I, respectively.

Fig. 4. (**a–c**) Three equally most parsimonious trees for species of *Ozarkodina* in analysis I; (**d & e**) consensus tree of three equally most parsimonious trees (**d**, 50% majority rule; **e**, strict consensus). Bold italics indicate out-group taxa.

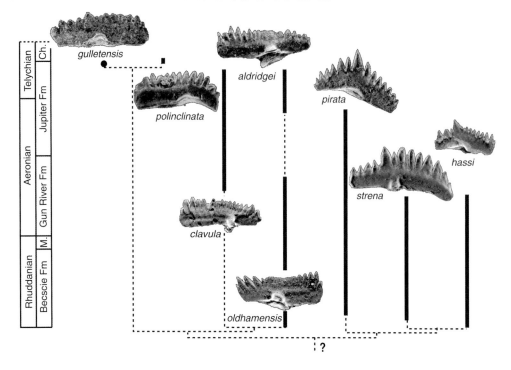

Fig. 6. Reconstruction of evolutionary tree for species of *Ozarkodina*, based on Figure 5.

of 2). In addition, angulate basal shape (1 of 1) is the synapomorphies of group I (Fig. 5). These synapomorphic characters support group II as being monophyletic, and questionably also group I. Thus, the species of *Ozarkodina* evolved through the two different lineages during the Llandovery on Anticosti Island.

Analysis II for prioniodinid species (of Oulodus and Rexroadus)

The second data matrix (Fig. 8) includes seven species as in-group taxa: five species of *Oulodus*– *Ou. panuarensis* Bischoff, *Ou. sigmoideus* Zhang & Barnes, *Ou. jeannae* Schönlaub, *Ou.? expansus* (Armstrong), and *Ou.? cf. Ou.? fluegeli* (Walliser), and two species of *Rexroadus*–*R. kentuckyensis* (Branson & Branson) and *R. nathani* (McCracken & Barnes), all the apparatus reconstructions are based on Zhang & Barnes (2002*a*), except for *Ou.? cf. Ou.? fluegeli* that is after Uyeno & Barnes (1983).

Twenty multistate characters of the apparatus were used in the *Oulodus* and *Rexroadus* analysis (Fig. 8):

(1)   Robustness of the apparatus: relatively slender (0); relatively robust (1).

(2)   Size of the basal cavity of all elements: large with flare (0); small with flare (1); small without flare (2).

(3)   Basal shape of Pa element 1: blade-like (0); ramiform (1).

(4)   Basal shape of Pa element 2: one process longer than the other (0); two processes equal (1).

(5)   Processes' orientation of Pa element: anteriorly–posteriorly (0); laterally (1).

(6)   Angle between two processes of Pa element: nearly 90° (0); 90–180° (1); nearly 180° (2); twisted (3).

(7)   Cusp of Pa element: prominent (0); not prominent (1).

(8)   Denticulation of Pa element: fused on anterior process (0); discrete on both processes (1).

(9)   Posterior protuberance of Pa element: present (0); absent (1).

(10)   Pb element: angulate-like with twisted posterior process (0); extensiform digyrate (1); breviform digyrate (2).

(11)   M element: dolobrate (0); makellate (1); dolobrate–makellate (2); breviform digyrate (3); makellate–breviform digyrate (4).

(12)   Processes' orientation of M element: anterior–posterior (0); lateral (1); between 0 and 1 (2).

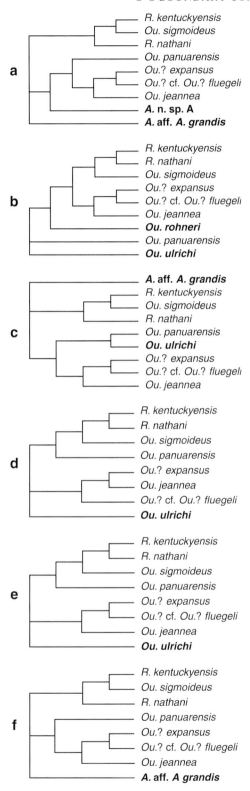

(13) Short process of M element: bent posteriorly (0); bent anteriorly (1); absent (2).

(14) Sa element: alate with cusp curved 90° posteriorly (0); alate with cusp curved posteriorly (1); alate with cusp almost erect (2).

(15) Angle between two processes of Sa element: about 90° (0); >90° (1); <90° (2).

(16) Sb element: breviform digyrate with cusp curved 90° posteriorly (0); breviform digyrate with cusp curved posteriorly (1); breviform digyrate with cusp almost erect (2).

(17) Aboral surface of S elements: inverted (0); non-inverted (1).

(18) Posterior protuberance of Sa and Sb elements: present (0); absent (1).

(19) Sc element: bipennate with anterior process curved posteriorly (0); bipennate with anterior process bent downward (1); bipennate with anterior process both curved posteriorly and bent downward (2).

(20) Interspaces of denticles: U shaped (0); V shaped (1).

Choosing the out-group taxa for this analysis is problematic, for example:

(1) When *Aphelognathus* aff. *A. grandis* Branson, Mehl & Branson (McCracken & Barnes 1981) and *A.* sp. nov. A Nowlan & Barnes (Nowlan & Barnes 1981), whose Pa element is similar to that of *Rexroadus*, were chosen as out-group taxa, one tree was produced, with a consistency index (CI) of 0.717 and a retention index (RI) of 0.629, and its tree-length is 46. In this case *Aphelognathus* sp. nov. A falls within the in-group (Fig. 7a).

(2) When *Oulodus ulrichi* (Stone & Furnish) and *Ou. rohneri* Ethington & Furnish (McCracken & Barnes 1981; Nowlan & Barnes 1981), whose Pa and apparatus are similar to *Ou. jeannae, Ou.?* *expansus* and *Ou.?* cf. *Ou.?* *fluegeli*, were assigned as out-group taxa, three equally most parsimonious cladograms were obtained, with a CI of 0.744 and a RI of 0.496, and the tree-length is 43. *A posteriori* reweighting results in only one tree from the three. In this case *Oulodus rohneri* falls within the in-group (Fig. 7b).

Fig. 7. The most parsimonious trees for prioniodinid species in analysis II. **a, b, c, d** and **e**, and **f** are from five different analyses, in which different species are chosen as out-group taxa. Out-group taxa are indicated by bold italics.

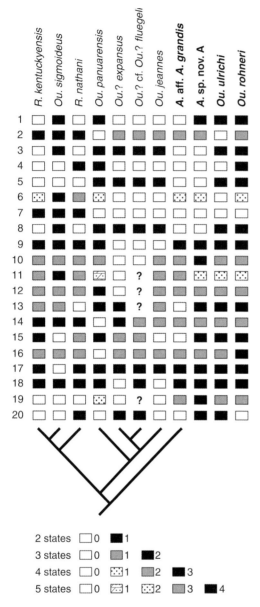

2 states □ 0 ■ 1

3 states □ 0 ■ 1 ■ 2

4 states □ 0 ▥ 1 ▦ 2 ■ 3

5 states □ 0 ▨ 1 ▥ 2 ▦ 3 ◣ 4

Fig. 8. Data box and one possible parsimonious reconstruction from one of the five analyses for prioniodinid species (based on Fig. 7f), in which *Aphelognathus* aff. *A. grandis* is chosen as an out-group taxon.

(3) When *Aphelognathus* aff. *A. grandis* and *Oulodus ulrichi* are selected as the out-group taxa, only one tree is gained, with a CI of 0.705 and an RI of 0.629, and its tree-length is 44. In this case, *Ou. ulrichi* falls within the in-group (Fig. 7c).

(4) When only one species – *Oulodus ulrichi* – was appointed as the out-group taxon, there were two equally most parsimonious cladograms, with a CI of 0.775 and an RI of 0.517, and the tree-length is 40. A posteriori reweighting affects neither the number nor the topology of trees. In this case, the topology of the cladogram shows that the species of the in-group are arranged in a reversed biostratigraphic order (Figs 7d & e).

(5) When only one species – *Aphelognathus* aff. *A. grandis* was used as the out-group taxon, one tree was obtained, with a CI of 0.750 and an RI of 0.482, and its tree-length is 40. In this case, the species are arranged on two branches of the in-group in a normal stratigraphic order (Fig. 7f).

In the former three cases, the most parsimonious solutions show that one of the out-group taxa falls within the in-group, and the initial assumption – the in-group is monophyletic, was wrong (Fig. 7a–c). Practically, *Aphelognathus* aff. *A. grandis* is employed as the out-group taxon, although it is better to have more than one out-group taxon. The out-group rooting gives support to the observation made by McCracken & Barnes (1981) that the presence of a blade-like Pa element in *Ou.? nathani* and *Ou.? kentuckyensis* argues against their derivation from Ordovician species of *Oulodus*, and their transference to the new genus *Rexroadus* (Zhang & Barnes 2002a). MacClade allows character tracing on its tree window, and the construction of an evolutionary tree could be made based on one of the most parsimonious trees and biostratigraphic distribution of the species (Fig. 9). However, present knowledge on the *Oulodus* and *Rexroadus* species involved in this analysis shows that the two genera may not share the common ancestor; in particular, the shape and orientation of the Pa element of the two genera may indicate that they are homoplastic. Additionally, some species probably originated outside of the Anticosti Basin (see later discussion).

Analysis III for species of Pterospathodus

The third data matrix (Fig. 11) includes eight species of *Pterospathodus* as in-group: *P.? originalis* Zhang & Barnes, *P.* cf. *P. celloni* (Walliser), *P. celloni* (Walliser), *P. pennatus pennatus* (Walliser), *P. pennatus procerus* (Walliser), *P. siluricus* (Pollock, Rexroad & Nicoll), *P. posteritenuis* Uyeno and *P. amorphognathoides* Walliser. Although their appara-

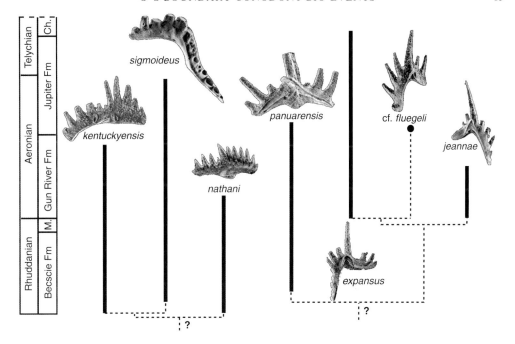

Fig. 9. Reconstruction of evolutionary tree for prioniodinid species (of *Oulodus and Rexroadus*), based on Figure 8.

tuses have been reconstructed by different authors, it is difficult to identify the homology, especially after *Carniodus* Walliser was considered as part of *Pterospathodus* and the latter as an apparatus with 14 elements (Männik 1998). Among the eight species that occur on Anticosti, the apparatus of *P. celloni, P. pennatus pennatus, P. pennatus procerus*, and *P. amorphognathoides* were reconstructed by Männik (1998) in his new concept. Among the Anticosti collections, *C. carnulus* indeed occurs with *P. amorphognathoides, P. celloni* and *P. pennatus procerus* in the same samples from younger strata – the Chicotte Formation (Uyeno & Barnes 1983), but there is not enough material to prove this for other species from the older strata – the Becscie, Gun River and Jupiter formations. If Männik's (1998) reconstructions were employed in this analysis, there would be too many unknown characters. Hence, the most simplistic solution is to include only the diagnostic Pa element of the eight species in this analysis.

The choice of out-groups for this analysis could lie within the Family Pterospathodontidae that includes *Apsidognathus, Astropentagnathus, Aulacognathus, Johnognathus* and *Pterospathodus*. However, none of these has been found in the early Llandovery, except for *Pterospathodus*

(Zhang & Barnes 2002*a*). Sweet (1988, p. 99) hypothesized that the simple or bifurcate lateral process on one or both sides of Pa element in the apparatus of *Pterospathodus* appears to have developed from *Ozarkodina*-like carminate elements through gradual lateral expansion of one or both sides at mid-length. Following this hypothesis, the two *Ozarkodina* species, *Oz. hassi* and *Oz. oldhamensis*, are included in the out-group.

Fourteen multistate characters of the Pa element of both in-group and out-group taxa are selected (Fig. 11).

(1) Shape of the Pa element: angulate (0); carminiscaphate (1); carminate (2); pastiniscaphate (3).

(2) Denticle shape: short and fused (0); long and fused with discrete tips (1); discrete (2).

(3) Denticle size on two processes: equal (0); those on anterior process larger than those on posterior process (1); those on anterior process smaller than those on posterior process (2).

(4) Denticle size on one process: equal (0); those on distal end larger than those in the middle (1); those on distal end smaller than those in the middle (2).

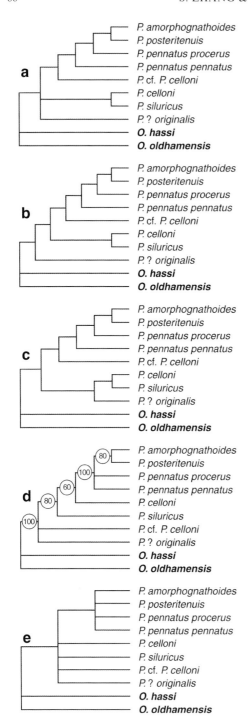

Fig. 10. (**a–c**) Three equally most parsimonious trees for species of *Pterospathodus* in analysis III; (**d–e**) consensus tree of the three equally most parsimonious trees (**d**, 50% majority rule; **e**, strict consensus). Bold italics indicate out-group taxa.

(5)   Lateral process: present (0); absent (1).

(6)   Character 1 of lateral expansion: on two sides (0); on outer side (1); no expansion (2).

(7)   Character 2 of lateral expansion: denticulate expansion (0); adenticulate (1); no expansion (2).

(8)   Character 3 of lateral expansion: one process forming an angle less than 90° with posterior process (0); with bifurcated process (1); no process (2); one process forming an angle of about 90° with posterior process (3).

(9)   Bifurcating process: posterior longer than anterior (0); anterior longer than posterior (1); bifurcating process absent (2).

(10) Under surface of lateral process: expanded (0); non-expanded (1); lateral process absent (2).

(11) Cusp: prominent (0); not prominent (1).

(12) Length of main processes: equal (0); anterior process longer than posterior (1); posterior process longer than anterior (2).

(13) Under surface of main processes: expanded posteriorly (0); expanded middle (1); expanded two processes (2); non-expanded (3).

(14) Platform ledge: present (0); absent (1).

In analysis III, 15 equally most parsimonious cladograms, with a consistency index (CI) of 0.737 and a retention index (RI) of 0.714, were obtained, whose shortest tree-length is 38. Again, for choosing the best one of the 15 rival trees, *a posteriori* reweighting was performed, which reduced the number of the trees to three (Figs 10a–c). One of the three (Fig. 10c) is chosen to trace characters (Fig. 11) and to reconstruct the evolutionary tree (Fig. 12), whose topology shows most of *Pterospathodus* species being arranged in the order of their biostratigraphic occurrence on Anticosti Island, with the exception of *P. posteritenuis*. A 50% majority rule and strict consensus trees are calculated, which summarize the parts in all the rival cladograms that are in agreement (Figs 10d–e).

Two groups can be recognized (Figs 11 & 12). Group I is composed of *Pterospathodus? originalis, P. siluricus* and *P. celloni*; and group II consists of *P.* cf. *P. celloni, P. pennatus pennatus, P. pennatus procerus, P. posteritenuis* and *P. amorphognathoides* (Fig. 11). Figure 11a shows that only character 7 provides synapomorphic evidence for group I, which is no lateral expansion/process related to the Pa element of the species (1 of 7). Within group II (Fig. 11a),

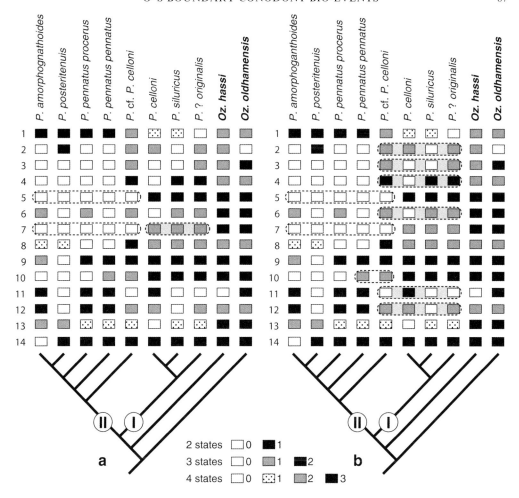

Fig. 11. Data box and one possible maximally parsimonious reconstruction from one most parsimonious tree (Fig. 10c) for species of *Pterospathodus* in analysis III. Dashed boxes and dashed box with shade in (**a**) indicate synapomorphies for group II and group I, respectively; dashed boxes and dashed boxes with shading in (**b**) indicate the derived and inherited characters of *Pterospathodus* cf. *P. celloni*, respectively. Bold italics indicate out-group taxa.

each species is at least supported by a derived character, i.e. *P.* cf. *P. celloni* by lateral process present (0 of 5) and denticulate lateral expansion (0 of 7), *P. pennatus pennatus* by pastiniscaphate shape (3 of 1), *P. pennatus procerus* by expanded underside (0 of 10) and *P. posteritenuis* by bifurcated lateral process (1 of 8) and underside of main processes expanded (2 of 13). In this case, four monophyletic groups and six additional paraphyletic groups can be recognized within group II by the different combinations of the stems. Herein the two character states derived at *P.* cf. *P. celloni*, i.e. lateral process present (0 of 5) and denticulate lateral expansion (0 of 7) are recognized as the synapomorphies of

group II, and the five taxa within group II as a monophyletic group.

This supports the idea that the species of *Pterospathodus*, or at least their Pa elements, evolved through the two different lineages during the Llandovery on Anticosti Island. However, the earliest representative of group II – *P.* cf. *P. celloni*, appeared much later than that of group: I – *P.?* *originalis*. *Pterospathodus* cf. *P. celloni* is an important species in linking the two groups: it is the last species retaining six characters of *P.?* *originalis* of the group I, and the first species deriving three new characters for group II (Fig. 11b).

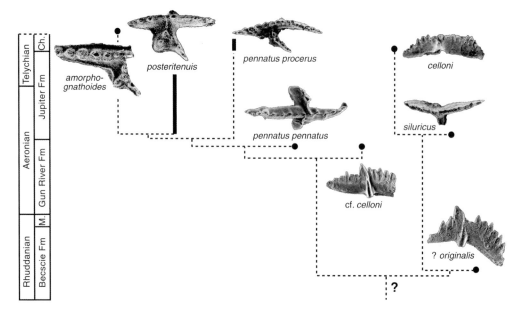

Fig. 12. Reconstruction of an evolutionary tree for species of *Pterospathodus*, based on Figure 11.

Conodont evolutionary cycles in the Llandovery

Cycle I: latest Ashgillian–earliest Rhuddanian

The marked conodont faunal turnover in the latest Ordovician has long been recognized, both on Anticosti Island (McCracken & Barnes 1981; Barnes 1988), and on a global scale (Barnes & Bergström 1988; Sweet, 1988; Armstrong 1995; Barnes *et al.* 1996). On Anticosti, there is a 1.5 m transitional interval in the uppermost Ellis Bay Formation that has a mixed fauna. In the overlying Becscie Formation, the Silurian conodont fauna comprises 17 species, 12 of which are unknown from older strata (Fig. 3). The absence of zonally diagnostic graptolites makes the precise time interval of the conodont faunal turnover uncertain. Armstrong (1995) argued that the conodont faunal turnover on Anticosti Island is of latest Ordovician age. In the Canadian Arctic, where zonal conodonts and graptolites co-occur in the Cape Phillips Formation, conodont turnover is in the latest Ordovician mid *Glyptograptus persculptus* Zone (Melchin *et al.* 1991; Jowett & Barnes 1999, 2000), slightly below the defined base of the Silurian which is the base of the overlying *Parakidograptus acuminatus* Zone.

This transitional turnover fauna (Cycle I) on Anticosti (Fig. 13) is a mixture of generalized species, represented by:

(1) long-ranging coniform taxa traced back to the Ordovician, such as *Panderodus* and *Walliserodus*;
(2) newly evolved prioniodontids, i.e. *Distomodus* and some *Icriodella* species;
(3) newly evolved ozarkodinids, such as all the *Ozarkodina* species; and
(4) newly evolved prioniodinids, i.e. the two species of *Rexroadus*.

Among this turnover fauna, the most abundant new species are *Ozarkodina hassi, Oz. oldhamensis, Rexroadus kentuckyensis* and *R. nathani*. The second most abundant species group comprises *Icriodella deflecta* Aldridge, *I. discreta* Pollock, Rexroad & Nicoll, and *I. dicrana* Zhang & Barnes. The lower and upper boundaries of Cycle I are defined by the first appearance of newly evolved ozarkodinids and last appearance of *I. dicrana* respectively (Fig. 13). Cycle I spans about 15 m of the lower Becscie Formation.

What was the origin of these new taxa? Was the faunal turnover a result of immigration or *in situ* speciation? Based on Smith (1994, p. 175), the appearance of a taxon that does not seem to be closely related to any earlier ones found within that region potentially represents an immigration event. For Anticosti Island, are the newcomers endemic or cosmopolitan species? To ascertain the endemic species, phylogenetic analyses are required to give support to the local branching history of the taxa; for the

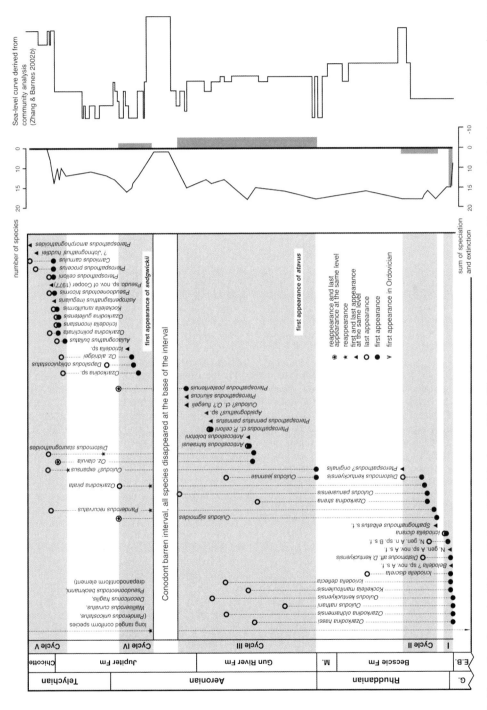

Fig. 13. Five cycles of conodont bio-events through the Llandovery (Early Silurian) sequence, Anticosti Island. The curve and shaded rectangular areas between the two scale bars represent the number of species and the sum of speciation and extinction, respectively; G., Gamachian; E.B., Ellis Bay Formation; M., Merrimack Formation.

cosmopolitan species, precise correlation is required to assess the relative timing of their appearance throughout their palaeogeographical range in addition to phylogenetic analysis. To determine the nature of the Ordovician–Silurian conodont turnover several different stocks are examined.

Speciation in the prioniodinid stock. The prioniodinid species in Cycle I on Anticosti Island comprise the only two species of *Rexroadus* already noted. All the Ordovician *Oulodus* species disappeared suddenly below the Ordovician–Silurian boundary; the new earliest Silurian prioniodinid species such as *Rexroadus nathani* and *R. kentuckyensis* have atypical characteristics for *Oulodus* (Zhang & Barnes 2002*a*), as indicated in the earlier cladistic analysis II.

Rexroadus nathani and *R. kentuckyensis* do not have a wide geographical distribution. They occur on Anticosti Island (McCracken & Barnes 1981) and Gaspé Peninsula (Nowlan 1981, 1983) of eastern Canada, and Arctic Canada (Jowett & Barnes 1999, 2000). A few questionable specimens of the two species have also been recovered from the western USA (Leatham 1985) and the Oslo region, Norway (Aldridge & Mohamed 1982; Idris 1984). In reconstructing the apparatus of *R. kentuckyensis*, components of *Oulodus* sp. A and *Ou.* sp. B described by Cooper (1975) from the Brassfield Limestone, Ohio, were considered to be synonymous with *R. kentuckyensis* (McCracken & Barnes 1981). Zhang & Barnes (2002*a*) regarded the latter and part of the former to belong to *Ou. sigmoideus*, and the P elements to belong to *Ou. panuarensis*. In both the Oslo region and the western USA, specimens assigned to *R. nathani* are questioned, and their first appearances are later than that of *Distomodus kentuckyensis*. The lowest occurrence of *D. kentuckyensis* on Anticosti Island is 49 m above that of *R. nathani* and *R. kentuckyensis*. If the first appearance of *D. kentuckyensis* is coeval, then the first appearance of *R. nathani* and *R. kentuckyensis* on Anticosti Island should be earlier than anywhere else that they have been found. Thus, the first appearance of *R. nathani* and *R. kentuckyensis* may represent an *in situ* speciation event in the Anticosti Basin. If true, then their possible ancestor should occur in the Anticosti Basin, and probably does not lie among the *Oulodus* species (see discussion of Analysis II).

Speciation in the ozarkodinid stock. The ozarkodinid genera that appear in the earliest Silurian on Anticosti Island include the spathognathodontid *Ozarkodina* and kockelellid *Kockelella*?. The former is far more abundant than the latter. Unlike *Rexroadus nathani* and *R. kentuckyensis, Ozarkodina hassi* and *Oz. oldhamensis* are relatively cosmopolitan, having widespread occurrence in many palaeotropical regions, and in a few higher-latitude locations. Based on known occurrence, the possible ancestor of *Oz. hassi* and *Oz. oldhamensis* could be limited to Anticosti Island and the Mackenzie Mountains, and the taxa could be *Ozarkodina* sp. s.f. and *Oz. sesquipedalis*, respectively, as discussed earlier in choosing the ideal candidates of out-group taxa that could be the possible ancestor for the in-group taxa in analysis I.

The Mackenzie Mountains section represents a basin-margin facies, whereas the Anticosti section represents a shallow-water subtidal facies, both located within Laurentia. Thus, the possible ancestor of Silurian spathognathodontids probably evolved within Laurentia. Although only two specimens of *Ozarkodina* sp. s.f. (Pa element) were recovered from the Upper Ordovician on Anticosti Island, and none of the other elements assigned to it have been reported from there, it is an Ordovician *Ozarkodina* representative on Anticosti. The first appearance of spathognathodontid species on Anticosti is an example of *in situ* speciation.

The first occurrences of *Ozarkodina hassi* and *Oz. oldhamensis* are at almost the same stratigraphic level. Morphologically, the former is more likely to be the direct descendant of *Ozarkodina* sp. s.f. or *Oz. sesquipedalis* than the latter. Cladistically, the former inherited far more characters from *Ozarkodina* sp. s.f. or *Oz. sesquipedalis* than did the latter (Fig. 5). However, the relationship between *Oz. oldhamensis* and *Oz. hassi* remains uncertain.

Kockelella? *manitoulinensis* (Pollock, Rexroad & Nicoll) is neither a typical spathognathodontid nor a typical kockelellid species. Its most likely ancestor is *Ozarkodina pseudofissilis* (Lindström), which has a much wider distribution than any spathognathodontid species in the Late Ordovician. The Pa element of *Oz. pseudofissilis* has a shorter posterior process, flexed laterally, forming an angle of about 145° with the anterior process, which is similar to the Silurian *Kockelella*? *manitoulinensis. Ozarkodina pseudofissilis* has been reported from the Upper Ordovician of the UK (Lindström 1959; Orchard 1980) and the Ashgillian Matapedia Group of Gaspé Peninsula, Québec (Nowlan 1981) to the south of Anticosti Island. Hence, it is likely that *in situ* speciation of *Kockelella*? *manitoulinensis* happened in the Anticosti Basin.

Speciation in the prioniodontid stock. The only prioniodontid genus present within Cycle I is *Icriodella*. It has a long stratigraphic range, from Middle Ordovician to Lower Silurian. Both Ordovician species (such as *I. superba* Rhodes) and Silurian species (such as *I. deflecta* and *I. discreta*) are widespread in North America and Europe. Within Cycle I (Fig. 13), *I. dicrana* is the only species that has so for only been found on Anticosti Island. This species is different from others in having blade-bearing denticles with laterally bifurcated tips.

Icriodella superba has been recovered from Ashgillian strata in Britain (Rhodes 1953; Lindström 1959; Orchard 1980), and in late Middle and Upper Ordovician strata in North America (e.g. Schopf 1966; Webers 1966; Sweet *et al.* 1971; Uyeno 1974). Nowlan (1981) reported the species from the Ashgillian Matapedia Group of the Gaspé Peninsula, Québec. Consequently, as with *Kockelella*? *manitoulinensis*, the earliest Silurian species of *Icriodella* probably originated from an *in situ* speciation event in the Anticosti Basin.

By examining the different stocks that appeared in the earliest Silurian, and deducing their possible ancestors, the conodont faunal turnover associated with the latest Ordovician mass extinction was probably followed by several *in situ* speciations, which mainly happened among the three genera: *Ozarkodina*, *Rexroadus* and *Icriodella* in the Anticosti Basin. The speciation in Cycle I is significant, with the sum of speciation and extinction being 14 (speciation defined as '+' and extinction as '–'), which is far larger than for any later cycles (Fig. 13).

Cycle II: early Rhuddanian

Cycle II, in the early Rhuddanian (Fig. 13), is characterized by the successive appearance of several new species, with branching events in different lineages, such as *Oulodus sigmoideus, Ozarkodina strena, Pterospathodus*? *originalis*, together with *Distomodus kentuckyensis* reported earlier from the lower Llandovery, and also *Ozarkodina pirata, Panderodus recurvatus* (Rhodes) and *Oulodus panuarensis* reported earlier from the upper Llandovery.

Cycle II is unlike Cycle I, in which all new species appear within a short interval near the Ordovician–Silurian boundary, but rather it is a longer interval with new species being introduced progressively. Cycle II starts with the lowest occurrence of *Oulodus sigmoideus* (about 15 m above the base of the Becscie Formation) and ends with the restricted occurrence of *Pterospathodus*? *originalis* (54 m above the base of the Becscie Formation).

Speciation in the ozarkodinid stock. Within Cycle II (Fig. 13), *Ozarkodina pirata, Oz. strena* and *Pterospathodus*? *originalis* belong to the ozarkodinid stock. *Ozarkodina pirata* has a moderately wide distribution geographically and stratigraphically. It has been reported from the upper Llandovery Jupiter Formation, Anticosti Island (Uyeno & Barnes 1983) and the middle to upper Llandovery rocks of North Greenland (Armstrong 1990). The form species *Ozarkodina* sp. nov. A (Pa), *Ozarkodina* cf. *Oz. media* Walliser (Pb), *Neoprioniodus planus* Walliser (M), *Trichonodella symmetrica* (Branson & Mehl) (Sa), *Plectospathodus flexuosus* Branson & Mehl (Sb) described by Pollock *et al.* (1970) from Michigan, have all been considered to be conspecific with *Oz. pirata* by Zhang & Barnes (2002a), but it is difficult to determine its exact stratigraphic level from these records. If the Michigan occurrence is neglected, then its lowest occurrence is in the lower Becscie Formation on Anticosti Island and probably represents the origination of the species.

Except for *Ozarkodina* cf. *O. strena* reported from the northern Rocky Mountains, British Columbia (Pyle & Barnes 2003), *Ozarkodina strena* has not been reported outside Anticosti Island; it may have its first appearance on Anticosti Island representing an *in situ* speciation event.

Both *Ozarkodina pirata* and *Oz. strena* occur on the same branch with *Oz. hassi* on the cladogram (Figs 4, 5 & 6). Figure 5 shows that *Oz. pirata* is characterized by the following autapomorphies: dolabrate M element with erect cusp (1 of 19), basal cavity of M element without flare (1 of 21), Sa element with posterior process (0 of 23), and Sc element with anterior process bent down (1 of 25); further, *Oz. strena* is characterized by following auapomorphies: Pa element's anterior process is more robust than posterior one (1 of 6); Pa element's round denticulation (1 of 7), Pb element's basal cavity with small flare on one side (0 of 12) and Sb element slightly asymmetrical (0 of 24). The hypothesis that *Oz. hassi* could be the common ancestor of *Oz. pirata* and *Oz. strena* is well supported by the synapomorphies as discussed earlier in analysis I (Fig. 5). So early Rhuddanian speciation events within the ozarkodinid stock probably happened mainly among those species having a Pa element that is angulate with a prominent cusp and basal cavity beneath the cusp.

Pterospathodus? *originalis* is the earliest representative of the pterospathodontids, and its Pa element is basically angulate with a strong offset lateral lobe of the base on the outer side and a prominent cusp. Although not a typical pterospathodontid, it probably represents the ancestral species of *Pterospathodus*, and gradually evolved into the more typical species by adding the offset lateral lobe on the inner side and reducing its cusp (Zhang & Barnes 2002*a*). This earliest representative of *Pterospathodus* may have evolved from a species of *Ozarkodina*, as discussed earlier in analysis III.

Speciation in the prioniodinid stock. *Oulodus sigmoideus* and *Ou. panuarensis* are the two species belonging to the prioniodinid stock within Cycle II. Cladistically, these two species evolved from the different clade, the *Ou. sigmoideus* is supported by a derived character, the inverted aboral surface of the S element (0 of 17), and the *Ou. panuarensis* by a large basal cavity with flare (0 of 2), makellate M element (1 of 11), bipennate Sc element with anterior process bent downward (1 of 19) (Fig. 8). *Oulodus sigmoideus* was recently described from Anticosti Island by Zhang & Barnes (2002*a*) who placed several informal names in synonymy. It is found in the Jupiter Formation, Anticosti Island (= *Oulodus* sp. Uyeno *in* Uyeno & Barnes 1983), the Welsh Borderland (= *Lonchodina* sp. A (Pa) and *Lonchodina walliseri* Ziegler (Pb), Aldridge 1972), and the Brassfield Formation, Ohio (= *Lonchodina*? sp. Rexroad (Pa) and *Lonchodina walliseri* (Pb), Rexroad 1967).

The Jupiter Formation contains the highest occurrence of *Oulodus sigmoideus*. In the Welsh Borderland, it ranges from Fronian through Telychian. It is difficult to correlate the lowest occurrence of this species between Anticosti Island and Ohio (Rexroad 1967), where it occurs throughout the Brassfield Formation that is within the *Distomodus kentuckyensis* Zone. There is a significant gap between the Silurian Brassfield Formation and the underlying Ordovician Belfast Member in Ohio. Rexroad (1967) considered the Brassfield conodont fauna to be equivalent to zone A_3. However, the Becscie Formation spans A_1–A_4. The lowest occurrence of *Ou. sigmoideus* is at about 29 m above the base of the Becscie Formation, and lower than the lowest occurrence of *D. kentuckyensis* – making it the lowest known occurrence.

Oulodus panuarensis was first described from the Lower Silurian in New South Wales, Australia (Bischoff 1986). *Oulodus* sp. B from

the Brassfield Formation of southern Ohio (Cooper 1975), *Ou.* sp. A from Jupiter Formation, Anticosti (Uyeno *in* Uyeno & Barnes 1983), and *Ou.* spp. indet. group 8 (Armstrong 1990) from northern Greenland, and part of the apparatus *Ou. angullongensis* from New South Wales (Bischoff 1986), were considered synonymous with *Ou. panuarensis* (Zhang & Barnes 2002*a*). Form species described as *Neoprioniodus planus* Walliser (M) by Rexroad (1967) from the Brassfield Formation, Ohio, and as *Neoprioniodus* cf. *N. excavatus* (Branson & Mehl) (M) and *Ligonodina* sp. nov. (Sc) by Pollock *et al.* (1970) from the Lower Silurian of Michigan and Ontario were also included in *Ou. panuarensis* (Zhang & Barnes 2002*a*).

In New South Wales, the first appearance of *Oulodus panuarensis* (= *Ou. angullongensis* Bischoff) occurs with that of *Distomodus combinatus* Bischoff and *D. tridens* Bischoff, and was correlated with the upper graptolite *Cystograptus vesiculosus* Zone – about A_3 time (Bischoff 1986). The exact stratigraphic level of *Oulodus* sp. B from the Brassfield Formation, Ohio, is unknown (Cooper 1975), but all *Oulodus* species at the West Union section occur later than *Distomodus kentuckyensis*. *Oulodus* spp. indet. group 8 (Armstrong 1990) from the Aleqatsia Fjord Formation, Kap Jefferson, northern Greenland occurs near the top of the formation, which lies close to the Rhuddanian–Aeronian boundary (Armstrong 1990). The lowest occurrence of *Ou. panuarensis* is lower than that of *Distomodus kentuckyensis* on Anticosti Island (Fig. 3). Thus, the first appearance of *Ou. panuarensis* on Anticosti Island is the earliest yet known.

Speciation in the prioniodontid stock. *Distomodus kentuckyensis* is a biostratigraphically important prioniodontid, widespread both in North America and Europe, and a zone fossil in the lower Llandovery. Its appearance is in the Idwian and early Fronian (Aldridge 1972). In North America, it occurs near the base of the Brassfield Formation, Ohio (Cooper 1975), and about 46 m above the base of the Becscie Formation, Anticosti Island, which might be the lowest known. The origin of *Distomodus kentuckyensis* probably lies among the Late Ordovician balognathids such as *Gamachignathus* (Sweet 1988). If true, then it is likely that *D. kentuckyensis* originated in the Anticosti Basin.

Thus, the faunal turnover exhibited by the three above-mentioned stocks in Cycle II represents a highly significant evolutionary event, but the sum of speciation and extinction of the species decreased from 14 in Cycle I to 3 in Cycle II (Fig. 13).

Cycle III: earliest to mid–late Aeronian

Cycle III (Fig. 13) lasted much longer than the other cycles, starting in the earliest Aeronian with the first appearance of *Oulodus*? *expansus* and *Ou. jeannae* until the mid- to late Aeronian with the last appearance of *Ou. panuarensis* and the temporary disappearance of almost all species. The recognition of Cycle III is based on:

(1) several short-lived species whose first and last appearances were almost at the same time;
(2) the extinction of many species that origi-nated in the early Rhuddanian; and
(3) the emigration of almost all conodont species at the end of the cycle.

Speciation in the ozarkodinid stock. Unlike Cycles I and II in the Rhuddanian, pterospathodontids played an important role in the ozarkodinid stock within Cycle III. Four species appeared in this cycle, mostly short-ranging, with their lowest and highest occurrences at almost the same level: *Pterospathodus* cf. *P. celloni*, *P. pennatus pennatus, P. siluricus* and *P. posteritenuis* (Figs 3, 12 & 13).

The biostratigraphic data (Figs 3 & 13), cladistic analysis (Figs 10 & 11) and the construction of a phylogenetic tree (Fig. 12) all indicate that the middle Aeronian was an important interval for *Pterospathodus* specia-tion. Analysis III reveals that *Pterospathodus* probably diversified through two lineages (Figs 10 & 11). Group I developed a carminiscaphate element with lateral lobes at mid-length (1 of 1), which is related to *P. siluricus* (Figs 11 & 12). Group II may have developed a lateral process (0 of 5) with a denticulate lateral expansion (0 of 7), which is related to *P.* cf. *P. celloni*; a pastiniscaphate element (3 of 1) with a lateral process forming an angle less than 90° with a posterior process (0 of 8), which is related to *P. pennatus pennatus*, a bifurcated lateral process (1 of 8); and the main processes having an expanded undersurface (2 of 13), which is related to *P. posteritenuis* (Figs 11 & 12). Although some species, such as *P. celloni, P. pennatus procerus* and *P. amorphognathoides* appeared in the early Telychian, the origination of some of their important characters can be traced back to the middle Aeronian in the Anticosti Basin.

Another interesting Cycle III pterospathodon-tid representative is *Apsidognathus*? sp. Although represented by a single specimen, probably a Pa element, it shows a broad, shallow, and completely excavated lower sur-face, and a row of broken denticles on the upper surface that bifurcate near the anterior (?) end – all basic characters of the genus (Zhang & Barnes 2002*a*). All previously known species of this genus occurred in or later than the *Pterospathodus celloni* Zone. The importance of this Anticosti discovery is that the character origination of the genus can be traced back to the middle Aeronian within the Anticosti Basin.

Ozarkodina clavula is the only spathognatho-dontid newcomer: a record in Cycle III from the Aeronian Gun River Formation (Zhang & Barnes 2002*a*) represents its first known appear-ance. A unique derived character, the Pa element's denticles at two ends being more robust than in the middle (2 of 6), supports the speciation of *Oz. clavula* (Figs 5 & 6). Thus, Cycle III is an important period for the speciation of *Pterospathodus* and the lineage of *Ozarkodina* lacking a prominent cusp.

Speciation in the prioniodontid stock. The important prioniodontid newcomer in Cycle III is *Distomodus staurognathoides* (Walliser), which has a world-wide distribution. In Britain (Aldridge 1972) and Oslo (Aldridge *et al.* 1993), the lower boundary of the *D. staurognathoides* Zone is assigned to the Fronian or mid-Aeronian *Monograptus sedgwickii* Zone. The lowest occurrence of *D. staurognathoides* is in the middle of member 3, Gun River Formation, about 50 m above the base of the formation (Zhang & Barnes 2002*a*). The associated graptolite *Atavograptus atavus* (Riva & Petryk 1981) indicates that the first appearance of *D. staurognathoides* is no later than the *Monograptus triangulatus* Zone, which is early Aeronian, and hence earlier than in Europe.

Two species of a recently described genus, *Anticostiodus fahraeusi* Zhang & Barnes and *A. boltoni* Zhang & Barnes, have an apparatus that shows similarity with the Ordovician prionio-dontids, although their position in the framework of the conodont classification is unknown. These species occur 13 m above the lowest occurrence of *Distomodus staurognathoides* (Zhang & Barnes 2000). The only earlier report of conodonts now referred to *A. fahraeusi* was made by Rexroad (1967) from the Brassfield Formation of the Cincinnati Arch area, and a new discovery of *A. fahraeusi* by Pyle & Barnes (2003) from the Kenny Formation, NE British Columbia.

Speciation in the prioniodinid stock. Both *Oulodus*? *expansus* and *Ou. jeannae* were recovered just above the Becscie–Gun River formational boundary, approximately at the Rhuddanian–Aeronian boundary (Zhang & Barnes 2002*a*). This is taken as the lower boundary of Cycle III (Figs 3 & 13). *Oulodus jeannae* was originally described from the *Pterospathodus celloni* Zone, Austria (Sweet & Schönlaub 1975). Its earlier appearance on Anticosti Island suggests a speciation event more likely from *Ou.*? *expansus*, an immigrant in the Anticosti Basin (see discussion below) than from *Ou. panuarensis*, which is cladistically supported by its sharing a synapomorphy with *Ou.*? *expansus* (Pa element with a posterior protuberance, 0 of 9), but none with *Ou. panuarensis* (Figs 8 & 9).

Immigration. *Oulodus*? *expansus* first occurs together with *Ou. jeannae* at the base of the Gun River Formation, which represents the earliest *Oulodus* species whose Pa element is similar to those of the Upper Ordovician species. The earliest-known occurrence of *Oulodus*? *expansus* is in northern Greenland (Armstrong 1990), where it was established as the zonal fossil for the upper shelf and slope facies of equivalent age to the *O.*? *nathani* Zone (McCracken & Barnes 1981) on Anticosti Island; the lower limit of the zone is close to the Ordovician–Silurian boundary. However, the Greenland section is incomplete. Recently, Jowett & Barnes (2000) found the M element of *Ou.*? *expansus* in the *Atavograptus atavus* Zone and the whole apparatus in the *Coronograptus cyphus* Zone from upper shelf and slope facies of the Cape Phillips Formation, Cornwallis Island, Arctic Canada. Evidently, *Ou.*? *expansus* appeared much later on Anticosti Island than in Greenland and Arctic Canada, indicating an immigration event.

Alternation of extinction and speciation. Although speciation in Cycle III happened in different stocks, the extinction rate in this cycle prevailed over the speciation rate (Fig. 13), with the sum of speciation and extinction within Cycle III being minus four. Nine species became extinct within Cycle III (Figs 3 & 13): *Rexroadus kentuckyensis, R. nathani, Oulodus panuarensis, Ozarkodina hassi, Oz. oldhamensis, Oz. strena, Icriodella deflecta* and *Kockelella*? *manitoulinensis* that originated in the early Rhuddanian, and *Ou. jeannae* that originated in the earliest Aeronian. The extinction event is based on their absence from younger strata on

Anticosti Island. Prior to the final disappearance of some species, notably *Kockelella*? *manitoulinensis, R. kentuckyensis, Ou. panuarensis, Oz. strena,* and *Oz. hassi,* there was a period of evolutionary stasis. In the lower Gun River Formation, few samples contain these species. Other species that first appeared, but did not become extinct in Cycle III, such as *Oulodus sigmoideus, Ou.*? *expansus, Distomodus staurognathoides* and *Ozarkodina clavula,* also experienced a period of stasis.

This was the first major extinction event after the latest Ordovician extinction, but it lasted longer and alternated with speciation events. Cycle III started with the immigration of *Oulodus*? *expansus* at the beginning of the Aeronian, which was followed by a period of stasis with no speciation or extinction. The extinction is recognized by the disappearance of *Rexroadus nathani, Ozarkodina strena, Oz. hassi* and *Kockelella*? *manitoulinensis,* accompanied later by the speciation of *Oz. clavula, Distomodus staurognathoides, Anticostiodus boltoni* and *A. fahraeusi.* It is also characterized by the loss of *Oulodus jeannae, Oz. oldhamensis, Icriodella deflecta* and *R. kentuckyensis,* which was followed by a major speciation of *Pterospathodus* near the Aeronian–Telychian boundary. Cycle III terminates with an extinction marked by the disappearance of *Ou. panuarensis* in the early Telychian and the local disappearance of all but one coniform species below the barren interval (Fig. 13).

Aldridge *et al.* (1993) recognized the Sandvika P–S event based on the Llandovery sequence in the Oslo region, and commented that the Sandvika event could be represented low in the Jupiter Formation, Anticosti Island. If the extinction event recognized in this study was related to the Sandvika event, then it would be much earlier, and have lasted longer than that in the Oslo region.

Emigration. Lazarus taxa (Flessa & Jablonski 1983) disappeared at mass extinction levels but later reappeared. Smith (1994) expanded the concept to refer to taxa that have a significant gap in their fossil record. Here, this term is used to indicate those species that disappeared in member 3 of the Jupiter Formation and then reappeared in member 4. Besides the extinction of *Oulodus panuarensis,* the upper limit of Cycle III is also marked by the sudden disappearance of Lazarus taxa. These include all coniform species that originated in the Ordovician and Early Silurian, such as *Panderodus unicostatus, P. recurvatus, Walliserodus curvatus,*

Pseudooneotodus beckmanni (Bischoff & Sannemann). *Decoriconus fragilis* (Branson & Mehl), and ramiform–pectiniform species that originated in the early Rhuddanian and early Aeronian, such as *Oulodus sigmoideus, Ou.? expansus, Ozarkodina pirata, Oz. clavula, Distomodus staurognathoides,* and *Pterospathodus posteritenuis.* Their disappearance marked an emigration event that is associated with a barren conodont interval in member 3 of the Jupiter Formation, which comprises about 30 m of green–grey shale, locally sandy (Uyeno & Barnes 1983). This is the longest duration with almost no conodonts through the entire Anticosti sequence.

The member 3 shale is of limited geographical extent, and is of uncertain depositional environmental interpretation. It may represent a brief period of deepening, with the clastics derived from the Appalachian Orogen to the south; or alternatively a local clastic influx from the Canadian Shield to the north, since shallowing is suggested by plant spores (Duffield 1985). Copper & Long (1990) revised the Jupiter Formation to combine members 1–3 as the Goéland Member, with an overlying biohermal unit as the East Point Member. They interpreted the Goéland Member to represent relatively deeper waters, with shallowing occurring in the biohermal East Point Member. This issue is discussed further by Zhang & Barnes (2002*b*).

During member 3 time, almost all conodont species migrated away from the Anticosti Basin to escape the harsh environment that even such species as *Panderodus unicostatus,* being the most eurytopic of all Early Silurian conodont species (Zhang & Barnes 2002*a*, 2002*b*, 2002*c*), could not tolerate.

Cycle IV: latest Aeronian

Cycle IV is recognized in the late Aeronian. Its lower boundary is marked by the reappearance of all coniform species and the long-ranging ramiform–pectiniform species: *Ozarkodina pirata.* The upper boundary is characterized by the extinction of several species, including *Oulodus sigmoideus, Oz. pirata* and *Pterospathodus posteritenuis.* The Cycle spans the upper *Oz. clavula* and lower *Oz. aldridgei* zones (Zhang & Barnes 2002*a*).

Reappearance of the Lazarus species. The lowest member 4 of the Jupiter Formation is dominantly lime mudstone – a marked change from the underlying shales of member 3. The base of member 4 yields all the long-ranging coniform

species extending from the Ordovician and earliest Silurian, including *Panderodus unicostatus, P. recurvatus, Walliserodus curvatus, Pseudooneotodus beckmanni,* and *Decoriconus fragilis,* and the ramiform–pectiniform species *Ozarkodina pirata.* Hence, these Lazarus conodont species reappeared largely because the appropriate environment was developed again in the Anticosti Basin after the conodont-barren interval. However, not all Lazarus species reappeared simultaneously, and the later reappearance of some other species, such as *Oulodus sigmoideus, Ou.? expansus, Ozarkodina clavula, Distomodus staurognathoides* and *Pterospathodus posteritenuis,* probably indicates their more stenotypic character.

Immigration of newcomer species. There was no remarkable speciation event in Cycle IV, with only a few newcomers such as *Dapsilodus obliquicostatus* (Branson & Mehl) and *Ozarkodina aldridgei.* The known lowest occurrence of *D. obliquicostatus* is at the Ordovician–Silurian boundary in the Cape Phillips Formation, the age-equivalent upper shelf and slope facies in the Arctic Islands (Jowett & Barnes 2000), and in the Hanson Creek and Roberts Mountains formations along the shelf-to-basin transect in Central Nevada (Sweet 2000). Hence, these two occurrences were earlier than on Anticosti Island.

Cladistic analysis (Figs 4, 5 & 6) identifies *Ozarkodina oldhamensis* and *Oz. aldridgei* as a clade at the terminus of the cladogram. Two characters, i.e. fused denticles without apices above the basal cavity (1 of 3) and a symmetrical flared basal cavity (1 of 5), could be synapomorphies to identify them as a monophyletic group.

In the discussion about extinctions within Cycle III, *Ozarkodina oldhamensis* was shown to have become extinct. Both *Oz. oldhamensis* and *Oz. hassi* had originated in the earliest Rhuddanian. The former possesses two derived character states: fused denticles without apices above the basal cavity (1 of 3), and a symmetrical flare-shaped basal cavity (1 of 5) (Fig. 5). These differ from the latter. This suggests that these two character states were derived first in the earliest Rhuddanian. However, they are also the states that identify *Oz. oldhamensis* and *Oz. aldridgei* as a clade, since both character states are also found in *Oz. aldridgei.* Based on cladistic theory, the monophyletic species *Oz. oldhamensis,* defined by the two apomorphic character states, had therefore not become extinct. There is a significant interval between the highest occurrence of *Oz. oldhamensis* in the upper Gun River Formation and the lowest occurrence of *Oz. aldridgei* in the middle Jupiter Formation. Thus, the disappearance of *Ozarkodina oldhamensis* in the Gun River Formation in Cycle III could be a termed pseudo-extinction (Stanley 1979), and the occurrence of *Oz. aldridgei* in the Jupiter Formation in Cycle VI could be termed a pseudo-origination. The appearance of the new-comer *Ozarkodina aldridgei* together with *Dapsilodus obliquicostatus* in Cycle IV suggests an immigration event.

Extinction. The upper boundary of Cycle IV is marked by the last appearance of *Oulodus sigmoideus*, *Ozarkodina pirata* and *Pterospathodus posteritenuis*. These species did not return immediately after the conodont-barren interval, as mentioned above, and did not appear during most of Cycle IV. Their reappearance was close to their last appearance, being at almost the same time. Although the number of species becoming extinct in Cycle IV is less than that in Cycle III, there was little speciation – thus the sum of speciation and extinction within Cycle IV is minus 3, marking the second conodont extinction event that occurred in the Llandovery. Compared to the extinction event in Cycle III, this one was of shorter duration, and occurred near the end of the cycle.

Cycle V: early Telychian

Speciation. Almost all species in Cycle V in the early Telychian can be recognized world-wide. On Anticosti Island, this cycle is remarkable for the sudden occurrence of 13 species near the Jupiter–Chicotte formational boundary, of which most have an apparatus with platform P elements (Figs 3 & 13).

Aulacognathus bullatus (Nicoll & Rexroad), *Ozarkodina polinclinata, Oz. gulletensis*, and *Icriodella inconstans* Aldridge make their lowest occurrence, and *Oz. clavula* and *Oulodus? expansus* make their return after their highest occurrence before the conodont barren interval in the uppermost lime mudstones of member 4, Jupiter Formation. The debut of *Kockelella ranuliformis* (Walliser), *Astropentagnathus irregularis* Mostler, *Apsidognathus tuberculatus* Walliser, *Pterospathodus celloni*, *P. pennatus procerus*, *Carniodus carnulus* Walliser, and two species of *Pseudooneotodus* coincided with the development of shallow-water crinoidal grainstones at the base of the Chicotte Formation. The last new Llandovery conodont representa-

tives on Anticosti Island, *?'Johnognathus' huddlei* Mashkova and *Pterospathodus amorphognathoides* made their lowest occurrence in the upper part of the exposed Chicotte Formation (Uyeno & Barnes 1983).

The major speciation in Cycle V happened within the Family Pterospathodontidae, representing an evolutionary burst of pterospathodontids in the Early Telychian. *Pterospathodus* and *Apsidognathus*, whose first appearances were in the early Middle Aeronian, along with *Aulacognathus, Astropentagnathus, Carniodus* and *Johnognathus*, are the only six genera included in the Family Pterospathodontidae (Sweet 1988). There is no evidence for the origin of the last few genera; in contrast, many characters of species of *Pterospathodus* within Cycle V can be traced back to the Aeronian (Figs 10–12). However, the following derived characters strongly support speciation in the early Telychian: under surface expanded posteriorly (0 of 13) supports the speciation of *P. celloni* with group I; anterior longer than posterior between the bifurcating lateral processes (1 of 9) and having a platform ledge (0 of 14) support the speciation of *P. amorphognathoides* at the terminus of group II. Further, within Group II, *P. pennatus procerus* is supported by a homoplasy character, lateral expansion on outer side (1 of 6), that has a disjunct distribution, indicating multiple independent derivation (Fig. 11). The other speciation occurred within the spathognathodontids, mainly within the ozarkodinids. The first appearance of *Ozarkodina polinclinata* and *Oz. gulletensis* is at the same level within Cycle V. The cladogram and evolutionary tree (Figs 4–6) suggest that the Llandovery *Ozarkodina* evolved through two different lineages. As discussed earlier, the main speciation of the lineage with prominent cusp happened in the early Rhuddanian; later, the main speciation of the lineage without prominent cusp, including *Oz. polinclinata* and *Oz. gulletensis*, occurred in the late Aeronian and early Telychian. *Ozarkodina polinclinata* is supported by a derived character – the basal cavity of Pa element near posterior end (2 of 4); however, *Oz. gulletensis* is supported by several homoplastic characters (Fig. 5).

Graptolites from the Jupiter Formation (Riva & Petryk 1981) are represented by *Monograptus sedgwickii* (Portlock), which is common in member 4. This species ranges through the *M. sedgwickii* and *Rastrites maximus* zones of the upper Llandovery in Britain (Toghill 1968).

Upper member 4 of the Jupiter Formation contains a conodont fauna that is correlated to those from the *Pterospathodus celloni* Zone in Norway and the *Icriodella inconstans* Zone in Britain (Uyeno & Barnes 1983). The fauna in Britain was compared with the C_5 – *Monoclimacis greistoniensis* Zone (Aldridge 1972), and in the Oslo Region with C_4 and C_5 – *Monograptus crispus* and *M. greistoniensis* zones. Although the fauna appears in uppermost member 4, it compares best with that of the *Rastrites maximus* Zone, suggesting that the first appearance of this fauna on Anticosti Island was earlier than those from Norway and Britain. This indicates that the conodont fauna appearing near the Jupiter– Chicotte boundary represent an *in situ* speciation event whose scale could match the earliest Rhuddanian event.

Pterospathodus amorphognathoides, the world-wide latest Llandovery zone fossil, makes its occurrence only in the upper Chicotte Formation on Anticosti Island, approximately 24 m above the base of the formation (note that the higher strata of the Chicotte Formation to the east were inaccessible at the time of sample collection; upper Chicotte here refers to strata cropping out both around and inland from Southwest Point). The *P. amorphognathoides* fauna equates with the C_6 subdivision of the Telychian, i.e. graptolite *Monoclimacis crenulata* Zone. It is uncertain whether its first appearance on Anticosti Island represents *in situ* speciation or immigration. However, as in the discussion of *Pterospathodus* speciation, the origination of some characters of *P. amorphognathoides* can be traced back to middle late Aeronian on Anticosti Island. Hence it seems more likely that it was an *in situ* speciation event.

Extinction?. Four species, *Oulodus? expansus, Ozarkodina clavula, Oz. aldridgei*, and *Distomodus staurognathoides* first appeared in the Aeronian. These made their highest occurrence near the Jupiter–Chicotte boundary. Other species that made both their first and last appearance in Cycle V include *Aulacognathus bullatus, Kockelella ranuliformis, Astropenta- gnathus irregularis, Apsidognathus tuberculatus, Pterospathodus celloni, P. pennatus procerus*, and *Carniodus carnulus*, as well as ?'*Johnognathus*' *huddlei* and *Pterospathodus amorphognathoides*. As only the lower 24 m of the Chicotte Formation was sampled, it is not known whether the last appearance of these species represents an extinction event on Anticosti Island. However, there was a world-wide conodont extinction event in the latest Telychian, named the Ireviken Event by Aldridge *et al.* (1993). If the last appearance of

these species on Anticosti Island did represent an extinction event, then the event may have happened earlier than elsewhere in the world, as none of the species are found in the exposed uppermost sample of Llandovery sequence. This sample contains the first and only appearance of *P. amorphognathoides*, whereas most species that disappeared in Cycle V can be found in the *P. amorphognathoides* Zone outside of Anticosti Island. However, the special crinoidal grainstone–rudstone facies development of the Chicotte Formation may have influenced particular species distributions. If the last appearance of these species represents an extinction event on Anticosti Island, then Cycle V would represent a mixture of speciations and extinctions.

Bio-events and sea-level changes

Sea-level changes can be controlled intrinsically (locally) or extrinsically (globally). The main glacio-eustatic drop during the latest Ordovician and the subsequent rise during the earliest Silurian have been used to explain the decline and recovery in faunal diversity (e.g. Barnes 1986; Brenchley 1989; Brenchley *et al.* 1994; Barnes *et al.* 1996; Zhang & Barnes 2002*b*). What is less clear is the role that sea-level plays in influencing conodont speciation, extinction, immigration and emigration in a basin-wide setting. The Llandovery sequence on Anticosti Island provides an opportunity to examine its role.

Methodology

In addition to the extensive terminal Ordovician glacial deposits across North Africa, Ordovician–Silurian glacial deposits have also been reported from Argentina, Bolivia, Brazil and Peru (Caputo & Lima 1984; Zalan *et al.* 1987; Grahn & Caputo 1992; Astini & Büggisch 1993; Büggisch & Astini 1993; Caputo 1998). In particular, three short-lived, waning phases of Silurian glaciation (early Aeronian, latest Aeronian–early Telychian, and latest Telychian–earliest Wenlock) have been recorded from the stratigraphic evidence in the Nhamundá Formation of the Trombetas Group in Brazil (Grahn & Caputo 1992; Grahn 1996; Caputo 1998) and from oxygen-isotope data (Azmy *et al.* 1998; Veizer *et al.* 1999). The three phases of Silurian glaciation correlate approximately with the *Monograptus triangulatus, M. sedgwickii* and *Cyrtograptus centrifugus* zones.

Were the Llandovery conodont faunas modified by these three Silurian glacial events? Copper & Long (1998), Jin & Copper (1999) and Dewing (1999) constructed sea-level curves based on the Llandovery sediments and brachiopods; the main low sea-levels were recognized in late Rhuddanian, earliest Aeronian and latest Aeronian. Those in the late Rhuddanian and latest Aeronian correlate to the *Coronograptus cyphus* and *Monograptus sedgwickii* zones.

The two immigration events, recognized by the invasion of *Oulodus? expansus* in the earliest Aeronian and *Dapsilodus obliquicostatus* in the latest Aeronian, could represent the two major transgressions during the Llandovery on Anticosti Island. Both species are regarded as indicative of deeper- and/or cooler-water environments.

The conodont extinction in the latest Ordovician and recovery in the earliest Silurian were probably induced by the glaciation and associated with the sea-level drop and subsequent rise. The pattern of conodont extinction and speciation that alternated through the Llandovery on Anticosti Island appears, at least in part, to correlate with the frequent sea-level changes (Zhang & Barnes 2002*b*).

The evolution and modification of conodont biofacies appear to have depended greatly on water depth (Zhang & Barnes 2002*c*). The changes of conodont biofacies through time are strongly correlated to the sea-level changes (Zhang & Barnes 2002*b*). Detailed studies of Llandovery sediments and brachiopods of Anticosti Island have been accomplished by Copper & Long (1998), Jin & Copper (1999), and Dewing (1999). Their reconstructed sea-level curves have been refined on a finer scale using conodont data (Zhang & Barnes 2002*b*).

Sea-level changes

Earliest Rhuddanian sea-level rise and speciation in Cycle I and Cycle II. The early Rhuddanian was a period of rapid sea-level rise resulting from melting of the North African continental ice sheets (Ziegler *et al.* 1979; Loydell 1998). The palaeobathymetric changes indicated by Ordovician–Silurian boundary strata on Anticosti Island have been interpreted as glacio-eustatic in origin by Petryk (1981*b*), McCracken & Barnes (1981), and Zhang & Barnes (2002*b*). Relatively high sea-level in the earliest Rhuddanian probably extended through member 1 of the Becscie Formation, which contains only rare brachiopods (Jin & Copper 1999) and is dominated by laminated, homogeneous mudstone (Sami & Desrochers 1992). It is interpreted to have been deposited below storm-wave base and in water depths of 70–100 m (Sami & Desrochers 1992). The

conodont community was dominated by a deeper-water assemblage of *Walliserodus curvatus, Ozarkodina oldhamensis* and *Rexroadus kentuckyensis*. In this short period, a burst of *in situ* conodont speciation within Cycle I was accomplished rapidly during the initial transgression. Shortly after Cycle I, another *in situ* speciation event introduced several new species within Cycle II during a period of stable high sea-level (Zhang & Barnes 2002*b*) (Fig. 13).

Early Rhuddanian sea-level drop and evolutionary stasis. Relatively low sea-level probably prevailed through the whole of member 2 of the Becscie Formation and the lower to middle part of the Merrimack Formation. This part of the Llandovery sequence (late Rhuddanian) has an abundant *Virgiana* brachiopod fauna (Jin & Copper 1999). Member 2 and the lower–middle part of the Merrimack Formation are dominated by laminated mudstone–grainstone and, at some localities, such as at Rivière Jupiter and Cap Henri-Rivière aux Cailloux, by laminated calcisiltite–grainstone. The former lithology is considered to represent deposition by episodic high-energy waning flows on the inner to outer ramp at water depths of 30–70 m; the latter lithology represents high-energy storm waves and currents on the inner ramp at water depths of 10–30 m (Sami & Desrochers 1992).

The dominant conodont community in member 2, Becscie Formation is *Ozarkodina strena–Rexroadus nathani* that reflects a shallow-water environment, above wave base (Zhang & Barnes 2002*b*) (Fig. 13). This community maintained a stable development through most of member 2 and the lower to middle part of the Merrimack Formation. Through this long interval, conodont speciation was stagnant and is probably related to the regression.

Latest Rhuddanian–earliest Aeronian transgression and conodont immigration in the beginning of Cycle III. The upper Merrimack Formation contains rare *Virgiana* (Jin & Copper 1999) and is composed of calcareous mudstone–shale that represents deposition on the outer ramp at water depths of 75–120 m (Sami & Desrochers 1992). This environment probably persisted until the earliest Aeronian, as the basal part of the Gun River Formation yields the common graptolite *Climacograptus rectangularis* (Riva & Petryk 1981) associated with the brachiopod *Fenestrirostra pyrrba* (Copper & Long 1989). Shortly afterwards, in member 3 of the Gun River Formation, the graptolite

Atavograptus atavus made its lowest occurrence, which ranges from *A. atavus* to *Monograptus triangulatus* zones in Britain. This was the highest sea-level stand since the earliest Rhuddanian. It is associated with a change to a deeper-water conodont community (Zhang & Barnes 2002*b*) (Fig. 13). *Oulodus*? *expansus*, which is interpreted as a deep-water specialist, first immigrated onto the Anticosti platform in the earliest Aeronian.

Early Aeronian alternating regression and transgression with faunal effects in Cycle III. The cause of early Aeronian sea-level drop is suggested to be glacio-eustasy (Grahn & Caputo 1992; Grahn 1996; Caputo 1998) correlated with the *Monograptus triangulatus* Zone (Azmy *et al.* 1998; Veizer *et al.* 1999). Graptolites from member 3 of the Gun River Formation (Riva & Petryk 1981) include *Atavograptus atavus*, a distinctive graptolite that ranges through *A. atavus* to *M. triangulatus* zones (Rickards 1970; Hutt 1974–1975), which spans middle Rhuddanian to early Aeronian. As noted earlier, this level is best correlated with the *M. triangulatus* Zone.

The first extinction phase within Cycle III started with the disappearance of *Rexroadus nathani*, and was over with the disappearance of *Ozarkodina hassi*. This interval is roughly equal to the range of *Atavograptus atavus*. Thus, this extinction phase correlates with the early Aeronian glaciation and regression. This extinction phase within Cycle III was the first extinction event after that of the latest Ordovician. It is interesting that most of the species that became extinct in this phase are those that had a preference for shallow-water environments, such as *Rexroadus nathani*, *Ozarkodina hassi*, and *Oz. strena*.

Termination of the short-lived glaciation in the early Aeronian likely resulted in a transgression. The Gun River Formation consists primarily of rhythmic micrites and shales that represent a deeper-water setting (Copper & Long 1998). This interval is the diversification phase in Cycle III, in which *in situ* speciation replaced the first extinction phase. This sea-level rise correlates with the appearance of newcomers to Anticosti such as *Distomodus staurognathoides, Ozarkodina clavula* and two new species of *Anticostiodus*. Within Cycle III, following this diversification, another extinction phase occurred that is characterized by the extinction of some deeper-water taxa such as *Ozarkodina oldhamensis, Oulodus jeannae* and *Rexroadus kentuckyensis*. Another diversification phase

followed, characterized by speciation within *Pterospathodus*. Most of these events happened within the Gun River Formation (Fig. 13). The principal conodont community in the Gun River is one dominated by *Ozarkodina pirata, Oulodus jeannae* and *Icriodella deflecta*, which remained stable through most of the formation (Zhang & Barnes 2002*b*). Stricklandiid brachiopods with low abundance were also prevalent through the whole formation, but brachiopods indicate shallowing toward the top (Jin & Copper 1999). These authors note a further shallowing in the base of the Goéland Member, Jupiter Formation, and the change to a *Pentamerus* community. This correlates with the last diversification phase of Cycle III, with the origination of several *Pterospathodus* species.

Late Aeronian regression and emigration of Lazarus conodonts at the end of Cycle III

The highest occurrence of *Oulodus panuarensis* is in the uppermost member 1 of the Jupiter Formation. Member 2 is not exposed on south coast. Member 3, equivalent to the upper part of the Goéland Member, or probably to the East Point Member that is a reefal unit (Copper & Long 1990), is the conodont-barren interval. This interval is dominantly of uniform green–grey shale and produced land-derived micro-fossils (Duffield 1985). As noted earlier, there is some debate whether this clastic interval represents a deepening or a shallowing event. If this interval is equivalent to East Point Member of Copper & Long (1990), then brachiopod studies indicate a very low abundance of *Pentamerus, Clorinda* and stricklandiids, which is interpreted as reflecting deposition below the normal storm wave base (Jin & Copper 1999). The virtual absence of conodonts indicates a hostile environment. This facies and faunal change may be caused by the latest Aeronian glaciation.

Azmy *et al.* (1998) and Veizer *et al.* (1999) documented the late Aeronian glaciation, which probably caused the sea-level drop both globally and locally – forcing all conodonts to migrate away from the Anticosti Basin. This glaciation was correlated to the graptolite *Monograptus sedgwickii* Zone by Azmy *et al.* (1998) and Veizer *et al.* (1999). However, on Anticosti Island the lowest occurrence of *M. sedgwickii* was accompanied by the reoccurrence of conodonts, just above the conodont-barren interval (Fig. 13).

Late Aeronian transgression and reappearance of Lazarus conodonts and the immigration of newcomers in Cycle IV. The lower part of member 4 of the Jupiter Formation is equivalent to the lower part of the Richardson Member (Copper & Long 1990). It contains the first appearance of *Monograptus sedgwickii* and is rich in stricklandiid brachiopods: indicative of deeper water. The lowest conodont sample from member 4 contains only long-ranging coniform species (Uyeno & Barnes 1983), which were interpreted as Lazarus taxa earlier in this paper. The reappearance of Lazarus taxa correlates with the transgression following the late Aeronian glaciation. Shortly after their reappearance (15 m and 17 m above the top of member 3), deeper-water conodont species, such as *Dapsilodus obliquicostatus* and *Ozarkodina aldridgei*, first immigrated into the Anticosti Basin (Fig. 13). This immigration was accompanied by the brachiopod *Dicoelosia*: a genus that indicates a deep-water environment (BA5 or deeper); with a suggested depth of about 120 m (Jin & Copper 1999), this marks the deepest environment in the Anticosti sequence. Therefore, the reappearance of Lazarus species and the subsequent invasion of deep-water conodont species probably indicate a deepening process (Fig. 13).

Latest Aeronian and earliest Telychian regression and mixture of speciation and extinction in Cycle V. The uppermost part of member 4 of the Jupiter Formation, equivalent to the Pavillon Member of Copper & Long (1990), is a recessive, greenish-grey shale and interbedded limestone unit, and has the most diverse fauna of brachiopods and corals found in the Jupiter Formation. It is capped by a thick blanket of crinoidal thickets and reefal development of the overlying Chicotte Formation. This appears to represent a regional event that transformed the Anticosti Basin in late Llandovery time into a very shallow environment (Copper & Long 1990). In this short interval, 13 conodont species made their first appearance in the Anticosti Basin – some probably representing *in situ* speciation. There is insufficient evidence to prove that the last appearance of all conodont species in Cycle V represents their extinction, because of the sampling limitation. However, based on their world-wide distribution, several species such as *Aulocognathus bullatus, Icriodella inconstans, Ozarkodina gulletensis,* and *Pterospathodus celloni* became extinct at this level. Thus, Cycle V represents a mixture of speciation and extinction, which happened during a regression spanning the *P. celloni* and lower *P. amorphognathoides* zones (Zhang & Barnes 2002*b*).

It is difficult to precisely correlate this event with the graptolite zonation, as no zonal graptolites have been found in the interval of Cycle V. On the basis of conodont and brachiopod biostratigraphy (Barnes 1989), the Chicotte ranges at least as high as Telychian C_5 and the graptolite *Monoclimacis crenulata* Zone. The lowstand recognized in Cycle V does not support the highstand related to the *M. crenulata* Zone and conodont *Pterospathodus amorphognathoides* Zone recognized by Ross & Ross (1996) and Johnson (1996), and may represent the third and final minor glacio-eustatic event within the Llandovery (Azmy *et al.* 1998).

Conclusions

The Ordovician–Silurian boundary interval is characterized by the second-most severe mass extinction in the Phanerozoic. It contains an intriguing pattern of evolutionary and ecological changes in the recovery phase through the Llandovery. Recent completion of taxonomic studies of early Llandovery conodont faunas, along with a reassessment of former studies of later Llandovery faunas (from the virtually complete Llandovery sequence on Anticosti Island, Québec) has provided a clearer picture of the evolutionary and ecological dynamics of the post-mass-extinction faunal recovery. The pattern of conodont bio-events is interpreted as reflecting a series of speciation, extinction, immigration and emigration events. Five conodont evolutionary cycles (I–V) are recognized and supported by new cladistic analyses for four key genera: *Oulodus, Ozarkodina, Pterospathodus* and *Rexroadus*. One particular, but differing, kind of bio-event played a leading role in each cycle, rather than cycles simply repeating themselves, and this suggests a more complex ocean-climate state than the model for P and S cycles proposed by Jeppsson (1990) and Aldridge *et al.* (1993). Although influenced by several environmental parameters, the bio-events correlate closely to phases of transgression or regression that were generated by the terminal Ordovician and Early Silurian glaciations on Gondwana. The effects of Llandovery glaciations on conodont faunas should be felt globally. The conodont bio-events and evolutionary cycles recognized herein, based on the shallow-water facies of Anticosti sequence, need to be compared with those from different palaeoenvironments, particularly from deep-water basinal facies. Only when these have been more rigorously/extensively correlated, will it be possible to fully assess the influence of sea-level changes caused largely by glaciations on Llandovery conodont bio-events. The Anticosti Basin may have been an important centre of evolutionary radiation, given that several species have their first appearances in this region and that initial evolutionary lineages can be established for many taxa.

Financial support by a Pan-LITHOPROBE grant (LITHOPROBE Contribution No. 1334) and ongoing support from both the Natural Sciences and Engineering Research Council of Canada (NSERC) and the Earth System Evolution Program of the Canadian Institute for Advanced Research are appreciated. G. S. Nowlan, A. D. McCracken, S. L. Duffield and S. Gardiner provided field assistant support that allowed the development of the conodont database. Advice on stratigraphic sections was generously provided by T. E. Bolton, M. J. Copeland and A. A. Petryk. Permission and support to undertake geological fieldwork on Anticosti Island was given by Ministère des Richesses Naturelles, Québec and the Ministère du Tourisme, de la Chasse et de la Pêche, Québec.

References

ALDRIDGE, R. J. 1972. Llandovery conodonts from the Welsh Borderland. *Bulletin of the British Museum (Natural History) Geology*, **22**, 127–231.

ALDRIDGE, R. J. 1988. Extinction and survival in the Conodonta. *In*: LARWOOD, G. P. (ed.) *Extinction and Survival in the Fossil Record*. Systematics Association Special Volume, **34**, 231–256, Clarendon Press, Oxford.

ALDRIDGE, R. J. & MOHAMED, I. B. 1982. Conodont biostratigraphy of the Early Silurian of the Oslo Region. *In*: WORSLEY, D. (ed.) *IUGS Subcommission on Silurian Stratigraphy, Field Meeting, Oslo Region 1982*. Paleontological Contributions from the University of Oslo, **278**, 109–120.

ALDRIDGE, R. J., JEPPSSON, L. & DORNING, K. J. 1993. Early Silurian oceanic episodes and events. *Journal of the Geological Society, London*, **150**, 501–513.

ARMSTRONG, H. A. 1990. *Conodonts from the Upper Ordovician–Lower Silurian Carbonate Platform of North Greenland*. Bulletin Grønlands Geologiske Undersogelse, **159**, 151 pp.

ARMSTRONG, H. A. 1995. High-resolution biostratigraphy (conodonts and graptolites) of the Upper Ordovician and Lower Silurian – evaluation of the Late Ordovician mass extinction. *Modern Geology*, **20**, 41–68.

ASTINI, R. A. & BÜGGISCH, W. 1993. Aspectos sedimentológicos y paleoambientales de los depósitos de la Formacion Don Braulio, Ordovícico tardío de la Precordillera Argentina. *Revista de la Asociación Geológica Argentina*, **48**, 217–232.

AZMY, K., VEIZER, J., BASSETT, M. G. & COPPER, P. 1998. Oxygen and carbon isotopic composition of Silurian brachiopods: implications for seawater isotopic composition and glaciation. *Geological Society of America Bulletin*, **110**, 1499–1512.

BARNES, C. R. 1986. The faunal extinction event near the Ordovician–Silurian boundary: a climatically induced crisis. *In*: WALLISER, O. H. (ed.) *Global Bioevents*. Lecture Notes in Earth Sciences, **8**, 121–126.

BARNES, C. R. 1988. Stratigraphy and paleontology of the Ordovician–Silurian boundary interval, Anticosti Island, Québec, Canada. *In*: COCKS, L. R. M. & RICKARDS, R. B. (eds) *A Global Analysis of the Ordovician–Silurian Boundary*. Bulletin of the British Museum (Natural History) Geology, **43**, 195–219.

BARNES, C. R. 1989. Lower Silurian chronostratigraphy of Anticosti Island, Quebec. *In*: HOLLAND, C. H. & BASSETT, M. G. (eds) *A Global Standard for the Silurian System*. National Museum of Wales Geological Series, **9**, 101–108.

BARNES, C. R. & BERGSTRÖM, S. M. 1988. Conodont biostratigraphy of the uppermost Ordovician and lowermost Silurian. *In*: COCKS, L. R. M. & RICKARDS, R. B. (eds) *A Global Analysis of the Ordovician–Silurian Boundary*. Bulletin of the British Museum (Natural History) Geology, **43**, 325–343.

BARNES, C. R. & MCCRACKEN, A. D. 1981. Early Silurian chronostratigraphy and a proposed Ordovician–Silurian boundary stratotype, Anticosti Island, Québec. *In*: LESPÉRANCE, P. J. (ed.) *Field Meeting, Anticosti–Gaspé, Québec 1981, 2, Stratigraphy and Paleontology*. Subcommission on Silurian stratigraphy, Ordovician–Silurian Boundary Working Group, Université de Montréal, Montréal, pp. 71–79.

BARNES, C. R., FORTEY, R. A. & WILLIAMS, S. H. 1996. The pattern of global bio-events during the Ordovician Period. *In*: WALLISER, O. H. (ed.) *Global Events and Event Stratigraphy*. Springer-Verlag, pp. 139–172.

BISCHOFF, G. C. O. 1986. *Early and Middle Silurian Conodonts from Midwestern New South Wales*. Courier Forschungsinstitut Senckenberg, **89**, 335 pp.

BRENCHLEY, P. J. 1989. The late Ordovician extinction. *In*: DONOVAN, S. K. (ed.) *Mass Extinction: Processes and Evidence*. Belhaven Press, London, pp. 104–132.

BRENCHLEY, P. J., CARDEN, G. A. ET AL. 2003. High-resolution stable isotope stratigraphy of Upper Ordovician sequences: constraints on the timing of bioevents and environmental changes associated with mass extinction and glaciation. *Bulletin of the Geological Society of America*, **115(1)**, 89–104.

BRENCHLEY, P. J., MARSHALL, J. D. ET AL. 1994. Bathymetric and isotope evidence for a short-lived Late Ordovician glaciation in a greenhouse period. *Geology*, **22**, 295–298.

BÜGGISCH, W. & ASTINI, R. A. 1993. The Late Ordovician ice age: new evidence from the Argentine Precordillera. *In*: FINDLEY, H. R., UNRUG, R., BANKS, M. R. & VEEVERS, J. J. (eds) *Gondwana Eight: Assembly, Evolution and Dispersal*. Balkema, Rotterdam, pp. 439–447.

CAPUTO, M. V. 1998. Ordovician–Silurian glaciations and global sea-level changes. *In*: LANDING, E. & JOHNSON, M. (eds) *Silurian Cycles: Linkages of*

Dynamic Stratigraphy with Atmospheric, Oceanic, and Tectonic Changes. New York State Museum Bulletin, **491**, 15–25.

CAPUTO, M. V. & LIMA, E. C. 1984. Estratigrafia, idade e correlação do Grupo Serra Grande-Bacia do Parnaíba. *Anais 33 Congresso Brasileiro de Geologia (Rio de Janeiro), Sociedade Brasileira de Geologia*, **2**, 740–753.

CARPENTER, J. M. 1988. Choosing among multiple equally parsimonious cladograms. *Cladistics*, **4**, 291–296.

COCKS, L. R. M. 1985. The Ordovician–Silurian boundary. *Episodes*, **8**, 98–100.

COOPER, B. J. 1975. Multielement conodonts from the Brassfield Limestone (Silurian) of Southern Ohio. *Journal of Paleontology*, **49**, 984–1008.

COOPER, B. J. 1977. Toward a familial classification of Silurian conodonts. *Journal of Paleontology*, **51**, 1057–1071.

COPPER, P. & LONG, D. G. F. 1989. Stratigraphic revisions for a key Ordovician/Silurian boundary section, Anticosti Island, Canada. *Newsletters on Stratigraphy*, **21(1)**, 59–73.

COPPER, P. & LONG, D. G. F. 1990. Stratigraphic revision of the Jupiter Formation, Anticosti Island, Canada: a major reference section above the Ordovician–Silurian boundary. *Newsletters on Stratigraphy*, **23**, 11–36.

COPPER, P. & LONG, D. G. F. 1998. Sedimentology and paleontology of the Late Ordovician through Early Silurian shallow water carbonates and reefs of the Anticosti Island, Québec. *Field Trip B8 Guidebook*, Geological Association of Canada (GAC), Mineralogical Association of Canada (MAC), Association des géologues et géophysicien du Québec (APGGQ), International Association of Hydrogeologists (IAH), Canadian Geophysical Union (CGU) Joint Annual Meeting, 1998, Québec, pp. 55–94.

DEWING, K. 1999. *Late Ordovician and Early Silurian Strophomenid Brachiopods of Anticosti Island, Quebec, Canada.* Palaeontographica Canadiana, **17**, 143 pp.

DONOGHUE, P. C. J. 2001. Conodonts meet cladistics: recovering relationships and assessing the completeness of the conodont fossil record. *Palaeontology*, **44(1)**, 65–93.

DUFFIELD, S. L. 1985. Land-derived microfossils from the Jupiter Formation (Upper Llandoverian), Anticosti Island, Quebec. *Journal of Paleontology*, **59**, 1005–1010.

FÅHRAEUS, L. E. & BARNES, C. R. 1981. Conodonts from the Becscie and Gun River formations (Lower Silurian) of Anticosti Island, Québec. *In:* LESPÉRANCE, P. J. (ed.) *Field Meeting, Anticosti-Gaspé, Québec 1981, 2, Stratigraphy and Paleontology.* Subcommission on Silurian stratigraphy, Ordovician–Silurian Boundary Working Group, Université de Montréal, Montréal, 165–172.

FLESSA, K. M. & JABLONSKI, D. 1983. Extinction is here to stay. *Paleobiology*, **9**, 315–321.

GOLDMAN, D., MITCHELL, C. E. & JOY, M. P. 1999. The stratigraphic distribution of graptolites in the classic upper Middle Ordovician Utica Shale of

New York State: an evolutionary succession or a response to relative sea-level change? *Paleobiology*, **25**, 273–294.

GRAHN, Y. 1996. Ordovician and Silurian glaciations in Brazil. Abstract. *In: 1 Simposio Sul Americano do Siluro–Devoniano – Estratigrafia e Paleontologia. Anais di 1 Simpósio Sul Americano do Siluro–Devoniano: Estratigrafia e Paleontologia*, Ponta Grossa, Pr. Gráfica Planeta, pp. 299– 308.

GRAHN, Y. & CAPUTO, M. V. 1992. Early Silurian glaciations in Brazil. *Palaeogeography, Palaeoclimatology, Palaeoecology*, **99**, 9–15.

HAWKINS, J. A., HUGHES, C. E. & SCOTLAND, R. W. 1997. Primary homology assessment, characters and character states. *Cladistics*, **13**, 275–283.

HUTT, J. E. 1974–1975. *The Llandovery graptolites of the English Lake District.* Palaeontographical Society Monographs, Parts **1–2**, 56 pp.

IDRIS, M. B. 1984. Local variations in the distribution of Silurian conodonts of the *Distomodus kentuckyensis* Zone of the Oslo Region, Norway. *Norsk Geologisk Tidsskrift*, **64**(3): 181–191.

JEPPSSON, L. 1988. Towards an oceanic model for Silurian lithologic and faunistic changes. *Courier Forschungsinstitut Senckenberg*, **102**, p. 242.

JEPPSSON, L. 1990. An oceanic model for lithological and faunal changes tested on the Silurian record. *Journal of the Geological Society, London*, **147**, 663–674.

JEPPSSON, L. 1997. The anatomy of the mid-Early Silurian Ireviken Event. *In:* BRETT, C. E. & BAIRD, G. (eds) *Paleontological Event Horizons – Ecological and Evolutionary Implications.* Columbia University Press, pp. 451–492.

JEPPSSON, L. 1998. Silurian oceanic events: summary of general characteristics. *In:* LANDING, E. & JOHNSON, M. (eds) *Silurian Cycles: Linkages of Dynamic Stratigraphy with Atmospheric, Oceanic, and Tectonic Changes.* New York State Museum Bulletin, **491**, 239–257.

JIN, JI-SUO & COPPER, P. 1999. The deep-water brachiopod *Dicoelosia* King, 1850, from the Early Silurian tropical carbonate shelf of Anticosti Island, eastern Canada. *Journal of Paleontology*, **73**, 1042–1055.

JOHNSON, M. E. 1996. Stable cratonic sequences and a standard for Silurian eustasy. *In:* WITZKE, B. J., LUDVIGSON, G. A. & DAY, J. (eds) *Paleozoic Sequence Stratigraphy: Views from the North American Craton.* Geological Society of America Special Papers, **306**, 203–211.

JOWETT, D. M. S. & BARNES, C. R. 1999. Conodont biostratigraphy of the Cape Phillips Formation (Lower Silurian), Cornwalls Island, Canadian Arctic. *American Association of Petroleum Geologists Bulletin*, **83(11)**, 1888–1889.

JOWETT, D. M. S. & BARNES, C. R. 2000. Lower Silurian conodont biostratigraphy: integrating traditional paleontological data. GeoCanada 2000 Geoscience Summit, Abstract on conference CD.

LEATHAM, W. B. 1985. Age of the Haven and Lowermost Laketown Dolomites in the Bear River Range, Utah. *Utah Geological Association Publication*, **14**, 29–38.

LESPÉRANCE, P. J., BARNES, C. R., BERRY, W. B. N., BOUCOT, A. J. & MU, E. 1987. The Ordovician–Silurian boundary stratotype: consequences of its approval by the IUGS. *Lethaia*, **20(3)**, 217–222.

LINDSTRÖM, M. 1959. Conodont from the Crug Limestone (Ordovician, Wales). *Micropaleontology*, **5**, 427–452.

LOYDELL, D. K. 1998. Early Silurian sea-level changes. *Geological Magazine*, **135**, 447–471.

MCCRACKEN, A. D. & BARNES, C. R. 1981. Conodont biostratigraphy and paleoecology of the Ellis Bay Formation, Anticosti Island, Quebec, with special reference to Late Ordovician–Early Silurian chronostratigraphy and the systemic boundary. *Geological Survey of Canada Bulletin*, **329**, 51–134.

MACNIOCALL, C., VAN DER PLUIJM & VAN DER VOO, R. 1997. Ordovician paleogeography and the evolution of the Iapetus ocean. *Geology*, **25**, 159–162.

MADDISON, W. P. & MADDISON, D. R. 1992. *MacCLADE: analysis of phylogeny and character evolution, Version 3.0* (Computer program and manual). Sinauer Associates, Sunderland, Massachusetts.

MÄNNIK, P. 1998. Evolution and taxonomy of Silurian conodont *Pterospathodus*. *Palaeontology*, **41**, 1001–1050.

MÄNNIK, P. & VIIRA, V. 1993. Events in the conodont history during the Silurian in Estonia. *Proceedings of the Estonian Academy of Science*, **42(2)**, 58–69.

MELCHIN, J. M., MCCRACKEN, A. D. & OLIFF, F. J. 1991. The Ordovician–Silurian boundary on Cornwallis Island and Truro Island, Arctic Canada: preliminary data. *Canadian Journal of Earth Sciences*, **28**, 1854–1862.

NOWLAN, G. S. 1981. Late Ordovician–Early Silurian conodont biostratigraphy of the Gaspé Peninsula – a preliminary report. *In*: LESPÉRANCE, P. J. (ed.) *Field Meeting, Anticosti–Gaspé Québec 1981, 2, Stratigraphy and Paleontology*. Subcommission on Silurian stratigraphy, Ordovician–Silurian Boundary Working Group, Université de Montréal, Montréal, pp. 257–291.

NOWLAN, G. S. 1983. Early Silurian conodonts of eastern Canada. *Fossil and Strata*, **15**, 95–110.

NOWLAN, G. S. & BARNES, C. R. 1981. Late Ordovician conodonts from the Vauréal Formation, Anticosti Island, Quebec. *Geological Survey of Canada Bulletin*, **329**, 1–49.

NOWLAN, G. S., MCCRACKEN, A. D. & CHATTERTON, B. D. E. 1988. *Conodonts from Ordovician–Silurian Boundary Strata, Whittaker Formation, Mackenzie Mountains, Northwest Territories*. Geological Survey of Canada Bulletin, **373**, 99 pp.

ORCHARD, M. J. 1980. Upper Ordovician conodonts from England and Wales. *Geologica et Palaeontologica*, **14**, 9–44.

PETRYK, A. A. 1981*a*. Stratigraphy, sedimentology and paleogeography of the Upper Ordovician–Lower Silurian of Anticosti Island, Québec. *In*: LESPÉRANCE, P. J. (ed.) *Field Meeting, Anticosti–Gaspé, Québec 1981, 2, Stratigraphy and Paleontology*. Subcommission on Silurian stratigraphy,

Ordovician–Silurian Boundary Working Group, Université de Montréal, Montréal, pp. 11–39.

PETRYK, A. A. 1981*b*. Upper Ordovician glaciations: effects of eustatic fluctuations on the Anticosti platform succession, Quebec. *In*: LESPÉRANCE, P. J. (ed.) *Field Meeting, Anticosti–Gaspé, Québec 1981, 2, Stratigraphy and Paleontology*. Subcommission on Silurian stratigraphy, Ordovician–Silurian Boundary Working Group, Université de Montréal, Montréal, pp. 81–85.

POLLOCK, C. A., REXROAD, C. B. & NICOLL, R. S. 1970. Lower Silurian conodonts from Northern Michigan and Ontario. *Journal of Paleontology*, **44**, 743–764.

POUSSART, P., WEAVER, A. J. & BARNES, C. R. 1999. Late Ordovician glaciation under high atmospheric CO_2: a coupled model analysis. *Paleoceanography*, **14**, 542–558.

PURNELL, M. A., DONOGHUE, P. C. J. & ALDRIDGE, R. J. 2000. Orientation and anatomical notation in conodonts. *Journal of Paleontology*, **74(1)**, 113–122.

PYLE, L. J. & BARNES, C. R. 2003. Conodonts from a platform-to-basin transect, Lower Ordovician to Lower Silurian, Northeastern British Columbia, Canada. *Journal of Paleontology*, **77(1)**, 146–171.

REXROAD, C. B. 1967. *Stratigraphy and Conodont Paleontology of the Brassfield (Silurian) in the Cincinnati Arch Area*. Indiana Geological Survey Bulletin, **36**, 64 pp.

RHODES, F. T. H. 1953. Some British Lower Palaeozoic conodont faunas. *Philosophical Transactions of the Royal Society, Series B*, **237**, 261–334.

RICKARDS, R. B. 1970. *The Llandovery (Silurian) Graptolites of the Howgill Fells, Northern England*. Palaeontographical Society Monographs, 108 pp.

RIVA, J. & PETRYK, A. A. 1981. Graptolites from the Upper Ordovician and Lower Silurian of Anticosti Island and the position of the Ordovician–Silurian boundary. *In*: LESPÉRANCE, P. J. (ed.) *Field Meeting, Anticosti–Gaspé, Québec 1981, 2, Stratigraphy and Paleontology*. Subcommission on Silurian stratigraphy, Ordovician–Silurian Boundary Working Group, Université de Montréal, Montréal, pp. 159–164.

ROSS, C. A. & ROSS, R. P. 1996. Silurian sea-level fluctuations. *In*: WITZKE, B. J., LUDVIGSON, G. A. & DAY, J. (eds) *Paleozoic Sequence Stratigraphy: Views from the North American Craton*. Geological Society of America Special Papers, **306**, 187–192.

SAGEMAN, B. B., KAUFFMAN, E. G., HARRIES, P. J. & ELDER, W. P. 1997. Cenomanian/Turonian bioevent and ecostratigraphy in the Western Interior Basin: contrasting scales of local, regional, and global events. *In*: BRETT, C. E. & BAIRD, G. C. (eds) *Paleontological Events – Stratigraphic, Ecological and Evolutionary Implications*. Columbia University Press, New York, United States, pp. 520–570.

SAMI, T. & DESROCHERS, A. 1992. Episodic sedimentation on an early Silurian, storm-dominated carbonate ramp, Becscie and Merrimack formations, Anticosti Island, Canada. *Sedimentology*, **39**, 355–381.

SCHOPF, T. J. M. 1966. *Conodonts of the Trenton Group (Ordovician) in New York, Southern Ontario, and Québec.* New York State Museum Bulletin, **405**, 105 pp.

SEPKOSKI, J. J. Jr 1995. The Ordovician radiation: diversification and extinction shown by global genus-level taxonomic data. *In:* COOPER, J. D., DROSER, M. L. & FINNEY, S. C. (eds) *Ordovician Odyssey: Short Papers for the Seventh International Symposium on the Ordovician System.* Pacific Section, SEMP Book, **77**, 393–396.

SERPAGLI, E. 1967. I Conodonti dell'Ordoviciano Superiore (Ashgilliano) delle Alpi Carniche. *Bollettino della Società Paleontologica Italiana*, **6**, 30–111.

SHEEHAN, P. M. 2001. The Late Ordovician mass extinction. *In:* JEANLOZ, R., ALBEE, A. L. & BURKE, K. C. (eds) *Annual Review of Earth and Planetary Sciences*, **29**, 331–364.

SMITH, A. B. 1994. *Systematics and the Fossil Record: Documenting Evolutionary Patterns.* Blackwell Science, Oxford, 223 pp.

STANLEY, S. M. 1979. *Macroevolution: Pattern and Process.* W. H. Freeman, San Francisco, 332 pp.

SWEET, W. C. 1981. Macromorphology of elements and apparatuses. *In:* ROBISON, R. A. (ed.) *Treatise on Invertebrate Paleontology, Part W Miscellanea, Supplement 2: Conodonta.* Geological Society of America and University of Kansas, pp. W5–W20.

SWEET, W. C. 1985. Conodonts: those fascinating little whatzits. *Journal of Paleontology*, **59**, 485–494.

SWEET, W. C. 1988. *The Conodonta: Morphology, Taxonomy, Paleoecology, and Evolutionary History of a Long-extinct Animal Phylum.* Oxford Monographs on Geology and Geophysics, **10**, 212 pp.

SWEET, W. C. 2000. Conodonts and biostratigraphy of Upper Ordovician strata along a shelf to basin transect in central Nevada. *Journal of Paleontology*, **74**, 1148–1160.

SWEET, W. C. & SCHÖNLAUB, H. P. 1975. Conodonts of the Genus *Oulodus* Branson and Mehl, 1933. *Geologica et Palaeontologica*, **9**, 41–59.

SWEET, W. C., ETHINGTON, R. L. & BARNES, C. R. 1971. North American Middle and Upper Ordovician conodont fauna. *In:* SWEET, W. C. & BERGSTRÖM S. M. (eds) *Symposium on Conodont Biostratigraphy.* Geological Society of America Memoirs, **127**, 163–193.

SWOFFORD, D. L. 1993. PAUP: phylogenetic analysis using parsimony, Version 3.1 (computer program and manual). Champaign, Illinois.

TOGHILL, P. 1968. The graptolite assemblages and zones of the Birkhill Shales (Lower Silurian) at Dob's Linn. *Palaeontology*, **11**, 654–668.

UYENO, T. T. 1974. *Conodonts of the Hull Formation, Ottawa Group (Middle Ordovician), of the Ottawa–Hull Area, Ontario and Québec.* Geological Survey of Canada Bulletin, **248**, 31 pp.

UYENO, T. T. & BARNES, C. R. 1983. *Conodonts of the Jupiter and Chicotte formations (Lower Silurian), Anticosti Island, Québec.* Geological Survey of Canada Bulletin, **355**, 49 pp.

VAN STAAL, C. R., DEWEY, J. F., MACNIOCAILL, C. & MCKERROW, W. S. 1998. The Cambrian–Silurian tectonic evolution of the northern Appalachians and British Caledonides: history of a complex, west and southwest Pacific-type segment of Iapetus. *In:* BLUNDEL, D. J. & SCOTT, A. C. (eds) *Lyell: the Past is the Key to the Present.* Geological Society, London, Special Publications, **143**, 199–242.

VEIZER, J., ALA, D. *ET AL.* 1999. $^{87}Sr/^{86}Sr$, $\delta^{13}C$ and $\delta^{18}C$ evolution of Phanerozoic seawater. *Chemical Geology*, **161**, 59–88.

WEBERS, G. F. 1966. The Middle and Upper Ordovician conodont faunas of Minnesota. *Minnesota Geological Survey Special Publication*, **4**, 1–123.

ZALAN, P. V., WOLFF, S., CONCEIÇÃO, J. C. J., VIEIRA, I. S., ASTOLFI, M. A. M., APPI, V. T. & ZANOTTO, O. A. 1987. A divisão tripartite do Siluriano da Bacia do Paraná. *Revista Brasileira de Geociências*, **172**, 242–252.

ZHANG, S. & BARNES, C. R. 2000. *Anticostiodus*, a new multielement conodont genus from the Lower Silurian, Anticosti Island, Québec. *Journal of Paleontology*, **74**, 662–669.

ZHANG, S. & BARNES, C. R. 2002a. A New Llandovery (Early Silurian) Conodont Biozonation and Conodonts from the Becscie, Merrimack and Gun River Formations, Anticosti Island, Québec. Paleontological Society Memoirs, **57** (Journal of Paleontology, **76**, supplement to No. 2), 46 pp.

ZHANG, S. & BARNES, C. R. 2002b. Late Ordovician–Early Silurian (Ashgillian–Llandovery) sea level curve derived from conodont community analysis. Anticosti Island, Québec. *Palaeogeography, Palaeoclimatology, Palaeoecology*, **180(1–3)**, 5–32.

ZHANG, S. & BARNES, C. R. 2002c. Paleoecology of Llandovery conodonts, Anticosti Island, Québec. *Palaeogeography, Palaeoclimatology, Palaeoecology*, **180(1–3)**, 33–55.

ZHANG, S. BARNES, C. R. & POHLER, S. M. L. 2002. Relationship between lithofacies belt and conodont faunas, Gun River Formation (Lower Silurian), Anticosti Island, Québec: a statistical approach. *Canadian Journal of Earth Sciences*, **39**, 1767–1782.

ZHEN, Y. Y., WEBBY, B. D. & BARNES, C. R. 1998. Upper Ordovician conodonts from the Bowan Park succession, central New South Wales, Australia. *Geobios*, **32(1)**, 73–104.

ZIEGLER, A. M., SCOTESE, C. R., MCKERROW, W. S., JOHNSON, M. E. & BAMBACH, R. K. 1979. Paleozoic paleogeography. *Annual Review of Earth and Planetary Sciences*, 7, 473–502.

Conodont sample-population approach to defining the base of the Changhsingian Stage, Lopingian Series, Upper Permian

SHILONG MEI[1], CHARLES M. HENDERSON[1] & CHANGQUN CAO[2]

[1]*Department of Geology and Geophysics, University of Calgary, Calgary, Alberta, Canada T2N 1N4 (e-mail: charles.henderson@ucalgary.ca)*

[2]*Nanjing Institute of Geology and Palaeontology, Nanjing, China 210008*

Abstract: Conodonts have been restudied in order to define the base of the Changhsingian Stage boundary at Meishan, Changxing County, Zhejiang Province, China. The Changhsingian represents the second and last stage of the Upper Permian, which is also known as the Lopingian Series. A sample-population based taxonomic approach has been used and described. This approach usually views the entire collection within a given sample as a population and recognizes the most consistent and stable characters within that 'sample-population' for identification. Three related conodont species, *Clarkina longicuspidata* Mei & Wardlaw *in* Mei *et al.* 1994, *C. wangi* (Zhang 1987) and *C. subcarinata* (Sweet *in* Teichert *et al.* 1973) have been redefined and redescribed using this new approach that recognizes carinal development as an apomorphic character for these taxa. A consistent change in denticulation has been observed between *Clarkina longicuspidata* and *Clarkina wangi* wherein *C. longicuspidata* has a prominent gap in front of the cusp, whereas *C. wangi* has a 'wall'-like carina. The carinal change may have resulted from a heterochronic process involving acceleration, since juvenile descendants exhibit features of ancestral adults; the change may be related to the evolution of other biota that may represent potential food sources for the conodont animal, given the apparent importance of the conodont carina for food processing. It is suggested that the base of the Changhsingian Stage could be defined within the *C. longicuspidata*–*C. wangi* lineage, based on the newly refined taxonomy. This boundary occurs close to the flooding surface that represents at least the second parasequence within the Changxing Limestone. The proposed boundary is close to, but not identical with, the traditionally defined boundary.

The base of the Changhsingian Stage was studied extensively by Zhao *et al.* (1981) and Wang & Wang (1981*a*), but formal recognition of this stage boundary has not yet been presented to the International Union of Geological Sciences for ratification. The Changhsingian represents the second and last stage of the Upper Permian, which is also known as the Lopingian Series. Zhao *et al.* (1981) documented changes in different fossil groups around this boundary. They formally recommended that the base of the Changhsingian Stage be defined as the horizon between the *Clarkina orientalis* Zone and the *C. subcarinata* Zone that is located at the base of bed 2 (*sensu* Zhao *et al.* 1981), which is the base of the Changxing Limestone in section D at Meishan, Changxing County, Zhejiang Province, China (Fig. 1). The Changhsingian Stage (historic name and spelling; see Jin *et al.* 1997) is named for the succession in the Changxing County (latter spelling is modern Pinyin transliteration; both pronounced Chang-

sing). This section is also the Global Stratotype Section and Point (GSSP) for the Permian–Triassic boundary. The boundary defined by Zhao *et al.* (1981) has been widely used since it was defined, as it reflects the well-defined faunal changes in major fossil groups such as conodonts, brachiopods, ammonoids, corals and fusulinaceans (Zhao *et al.* 1981). These faunal changes may, however, be accentuated by the presence of a significant unconformity at, or just below, the base of the Changxing Limestone. Proximity to this unconformity has led others to look for a suitable boundary a little higher in the section. Wardlaw & Mei (2000) suggested that the First Appearance Datum (FAD) of *C. subcarinata sensu stricto* would be a suitable boundary at 13.71 m above the base of the Changxing Limestone at Section D, based on a significant change in the denticulation of gondolellid conodonts. Later, Mei & Henderson (2001) suggested that the base of the Changhsingian Stage could be defined within the *C.*

From: BEAUDOIN, A.B. & HEAD, M.J. (eds) 2004. *The Palynology and Micropalaeontology of Boundaries.* Geological Society, London, Special Publications, **230**, 105–121. 0305-8719/04/$15 © The Geological Society of London 2004.

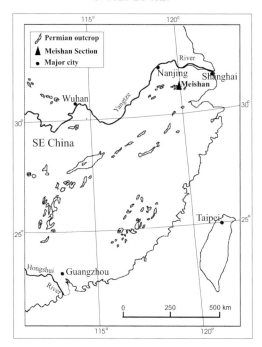

Fig. 1. Location map for the Meishan locality near Changxing, Zhejiang in SE China. The exact location of Meishan section D depicted in Figure 2 is 31° 4′ 55″ N and 119° 42′ 22.9″ E.

longicuspidata–C. wangi lineage in Bed 4 based on revised taxonomic definitions. The latter definition is only about 80 cm higher than the traditional boundary suggested by Zhao *et al.* (1981), providing historical support for this position. The proposed boundary (Fig. 2) is defined by the gradual change within a conodont evolutionary lineage that is recognized by a sample-population approach; this accounts for the considerable variability exhibited by these species. The proposed boundary occurs near the flooding surface in the second parasequence of the Changxing Limestone, and is therefore a more suitable position with respect to continuity of deposition. This paper presents the detailed definition of this boundary, highlights the conodont taxonomy necessary for this definition, and demonstrates that the refined taxonomy is based on a sample-population approach.

Material

Zhao *et al.* (1981), Yin *et al.* (1996) and Zhang *et al.* (1997) described the Meishan section in detail. The bed numbering system used by Yin *et al.* (1996) is followed here, with slight modification of the measured thickness of related beds. Conodont samples were collected continuously from the boundary interval

between the Longtan Formation and the Changxing Limestone in section D at Meishan, Zhejiang, China (Fig. 2). This interval includes beds 1, 2, 3, 4a, 4b and 5 of Yin *et al.* (1996). The boundary between beds 1 and 2 is the boundary between the underlying Longtan Formation and the overlying Changxing Limestone.

Abundant conodonts have been recovered from beds 2 to 5. They are exclusively dominated by species of *Clarkina,* but also include species of rare *Sweetina* and *Hindeodus* as well as *Iranognathus tarazi*. Samples from Bed 1 are barren of conodonts. In addition, conodonts from sample Mc-10 of Mei *et al.* (1998) and sample 69SA-10M of Teichert *et al.* (1973) are illustrated herein for comparison. Sample Mc-10 is from the middle of bed 8 of Sheng *et al.* (1984), which probably corresponds with the middle of Bed 11 of Yin *et al.* (1996). The holotype of *Clarkina subcarinata* is from sample 69SA-10M at Locality 1 in Julfa, NW Iran *sensu* Teichert *et al.* (1973).

Stratigraphy and sequence stratigraphy

Regionally, the Longtan Formation is a coal-bearing, marginal-marine unit (Wu & He 1999) in which the top represents the maximum regression during the Wuchiapingian Stage.

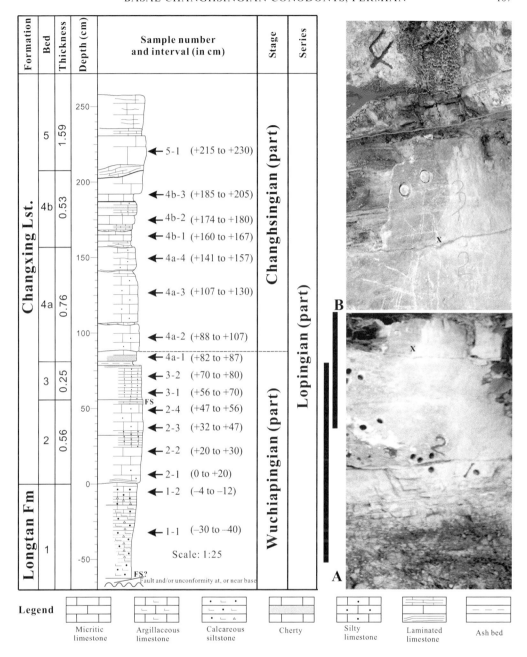

Fig. 2. Stratigraphic column of the lower part of the Meishan D section (Fig. 1), which is the proposed stratotype for a GSSP of the Changhsingian Stage (uppermost stage of the Permian); the boundary position is dashed, since it has not yet been submitted for ratification. Sample numbers and positions are provided. The base of the section is at, or near, a fault and/or unconformity. Two flooding surfaces (FS) define the base of interpreted parasequences. The photos on the right overlap ('x' marks the same point on the two photos and a black vertical bar indicates the position of the lower (A) photo and the upper (B) photo).

Transgressive deposits (fine cherty siliciclastics) of the Talung and the basal Changxing Limestone overlie the Longtan Formation, presum-

ably in an unconformable contact; however, the extent of this unconformity is uncertain. Regionally, the boundary between the Longtan Formation and the Changxing Limestone is regarded as a sequence boundary (Zhang *et al.* 1997). However, in section D at Meishan, this boundary is represented by a smooth transition from calcareous mudstone beds that increase in thickness upward in bed 1 to thick-bedded bioclastic limestone in bed 2. The exposure at the Meishan D section contains only the uppermost part of the Longtan Formation (Fig. 2); the base is either faulted or near the unconformity mentioned above. These beds include earthy yellow, calcareous siltstone and mudstone with horizontal beds of increasing thickness that contain ammonoids and brachiopods (Yin *et al.* 1996). This unit appears to be conformable with the overlying Baoqing Member of the Changxing Limestone and may represent the first transgressive cycle above the unconformity near the top of the Longtan Formation; the unit is not assigned to the Talung Formation because of the lack of chert. The lowest bed (bed 2) of the Changxing Limestone, which is represented by dark grey, thick-bedded silty wackestone, appears to form the upper part of a cycle or parasequence. Bed 3 contains greyish black calcareous mudstone and thin-bedded argillaceous mudstone that may represent the flooding unit of a second parasequence in the section. Beds 4 and 5 include thin- to medium-bedded wackestone and represent the regressive portion of this second parasequence. The speciation event from *C. longicuspidata* to *C. wangi* occurs just above the maximum flooding surface of the second parasequence. Yin *et al.* (1996) and Zhang *et al.* (1997) illustrate numerous high-frequency cycles throughout the Changxing Limestone.

The descriptions and identified fossils from each unit or bed (the bed numbering system does not always conform to the standard definition of a bed and may include more than one depositional bed) are summarized below from Zhao *et al.* (1981) and Yin *et al.* (1996). Bed thickness measurements are slightly modified by us.

Upper Permian (Lopingian) Changxing Limestone

Bed 5 (depth, 210–370 cm). Dark-grey thin- to medium-bedded bioclastic micritic limestone with siliceous banding, with normal graded bedding and small-scale sandy wavy bedding. Non-fusulinacean foraminifera (230–370 cm, ACT 109): *Glomospira* sp.; (290–330 cm, ACT 109): *Frondicularia ovata, Damgarita* sp., *Nodosaria krotovi* (250–290 cm, ACT 108):

Geinitzina uralica, Globivalvulina distensa, Nodosarina longissima, Damgarita sp., *Pseudonodosarlina* sp. (210–250 cm, ACT 107): *Damgarita* sp., *Frondicularia* sp., *Geinitzina splandli;* fish (210–370 cm): Palaeomiscoidei gen. *et* sp. indet., *Sinohelicoprion changxingensis* Liu & Chang, *Sinoplatysomus meishanensis* Wei; ostracodes (210–370 cm): *Bairdiacypris fornicata* Shi, *Bairdia wrodeloformis* Chen, *Basslerella firma* Kellett, *Eumiraculum changxingensis* Chen, *Petasobairdia bicornuta* Chen, *Silenmites sockakwaformis* Shi.

Bed 4b (depth, 158–211 cm). Grey, thin- to medium-bedded bioclastic micritic limestone, intercalated with light-grey thin-bedded calcareous mudrock in the upper part, with slightly wavy bedding. Non-fusulinacean foraminifera (158–211 cm, ACT 106): *Geinitzina splandli, Pseudoglandulina conicula;* fusulinaceans (158–211 cm): *Palaeofusulina minima* Sheng & Chang; fish (158–211 cm): Amblypteridae? Coelacanthidae gen. *et* sp. indet., Palaeoniscoidei gen. *et* sp. indet., *Sinonelicoprion changxingensis* Liu & Chang, *Sinoptatysomusg meishanensis* Wei; ostracodes (158–211 cm): *Basslerella obesa* Kellett, *Petasobairdia bicornuta* Chen.

Bed 4a (depth, 82–158 cm). Grey thick-bedded bioclastic micritic limestone. Fusulinaceans (85–125 cm, ACT 104): *Palaeofusulina minima, Reichelina pulchra;* non-fusulinacean foraminifera (125–158 cm, ACT 105): *Frondicularia palmate, Geinitzina splandli, Globivalvulina* sp., *Nodosaria longissma* (85–125 cm, ACT 104): *Nodosaria delicata, Damgarita* sp.; brachiopods (85–158 cm) *Cathaysia chonetoides* (Chao), *C. parvalia* Chang.

Bed 3 (depth, 56–82 cm). Greyish yellow illite–montmorillonite clay, U–Pb age: 257 Ma (Mundil *et al.* 2001) (56–82 cm) Greyish black silty and calcareous mudrock intercalating argillaceous mudrock, with horizontal bedding.

Bed 2 (depth, 0–56 cm). Dark-grey thick-bedded silt-bearing micritic limestone. Non-fusulinacean foraminifera (0–55 cm, ACT 103): *Collaniella* sp., *Eacristellaria* sp., *Geinitzina postcarbonica* Spandel, *Pseudoglandulina conica.*

–Conformable contact–

Upper Permian (Lopingian) Longtan Formation

Bed 1 (depth of upper part, 0 to −30 cm). Dark, dolomitized calcirudite with fragments of limestone, siltstone and phosphate. Non-fusulinacean foraminifera (0 to −30 cm, ACT 102): *Geinitzina uralica, Hemigardius* sp., brachiopods (0 to −30 cm, ACT 102): *Orbiculoidea* sp., *Cathaysia chonetoides* (Chao), *Paryphella gouwaensis* Liao, *Spinomarginifera* sp.

Bed 1 (depth of lower part, −30 to −70 cm). Dark, medium-bedded calcareous siltstone with horizontal beddings. The corresponding bed in Section C contains ammonoids (ACT 32): Araxoceratidae gen. et sp. indet., *Pseudogastrioceras* sp.; bivalves: *Palaeoneilo sunanensis* Liu, *P.* cf. *leiyangensis* Liu, *Pernopecten* sp., *Schizodus* cf. *dubiiformis* Waagen; brachiopods (ACT 32): *Anidanthus* cf. *sinosus* (Huang), *Acosarina* sp., *Cathaysia chonetoides* (Chao), *Crurithyris* sp., *Neowellerella* sp., *Orbiculoidea minuta* Liao, *Orthotichia* sp., *Paryphella gouwaensis* Liao, *Spinomarginifera lopingensis* (Kayser), *Streptorhynchus* sp.

The taxonomic changes used to define a potential Changhsingian Stage base occur in the lower part of bed 4 just above a flooding surface defining a second parasequence in the Changxing Limestone.

Discussion

The configuration of the denticles of the Pa element of *Clarkina* species (Fig. 3) is the most stable characteristic within the sample-populations of this study, and can be used to define the Wuchiapingian–Changhsingian boundary. The evolution of the denticulation around the boundary between the Longtan Formation and the Changxing Limestone in the D section can be characterized in adult specimens. Lambert (1994) discussed a methodology for using size as a proxy of relative maturity, by using the relationship of number of denticles to carina length in neogondolellid platform elements. Small, juvenile forms generally show more discrete denticles than large, adult forms, and are similar throughout the Changxing Limestone. Very large, gerontic forms display excessive fusion and commonly pathological, bizarre characters. In the basal part of the Changxing Limestone, a distinctive change in the configuration of the denticles of *Clarkina* Pa elements

has been observed around the base of bed 4. The carina in adult Pa elements of *Clarkina* species from bed 2 and bed 3 has a proclined and recurved cusp that appears erect and is as high as or a little higher than the penultimate denticle (Fig. 3). The slope of the cusp is gentle, low and usually one and a half to twice as long as the height of the cusp. The cusp joins the penultimate posterior denticle by a ridge that gently slopes down from the cusp and forms the lowest and narrowest part of the carina, just posterior to the penultimate posterior denticle, which is usually considerably reduced and fused; the connecting ridge forms a wide concave arc in lateral view (Fig. 4a–o, Fig. 5a–h, Fig. 6a–n). This denticulation cannot be differentiated from that of *Clarkina longicuspidata* (Mei *et al.* 1994). As a result, *C. longicuspidata* is used herein as a species defined by a sample-population concept to include morphotypes with various platform outlines, but the same denticulation as mentioned above. The denticulation in adult Pa elements of *Clarkina* from Bed 4 to Bed 9 (*sensu* Yin *et al.* 1996) has posterior denticles that are not reduced and a cusp that connects the carina with a high ridge with no clear separation from the highly fused remaining carina (Fig. 7a–k). As a result, the carina in lateral view remains about the same height toward the end of the platform and commonly looks like a high 'wall'. We apply the name *Clarkina wangi* to specimens from this interval bearing this type of denticulation. *Clarkina subcarinata sensu stricto* has a similar denticulation to *C. wangi*, but the posterior denticles are usually moderately reduced in height and partially discrete (Fig. 8a–m).

While it is true that the smallest juveniles of *Clarkina* species appear to be very similar, we can get some hint of the evolutionary process by looking at juveniles of *C. longicuspidata* and *C. wangi*. Juveniles of *C. longicuspidata* (Figs 4a–d, 6a–d) have relatively discrete denticles compared to the increasingly fused denticles of intermediate (Figs 5e–f, 6i–j) and larger mature forms (Figs 5g–h, 6n). In contrast, denticles of juveniles of *C. wangi* (Fig. 7b, e, f & h) are already partially fused, and in adults this fusion is completed by closing of the anterior gap adjacent to the cusp, forming a high wall-like carina. This would imply a heterochronic process involving acceleration of development (Gould 1977) or recapitulation. In contrast, Henderson *et al.* (2002) demonstrated that the presence of discrete denticles, typical of juveniles of *Jinogondolella granti*, in adults of the descendant *Clarkina postbitteri* may result from paedomorphosis. It is noteworthy that the latter process occurred at a major sequence boundary

(Guadalupian–Lopingian Series boundary) involving the evolution of a new gondolellid genus *Clarkina*, defined by the lack of serration and change in platform outline. In contrast, the subject of this paper involves a small evolutionary event within an anagenetic series of *Clarkina* species occurring near a relatively minor flooding surface. This suggests that evolution involving these taxa may be influenced by the same environmental factors that influence

sequence stratigraphy, and that the scale of the effects is similar.

Our species concept interprets platform outline as a plesiomorphic character because pointed, rounded and squared platforms are seen in all *Clarkina* taxa; all platform shapes are represented in all collections over the interval studied herein. Platform outline is therefore not suitable for phylogenetic analysis. Our phylogenetic species concept (Wheeler & Platnick 2000)

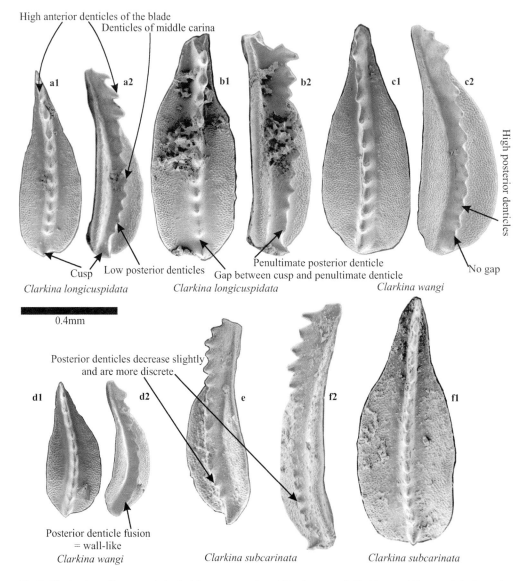

Fig. 3. Illustration of key morphological features on selected Pa elements of *Clarkina* spp. Figures a1 & a2 are the same as Figure 4m1 & m2. Figures b1 & b2 are the same as Figure 6l1 & l2. Figures c1 & c2 are the same as Fig. 7j1 & j2. Figures d1 & d2 are the same as Figure 7h1 & h2. Figure e is the same as Figure 8e. Figures f1 and f2 are the same as Figure 8mi & m2. Scale bar is 0.4 mm.

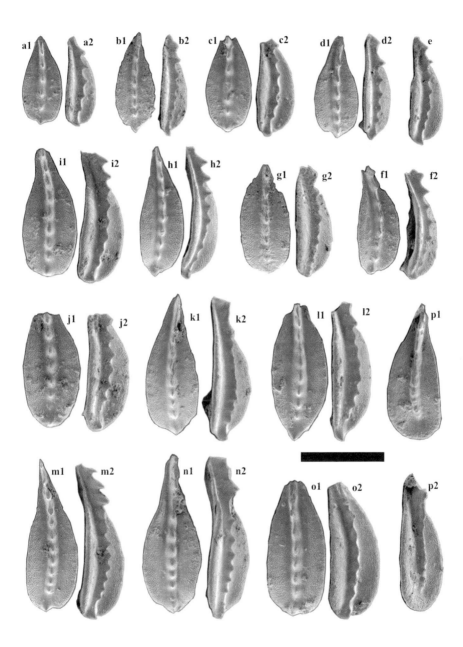

Fig. 4. All specimens are Pa elements; scale bar is 0.4 mm. Specimens illustrated are from the Meishan Section, Changxing, Zhejiang, China. The upper view and oblique view are denoted respectively by 1 and 2 after the letter. (**a–o**) *Clarkina longicuspidata* Mei & Wardlaw *in* Mei *et al.* 1994. Pa elements showing ontogeny and different morphologies of the posterior end. See Fig. 5a–e & g for bigger specimens. From samples 2-3. (**p**) *Clarkina orientalis* (Barskov & Koroleva 1970). From sample 2-3.

Fig. 5. All specimens are Pa elements, scale bar is 0.4 mm. Specimens illustrated are from the Meishan Section, Changxing, Zhejiang, China. The upper view and oblique view are denoted respectively by 1 and 2 after the letter. (**a–e & g**). *Clarkina longicuspidata* Mei & Wardlaw *in* Mei *et al.* (1994) Pa elements showing different morphologies of the posterior end. See Fig. 4a–o for smaller specimens. From sample 2-3. (**f & h**). *Clarkina longicuspidata* Mei & Wardlaw in Mei *et al.* (1994). Pa elements showing a small and a large specimen. From sample 2-4.

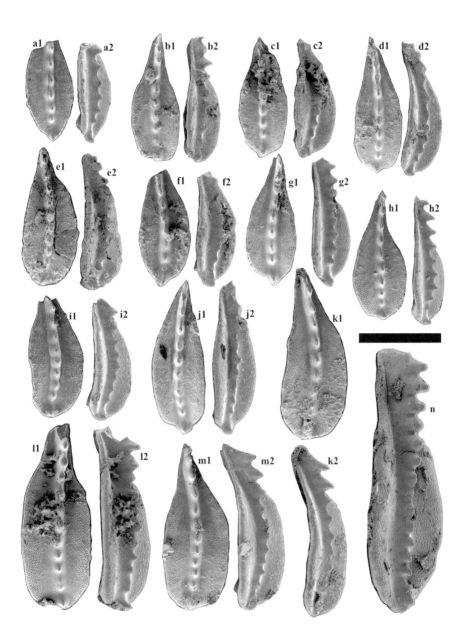

Fig. 6. All specimens are Pa elements; scale bar is 0.4 mm. Specimens illustrated are from the Meishan Section, Changxing, Zhejiang, China. The upper view and oblique view are denoted respectively by 1 and 2 after the number. (**a–e**) *Clarkina longicuspidata* Mei & Wardlaw in Mei *et al.* 1994. Pa elements showing small specimens and different morphologies of the posterior end. From sample 3-1. (**f–n**) *Clarkina longicuspidata* Mei & Wardlaw *in* Mei *et al.* 1994. Pa elements showing ontogeny and different morphologies of the posterior end. From sample 3-2.

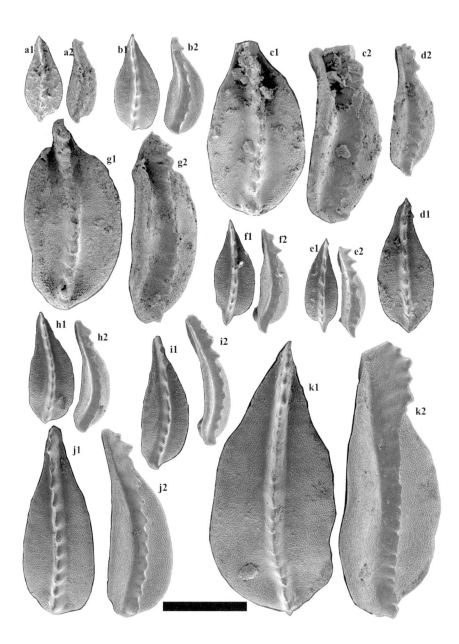

Fig. 7. All specimens are Pa elements; scale bar is 0.4 mm. Specimens illustrated are from the Meishan Section, Changxing, Zhejiang, China. Upper views and oblique views are denoted respectively by 1 and 2 after the letter. (**a–c**). *Clarkina wangi* (Zhang 1987). Pa elements showing ontogeny. From sample 4a-2. (**d & g**) *Clarkina wangi* (Zhang 1987). Pa elements showing a small and a big specimen. From sample 4a-3. (**e, f & h–k**) *Clarkina wangi* (Zhang 1987). Pa elements showing ontogeny and different morphologies. From the sample at the base of Bed 5.

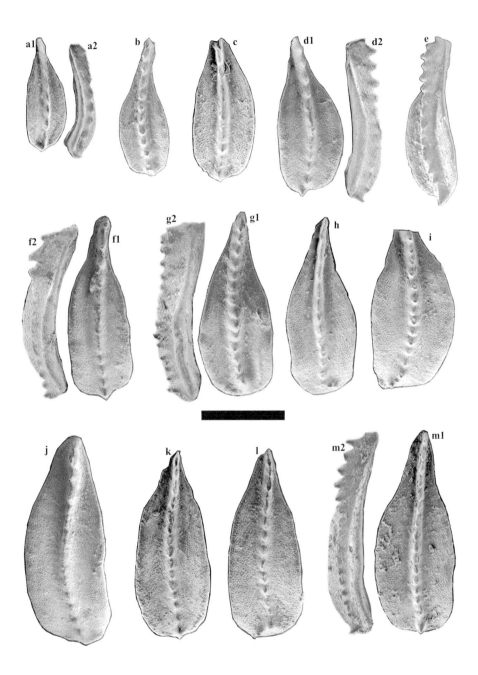

Fig. 8. All specimens are Pa elements; scale bar is 0.4 mm. Specimens illustrated as **a, c, h, k & m** are from the Meishan section, Changxing, Zhejiang, China, and those as **b, d–g, i, j & l** are from the section at Locality 1 in Julfa, NW Iran, *sensu* Teichert *et al.* (1973). The upper view and oblique view are denoted respectively by 1 and 2 after the letter. (**a–m**) *Clarkina subcarinata* (Sweet *in* Teichert *et al.* 1973). Pa elements showing ontogeny. **a, c, h, k & m** are from the sample Mc-10 of Mei *et al.* (1998) at the Meishan section, Changxing, Zhejiang, China; **b, d–g, i, j & l** are from Sweet's collection and from the sample 69SA-10M of Teichert *et al.* (1973) at the section at Locality 1 in Julfa, NW Iran.

recognizes the carinal configuration as an important apomorphic character and completely encompasses the holotype and topotypes of *Clarkina subcarinata* (Sweet *in* Teichert *et al.* 1973), *C. longicuspidata* and *C. wangi*. These species are based on unique patterns of shared characters within populations with emphasis on the carinal configuration. *Clarkina orientalis* (Fig. 4p), the most easily identifiable *Clarkina* species for the Lopingian, ranges from bed 2 to bed 4. Its distinct denticulation may suggest that it belongs to a different lineage. The transition from the denticulation of *Clarkina longicuspidata* to that of *C. wangi* occurs in a very short interval (about 20 cm within the basal part of bed 4) and thus allows us to distinguish these two species fairly consistently. The sample from the lower part of bed 4 yielded abundant adult forms with a high, wall-like carina, and the sample from the top of bed 3 (*sensu* Yin *et al.* 1996) yielded abundant adult specimens with a typical denticulation of *Clarkina longicuspidata*. Rare specimens from the top of bed 3 and basal part of bed 4 have a penultimate denticle that is only slightly reduced, and are therefore similar to that of *Clarkina wangi*. Rare morphotypes within sample-populations that resemble closely related taxa are not recognized as separate taxa unless a distinct growth series can be demonstrated. The first occurrence of *Clarkina wangi* is somewhere within the basal part of bed 4. However, conodonts recovered from the basal part of bed 4 (Sample 4a–1) are not common and are therefore not adequate for examining population variation. As a result, larger samples around this interval are necessary to determine a precise speciation point. We suggest that the base of the Changhsingian be defined by the FAD of *Clarkina wangi* in section D at Meishan, Changxing County, China, because it is close to the traditional boundary defined by Zhao *et al.* (1981), it is recognized by a distinct change in conodont carinal configuration, and it occurs in beds of continuous deposition at least one parasequence above an unconformity.

Our population approach might imply that differences occur by gradually increasing the proportion of new characters over an extended interval, but in fact, the changes appear to occur over a relatively narrow interval, which is why we can recognize this boundary with a reasonable degree of consistency.

Donoghue & Purnell (1999) have demonstrated mammal-like occlusion in ozarkodinid conodonts that may provide a palaeobiological basis for relating the evolution of morphological variation used in biostratigraphic analyses. Ozarkodinid Pa elements as in *Streptognathodus* (their *Idiognathodus sensu lato*) have a long anterior blade that constrains element motion to the transverse plane and maximizes food-processing efficiency. The high anterior (ventral in Purnell *et al.* 2000) blade in the ozarkodinid genus *Clarkina* may have served a similar function. The importance of the carinal shape in these taxa may be related to the parallel evolution of taxa representing potential food sources or to the availability of food sources along some environmental gradient. It is possible that the minor variation recognized herein at the specific level may be related to ecological factors. This hypothesis is testable by examining correlative intervals in other sections, from basin to margin, and in other geographical regions. The cosmopolitan nature of many of these taxa appears to suggest that the variations reflect true evolutionary change.

Taxonomy

The genus *Clarkina* was referred to as a prioniodinid by Sweet (1988), based on the presence of digyrate elements in both P-positions, but this is true only if the segminiplanate Pa elements like those illustrated in this paper are part of an unimembrate apparatus that is distinct from the elements attributed to the genus *Xaniognathus*. Orchard & Rieber (1999) classify *Neogondolella* as an Upper Permian through Middle Triassic ozarkodinid genus. They indicated that natural assemblages clearly show that the P-positions are not occupied by digyrate elements and that the apparatus plan is typical of the Ozarkodinida. We recognize Late Permian gondolellids as belonging to the genus *Clarkina* on the basis of the distinctive Pa-element with its abrupt anterior narrowing; the rest of the apparatus plan is characteristic of suprageneric classification.

The Pa elements of Permian gondolellids are not highly diversified in morphology and therefore are difficult to classify. Rare individuals within a population of a particular species may exhibit one or several characteristics that are thought to be diagnostic of different species (Wardlaw & Collinson 1979). The analysis of large numbers of individuals is necessary to understand the ontogeny and intra-specific variation of these taxa. We have found that to effectively differentiate among Permian gondolellid species and maximize their value for stratigraphic correlation, it is necessary to examine the entire sample-population and choose the most consistent and stable character within this sample-population for identification. In many cases, the most consistent and reliable character for Permian gondolellids is the general configuration of the denticles, which can be used to define a natural sample-population or an apparatus species (Orchard *et al.* 1994; Mei 1996; Mei *et al.* 1998; Henderson 2001). In some cases, the overall configuration of the anterior, middle and posterior platform of Pa elements is stable and thus useful for identification of a sample-population (Mei & Henderson 2001). In the past, platform outline was emphasized and this taxonomic practice has resulted in many form species with long stratigraphic ranges.

We recognize that the denticulation configuration of the Pa element of *Clarkina* is the most stable characteristic within sample-populations of *Clarkina* species near the Wuchiapingian–Changhsingian boundary, whereas the platform outline is highly variable within sample-populations. As Mei *et al.* (1998) demonstrated, conodont morphotypes with the same platform outline occur throughout the Upper Wuchiapingian and the entire Changhsingian stages, whereas the denticulation configuration changes throughout the succession. In an attempt to consolidate the disparate morphological form taxa that have been previously identified as species, Mei *et al.* (1998) recognized several assemblage zones within the Changxing Limestone, based on the change in denticulation pattern and noting four 'shape classes' or morphotypes in each zone. The shapes were round-, square-, narrow- and transitional morphotypes (transitional among square, narrow and round). Typically, the names applied to these morphotypes include '*C. deflecta*' for the square-morphotype, '*C. changxingensis*' for the round-morphotype, '*C. wangi*' for the narrow-morphotype, and '*C. subcarinata*' for the transitional morphotype. All four morphotypes occur in every sample throughout the entire Changxing Limestone, and clearly do not serve as valid species identifiers. Based on the study of many topotypes for each morphospecies and our abundant new material from the Changxing Limestone, we suggest that species of *Clarkina* be redefined on the clear evolutionary progression of denticulation pattern in the Pa elements; this would provide a powerful boundary definition, rather than platform outline morphologies that provide little variation throughout the Changxing Limestone. As a result, a taxonomic approach that emphasizes consistent characters in a sample-population, including denticulation and configuration of platform, has been adopted for Permian gondolellids (Henderson *et al.* 2002); for the interval of interest, carinal denticulation is considered as an apomorphic character and is therefore emphasized. The

difference between this sample-population taxonomic approach and the conventional platform outline form-taxa approach was demonstrated by Henderson (2001, pp. 127–129) using Guadalupian–Lopingian boundary conodonts illustrated by Wang (2000). The sample-population taxonomic approach emphasizes the need to document the total sample-population variation, including ontogenetic variation, by illustrating numerous specimens in order to facilitate understanding of verbal descriptions that are often limited by the complexity of describing the total variation within any sample-population.

Purnell *et al.* (2000) have introduced new orientations and elemental notations in light of palaeobiological considerations of the conodont apparatus. In this scheme, the anterior blade of the P_1 element (or Pa) would be ventral and the posterior platform dorsal. The inner side of the platform would be caudal or posterior and the outer side rostral or anterior. The upper surface view would be oral or adaxial and the lower surface view would be aboral or abaxial. While this orientation terminology may reflect true biological orientation, we have chosen to continue to use the conventional terms to facilitate comparison with previous descriptions.

Systematics

Phylum **Chordata** Bateson 1886

Class **Conodonta** Eichenberg 1930

Subclass **Conodonti** Branson 1938

Order **Ozarkodinida** Dzik 1976

Superfamily **Gondolellacea** Lindstrom 1970

Family **Gondolellidae** Lindstrom 1970

Genus *Clarkina* Kozur 1989

Clarkina longicuspidata Mei & Wardlaw *in* Mei *et al.* 1994
Figs 3a–b, 4a–o, 5a–h, 6a–n

Clarkina longicuspidata Mei & Wardlaw *in* Mei *et al.* 1994, p. 136, pl. II, figs 7–9.

Original diagnosis: A species of *Clarkina* characterized by a Pa element with a square to bluntly rounded posterior termination to the platform which is widest near the middle part, a terminally located long and large proclined cusp, a marked gap between the cusp and the posteriormost denticle, denticles increasing in height anteriorly except for distal few, with the widest one near the anterior narrowing of platform, well-developed smooth furrows, upturned lateral margins and a smoothly abrupt anterior narrowing of the platform (Mei *et al.* 1994, p. 136).

Emended diagnosis: A species of *Clarkina* with a denticulation in adult Pa elements that has a more or less erect cusp that is as high as or a little bit higher than the posteriormost denticle. The slope of the cusp is gentle, low and usually 1.5 to 2 times as long as the height of the cusp. The cusp joins the penultimate posterior denticle by a ridge that gently slopes down from the cusp and forms the lowest and narrowest part of the carina, just posterior to the penultimate posterior denticle, which is usually considerably reduced and fused; the connecting ridge forms a wide concave arc in lateral view. This wide gap becomes less prominent in larger gerontic specimens and in stratigraphically younger specimens. The platform is usually elongate, usually widest around the middle and tapering toward the anterior. The posterior platform termination ranges from narrowly pointed to rounded and squared.

Holotype: The specimen illustrated on pl. II, fig. 7 (Mei & Wardlaw *in* Mei *et al.*, 1994) with the depository number of NIGP121717. This specimen is from Sample QT-67 in the upper Wuchiaping Formation at Nanjiang Section, Sichuan, South China.

Remarks: This species is differentiated from *Clarkina subcarinata* (Figs 3e–f, 8a–m) by its prominent gap anterior to the cusp. However, this wide posterior carinal gap becomes considerably reduced in larger gerontic specimens (Figs 5g & h) and in stratigraphically younger specimens. *Clarkina wangi* differs from this species by lacking a gap between the cusp and the posterior denticles.

Occurrence: Late Wuchiapingian, South China.

Clarkina subcarinata (Sweet *in* Teichert *et al.* 1973)

Figs 3e–f, 8a–m

Neogondolella carinata subcarinata Sweet *in* Teichert *et al.* 1973, p. 437, pl. 13, figs 12–17; fig. 16E–H.
Neogondolella subcarinata subcarinata (Sweet *in* Teichert *et al.* 1973). Wang & Wang *in* Zhao *et al.* 1981, pl. V, figs 1–5, 8, 9, 15 & 16.
Neogondolella subcarinata (Sweet *in* Teichert *et al.* 1973). Orchard *et al.* 1994 (in part as morphotype 2), p. 835, pl. 1, figs 3, 4 & 9.

Neogondolella subcarinata (Sweet *in* Teichert *et al.* 1973). Tian 1993, figs 6–8.
Clarkina subcarinata (Sweet *in* Teichert *et al.* 1973). Mei *et al.* 1998, pl. II, fig. K.
Clarkina wangi (*auct. non* Zhang, 1987). Mei *et al.* 1998, pl. III, fig. J.

Original diagnosis: A subspecies of *Neogondolella carinata* (Clark) with elements distinguished from those of the typical subspecies by a somewhat broader platform; a shorter, wider keel; and a less distinctly set-off buttress beneath the posterior platform brim (Sweet *in* Teichert *et al.* 1973, p. 436).

Emended diagnosis: A species of *Clarkina* with denticulation in adult Pa elements similar to *C. wangi*; however, the posterior denticles are partially discrete and usually moderately reduced in height.

Syntypes: The specimens illustrated by Sweet (*in* Teichert *et al.* 1973, pl. 13, figs 12–17). They are from Sample 69SA-10M at the section of Locality 1 in Julfa, NW Iran (Teichert *et al.* 1973). Sweet illustrated, using light photography, the upper and lower surfaces of three specimens in growth series as syntypes, presumably in an attempt to illustrate multiple specimens as a population subset. We empathize with this approach, but feel that it is still better to designate a single specimen as a holotype.

Holotype: We designate the adult specimen from Sweet *in* Teichert *et al.* 1973 (pl. 13, figs 12 & 13) as a lectotype and provide SEM photos of topotype material in Figs 8a–m.

Remarks: We found that denticulation is the most reliable character for differentiating this species from related species, as illustrated diagrammatically by Sweet (*in* Teichert *et al.* 1973, text-fig. 16); other features such as the platform outline are not as useful. *Clarkina carinata* (Clark 1959) differs from *Clarkina subcarinata* by having a much more prominent cusp and a carina in which the posterior denticles are not reduced, but often increase in size posteriorly. Sweet (1973) discussed the stratigraphic ranges of these taxa in various sections around the world. *Clarkina wangi* differs from this species by having posterior denticles that are usually mostly fused and are of the same height. It is possible that the minor differences between *Clarkina subcarinata* and *Clarkina wangi* are due to an ecological response, as opposed to a stratigraphic evolutionary change. Our current interpretation is that these differences represent stratigraphic evolutionary change, since *Clarkina subcarinata* succeeds *Clarkina wangi* over an interval at the Meishan section that demonstrates very little apparent ecological change.

Clarkina wangi (Zhang 1987)
Figs 3c–d, 7a–k

Neogondolella subcarinata elongata Wang & Wang 1981*a*, p. 118, pl. II, figs 1–4.
Neogondolella subcarinata elongata Wang & Wang 1981*b*, pl. 1, figs 21 & 25.
Neogondolella subcarinata elongata Wang *in* Zhao *et al.* 1981, p. 80, pl. VI, figs 1–5.
Gondolella wangi Zhang 1987, pl. 1, fig. 4.
Not *Neogondolella wangi* Dai & Zhang 1989, p. 234, pl. 49, figs 19–22.
Neogondolella wangi Dai, Tian & Zhang *in* Tian 1993, pl. 4, figs 23a & 23b.
Clarkina wangi (Zhang). Mei *et al.* 1998, p. 225, pl. III, fig. K.
Clarkina subcarinata (*auct. non* Sweet *in* Teichert *et al.* 1973). Mei *et al.* 1998, pl. I, fig. E, pl. II, fig. I.
Clarkina prechangxingensis Mei *et al.* 1998, pl.1, fig. I.
Clarkina predeflecta Mei *et al.* 1998, pl. II, figs E, J, pl. III, fig. C.

Original diagnosis: Unit wide, widest around the middle of the unit, tapering considerably both anteriorly and posteriorly, usually no free blade. The posterior end of the unit extends posteriorly and is sharp, with a prominent and reclined cusp. The anterior blade is a little higher than the rest of the carina, and decreases in height toward the posterior. The attachment surface on the lower surface is wide. Unit is prominently arched in the middle (translated from Chinese in Wang &Wang 1981*a*).

Original English diagnosis: A subspecies of *Neogondolella subcarinata* characterized by an elongated and posteriorly inclined cusp and by a wide platform that abruptly narrows anteriorly (Wang & Wang 1981*b*, p. 231).

Original description: Platform wide, arched, and slightly curved laterally, its greatest width near middle or mid-posterior. Cusp commonly projects beyond posterior platform, forming a posterior separate wedge, commonly forming part of margin of platform. Denticles on carina partly fused: increasing in size and spacing anteriorly. Platform abruptly tapering at posterior end and at anterior one-third to one-fourth of unit. Free blade not well developed. Lower attachment surface wide and having a pit, surrounded by an elevated loop posteriorly; keel gradually elevated from pit (Wang & Wang 1981*b*, p. 231).

Emended diagnosis: A species of *Clarkina* with a platform of the narrow type, widest at the mid-

length of the posterior and middle platform, where the platform tapers to both the anterior and posterior and is thus lenticular in outline. Denticles and the reclined cusp are largely fused as a continuous carina that keeps nearly the same height, extends beyond the posterior platform margin and thus makes the platform end pointed. In advanced forms the carina is less fused and decreases in height up to the reclined cusp (Mei *et al.* 1998, p. 225).

New emended diagnosis: A species of *Clarkina* with a denticulation in adult Pa elements that has posterior denticles that are of near equal height and a cusp that is attached to the carina bearing mostly fused denticles. The carina in lateral view keeps about the same height towards the end of the platform and very often looks like a high 'wall'. The carina extends beyond the posterior platform margin and thus makes the platform end pointed. In advanced forms the carina is less fused and decreases slowly in height until the reclined cusp.

Remarks: This species was originally named by Wang & Wang (1981*a*, 1981*b*) as a subspecies of *Neogondolella subcarinata: N. subcarinata elongata*. Later, this subspecies was elevated to species level by both Zhang (1987) and Dai & Zhang (1989). Since the species name '*elongata*' has been used for a Lower Triassic species by Sweet (1970), both Zhang (1987) and Dai & Zhang (1989) renamed it '*wangi*'. Specimens designated as *N. wangi* by Dai & Zhang are from the Shangsi section and have a different denticulation pattern – they are not *Clarkina wangi*. Mei *et al.* (1998) tentatively limited this species to specimens with a narrow-type platform and a wall-like carina. Specimens with this type of denticulation, but with different shapes of platform outline were tentatively named *Clarkina prechangxingensis* (round morphotype), *C. wangi* (narrow morphotype), *C. predeflecta* (square morphotype) and *C. subcarinata* (transitional mophotype) by Mei *et al.* (1998) in an attempt to consolidate the disparate form taxa identified previously. Mei *et al.* (1998) stated: 'The taxonomy of form species is tentatively followed here to avoid dramatic taxonomic change, although the present authors are ready to accept taxonomic adjustments to the multi-element species in the near future.' Following this trend, and based on the holotypes of the form species, we apply the names *Clarkina wangi* to the forms with the high, wall-like carina with various platform outlines (Fig. 7a–k), and *Clarkina subcarinata sensu stricto* to the forms with a similar denticulation to *C. wangi*, but the posterior denticles are usually moderately reduced in height and partially discrete (Fig. 8a–m).

Holotype: The specimen illustrated with the depository number of 53222 by Wang & Wang (1981a; pl. II, figs 3, 4) and by Wang & Wang (1981b; pl. 1, figs 21, 25). This specimen is from Sample ACT-116, which is from the middle Bed 5 of Sheng *et al.* (1984). The stratigraphic position is approximately corresponding with the middle Bed 8 of Yin *et al.* (1996).

Occurrence: Lower Changhsingian, South China.

This study was supported by the State Science and Technology Commission of China (Project G2000077700) and received funding from the industry supported Applied Stratigraphy Research Group at the University of Calgary (www.geo.ucalgary.ca/asrg/) and a NSERC Discovery Grant to C. Henderson. We thank the editors of this special publication (M. Head and A. Beaudoin), as well as B. Wardlaw, M. Orchard and an anonymous reviewer for their valuable scientific and editorial comments. Comments from Yugan Jin of the Nanjing Institute of Geology and Palaeontology were also beneficial. We also thank W. Sweet for providing slides of the syntypes of *C. subcarinata* to Shilong Mei.

References

BARSKOV, I. S. & KOROLEVA, N. V. 1970. Pervaya nakhodka verkhnepermskikh konodontovna territorii SSSR. *Doklady Akademii Nauk SSSR*, **194**, 933–934.

BATESON, W. 1886. The ancestry of the Chordata. *Quarterly Journal of Microscopical Science*, **26**, 218–571.

BRANSON, E. B. 1938. Stratigraphy and paleontology of the Lower Mississippian of Missouri. Part I. *University of Missouri Studies*, 13(3), 1–208.

CLARK, D. L. 1959. Conodonts from the Triassic of Nevada and Utah. *Journal of Paleontology*, **33(2)**, 305–312.

DAI, JINYE & ZHANG, JINGHUA 1989. Conodonts. *In*: LI, ZISHUM, ZHAN, LIPEI & ZHANG, JINGHUA (eds), *Study on the Permian–Triassic biostratigraphy and event stratigraphy of northern Sichuan and southern Shansi*. Geological Memoirs, Series, **2(9)**, 220–238.

DONOGHUE, P. C. J. & PURNELL, M. A. 1999. Mammal-like occlusion in conodonts. *Paleobiology*, **25(1)**, 58–74.

DZIK, J. 1976. Remarks on the evolution of Ordovician conodonts. *Acta Palaeontologica Polonica*, **36(3)**, 265–323.

EICHENBERG, W. 1930. Conodonten aus dem Culm des Harzes. *Palaontologische Zeitschrift*, **12**, 177–182.

GOULD, S. J. 1977. *Ontogeny and Phylogeny*. Belknap Press of Harvard University Press, Cambridge, Massachusetts, 501 pp.

HENDERSON, C. M. 2001. Conodonts around the Guadalupian and Lopingian boundary in Laibin

area, South China: a report of independent test. *Acta Micropaleontologica Sinica*, **18(2)**, 122–132.

HENDERSON, C. M., MEI, S. & WARDLAW, B. R. 2002. New conodont definitions at the Guadalupian–Lopingian boundary. *In*: HILLS, L. V., HENDERSON, C. M. & BAMBER, E. W. (eds), Carboniferous and Permian of the World, *Canadian Society of Petroleum Geologists, Memoir*, **19**, 725–735.

JIN, Y., WARDLAW, B. R., GLENISTER, B. F. & KOTLYAR, C. V. 1997. Permian chronostratigraphic subdivisions. *Episodes*, **20(1)**, 11–15.

KOZUR, H. 1989. The taxonomy of the Gondolellid conodonts in the Permian and Triassic. *Courier Forschungsinstitut Senckenberg*, **117**, 409–469.

LAMBERT, L. L. 1994. Morphometric confirmation of the *Mesogondolella idahoensis* to *M. nankingensis* transition. *Permophiles*, **24**, 28–35.

LINDSTROM, M. 1970. A suprageneric taxonomy of the conodonts. *Lethaia*, **3**, 427–445.

MEI, S. 1996. Restudy of conodonts from the Permian–Triassic boundary beds at Selong and Meishan and the natural Permian–Triassic boundary. *In*: WANG, H., WANG, X. (eds) *Centennial Memorial Volume of Professor Sun Yunzhu (Y. C. Sun) – Stratigraphy and Palaeontology*, China University of Geosciences Press, Wuhan, pp. 141–148.

MEI, S. & HENDERSON, C. M. 2001. Evolution of Permian conodont provincialism and its significance in global correlation and paleoclimate implication. *Palaeogeography, Palaeoclimatology, Palaeoecology*, **170(3–4)**, 237–260.

MEI, S, JIN, YUGAN & WARDLAW, B. R. 1994. Succession of Wuchiapingian conodonts from northeast Sichuan Province and its worldwide correlation. *Acta Micropalaeontologica Sinica*, **11(2)**, 121–139.

MEI, S., ZHANG, K. & WARDLAW, B. R. 1998. A refined succession of Changhsingian and Griesbachian neogondolellid conodonts from the Meishan section, candidate of the global stratotype section and point of the Permian–Triassic boundary. *Palaeogeography, Palaeoclimatology, Palaeoecology*, **143**, 213–226.

MUNDIL, R., METCALFE, I., LUDWIG, K. R., RENNE, P. R., OBERLI, F. & NICOLL, R. S. 2001. Timing of the Permian–Triassic biotic crisis: implications from new zircon U/Pb age data (and their limitations). *Earth and Planetary Sciences Letters*, 187, 133–147.

ORCHARD, M. J., NASSICHUK, W. W. & RUI, L. 1994. Conodonts from the Lower Griesbachian *Otoceras latilobatum* bed of Selong, Tibet and the position of the Permian–Triassic boundary. *In*: EMBRY, A. F., BEAUCHAMP, B. & GLASS, D. J. (eds) Pangea–Global Environmental Resources. Canadian Society of Petroleum Geologists, Memoirs, **17**, 823–843.

ORCHARD, M. J. & RIEBER, H. 1999. Multielement *Neogondolella* (Conodonta, Upper Permian–Middle Triassic). *Bollettino della Societa Paleontologica Italiana*, **37(2–3)**, 475–478.

PURNELL, M. A., DONOGHUE, P. C. J. & ALDRIDGE, R. J. 2000. Orientation and anatomical notation in conodonts. *Journal of Paleontology*, **74**, 113–122.

SHENG, J., CHEN, C. *ET AL.* 1984. Permian–Triassic boundary in middle and eastern Tethys. *Journal of the Faculty of Science, Hokkaido University, Series IV*, **21(1)**, 133–181.

SWEET, W. C. 1970. Uppermost Permian and Lower Triassic conodonts of the Salt Range and Trans-Indus Ranges, West Pakistan. *In*: KUMMEL, B. & TEICHERT, C. (eds) *Stratigraphic Boundary Problems, Permian and Triassic of West Pakistan*. University of Kansas, Department of Geology, Special Publications, Lawrence, Kansas, 4, 207–275.

SWEET, W. C. 1973. Late Permian and Early Triassic conodont faunas. *In*: LOGAN, A. & HILLS, L. V. (eds.) *The Permian–Triassic Systems and their Mutual Boundary*. Canadian Society of Petroleum Geologists, Memoirs, **2**, 630–646.

SWEET, W. C. 1988. *The Conodonta: Morphology, Taxonomy, Paleoecology, and Evolutionary History of a Long-extinct Animal Phylum*. Oxford Monographs on Geology and Geophysics, **10**, 212 pp.

TEICHERT, C., KUMMEL, B. & SWEET, W. C. 1973. Permian–Triassic strata, Kuh-e-Ali Bashi, northwest Iran. *Bulletin of the Museum of Comparative Zoology*, **145(8)**, 359–472.

TIAN, S. 1993. Evolution of conodont genera *Neogondolella, Hindeodus* and *Isarcicella* in northwestern Hunan, China. *Stratigraphy and Paleontology*, **2**, 173–191.

WANG, C. 2000. The base of the Lopingian series – Restudy of the Penglaitan Section. *Acta Micropalaeontologica Sinica*, **17(1)**, 1–17.

WANG, C. & WANG, Z. 1981a. Permian conodonts from the Longtan Formation and Changxing Formation of Changxing, Zhejiang and their stratigraphical and palaeoecological significance. *Selected Papers of 1st Convention Micropaleontological Society of China, 1979*, pp. 114–120 (in Chinese).

WANG, C. & WANG, Z. 1981b. Permian conodont biostratigraphy of China. *Geological Society of America, Special Paper*, **187**, 227–236.

WARDLAW, B. R. & COLLINSON, J. W. 1979. Youngest Permian conodont faunas from the Great Basin and Rocky Mountain regions. *In*: SANDBERG, C. A. & CLARK, D. L. (eds) Conodont biostratigraphy of the Great Basin region. *Brigham Young University Geology Studies*, **26**, 151–163.

WARDLAW, B. R. & MEI, S. 2000. Conodont definition for the basal boundary of the Changhsingian Stage. *In*: JIN, YUGAN (ed.) *Conodont Definition on the Basal Boundary of Lopingian Stages: A Report From the International Working Group on the Lopingian Series*. Permophiles, **36**, 39–40.

WHEELER, Q. D. & PLATNICK, N. I. 2000. The Phylogenetic species concept (*sensu* Wheeler and Platnick). *In*: WHEELER, Q. D. & MEIER, R. (eds) *Species Concepts and Phylogenetic Theory – A Debate*. Columbia University Press, New York, pp. 55–69.

WU, S. & H. WEILONG 1999. The subdivision and correlation of three series' boundary of Permian in Lower Yangtze region. *In*: YIN, HONGFU & TONG, JINNAN (eds) *Proceedings of the International Conference on Pangea and the Paleozoic–Mesozoic transition*, China University of Geosciences Press, pp. 48–56.

YIN, H. SWEET, W. C. *ET AL.* 1996. Recommendation of the Meishan section as Global Stratotype Section and Point for basal boundary of Triassic System. *Newsletter of Stratigraphy*, **34(2)**, 81–108.

ZHANG, K. 1987. The Permo-Triassic conodont fauna in Changxing area, Zhejiang Province and its stratigraphic significance. *Earth Science Journal of Wuhan College of Geology*, **12(2)**, 193–200 (in Chinese with English abstract).

ZHANG, K. TONG, J., YIN, H. & WU, S. 1997. Sequence stratigraphy of the Permian–Triassic boundary section of Changxing, Zhejiang. *Acta Geologica Sinica*, **71(1)**, 90–103.

ZHAO, J. K., SHENG, J. Z., YAO, Z. Q., LIANG, X. L., CHEN, C. Z., RUI, L. & LIAO, Z. T. 1981. The Changhsingian and Permian–Triassic boundary in South China. *Bulletin Nanjing Institute Geology and Palaeontology, Academia Sinica*, **2**, 1–128.

Palynostratigraphy of the Upper Carboniferous Langsettian–Duckmantian Stage boundary in Britain

DUNCAN MCLEAN, BERNARD OWENS & DAVID BODMAN

Palynology Research Facility, Department of Animal and Plant Sciences, Alfred Denny Building, University of Sheffield, Western Bank, Sheffield S10 2TN, UK
(e-mail: d.mclean@sheffield.ac.uk)

Abstract: A critique of palynostratigraphic zonation schemes associated with the Langsettian–Duckmantian Stage boundary shows that, at high levels of stratigraphic resolution, most criteria used as palynological proxies for the position of the boundary are unsuitable. Most importantly, in the Duckmantian stratotype section the highest stratigraphic occurrence of the index species *Schulzospora rara* is above (rather than below or within) the Vanderbeckei Marine Band, the base of which defines the Duckmantian Stage. A cored section through the boundary in southern North Sea well 44/22–1 displays comparable microfloral distributions. While data are as yet too sparse to provide detailed answers, the findings have implications for understanding how marine flooding events affected Carboniferous microfloral evolution and extinction. Ultimately this influences how microfloral biozone boundaries relate to the regional European Upper Carboniferous stage boundaries, which are largely defined in relation to strata deposited during marine flooding events similar to that associated with the Langsettian–Duckmantian boundary. The miospore genus *Sinuspores* Artüz is emended, and two new taxa are described: *Gondisporites bulboides* sp. nov. and *Hymenospora murdochensis* sp. nov.

The Second International Congress on Carboniferous Stratigraphy in Heerlen in 1935 defined contiguous stages within the Westphalian Series of the European Carboniferous as Westphalian A, B, C and D in ascending sequence (Jongmans & Gothan 1937). Following suggestions by George & Wagner (1972), Calver & Owens (1977) and Ramsbottom (1981), Owens *et al.* (1985) proposed replacement of the Heerlen terminology with stage names based on stratotypes within the British Isles. In their classification, the Westphalian A is replaced by the Langsettian, the Westphalian B by the Duckmantian and the Westphalian C by the Bolsovian. These nomenclatural changes and associated designation of stratotype sections were ratified by the Subcommission on Carboniferous Stratigraphy in 1989 (Engel 1989). The Duckmantian thus represents a regional Stage for the European Carboniferous. Use of the name is continued and widespread (Wagner & Winkler Prins 1997; Heckel 2001). The base of the Duckmantian has been correlated within the Lower Moscovian (Wagner & Winkler Prins 1997) or within the Upper Bashkirian stages of the former Soviet Union (Peppers 1996) (Fig. 1). Results from the Subcommission on Carboniferous Stratigraphy Task Group to identify and

define a global chronostratigraphic boundary close to the Bashkirian–Moscovian Boundary may help to resolve this discrepancy.

The base of the Duckmantian Stage is defined by a stratotype section (55° 13′ 33″ N, 01° 21′ 53″ W, national grid reference SK4237,7040) in a disused railway cutting at Duckmanton near Chesterfield, Derbyshire, UK (Fig. 2). The stage boundary is defined by the first appearance of marine macrofossils at the base of the Vanderbeckei Marine Band. The nomenclature of the marine band was defined and standardized by Ramsbottom *et al.* (1978). The marine band represents a widely correlatable horizon. Calver (1968) estimated that the horizon could be consistently recognized over an area of 960 × 50 km in sequences of fluvio-deltaic coal measures that are otherwise characterized by rapid lateral and vertical facies changes. No other marine bands are recognized in the upper Langsettian to mid-Duckmantian sequence and, as such, the Vanderbeckei Marine Band provides ready lithostratigraphic correlation even without the presence of diagnostic goniatite macrofaunas. Fossil groups other than marine faunas may provide evidence for the stratigraphic location of the marine band. It is the only marine band to occur within the non-

From: BEAUDOIN, A.B. & HEAD, M.J. (eds) 2004. *The Palynology and Micropalaeontology of Boundaries.* Geological Society, London, Special Publications, **230**, 123–135. 0305-8719/04/$15 © The Geological Society of London 2004.

Europe		C.I.S.	
Series	**Stages**	**Wagner & Winkler Prins (1997)**	**Peppers (1996)**
			Kasimovian (pars.)
	Westphalian D		
		Moscovian (pars.)	Moscovian
Westphalian	Bolsovian		
	Duckmantian		
	⊛		Bashkirian (pars.)
	Langsettian	Bashkirian (pars.)	

Fig. 1. Subdivisions of the European Westphalian and their correlation with the Late Carboniferous Stages of the former Soviet Union (CIS). The Duckmantian–Langsettian boundary is emphasized by a star. No vertical scale is implied.

Fig. 2. Location of the studied sections.

marine bivalve *Modiolaris* Chronozone, and its position has been correlated with significant changes in macro- and microfloral assemblages across northwestern Europe (Clayton *et al.* 1977; Wagner 1984).

Changes in the microflora across the Langsettian–Duckmantian boundary have long been recognized (Tomlinson 1940, reported in Smith & Butterworth 1967, p. 28; Balme & Butterworth 1952) and have formed the basis for biozonal subdivision of the associated strata. Smith & Butterworth (1967) recognized changes in assemblages recovered from coal seams above and below the boundary. They carefully avoided defining any biozones (Smith & Butterworth 1967, p.12), although their 'assemblages' have subsequently been interpreted as assemblage biozones (e.g. Clayton *et al.* 1977). Care is needed in extending the application of these assemblages to those from other lithologies. Miospores from coals represent a limited part of the total microflora (Neves 1958), and it is expected that abundance and total stratigraphic range characteristics of taxa will vary between coal and non-coal lithologies. Furthermore, the sampling strategy of Smith & Butterworth (1967) appears to have been defined by economic interests, such that small, unworkable coal seams were largely ignored. Their coal assemblages are recognizable by the ranges of several index taxa (Smith & Butterworth 1967, text-fig. 5) and some abundance criteria (summarized in Smith & Butterworth 1967, pp 81–82, text-fig. 55). The base of their *Schulzospora rara* (VII) assemblage was defined by the first seam (above their *Radiizonates aligerens* (VI) assemblage) to be without *R. aligerens*. The base of their *Dictyotriletes bireticulatus* (VIII) assemblage was explicitly correlated with the Vanderbeckei Marine Band (Smith & Butterworth 1967, p. 81), but is in effect defined as the first coal seam to contain *Endosporites globiformis* and *Radiizonates tenuis* and to be without *S. rara*. *Vestispora pseudoreticulata* is 'almost invariably' confined to the VIII and overlying assemblages (Smith & Butterworth 1967, p. 82).

Clayton *et al.* (1977) defined a series of biozones, using several criteria. They correlated their *Radiizonates aligerens* (RA) Biozone with the *Radiizonates aligerens* (VI) and *Schulzospora rara* (VII) assemblages of Smith & Butterworth (1967). The overlying *Microreticulatisporites nobilis–Florinites junior* (NJ) Biozone was defined by the lower limits of *M. nobilis* and *F. junior*, and the upper limits of *Sinuspores sinuatus* and *Schulzospora rara*. The base of the NJ Biozone was correlated with the Vanderbeckei Marine Band across northwestern Europe.

Boundary sections

Stratotype section

The boundary stratotype section in the Duck-manton railway cutting displays a series of upper Langsettian to lower Duckmantian coal measures. Elements of the geology of the section were described by Smith *et al.* (1967) and Anon. (1978). Ramsbottom (1981) described the stratigraphy of the basal Duckmantian in the section in detail, and palaeontological data were collated by Edwards & Stubblefield (1948); Smith *et al.* (1967); Eagar *in* Anon. (1978); Ramsbottom (1981) and Owens *et al.* (1985). These studies show the distribution of marine faunas, non-marine bivalves, ostracodes and miospores. The Langsettian–Duckmantian boundary is defined at the point in the section at which the first marine macrofauna occurs in the marine mudstones of the *Anthracoceratites vanderbeckei* Marine Band. This is immediately above the Joan Coal, which is succeeded by 38 cm of mudstones containing a fauna (*Lingula, Praehollinella*) representative of a transgressive marine phase, and 56 cm of mudstones with iron carbonate concretions containing a pectinoid fauna (*Dunbarella, Myalina*). The latter unit represents the acme phase of the marine flooding event (*sensu* Calver 1968). It is succeeded by 2.7 m of mudstones representing the regressive phase of marine flooding. Towards the top of this unit are intercalations of strata containing marine fossils (*Ammodiscus, Glomospira*) and stunted non-marine fossils (*Geisinia*) that are typical of the Vanderbeckei Marine Band in this part of the Pennine Basin (Calver 1968). The marine band is overlain by non-marine mudstones with some prominent ironstone horizons containing non-marine bivalves.

Recognizable macrofloras have not been recovered from the section (Cleal & Thomas 1996). The section is now largely overgrown. Sample material for the present study covered the interval from the First Piper Coal to the Top First Waterloo Coal (Fig. 3), and was acquired from trenches dug by the British Geological Survey in 1972 and from shallow workings opened during the miners' strike of 1984. The full sequence of strata was thus not available for sampling, but a BGS trench provided closely spaced samples over the interval of the Vanderbeckei Marine Band and immediately adjacent strata (Fig. 4).

Well 44/22-1

Conoco UK Ltd well 44/22-1 (54° 15′ 24″ N, 02° 20′ 49″ E; Fig. 2) was drilled in 1984, and penetrated a thick Langsettian–Duckmantian sequence truncated by the Saalian unconformity (Fig. 5). The strata belong to the Westoe Coal Formation and the Caister Coal Formation of Cameron (1993). Hydrocarbon-bearing sandstone reservoirs in this and neighbouring wells define the Murdoch Gas Field. Recovery of an extensive cored section from well 44/22-1 allowed the recognition of a limited macrofauna typical of the Vanderbeckei Marine Band. In the core a thin coal is overlain by 5.2 m of non-marine strata, followed by 2.3 m of siltstones containing *Lingula* (incursion faunal phase) and 1.7 m of silty mudstones and iron carbonate concretions containing *Spirifer pennystonensis, Levipustula piscarae* and crinoid columnals (acme faunal phase). A specimen of *Lingula* recovered from 3.2 m higher in the sequence represents the highest recorded marine fossil, suggesting a total thickness of 7.2 m of marine strata. Occurrence of the marine brachiopods *S. pennystonensis* and *L. piscarae* is typical of the productoid facies of the Vanderbeckei Marine Band (George 1928; Mason 1957; Calver 1968). The marine strata are succeeded by a coarsening-upwards sequence of siltstones and fine sandstones overlain by a thick development of coarse sandstones and conglomerates of the Murdoch–Caister sandstone unit (McLean & Murray 1996). A total of 62 core and eight side-wall core samples were analysed from throughout this section, with a concentration of 24 core samples around the horizon of the Langsettian–Duckmantian boundary (Fig. 6).

Palynostratigraphy

Both study sections provided abundant and diverse palynological assemblages, with more than 200 miospore taxa recorded from each. Figures 3 & 5 illustrate the distributions of particular miospore taxa in composite sections of upper Langsettian and lower Duckmantian strata in the area of Duckmanton, and in the southern North Sea Murdoch Gas Field. The detailed distributions of selected palynomorphs around the Langsettian–Duckmantian boundary are shown in Figures 4 & 6. The data have been interpreted in terms of the criteria used to define the assemblages of Smith & Butterworth (1967) and the biozones of Clayton *et al.* (1977). In both sections, the

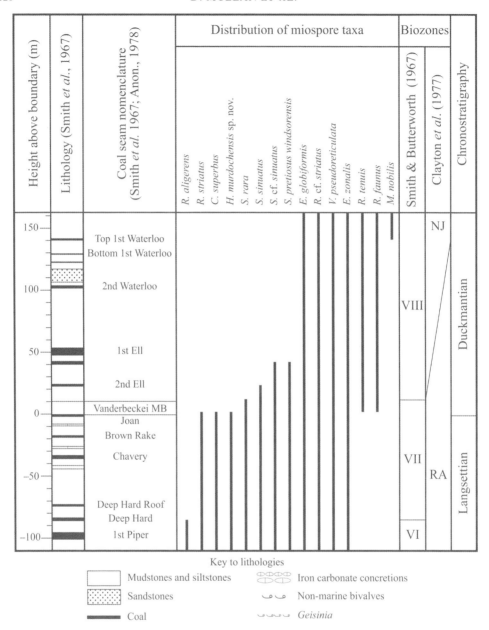

Fig. 3. Distribution of stratigraphically significant miospore species in the Duckmanton railway cutting and neighbouring area. Key to lithologies for Figures 3–6.

boundary between the VI and VII assemblages is identified by the range top of *Radiizonates aligerens*. The VII–VIII assemblage boundary is less readily recognizable. In both areas, occurrences of *Endosporites globiformis* and *Vestispora pseudoreticulata* extend down into Langsettian strata and are even associated with *R. aligerens*, and the ranges of *Schulzos-*

pora rara and *Radiizonates tenuis* overlap (Figs 3–6). Here the boundary between the assemblages has been taken at the total range top (irrespective of lithology) of *S. rara*. If non-coal microfloras are excluded, the range top of *S. rara* would be placed at the Joan Coal in Duckmanton and at the −1 Coal (*sensu* McLean & Murray 1996) in the

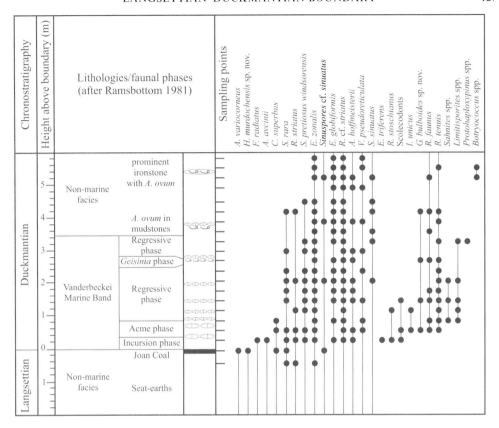

Fig. 4. Distribution of selected palynomorphs in the Duckmantian boundary stratotype section. For key to lithologies, see Figure 3.

Murdoch Gas Field. Recognition of the biozonal boundaries of Clayton *et al.* (1977) is also problematic, because the stratigraphic criteria that are used to define the base of the NJ Biozone (range top of *S. rara*, range top of *Sinuspores sinuatus*, range base of *Microreticulatisporites nobilis*) do not occur at the same horizon.

The difficulties in these interpretations relate to using several criteria to define assemblages or assemblage biozones. A more suitable approach may be to define biostratigraphic units using events specific to a single taxon. In the case of the Langsettian–Duckmantian boundary, the following events may prove suitable:

(1) Range base of *Microreticulatisporites nobilis*;
(2) Range top of *Sinuspores* spp. (*S. sinuatus* and *S.* cf. *sinuatus*) or *Spelaeotriletes pretiosus windsorensis*;
(3) Range top of *Schulzospora rara*;
(4) Range base of *Protohaploxypinus* spp.;

(5) Range top of *Camptotriletes superbus*, or range base of *Radiizonates faunus* or *R. tenuis*;
(6) Range top of *R. aligerens*.

Establishment of such units awaits the consideration of the consistency of these events over a wider geographical area. These events generally concur with observations of the distribution of particular taxa across NW Europe, but published records are all at low levels of stratigraphic resolution. The range base of *Protohaploxypinus* spp. as recognized here is considerably lower than previously described. Clayton *et al.* (1977) and Van de Laar & Fermont (1989) showed *Protohaploxypinus* spp. occurring in the Lower Bolsovian. Farther afield, however, the genus is known from the questionable Upper Namurian (Zhu 1993) and Lower Westphalian (Playford & Dino 2000). Several other taxa have ranges that may appear suitable. However, the range of *Fragilipollenites radiatus* (Fig. 4) extends into younger strata than

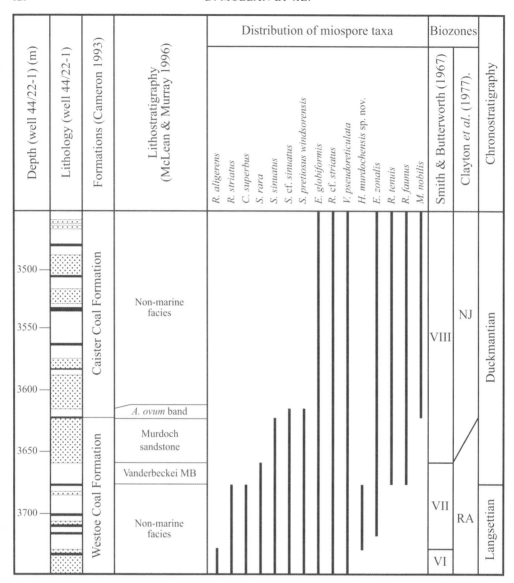

Fig. 5. Distribution of stratigraphically significant miospore species in the upper Langsettian and Duckmantian of the Murdoch Gas Field. For key to lithologies, see Figure 3.

in this study (McLean 1997). The range top of *Hymenospora murdochensis* sp. nov. appears to lie consistently in the coal beneath the Vanderbeckei Marine Band, but additional records are needed before the suitability of this species can be assessed. Similarly there are too few European records of *Anafoveosporites avcinii* to assess its biostratigraphic utility.

It may be that at low levels of stratigraphic resolution (low sample density or sampling confined to coals) there is an apparent change

in the microflora across the Langsettian–Duckmantian boundary, but the ranges of taxa illustrated in Figures 4 & 6 show that at high levels of stratigraphic resolution the boundary is typified by a gradual turnover of taxa. Furthermore, at this level of resolution there is little consistency in the order of these biostratigraphic events. This is illustrated by the different positions of the range tops of *Apiculatasporites variocorneus* and *Radiizonates striatus*, and the range bases of *Alatisporites hoffmeisterii* and

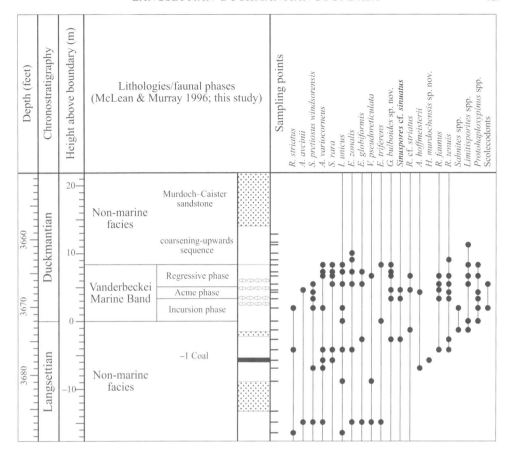

Fig. 6. Distribution of selected palynomorphs in the Duckmantian boundary section in southern North Sea well 44/22-1. For key to lithologies, see Figure 3.

Gondisporites bulboides sp. nov. relative to the the six events listed above.

Palaeoenvironments

Few unequivocal marine palynomorphs are recognized in Upper Carboniferous marine strata in northwestern Europe (McLean & Chisholm 1996), although scolecodonts (the jaw apparatuses of marine annelids) occur rarely in many marine bands. Palynological identification of Upper Carboniferous marine bands thus relies upon changes in miospore assemblage composition (Neves 1958; Davies & McLean 1996) and palynofacies (Van de Laar & Fermont 1990). Most significant is the increase in abundance of certain saccate pollen taxa in marine strata. In the studied sections, both striate and non-striate bisaccate pollen (*Illinites unicus, Protohaploxypinus* spp., *Sahnites* spp., *Limitisporites* spp.) occur throughout the Van-

derbeckei Marine Band and, except for specimens of *Limitisporites* spp. in the overlying non-marine unit in well 44/22-1, are restricted to it. Similarly, the sphenopsid miospore *Elaterites triferens* may occur elsewhere, but is often common in the incursion phase of the marine band. There are clearly palaeoecological effects on the distribution of these forms (Chaloner 1958; Chaloner & Muir 1968) that allow their presence to suggest the position and extent of marine strata. Ultimately the driving force behind these distributions is palaeoclimatic, reflecting changes in the availability of low-lying habitats suitable for land plants, in turn brought about by glacial–interglacial sea-level fluctuations. Sea-level fluctuations have been envisaged as driving vegetational compositional changes (Chaloner 1958) and also the overall evolution of the microflora. In recognizing that Upper Carboniferous microfloral biozonal boundaries coincide with marine band horizons, Owens *et al.* (1977) suggested a causal link, whereby evolutionary stress was produced by marine flooding of lowland habitats. If this model is correct, then most miospore range tops would coincide with the incursion phase of a marine flooding event. In the Vanderbeckei Marine Band this is not the case (Figs 4 & 6). Of the taxa which have their range tops in proximity to the marine band, none are consistently in the lower part of the incursion phase. In fact, most extend into the regressive phase or higher. Significantly, *Schulzospora rara* and *Radiizonates striatus* both occur in the non-marine strata above the marine band. Given the limited data-set available, the implication is that periods of marine flooding alone did not exert particular evolutionary stress upon the microflora, but that evolution and extinction took place throughout the complete transgressive–regressive (i.e. interglacial) event.

Conclusions

It appears that, at high levels of stratigraphic resolution, there is no palynostratigraphic event that consistently equates to the horizon of the Langsettian–Duckmantian boundary. However, a series of events recognized within a gradual turnover of taxa across the boundary may prove to provide a framework within which the boundary can be located. In addition, palaeoecological changes apparent in microfloral assemblages allow recognition of the marine strata of the Vanderbeckei Marine Band – the base of which defines the Duckmantian Stage. The distribution of palynomorph range tops and bases across the boundary suggests that marine flooding did not drive the evolution of the microflora, but that the vegetational response to both transgression and regression may have been important.

Systematic palaeontology

All described and figured specimens are housed in the collection of the Palynology Research Facility, Department of Animal and Plant Sciences, University of Sheffield, UK, collection numbers ML5742 to ML5747.

Anteturma SPORITES Potonié 1893
Turma TRILETES Reinsch emend.
Dettmann 1963
Subturma   AZONOTRILETES   Luber
emend. Dettmann 1963

Infraturma LAEVIGATI Bennie & Kidston emend. Potonié 1956
Sinuspores Artüz emend. nov.

Synonymy: Sinuspores Artüz 1957, p. 254.
Sinuspores Artüz emend. Ravn 1986, p. 80.

Type of genus: Sinuspores sinuatus Artüz emend. Ravn 1986.
Original diagnosis: Translated from Artüz (1957, p. 254). Trilete iso- and microspores with a rounded equatorial outline. 'Y' mark generally distinct, straight, reaching three-quarters of the spore diameter. There are sinusoidal, curved structures ('Sinuskurven') on the surface of the spore. These structures appear as light areas against a dark background. There is a structureless and sculptureless, dark-brown cingulum ('Gürtelzone') around the spore.
Emended diagnosis: Miospores radial, trilete, acamerate; amb circular. Ends of the laesurae extend into a broad, rounded curvatural ridge that lies in a subequatorial, proximal position. Exine proximally laevigate, distally sculptured with low, broad, sinuous muri and sometimes also with low, broad verrucae. Areas of relatively thin exine between the muri are sinuous to irregular in shape.
Remarks: Artüz (1957, p. 254) provided a clear, descriptive diagnosis for the genus. Ravn (1986, p. 80) provided an interpretative emendation that emphasized the curvatural nature of the subequatorial thickening but described the exine as 'laevigate or nearly so'. This description of the exine is misleading, since all species (and the genus remained monospecific until now) have a distinctive and characteristic distal exine sculpture. Indeed, it is to the existence of sinusoidal areas ('Sinuskurven' of Artüz, 1957, p. 245) between these sculptural thickenings that the name *Sinuspores* refers. In removing reference to the distal sculpture, Ravn (1986) described a genus that is indistinguishable from *Retusotriletes* Naumova emend. Richardson 1965. The current emendation restates the importance of the distal sculpture, while including the interpretation of the subequatorial proximal structure as a curvatural ridge. Examination of the illustrations provided by Artüz (1957, pl. 7, figs 48a, b); of all subsequently illustrated specimens assigned to this genus; and of voucher material prepared from the type locality, indicate that the areas ('Sinuskurven') between the distal sculptural thickenings vary on any one specimen from sinuosidal to irregular. Further, amongst the linear muri, the positive sculpture includes

elements that are more or less equidimensional in plan view and are best described as verrucae. These consistent features have been included in the emendation of the generic diagnosis.

Sinuspores cf. *sinuatus*
Fig. 7a & b

Description: Radial, trilete, acamerate miospores. Amb circular to subcircular. Laesurae straight or slightly sinuous, accompanied by narrow labra less than 1 μm wide. Labra broaden at their equatorial extremities, where they extend to a broad, proximal subequatorial curvatural crassitude, 4.0–8.0 μm wide. Exine 1.0–2.0 μm thick. Contact faces and curvatural ridge laevigate; distal surface ornamented with broad, low, elongate, meandering muri (1.0–2.0 μm high, 2.0–8.0 μm wide and up to 20 μm long), which do not anastomose. Size of miospores 40(55)70 μm. Based on 20 specimens.
Comparison. Specimens assigned to this taxon are smaller and have narrower labra than *Sinuspores sinuatus* Artüz 1957. Their distal ornament may resemble that of *Punctatisporites edgarensis* Peppers 1970, but they have a well-developed curvatural crassitude characteristic of the genus *Sinuspores*. *Orbisporis convolutus* Butterworth & Spinner 1967 is larger (69–116 μm) and has wider labra of regular width. Butterworth & Spinner (1967, p. 9) state that the labra of *O. convolutus* 'terminate against' a wide proximal subequatorial thickening. This suggests a similarity to the structure of *Sinuspores*, but examination of the type material of *O. convolutus* indicates that the labra invariably terminate before reaching the subequatorial thickening. A distinct area of thin exine between 2 μm (as on the holotype) and 8 μm separates the two thickened structures. In addition, there is no evidence for invagination of the subequatorial structure of *O. convolutus*.
Remarks: Miospore size may be affected by preparation techniques (Butterworth & Williams 1954), and so it should only be used with caution as a discriminatory taxonomic attribute. In the present instance, the sizes of *S. sinuatus* and *S.* cf. *sinuatus* remain discrete within any assemblage. Further, specimens of *S.* cf. *sinuatus* do not reach the published minimum size of *S. sinuatus* (75 μm, Butterworth & Williams 1958).

Subturma SOLUTITRILETES Neves & Owens 1966

Infraturma DECORATI Neves & Owens 1966
Gondisporites Bharadwaj 1962
Type of genus: *G. raniganjemsis* Bharadwaj 1962, pl. 2, fig. 48

Gondisporites bulboides sp. nov.
Fig. 7c–h

Diagnosis: Circular to subcircular, distinctly camerate miospores with narrow, subequatorial curvaturae perfectae with a narrow equatorial zona developed beyond; distal ornament of fine grana and scattered spinae-coni.
Description: Radial, trilete, camerate miospores. Amb circular. Laesurae straight or slightly flexuous, accompanied by weakly developed labra less than 1.0 μm high, reaching to the equator and developing into curvaturae perfectae. Intexine thin but distinct, laevigate, three-quarters of the spore diameter. Exoexine equatorially developed into a narrow zona 2.0 μm to 3.5 μm wide. Proximal exoexine punctate or faintly granulate. Distal ornament of densely set, faint grana, less than 0.5 μm in diameter, with scattered spinae–coni, 0.5 μm in diameter and 1.0 μm to 2.0 μm high. Size of miospores 68(79.5)85 μm. Based on 20 specimens.
Derivation of name: Latin *bulbus* – onion, with reference to the appearance of the spore as having several concentrically arranged layers.
Type locality: Well 44/22-1; southern North Sea.
Type horizon: Mudstones in core at 3638.04 m; lower Duckmantian.
Holotype: Fig. 7c & d Well 44/22-1, core at 3638.04 m, slide 1, collection number ML5744 England Finder reference E56/1.
Comparison: This is the only species of *Gondisporites* so far described from the European Carboniferous. It differs from species of *Kraeuselisporites* and *Spelaeotriletes* by the presence of the equatorial zona. *Gondisporites ewingtonensis* Backhouse 1988 and *G. wilsonii* Backhouse 1988 have coarser distal ornament. *G. raniganjensis* Bharadwaj 1962 has an equatorial zona which is distinctly thickened along its inner margin.

Subturma MEMBRANATITRILETES Neves & Owens 1966
Infraturma MEMBRANATI Neves 1961
Hymenospora Neves 1961
Type of genus: *H. palliolata* Neves 1961, pl. 33, fig. 11

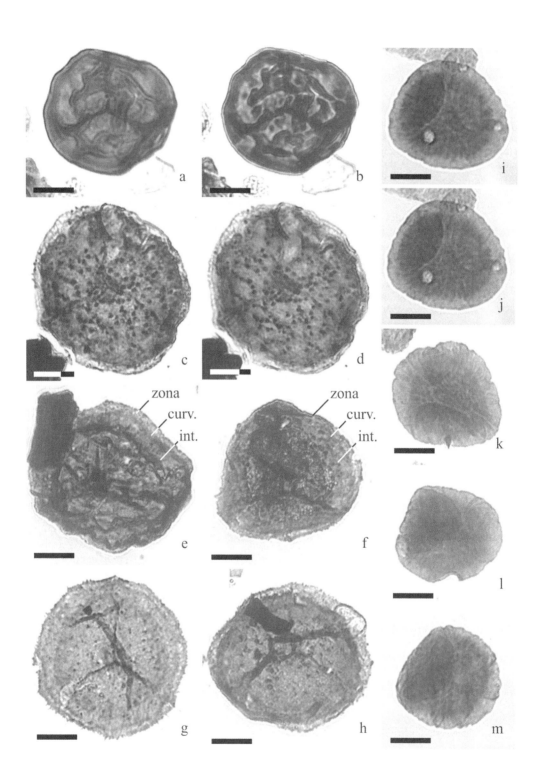

Hymenospora murdochensis sp. nov.

Fig. 7i–m

Diagnosis: Camerate trilete miospore with numerous, radially arranged plications of the finely granulate exoexine. Exoexine attached to intexine in furrows of plications. Cameration of more or less constant width around the intexine.

Description: Radial, trilete, camerate miospores. Amb subcircular, broadly rounded triangular or elongate-oval. Laesurae straight, simple, reaching to the margin of intexine, often difficult to discern. Intexine laevigate, three-quarters radius of spore. Cameration of more or less constant width around the intexine. Exoexine finely granulate, grana largest (up to 1.0 μm diameter) on the distal surface towards the distal pole; folded into 30 to 50, more or less radial plications on both proximal and distal faces; exoexine attached to intexine in furrows of plications. Size of miospores 46(53.3)59 μm. Based on 20 specimens.

Derivation of name: Named after the Murdoch Gas Field in which the species was first recognized.

Type locality: Well 44/22-1, southern North Sea.

Type horizon: Coal in core at 3679.52 m; upper Langsettian.

Holotype: Fig. 7i & j. Well 44/22-1, core at 3679.52 m, slide 1, collection number ML5742 England Finder reference V58/0.

Comparison: Hymenospora palliolata Neves 1961 is larger, has fewer radial plications and a laevigate exoexine. *H. multirugosa* Peppers 1970 has prominent, labrate laesurae and a relatively thick, infrapunctate exoexine. *Schulzospora plicata* Butterworth & Williams 1958 is

---

Fig. 7. Illustration of miospore taxa. Scale bar represents 20 μm. Specimens are identified by location, sample depth, slide number, University of Sheffield slide reference and England Finder reference. (**a**) *Sinuspores* cf. *sinuatus*, 44/22-1, 3699.65 m, 1, ML5747, H56/4. Proximal focus. (**b**) Same specimen, distal focus. (**c–h**) *Gondisporites bulboides* sp. nov. (**c**) Holotype, 44/22-1, 3638.04 m, 1, ML5744, E56/1. Proximal focus. (**d**) Holotype, distal focus. (**e**) Paratype, 44/22-1, 3638.04 m, 1, ML5744, Q38/3. 'zona' indicates narrow equatorial zona; 'curv.' indicates curvatural ridge; 'int.' indicates outer margin of intexine. (**f**) Paratype, 44/22-1, 3638.04 m, 1, ML5744, V50/2. (**g**) 44/22-1, 3622.79 m, 1, ML5746, H47/2. (**h**) Paratype, 44/22-2, 3638.04 m, 2, 40.1. (**i–m**) *Hymenospora murdochensis* sp. nov. (**i**) Holotype, 44/22-1, 3679.52 m, 1, ML5742, V58/0. Proximal focus. (**j**) Holotype, distal focus. (**k**) Paratype, 44/22-1, 3679.52 m, 1, ML5742, M68/3. (**l**) Paratype, 44/22-1, 3679.52 m, 1, ML5742, U63/4. (**m**) Paratype, 44/22-1, 3679.52 m, 1, S64/0.

---

consistently elongate–elliptical in outline due to the median constriction of the exoexine. It therefore does not have the consistent width of cameration of *H. murdochensis*.

W. H. C. Ramsbottom identified macrofaunas from the Murdoch Gas Field. The authors wish to thank ConocoPhillips UK Ltd and partners GDF Britain Ltd and Tullow Oil UK for permission to publish data from well 44/22-1. B. O. publishes with the approval of The Director, British Geological Survey (NERC).

Appendix I

List and author citations of palynomorph taxa mentioned in this paper:

Alatisporites hoffmeisterii Morgan 1955

Anafoveosporites avcinii (Ravn & Fitzgerald) Ravn 1986

Apiculatasporites variocorneus (Sullivan) Ravn 1986

Botryococcus Kützing 1849

Camptotriletes superbus Neves 1961

Dictyotriletes bireticulatus (Ibrahim) Potonié & Kremp emend. Smith & Butterworth 1967

Elaterites triferens Wilson 1943

Endosporites globiformis (Ibrahim) Schopf *et al.* 1944

Endosporites zonalis (Loose) Knox 1950

Florinites junior Potonié & Kremp 1956

Fragilipollenites radiatus Konyali *in* Agrali *et al.* emend. McLean 1997

Gondisporites bulboides sp. nov.

Gondisporites ewingtoneneis Backhouse 1988

Gondisporites raniganjensis Bharadwaj 1962

Gondisporites wilsonii Backhouse 1988

Hymenospora multirugosa Peppers 1970

Hymenospora murdochensis sp. nov.

Hymenospora palliolata Neves 1961

Illinites unicus Kosanke emend. Jansonius & Hills 1976

Kraeuselisporites Leschik emend. Scheuring 1974

Limitisporites Leschik emend. Klaus 1958

Microreticulatisporites nobilis (Wicher) Knox 1950

Orbisporis convolutus Butterworth & Spinner 1967

Protohaploxypinus Samoilovich emend. Morbey 1975

Punctatisporites edgarensis Peppers 1970

Radiizonates aligerens (Knox) emend. Staplin & Jansonius 1964

Radiizonates difformis (Kosanke) Staplin & Jansonius 1964

Radiizonates faunus (Ibrahim) Smith & Butterworth 1967

Radiizonates striatus (Knox) Staplin & Jansonius 1964

Radiizonates cf. *striatus sensu* Smith & Butterworth 1967

Radiizonates tenuis (Loose) Butterworth & Smith *in* Butterworth *et al.* 1964

Reduviasporonites stoschianus (Balme) Elsik 1999

Sahnites Pant *ex* Pant 1955

Schulzospora plicata Butterworth & Williams 1958

Schulzospora rara Kosanke 1950

Sinuspores sinuatus Artüz emend. Ravn 1986

Spelaeotriletes Neves & Owens 1966

Spelaeotriletes pretiosus windsorensis Utting 1987

Vestispora pseudoreticulata Spode *in* Smith & Butterworth 1967

References

ANON. 1978. *The W. H. Wilcockson Nature Reserve Duckmanton Railway Cutting Geological Trail.* Derbyshire Naturalists' Trust, pp. 1–17.

ARTÜZ, S. 1957. Die sporae dispersae der Turkischen Steinkohle von Zonguldak–Gebiet (mit besonderer Beachtung der neuen Arten und Genera). *Istanbul Üniversitesi fen Fakültesi Mecmuasi B*, **22**, 239–263.

BALME, B. E. & BUTTERWORTH, M. A. 1952. The stratigraphic significance of certain fossil spores in the central group of British coalfields. *Transactions of the Institute of Mining Engineers*, **111**, 3–17.

BUTTERWORTH, M. A. & SPINNER, E. G. 1967. Lower Carboniferous spores from North-West England. *Palaeontology*, **10**, 1–24.

BUTTERWORTH, M. A. & WILLIAMS, R. W. 1954. Descriptions of nine species of small spores from the British Coal Measures. *Annals and Magazine of Natural History*, **7**, 753–764.

BUTTERWORTH, M. A. & WILLIAMS, R. W. 1958. The small spore floras of coals in the Limestone Coal Group and Upper Limestone Group of the Lower Carboniferous of Scotland. *Transactions of the Royal Society of Edinburgh*, **63**, 353–392.

CALVER, M. A. 1968. Distribution of Westphalian marine faunas in northern England and adjoining areas. *Proceedings of the Yorkshire Geological Society*, **37**, 1–72.

CALVER, M. A. & OWENS, B. 1977. Progress report of Working Group on proposed boundary–stratotypes for Westphalian A, B and C. *In*: HOLUB, V. M. & WAGNER, R. H. (eds) *Symposium on Carboniferous Stratigraphy*, Geological Survey of Prague, pp. 65–70.

CAMERON, T. D. J. 1993. Carboniferous and Devonian of the Southern North Sea. *In*: KNOX, R. W. O'B. & CORDEY, W. G. (eds) *Lithostratigraphic Nomenclature of the UK North Sea*. British Geological Survey, Nottingham, pp. 1–93.

CHALONER, W. G. 1958. The Carboniferous upland flora. *Geological Magazine*, **95**, 261–262.

CHALONER, W. G. & MUIR, M. 1968. Spores and floras. *In*: MURCHISON, D. G. & WESTOLL, T. S. (eds) *Coal and Coal-bearing Strata*. Oliver and Boyd, Edinburgh, pp. 127–146.

CLAYTON, G., COQUEL, R., DOUBINGER, J., GUEINN, K. J., LOBOZIAK, S., OWENS, B. & STREEL, M. 1977. Carboniferous miospores of western Europe: illustration and zonation *Mededelingen Rijks Geologische Dienst*, **29**, 1–71.

CLEAL, C. J. & THOMAS, B. A. 1996. *British Upper Carboniferous Stratigraphy*. Joint Nature Conservation Committee, Geological Conservation Review Series, Chapman & Hall, London, pp. 1–339.

DAVIES, S. J. & MCLEAN, D. 1996. Spectral gamma-ray and palynological characterization of Kinderscoutian marine bands in the Namurian of the Pennine Basin. *Proceedings of the Yorkshire Geological Society*, **51**, 103–114.

EDWARDS, W. & STUBBLEFIELD, C. J. 1948. Marine bands and other faunal marker horizons in relation to the sedimentary cycles of the Middle Coal Measures of Nottinghamshire and Derbyshire. *Quarterly Journal of the Geological Society of London*, **103**, 209–260.

ENGEL, B. A. 1989. S.C.C.S. ballot results. *Newsletter on Carboniferous Stratigraphy*, **7**, 7–8.

GEORGE, T. N. 1928. *Spirifer pennystonensis* sp. nov. from the Coal Measures of Coalbrookdale. *Annals and Magazine of Natural History*, **1**, 108–112.

GEORGE, T. N. & WAGNER, R. H. 1972. International Union of Geological Sciences Subcommission on Carboniferous Stratigraphy, Proceedings and report of the General Assembly at Krefeld, August 21–22. *Compte rendu 7ème Congrès Internationale de Stratigraphie et de Géologie du Carbonifère, Krefeld, 1971*, Geologisches Landesamt Nordrhein-Westfalen, Krefeld, **1**, 139–147.

HECKEL, P. H. 2001. New proposals for Series and Stage subdivision of the Carboniferous system. *Newsletter on Carboniferous Stratigraphy*, **19**, 12–14.

JONGMANS, W. E. & GOTHAN, W. 1937. Betrachtungen über die Ergebnisse des Zweiten Kongresses für Karbonstratigraphie. *Compte rendu 2ème Congrès Internationale de Stratigraphie et de Géologie du Carbonifère, Heerlen, 1935*, Ernst Van Aelst, Maestricht, **1**, 1–40.

MCLEAN, D. 1997. The miospore genus *Fragilipollenites* Konyali emend. from the Silesian of Great Britain. *Journal of Micropalaeontology*, **16**, 85–90.

MCLEAN, D. & CHISHOLM, J. I. 1996. Reworked palynomorphs as provenance indicators in the Yeadonian of the Pennine Basin. *Proceedings of the Yorkshire Geological Society*, **51**, 141–151.

MCLEAN, D. & MURRAY, I. 1996. Subsurface correlation of Carboniferous coal seams and inter-seam sediments using palynology: applications to exploration for coalbed methane. *In*: GAYER, R. & HARRIS, I. (eds) *Coalbed Methane and Coal Geology*, Geological Society, London, Special Publications **109**, 315–324.

MASON, W. 1957. On the occurrence of a marine band in the *Anthraconaia modiolaris* Zone of the Scottish Coal Measures. *Bulletin of the Geological Survey of Great Britain*, **12**, 66–86.

NEVES, R. 1958. Upper Carboniferous plant spore assemblages from the *Gastrioceras subcrenatum* horizon, North Staffordshire. *Geological Magazine*, **95**, 1–19.

OWENS, B., NEVES, R., GUEINN, K. J., MISHELL, D. R. F., SABRY, H. S. M. Z. & WILLIAMS, J. E. 1977. Palynological division of the Namurian of northern England and Scotland *Proceedings of the Yorkshire Geological Society*, **44**, 381–398.

OWENS, B., RILEY, N. J. & CALVER, M. A. 1985. Boundary stratotypes and new stage names for the Lower and Middle Westphalian sequences in Britain. *Compte rendu 10ème Congrès Internationale de Stratigraphie et de Géologie du Carbonifère, Madrid, 1983*, **4**, 461–472.

PEPPERS, R. A. 1996. Palynological correlation of major Pennsylvanian (Middle and Upper Carboniferous) chronostratigraphic boundaries in the

Illinois and other coal basins. *Geological Society of America Memoir*, **188**, 1–111.

PLAYFORD, G. & DINO, R. 2000. Palynostratigraphy of Upper Palaeozoic strata (Tapajos Group), Amazonas Basin, Brazil: Part Two. *Palaeontographica Abteilung B*, **255**, 87–145.

RAMSBOTTOM, W. H. C. 1981. *Field Guide to the Boundary Stratotypes of the Carboniferous Stages in Britain*. IUGS Subcommission on Carboniferous Stratigraphy, Leeds, pp. 1–105.

RAMSBOTTOM, W. H. C., CALVER, M. A., EAGAR, R. M. C., HODSON, F., HOLLIDAY, D. W., STUBBLEFIELD, C. J. & WILSON, R. B. 1978. A correlation of Silesian rocks in the British Isles. *Geological Society of London Special Report*, **10**, 1–81.

RAVN, R. L. 1986. Palynostratigraphy of the lower and middle Pennsylvanian coals of Iowa. *Iowa Geological Survey Technical Paper*, **7**, 1–245.

SMITH, A. H. V. & BUTTERWORTH, M. A. 1967. Miospores in the coal seams of the Carboniferous of Great Britain. *Special Papers in Palaeontology*, **1**, 1–324.

SMITH, E. G., RHYS, G. H. & EDEN, R. A. 1967. Geology of the country around Chesterfield, Matlock and Mansfield. *Memoir of the Geological Survey of Great Britain, Sheet 112*, 1–430.

VAN DE LAAR, J. G. M. & FERMONT, W. J. J. 1989. On-shore Carboniferous palynology of The Netherlands. *Mededelingen Rijks Geologische Dienst*, **43**, 35–73.

VAN DE LAAR, J. G. M. & FERMONT, W. J. J. 1990. The impact of marine transgressions on palynofacies; the Carboniferous Aegir Marine Band in borehole Kemperkoul-1. *Mededelingen Rijks Geologische Dienst*, **45**, 75–89.

WAGNER, R. H. 1984. Megafloral zones of the Carboniferous *Compte rendu 9ème Congrès Internationale de Géologie et de Stratigraphie du Carbonifère, Washington and Champaign-Urbana, 1979*, **2**, 109–134.

WAGNER, R. H. & WINKLER PRINS, C. F. 1997. Carboniferous chronostratigraphy: *quo vadis? Proceedings of the 13th International Congress on the Carboniferous and Permian*, Polish Geological Institute Warsaw, Remigraf Sp. z.o.o, Warszawa, **1**, 187–196.

ZHU, H. 1993. A revised subdivision of the Namurian of Jingyuan, northwest China. *Review of Palaeobotany and Palynology*, **77**, 273–300.

Foraminifera and ostracodes across the Pliensbachian–Toarcian boundary in the Arctic Realm (stratigraphy, palaeobiogeography and biofacies)

BORIS L. NIKITENKO[1] & MICHAEL B. MICKEY[2]

[1]*Institute of Petroleum Geology, Siberian Branch of RAS, Koptyug av. 3, Novosibirsk, 630090, Russia (e-mail: NikitenkoBL@uiggm.nsc.ru)*
[2]*Micropaleo Consultants Inc., 329 Chapalita Drive, Encinitas, CA 92024, USA (e-mail: micropaleo@cox.net)*

Abstract: The analysis of samples from numerous Pliensbachian and Toarcian sections from the northern regions of Russia and northern Alaska, as well as published data, allow us to estimate the correlative significance of foraminifera and ostracodes, and to develop an Arctic zonal standard based on these microfauna. During the Late Pliensbachian–Early Toarcian depositional period in the Arctic Basin and northwestern seas of Western Europe, a succession of almost simultaneous biotic and abiotic events occurred: widespread development of black bituminous shale at the beginning of the Early Toarcian, and a microbiota crisis (mass extinction event) in the Northern Hemisphere. The Early Toarcian microbiotic crisis was very sharp in both Arctic and Western European palaeobasins. In the Arctic seas, the generic and family composition of ostracode communities was completely replaced by new taxa. The species composition of foraminiferal assemblages changed considerably, while the generic composition of the foraminifera is only characterized by partial changes. In the Western European seas, the Early Toarcian microbenthos crisis caused taxonomic changes generally at the species level among foraminifera and at the generic level among ostracodes. The comprehensive analysis of the biogeographical distribution of Late Pliensbachian and Early Toarcian foraminifera and ostracodes, as well as Jaccard cluster analysis, allow us to define several biogeographical units within the Arctic and Boreal–Atlantic realms. A pattern of ecological distribution of microbenthos in bathymetric zones in Siberian palaeobasins has been developed, providing the basis for palaeoenvironmental reconstructions.

Upper Pliensbachian and Lower Toarcian deposits are widespread in both the Arctic Basin and in NW Europe (Fig. 1). Numerous sections of Upper Pliensbachian–Lower Toarcian microfossils (foraminifera and ostracodes) from the Barents Sea shelf, NW and eastern Siberia, NE Russia and northern Alaska have been investigated by the authors. For comparative analysis, the published data on lithostratigraphy, biostratigraphy and micropalaeontology of Upper Pliensbachian–Lower Toarcian sections from the NW portion of Western Europe, the North Sea, the Barents Sea shelf and Arctic Canada were included in this study (Norling 1972; Bate & Coleman 1975; Souaya 1976; Løfaldli & Nagy 1980; Copestake & Johnson 1981, 1984, 1989; Wall 1983; Riegraf 1985; Ainsworth 1986, 1987; Gramberg 1988; Malz & Nagy 1989; Basov et al. 1989; Nagy & Johansen 1991; Leith et al. 1992; Embry 1993; Dibner 1998; Arias 2000).

During the Late Pliensbachian–Early Toarcian in the Arctic basin and northwestern seas of western Europe, a succession of almost simultaneous biotic and abiotic events occurred. The widespread development of black bituminous shale during the earliest Toarcian coincided with a biotic crisis (mass extinction event) in the Early Toarcian within the Northern Hemisphere. In Northern Europe, this biotic event has been well publicized by authors such as Hallam (1975, 1986), Copestake & Johnson (1981, 1984, 1989), Jenkyns (1985, 1988), Riegraf (1985), Ainsworth (1986, 1987), Little & Benton (1995), Hylton & Hart (1998), Liu et al. (1998), Hallam & Wignall (1999), Harries & Little, (1999), Arias (2000), and Röhl et al. (2001).

Data on the Pliensbachian–Toarcian microfauna of Arctic regions are not so numerous: mainly comprising descriptions of the foraminifera and ostracodes, as well as taxonomic lists of microfauna from the Pliensbachian–Toarcian

From: BEAUDOIN, A.B. & HEAD, M.J. (eds) 2004. *The Palynology and Micropalaeontology of Boundaries.* Geological Society, London, Special Publications, **230**, 137–174. 0305-8719/04/$15 © The Geological Society of London 2004.

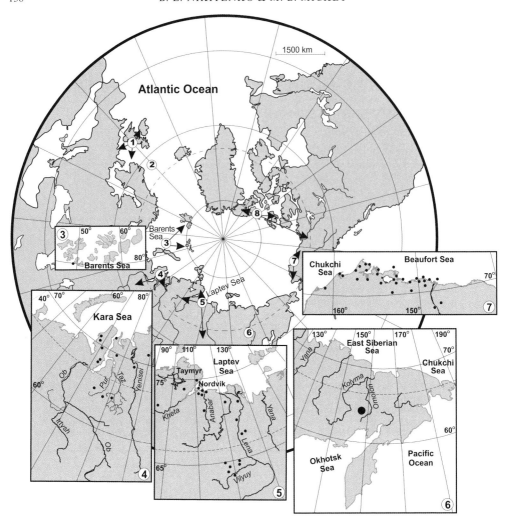

Fig. 1. The main Arctic Basin and NW Europe Pliensbachian–Toarcian study areas, showing the location of the studied sections. 1, NW of Western Europe (England, Fastnet Basin, Sweden); 2, North Sea; 3, Barents Sea area: South Barents depression, Franz Josef Land, Svalbard; 4, NW Siberia; 5, NE Siberia; 6, NE Russia; 7, northern Alaska (Arctic platform of Alaska); 8, Canadian Arctic archipelago and Northwest Territories of Canada.

deposits of eastern and western Siberia, northern Alaska, the Barents Sea region and Canadian Arctic, or investigations concentrated on zonal stratigraphy (Tappan 1955; Gerke 1961; Bergquist 1966; Saks 1976; Souaya 1976; Wall 1983; Mickey & Haga 1987; Basov *et al.* 1989; Azbel & Grigelis 1991; Nikitenko 1992, 1994; Nikitenko & Shurygin 1994*a*; Shurygin *et al.* 2000). Some studies have concentrated on the details of the Pliensbachian–Toarcian biotic crisis (Nikitenko & Shurygin 1994*b*; Nikitenko & Pospelova 1996).

The aim of this paper is to summarize all the data on the distribution of foraminifera and ostracodes in the Upper Pliensbachian and

Lower Toarcian deposits of the Arctic regions, evaluate the correlative potential of the foraminifera and ostracodes, and develop an Arctic zonal standard based on these data. Also, we will describe and characterize the Pliensbachian–Toarcian microfaunal turnover of the Arctic region. Despite the fact that the foraminifera and ostracodes are the most widespread groups of Jurassic microfossils present in the differing facies (from brackish to normal marine), these groups are very seldom utilized for palaeobiogeographical purposes (Gordon 1970; Basov 1983). This necessitates the analysis of the biogeographical distribution of the foraminifera and ostracodes at the end of the Late Pliensbachian–earliest Toarcian in the Arctic regions on the basis of well-developed biostratigraphy, as well as the development of the patterns of ecological distribution of the microfauna in bathymetric zones in the studied palaeobasins, and the reconstruction of palaeoenvironments.

Stratigraphy

Upper Pliensbachian–Lower Toarcian deposits, both from the Arctic and northwestern areas of Western Europe, are characterized by a succession of sedimentological cycles caused by eustatic events in the world's oceans. The widespread development of Lower Toarcian organic-rich shales allows us to divide the Upper Pliensbachian–Lower Toarcian deposits of the NW areas of Western Europe and the Arctic into two parts: Upper Pliensbachian and Lower Toarcian (Fig. 2). The Lower Toarcian bituminous clays are now regarded as an interregional stratigraphic marker-level, due to typical homogeneous argillaceous composition and comparable thickness (20–40 m) over the vast territory of the Arctic and Europe.

Any stratigraphic and palaeobiogeographical reconstructions are only possible on the basis of reliable and detailed biostratigraphic information. All the deposits of the different Arctic regions are characterized by rich assemblages of foraminifera, ostracodes and palynomorphs, as well as less-abundant ammonites and bivalves, allowing for the definitive correlation of these deposits.

Northeastern Siberia and northeastern Russia

Pliensbachian–Toarcian deposits in northeastern Siberia and northeastern Russia are distributed in numerous outcrops and well-sections, and are characterized by macrofaunas, including ammonites, belemnites and bivalves, and also rich and diverse foraminiferal and ostracode assemblages. During the 1990s, zonation schemes for both Siberia and northeastern Russia based on the foraminiferal (f-zones) and ostracode (o-zones) have been developed and correlated with each other, and tied into the Boreal Ammonite zonal standard (Nikitenko 1992, 1994; Nikitenko & Shurygin 1994a, b; Zakharov et al. 1997; Shurygin et al. 2000). The combination of Jurassic zones based on foraminiferal and ostracode data has allowed us to calibrate the sections of Arctic Russia (Nikitenko 1992, 1994;

Nikitenko & Shurygin 1994a, b; Shurygin et al. 2000).

The Upper Pliensbachian in the northern portion of central Siberia is represented by sediments of the upper part of the Zimnyay Formation comprising marine and near-shore sandstones, mudstones and siltstones (Fig. 3). In the west, the Zimnyay Formation is overlain by argillites and clays with pebbles, and thin layers of organic-rich shale of the Levinskiy Formation. In the central areas, it is overlain by clays and silty clays of the lower part of the Airkat Formation, while in the eastern areas (lower reaches of the Lena River) it is overlain by clays and silts of the Kyra Formation. In the upper part of the Zimnyay Formation, and lower parts of the Levinskiy, Airkat and Kyra formations, the *Ammodiscus siliceus* JF3 Zone (uppermost Lower Pliensbachian–basal Upper Pliensbachian) has been established. Foraminiferal assemblages of this zone are characterized by an abundance of *Ammodiscus siliceus* (Fig. 3). *Trochammina inusitata* is subsidiary, while other foraminifera (*Turritellella volubilis, Jaculella jacutica, Spiroplectammina* sp. 1, *Astacolus varians, Geinitzinita tenera* and *Marginulinopsis hatangensis*) are rare. In this part of the section, the ostracodes (*Ogmoconcha longula,* 'Mandelstamia' sp.) are rare, characterizing the *Ogmoconcha longula* JO2 Zone (Hettangian–basal Lower Toarcian) assemblage (Figs 4 & 5).

The foraminiferal assemblage of the overlying *Trochammina lapidosa–Frondiculinita dubiella* JF5 Zone (middle *stokesi* Ammonite Zone) is more diverse (Fig. 6h, n & r). *Dentalina gloria, Neobulimina* sp., *Nodosaria turgida, Marginulina spinata orbicularis, M. prima, M. quinta* and *Ichthyolaria lustrata* have their inceptions in this zone. The assemblage is dominated by *Trochammina lapidosa,* while *Ammodiscus siliceus, Hyperammina odiosa* and *Glomospira* ex gr. *gordialis* are subsidiary. In some horizons, *Neobulimina* sp. dominate the assemblage. The *Trochammina lapidosa–Frondiculinita dubiella* JF5 Zone occurs in the lower part of the Levinskiy, Airkat and Kyra formations in NE Siberia (Shurygin et al. 2000). In the upper part of the *Trochammina lapidosa–Frondiculinita dubiella* JF5 Zone, the diversity of the ostracodes increases. The lowest occurrence of the *Ogmoconchella olenekensis, Ogmoconcha nordvikensis,* 'Mandelstamia' *linearis* and *Nanacythere costata* (Fig. 7l, o, p, s, r, u & w) was observed in the *Nanacythere costata* JO3 Zone (uppermost *stokesi* Ammonite Zone–lower part of *viligaensis* Ammonite Zone) (Fig. 5).

The *Anmarginulina gerkei* JF7 Zone ranges from the upper part of the *stokesi* Ammonite Zone to the lower part of the *margaritatus*

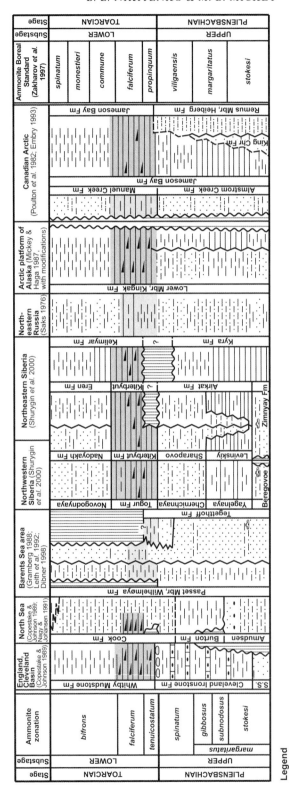

Fig. 2. Lithostratigraphic summary showing Lower Jurassic deposits and the age of organic-rich marine mudrock units in diverse geographical areas. Dark fill: Lower Toarcian organic-rich marine mudrock units.

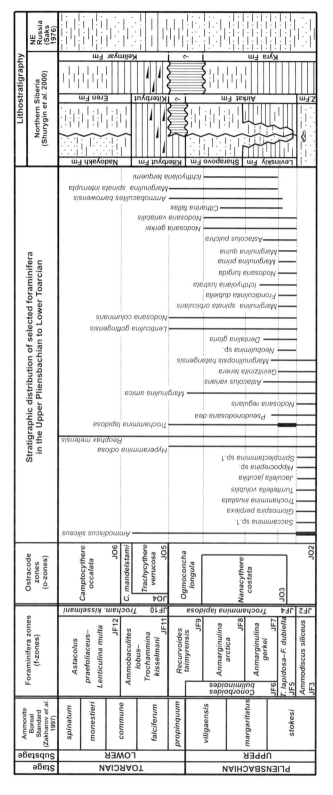

Fig. 3. Summary of the distribution of selected Upper Pliensbachian–Lower Toarcian foraminifera, NE Siberia and NE Russia (part 1). For legend, see Fig. 2.

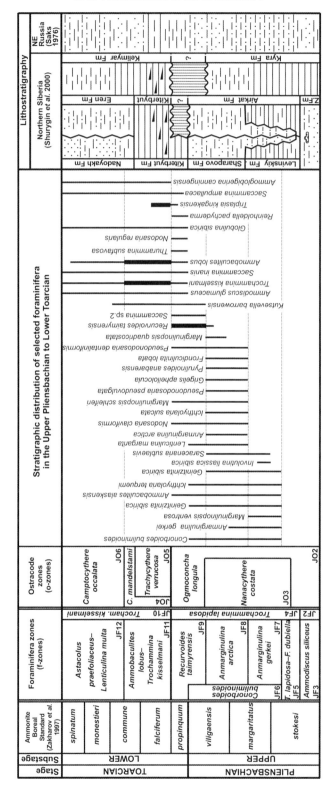

Fig. 4. Summary of the distribution of selected Upper Pliensbachian–Lower Toarcian foraminifera, NE Siberia and NE Russia (part 2). For legend, see Fig. 2.

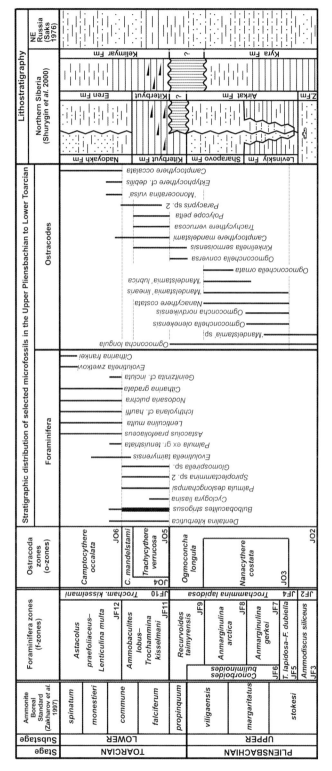

Fig. 5. Summary of the distribution of selected Upper Pliensbachian–Lower Toarcian foraminifers and ostracodes, NE Siberia and NE Russia. For legend, see Fig. 2.

Ammonite Zone (upper part of Levinskiy Formation, middle part of Airkat and Kyra Formations). It is characterized by a considerable change of the foraminiferal assemblages, with the inceptions of *Involutina liassica sibirica, Citharina fallax, Marginulinopsis ventrosa, Marginulina spinata interrupta, Saracenaria sublaevis, Ichthyolaria terquemi* and *Conorboides buliminoides* (Fig. 6a, d, e & q). Among the foraminifera, a large number of migrant taxa are recognized.

The foraminiferal assemblage from the overlying *Anmarginulina arctica* JF8 Zone (upper part of *margaritatus* Ammonite Zone–lower part of *viligaensis* Ammonite Zone) is characterized by a high diversity of the calcareous foraminifera, which sometimes dominate over the agglutinated foraminifera. This assemblage is characterized by *Lenticulina margarita, Pyrulinoides anabarensis, Ichthyolaria sulcata, Pseudonodosaria pseudovulgata, Grigelis apheilolocula* and *Frondiculinita lobata* (Fig. 6b, c, g, i, j, k, l, o, p, s, w, y, z & aa). The most diverse ostracodal assemblage of the *Nanacythere costata* JO3 Zone is found in this

part of the section. '*Mandelstamia*' *lubrica* and *Ogmoconchella ornata* (Fig. 7t & v) have their inceptions in these assemblages. These foraminifera (JF8 Zone) and ostracodes (JO3 Zone) occur in the clays in the top of the Levinskiy Formation and from the overlying siltstones with interbedded sandstone of the Sharapovo Formation, and also in the Airkat Formation and in the top of the Kyra Formation.

The *Recurvoides taimyrensis* JF9 Zone ranges from the uppermost Upper Pliensbachian to the lowermost Lower Toarcian (upper part of *viligaensis* Ammonite Zone–*propinquum* Ammonite Zone). At the base of foraminiferal zone (JF9), foraminifera greatly decrease in diversity. *Recurvoides taimyrensis* (Fig. 8a, b & c) becomes the dominant taxon, while *Kutsevella barrowensis* and locally *Trochammina lapidosa* are subsidiary. The characteristic feature of the foraminiferal assemblages from this Zone is the extinction of many of the most typical Pliensbachian species and the inception of the first Toarcian elements in the upper part of *Recurvoides taimyrensis* JF9 Zone (Figs 4 & 5).

Fig. 6. The foraminiferal assemblages of Upper Pliensbachian (**a, b, c, d, e, f, g, h, i, j, k, l, n, o, p, q, r, s, t, u, v, w, y, z & aa**) and lowermost Toarcian (**m & x**) from NE Siberia, NE Russia and the Franz Josef Land archipelago. Measurements (in brackets): length of specimens in micrometres.

(**a, d, e, q, r, t & u**) Northeastern Siberia, Anabar Bay, outcrop 12; Airkat Formation. (**a, d, e & q**) Upper Pliensbachian, *stokesi* Ammonite Zones, *Anmarginulina gerkei* JF7 Zone. (**r**) Upper Pliensbachian, *stokesi* Ammonite Zones, *Trochammina lapidosa–Frondiculinita dubiella* JF5 Zone. (**t & u**) Upper Pliensbachian, *margaritatus* Ammonite Zones, *Anmarginulina arctica* JF8 Zone. (**b, c, g, h, i, j, k, l, n, o, p, s, w, y, z & aa**) Northeastern Siberia, Yuryung–Tumus Peninsula; Airkat Formation. (**b, c, g, i, j, k, l, o, p, s, w, y, z & aa**) Upper Pliensbachian, *margaritatus* Ammonite Zones, *Anmarginulina arctica* JF8 Zone. (**h & n**) Upper Pliensbachian, *Trochammina lapidosa–Frondiculinita dubiella* JF5 Zone. (**v & x**) Northeastern Russia, left Kedon River basin, Astronomicheskaya River, outcrop 2.

(**a & b**) *Saracenaria sublaevis* (Franke 1936). (**a**) (883.1); 1048/302. Bed 50, sample 6. (**b**) (646.7); 1048/306. Outcrop 8, bed 1, sample 1. (**c**) *Citharina fallax* (Payard 1947) (1686); 892/31. Outcrop 8, bed 1, sample 3. (**d, e & f**) *Anmarginulina gerkei* Nikitenko, 1992. (**d**) (1050); 1048/101. Bed 50, sample 1. (**e**) (980.2); 1048/102. Bed 50, sample 1. (**f**) (555.6); 1048/103. Northeastern Siberia, Taymyr Peninsula, Cape Tsvetkova, outcrop 7, bed 32, sample 2; Airkat Formation, Upper Pliensbachian, *Anmarginulina gerkei* JF7 Zone. (**g**) *Frondiculinita lobata* (Gerke 1957) (810.5); 892/39. Outcrop 5, bed 1, sample 2. (**h & n**) *Frondiculinita dubiella* (Gerke 1957). (**h**) Microspheric test (1309.3); 892/37. Outcrop 10, bed 3, sample 1a. (**n**) Megalospheric test (1297.3); 892/38. Outcrop 9, bed 3, sample 3. (**i, j & k**) *Anmarginulina arctica* (Schleifer 1961). (**i**) Megalospheric test (752.9); 1048/95. Outcrop 5, bed 1, sample 4. (**j**) Megalospheric test, ventral view (737.2); 1048/96. Outcrop 5, bed 1, sample 1. (**k**) Megalospheric test (324.9); 1048/99. Outcrop 5, bed 1, sample 1. (**l, o & p**) *Pseudonodosaria pseudovulgata* (Gerke 1961). (**l**) Microspheric test (509.3); 1048/89. Outcrop 5, bed 1, sample 1. (**o**) Microspheric test (624.4); 1048/91. Outcrop 5, bed 1, sample 3. (**p**) Megalospheric test (619.2); 1048/93. Outcrop 5, bed 1, sample 3. (**m**) *Textularia areoplecta* Tappan 1955. (710.4); ZFI1/5. Franz Josef Land archipelago, Bell Island, outcrop 1, bed 5, sample 1/5; Tegetthoff Formation (upper part), uppermost Pliensbachian–lowermost Toarcian, *Recurvoides taimyrensis* JF9 Zone. (**q, r & v**) *Trochammina lapidosa* Gerke & Sossipatrova, 1961. (**q**) Microspheric test (886.2); 1048/69. Bed 50, sample 2. (**r**) Megalospheric test (788.9); 1048/74. Bed 45, sample 7. (**v**) Megalospheric test (422.3); 2N16/2. Bed 4, sample 16; Upper Pliensbachian, *viligaensis* Ammonite Zone, *Recurvoides taimyrensis* JF9 Zone. (**s, t & u**) *Pyrulinoides anabarensis* Nikitenko 2000. (**s**) Megalospheric test, (1157.9); 1048/122. Outcrop 5, bed 1, sample 1. (**t**) Microspheric test (536.2); 1048/119. Bed 55, sample 2. (**u**) Megalospheric test (1333.6); 1048/118. Bed 53, sample 2. (**w**) *Marginulina spinata interrupta* Terquem 1866. Megalospheric test (748.5); 1048/310. Outcrop 5, bed 1, sample 2. (**x**) *Lenticulina gottingensis* (Bornemann 1854) (567.2); 1048/301. Bed 6, sample 43; lowermost of Lower Toarcian, *propinquum* Ammonite Zone, *Recurvoides taimyrensis* JF9 Zone. (**y, z & aa**) *Conorboides buliminoides* (Gerke 1961). (**y**) Ventral view (291.2); 1048/125. Outcrop 5, bed 1, sample 2. (**z**) (370.6); 1048/127. Outcrop 5, bed 1, sample 3. (**aa**) Dorsal view (315.3); 1048/126. Outcrop 5, bed 1, sample 3.

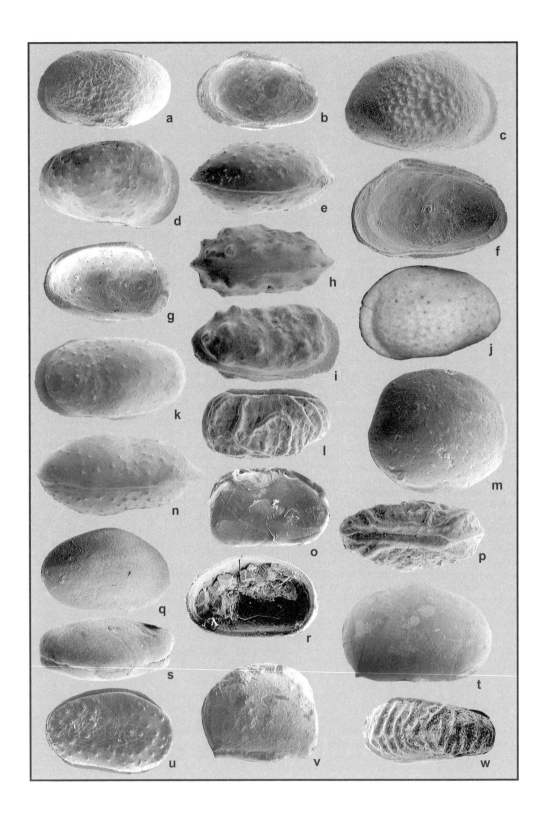

In many sections from the northern regions of eastern Siberia, the lowermost Toarcian (*propinquum* Ammonite Zone) is often eroded or absent. Therefore, the boundaries between foraminiferal and ostracodal zones in these sections are rather sharp and are associated with an almost complete change of microfaunal assemblages. Where this part of the lowermost Toarcian is present in the sections (NE Russia), the transition between the assemblages is gradational, with the complete change of microfaunal assemblages occurring at the boundary between the *propinquum* and *falciferum* Ammonite Zones. In the lowermost Toarcian, the highest occurrences of the Pliensbachian foraminifera (*Trochammina lapidosa*, *Recurvoides taimyrensis*, *Lenticulina margarita*, *Nodosaria claviformis* and *Marginulina spinata interrupta*) (Fig. 6x; Fig. 8p & q) and the ostracodes (*Ogmoconcha longula* and *Ogmoconchella conversa*), as well as the lowest occurrence of the Toarcian microfauna (*Trochammina kisselmani*, *Ammobaculites lobus*, *Ammodiscus glumaceus*, *Nodosaria regularis*, *Globulina sibirica*, *Triplasia kingakensis*, *Rein-*

holdella pachyderma and *Kinkelinella sermoisensis*) (Fig. 8f, g & r, Fig. 9n, o & p) characteristic for the upper part of this section have been observed. Depletion of the ostracode assemblages begins in the uppermost part of the Upper Pliensbachian, with the extinction of both *Nanacythere* and '*Mandelstamia*'. The *Recurvoides taimyrensis* JF9 Zone and the upper parts of *Ogmoconcha longula* JO2 Zone are present in the upper silty and sandy deposits of the Sharapovo and Airkat Formations, and probably into the base of the clayey deposits of the Kiterbyut Formation in some sections from NE Siberia, and in the Pliensbachian–Toarcian deposits of NE Russia.

Lower Toarcian black, locally bituminous shales of the Kiterbyut Formation occur throughout northern Siberia (Shurygin *et al.* 2000). Their stratigraphic analogues in western Siberia are the black mudstones of the Togur Formation, while in northeastern Russia these comprise clayey silty deposits. In sections of the coastal facies from the Anabar River and the lower sublittoral facies (Eastern Taymyr), the

---

Fig. 7. The ostracode assemblages of Upper Pliensbachian (**l, p, q, o, r, s, t, u, v & w**) and Lower Toarcian (**a, b, c, d, e, f, g, h, i, j, k, m & n**) from northeastern Siberia and northeastern Russia. Measurements (in brackets): length of specimens in micrometres.

(**a, b, c, d, e, f, h, i, k, m, n & v**) Northeastern Siberia, Taymyr Peninsula, Cape Tsvetkova, outcrop 7. (**a, c & f**) Bed 1, sample 2; Korotkiy Formation, Lower Toarcian, *commune–monestieri* Ammonite Zones, *Camptocythere occalata* JO6 Zone. (**d, e, h, i, k, m & n**) Bed 7; Kiterbyut Formation, Lower Toarcian, *Trachycythere verrucosa* JO5 Zone. (**v**) Bed 13, Airkat Formation, Upper Pliensbachian, *Nanacythere costata* JO3 Zone. (**g, l, p & s**) NE Siberia, Anabar Bay. (**g**) Outcrop 11, bed 1; Kiterbyut Formation, Lower Toarcian, *Camptocythere mandelstami* JO4 Zone. (**l, p & s**) Outcrop 12; Airkat Formation, Upper Pliensbachian, *Nanacythere costata* JO3 Zone. (**o, r, u & w**) NE Siberia, Olenek river basin, outcrop 1, bed 3, sample 7; Kyra Formation, Upper Pliensbachian, *Nanacythere costata* JO5 Zone.

(**a, b, c & f**) *Camptocythere occalata* Gerke & Lev, 1958. (**a**) 1. Male carapace, left side, lateral view (792.3); 1050/32. (**b**) Female, right valve, internal lateral view (810.3); M5524. East Siberia, Vilyuy Basin, Markha river, outcrop 5, bed 5, sample 23; Suntary Formation, Toarcian, *Camptocythere occalata* JO6 Zone. (**c**) Female, right valve, lateral view (963.8); 1048/5. (**f**) Female, right valve, internal lateral view (978.9); 1048/6. (**d, e, g, j, k & n**) *Camptocythere mandelstami* Gerke & Lev, 1958. (**d**) Female carapace, right side, lateral view (893.6); 1048/1. Sample 2. (**e**) Female carapace, dorsal view (914.1); 1048/2. Sample 2. (**g**) Female, left valve, internal lateral view (873.4); AB1113. Sample 3. (**j**) Female carapace, left side, lateral view (598.1); 2N51/1. Northeastern Russia, Left Kedon River basin, Astronomicheskaya River, outcrop 2, bed 8, sample 51; Lower Toarcian, *falciferum* Ammonite Zone, *Camptocythere mandelstami* JO4 Zone. (**k**) Male, carapace, left side, lateral view (1130.4); 1048/3. Sample 2. (**n**) Male carapace, dorsal view (1117.9); 1048/4. Sample 2. (**h & i**) *Trachycythere verrucosa* Triebel & Klingler 1959. (**h**) Carapace, dorsal view (845.9); 1048/16. Sample 1. (**i**) Carapace, right side, lateral view (845.9). (**l & p**) *Nanacythere costata* (Gerke & Lev 1958). (**l**) Carapace, left side, lateral view (427); 1048/17. *stokesi* Ammonite Zone, Bed 50, sample 9. (**p**) Carapace, dorsal view (426.5); 1048/18. Bed 50, sample 2. (**m**) *Polycope pelta* Fischer 1961. Carapace, lateral view (204.1); 1048/240. Sample 2. (**o & r**) *Ogmoconchella olenekensis* (Gerke & Lev 1958). (**o**) Carapace, right side, lateral view (641.3); 7/3a. (**r**) Right valve, internal lateral view (631.5); 7/4a. (**q & s**) *Ogmoconcha longula* Gerke & Lev 1958. (**q**) Carapace, right side, lateral view (684.5); 1048/28. Northeastern Siberia, Yuryung–Tumus Peninsula, outcrop 1, bed 6, sample 1; Airkat Formation, Upper Pliensbachian, *margaritatus* Ammonite Zone, *Ogmoconcha longula* JO2 Zone. (**s**) Carapace, dorsal view, (823.5); 1048/26. Bed 52, sample 2. (**t & v**) *Ogmoconchella ornata* (Gerke & Lev 1958). (**t**) Carapace, right side, lateral view, (731.6); 1048/236. Northeastern Siberia, Anabar River, outcrop 3, bed 7, sample 7; Airkat Formation, Upper Pliensbachian, *Nanacythere costata* JO3 Zone. (**v**) Carapace, right side, lateral view (792.8); 7/4a. Bed 12, sample 2. (**u**) *Ogmoconcha nordvikensis* Gerke & Lev 1958. Carapace, right side, lateral view, (621.8); 7/4b. (**w**) '*Mandelstamia*' linearis Gerke & Lev 1958. Carapace, left side, lateral view, (470); 1/7v.

maximum content of the pelitic fraction varies between 91% and 97%. A high concentration of organic carbon is also characteristic of these sediments (Kaplan 1976; Levchuk 1985). The thicknesses of the Kiterbyut Formation are between 22 m and 25 m and are remarkably consistent over the vast territory of the Siberian Platform (Shurygin *et al.* 2000).

In the Kiterbyut Formation, the lower part of the Kelimyar Formation, and at the base of the overlying sandy silts of the Nadoyakh and Eren Formations, foraminiferal assemblages of the *Ammobaculites lobus–Trochammina kisselmani* JF11 Zone (lower part of the Lower Toarcian, *falciferum* Ammonite Zone–lower half of the *commune* Ammonite Zone) have been found. The foraminiferal assemblages of the relatively deep-water facies are dominated by *Trochammina kisselmani*, *Bulbobaculites strigosus* and *Triplasia kingakensis* (Fig. 9a, b, c, j, k, l, q & r), while *Ammobaculites lobus* (Fig. 9d & g) and *Ammoglobigerina canningensis* are subdominant species. *Evolutinella taimyrensis*, *Globulina sibirica* (Fig. 9e, h & m), *Spiroplectammina* sp. 2 and *Lagenammina jurassica* are also common (Figs 4 & 5). The characteristic feature of this assemblage is the presence of migrant species from southern palaeobasins (*Palmula deslongchampsi*, *Cyclogyra liasina* and *Dentalina kiterbutica*). The near-shore shallow-water facies are distinguished by abundant *Ammobaculites lobus*, while *Trochammina kisselmani*, *Saccammina inanis* and *Triplasia kingakensis* are rare.

The *Camptocythere mandelstami* JO4 Zone (lower part of Lower Toarcian, *falciferum* Ammonite Zone–lower half of *commune* Ammonite Zone) is characterized by a monospecific assemblage in the shallow-water facies (Fig. 7d, e, k & n). In the deeper-water facies, migrant species from the west European basins occur (*Trachycythere verrucosa*, *Kinkelinella sermoisensis* and *Polycope pelta*) (Fig. 7h, i, & m) defining the *Trachycythere verrucosa* JO5 Zone (*falciferum* Ammonite Zone–lowest part of *commune* Ammonite Zone).

In the later part of the Early Toarcian, the differentiation of palaeoenvironments begins. The sandy silts of the Nadoykh and Eren Formations accumulated in the coastal areas of the Siberian palaeobasin, while the clayey silts of the Kelimyar Formation and their analogues were deposited in the more offshore areas. Foraminiferal assemblages of the *Lenticulina multa–Astacolus praefoliaceus* JF12 Zone, upper part of the Lower Toarcian–lower part of the Lower Aalenian (upper part of *commune* Ammonite Zone–lower part of *maclintocki* Ammonite Zone) are characterized by *Lenticulina multa*, *Astacolus praefoliaceus*, *Nodosaria pulchra*, *Citharina gradata*, *Evolutinella zwetkovi*, *Ammodiscus glumaceus* and *Saccammina inanis* (Fig. 8h, j, k, m & s; Fig. 9s & t). Rather

---

Fig. 8. The foraminiferal assemblages of uppermost Pliensbachian (**a, b, c & o**), lowermost Toarcian (**d, e, f, g, l, p, q & r**), Lower (**h, i, m, n & s**) and Upper (**j & k**) Toarcian from NE Siberia, NE Russia and the Franz Josef Land archipelago. Measurements (in brackets): length of specimens in micrometres.

(**a, c, h, i, n & s**) Northeastern Siberia, Taymyr Peninsula, Cape Tsvetkova, outcrop 7. (**a & c**) Airkat Formation, Upper Pliensbachian, *Recurvoides taimyrensis* JF9 Zone. (**h & s**) Korotkiy Formation, Lower Toarcian, *commune–monestieri* Ammonite Zones, *Ammobaculites lobus–Trochammina kisselmani* JF11 Zone. (**i & n**) Kiterbyut Formation, Lower Toarcian, *Ammobaculites lobus–Trochammina kisselmani* JF11 Zone. (**b & o**) Northeastern Siberia, Anabar Bay, outcrop 12, bed 65, Airkat Formation, Upper Pliensbachian, *Recurvoides taimyrensis* JF9 Zone. (**f, g, l, p, q & r**) Northeastern Russia, left Kedon river basin, Astronomicheskaya River, outcrop 2, lowermost Lower Toarcian, *propinquum* Ammonite Zone, *Recurvoides taimyrensis* JF11 Zone. (**j, k & m**) Northeastern Russia, left Kedon River basin, Saturn River, outcrop 1.

(**a, b, c, d & e**) *Recurvoides taimyrensis* Nikitenko 1992. (**a**) Dorsal view (285.9); 1048/277. Bed 10, sample 2. (**b**) Dorsal view (396.1); 1048/281. Sample 5. (**c**) Ventral view (282.7); 1048/278. Bed 10, sample 2. (**d**) Dorsal view (516.4); ZFI1/6. Franz Josef Land archipelago, Bell Island, outcrop 1, bed 5, sample 1/5; Tegetthoff Formation (upper part), uppermost Pliensbachian–lowermost Toarcian, *Recurvoides taimyrensis* JF9 Zone. (**e**) Lateral view (500). (**f & g**) *Reinholdella pachyderma* Hofker 1952. (**f**) Dorsal view (382.1); 2N43/1. Bed 6, sample 43. (**g**) Ventral view (508); 2N43/2. Bed 6, sample 43. (**h**) *Ammodiscus glumaceus* Gerke & Sossipatrova 1961 (514.3); 1048/244. Bed 3, sample 3. (**i & o**) *Kutsevella barrowensis* (Tappan 1951). (**i**) (510); 1048/260. Bed 5, sample 1. (**o**) (779); 1048/261, Sample 3. (**j, k & s**) *Lenticulina multa* Schleifer 1961. (**j & k**) Megalospheric test (1365.8); 1048/298. Bed 17, sample 124; Upper Toarcian, *falcodiscus* Ammonite Zone, *Astacolus praefoliaceus–Lenticulina multa* JF12 Zone. (**s**) Microspheric test (867.7); 1048/108. Bed 1, sample 2. (**l**) *Thurammina subfavosa* Franke 1936. (376.5); 2N35/3. Bed 5, sample 35. (**m**) *Astacolus praefoliaceus* (Gerke 1961) (345.8); 1N13/1. Bed 13, sample 95; Lower Toarcian, *commune* Ammonite Zone, *Astacolus praefoliaceus–Lenticulina multa* JF12 Zone. (**n**) *Globulina sibirica* Kisselman 1983 (335.1); 1048/320. Bed 5, sample 2. (**p**) *Marginulinopsis schleiferi* Gerke 1961 (496); 2N35/10. Bed 5, sample 35. (**q**) *Marginulina spinata interrupta* Terquem 1866 (777.6); 1048/318. Bed 5, sample 35. (**r**) *Trochammina kisselmani* Sapjanik & Sokolov, 1991 (218.1); 1048/290. Bed 5, sample 20.

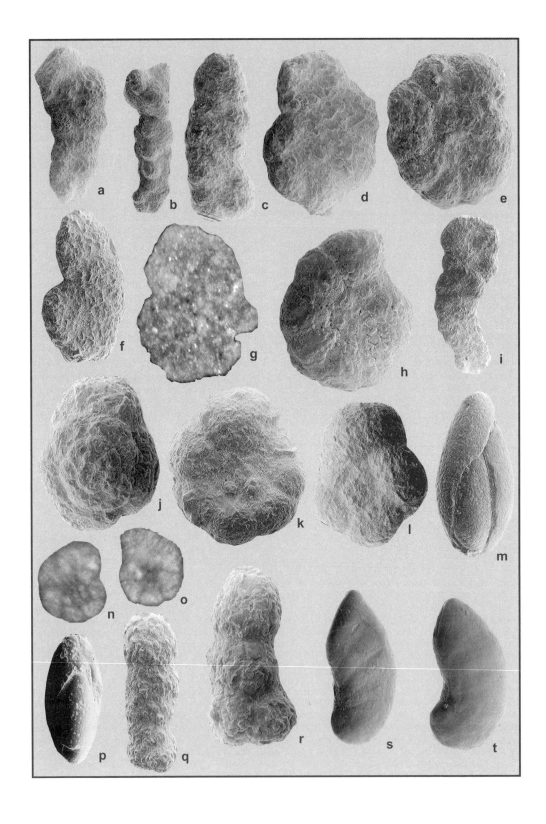

impoverished ostracodal assemblages of the *Camptocythere occalata* JO6 Zone, upper part of the Lower Toarcian to lower part of the Upper Toarcian (upper part of *commune* Ammonite Zone–lower part of *wurttenbergeri* Ammonite Zone), are mostly represented by rare occurrences of the index species (Fig. 7a, b, c & f).

When the data are insufficient (specific facies, rare samples) to distinguish this detailed Upper Pliensbachian–Lower Toarcian foraminiferal zonation, f-zones of a wider stratigraphic range have been established. For example, in the coastal shallow-water deposits at the base of the Upper Pliensbachian, the f-zone *Trochammina inusitata–Turritellella volubilis*, JF2 (Upper Sinemurian–lower part of Upper Pliensbachian) has been recognized. Above the *Ammodiscus siliceus* JF3 Zone, due to impoverished foraminiferal assemblages, an Upper Pliensbachian and lowermost Toarcian biostraton of wide stratigraphic range, the *Trochammina lapidosa* JF4 Zone, can be established. It is overlain by the *Trochammina kisselmani* JF10 Zone (Lower Toarcian). In the more offshore shallow-water facies, above the *Trochammina lapidosa–Frondiculinita dubiella* JF5 Zone, the *Conorboides buliminoides* JF6 Zone has been distinguished. This corresponds with the upper part of the Upper Pliensbachian.

Northwestern Siberia

In northwestern Siberia, Pliensbachian and Toarcian sediments have only been described from boreholes. Conventional core samples from these subsurface strata contain relatively rich foraminiferal and ostracodal assemblages

and rare bivalves. Autonomous Jurassic zonations based on the foraminifera and ostracodes, which have been developed from the ammonite-dated coastal outcrops of northeastern Siberia, are present over the northern regions of western Siberia. Some marker levels can be observed in central and even southern regions of western Siberia. The detailed (as in northern Siberia) subdivision of the Lower and Middle Jurassic of western Siberia based on microfauna is difficult to duplicate, due to the rare and incomplete recovery of microfaunal assemblages in core samples. However, marker levels are rather distinct and occur across the region (Nikitenko *et al.* 2000).

At the base of the Upper Pliensbachian, in the uppermost part of the Zimnyay Formation and lowermost part of the Levinskiy Formation, the *Ammodiscus siliceus* JF3 Zone has been identified (Fig. 10). The foraminiferal assemblages are characterized by abundant *Ammodiscus siliceus* and *Trochammina inusitata*, in association with rare *Pseudonodosaria dea, Marginulina prima* and *Verneuilinoides pudica* (Nikitenko *et al.* 2000).

In the central part of NW Siberia, clays of the Chernichnoe Formation and sandy silts of the Sarapovo Formation were deposited in subcontinental to nearshore marine palaeoenvironments. In layers of marine genesis, rare *Trochammina lapidosa, Ammodiscus siliceus, Hyperammina* ex gr. *odiosa, Saccammina* sp. and *Jaculella jacutica* have been recovered, characterizing the *Trochammina lapidosa* JF4 Zone, upper part of Upper Pliensbachian–basal Lower Toarcian (Nikitenko *et al.* 2000). In the more northern regions, where coastal marine environments were more stable, this part of the

---

Fig. 9. The foraminiferal assemblages of the Lower Toarcian from northeastern Siberia and northeastern Russia. Measurements (in brackets): length of specimens in micrometres.

(**a, b, c, d, e, f, h, i, j, k, l, m, q, r, s & t**) Northeastern Siberia, Taymyr Peninsula, Cape Tsvetkova, outcrop 7. (**a, b, c, e, h, i, j, k, l, m & q**) Kiterbyut Formation, Lower Toarcian, *Ammobaculites lobus–Trochammina kisselmani* JF11 Zone. (**r, s & t**) Korotkiy Formation. (**r**) Lower Toarcian, *Ammobaculites lobus–Trochammina kisselmani* JF11 Zone. (**s & t**) Lower Toarcian, *commune–monestieri* Ammonite Zones, *Astacolus praefoliaceus–Lenticulina multa* JF11 Zone. (**g, n, o & p**) Northeastern Russia, left Kedon River basin, Astronomicheskaya River, outcrop 2. (**g**) Lower Toarcian, *falciferum* Ammonite Zone, *Ammobaculites lobus–Trochammina kisselmani* JF11 Zone. (**n, o & p**) lowermost Lower Toarcian, *propinquum* Ammonite Zone, *Recurvoides taimyrensis* JF9 Zone.

(**a, b, c & i**) *Triplasia kingakensis* Loeblich & Tappan 1952. (**a**) (796.5); 1048/61. Bed 7, sample 4. (**b**) (1066.5); 1048/57. Bed 7, sample 4. (**c**) (722.2); 1048/58. Bed 7, sample 4. (**i**) (1047.7); 1048/59. Bed 7, sample 4. (**d, f & g**) *Ammobaculites lobus* Gerke & Sossipatrova 1961. (**d**) (562.3); 1048/250. Bed 7, sample 2. (**f**) (522.7); 1048/249. Bed 5, sample 1. (**g**) (570.8); 2N61/1. Bed 12, sample 61. (**e & h**) *Evolutinella taimyrensis* Nikitenko 2003. (**e**) (312.6); 1048/269. Bed 5, sample 1. (**h**) (169.4); 1048/265. Bed 5, sample 1. (**j, k, l, n & o**) *Trochammina kisselmani* Sapjanik & Sokolov 1991. (**j**) Microspheric test, dorsal view (302); 1048/81. Bed 5, sample 1. (**k**) Megalospheric test, ventral view (371.5); 1048/160. Bed 7, sample 4. (**l**) Megalospheric test, dorsal view (461.9); 1048/80. Bed 5, sample 1. (**n**) Megalospheric test, dorsal view (217.9); 2N27/2. Bed 5, sample 27. (**o**) Ventral view. (**m & p**) *Globulina sibirica* Kisselman 1983. (**m**) (281.8); 1048/319. Bed 5, sample 1. (**p**) (567.2); 1048/325. Bed 5, sample 35. (**q & r**) *Bulbobaculites strigosus* (Gerke & Sossipatrova 1961). (**q**) Megalospheric test (517); 1048/285. Bed 7, sample 2. (**r**) Megalospheric test (257.2); 1048/289. Bed 4, sample 2. (**s & t**) *Astacolus praefoliaceus* (Gerke 1961). (**s**) Megalospheric test (792.3); 1048/113. Bed 1, sample 2. (**t**) Microspheric test (522.6); 1048/112. Bed 1, sample 2.

Fig. 10. Summary of the distribution of selected Upper Pliensbachian–Lower Toarcian foraminifera and ostracodes, NW Siberia. For legend, see Fig. 2.

section can be further subdivided. For example, from the Levinskiy Formation and lower part of the Sharapovo Formation, *Trochammina lapidosa, Lenticulina gottingensis, Anmarginulina gerkei, Verneuilinoides* sp., *Marginulinopsis hatangensis, M. schleiferi, Pseudonodosaria pseudovulgata* and *Frondiculinita lobata* have been recovered (Glinskikh 2001). These taxa are typical of the undivided *Anmarginulina gerkei–A. arctica* JF7–JF8 Zones (middle part of Upper Pliensbachian). In the uppermost part of the Sharapovo Formation, and in its analogue (Chernichnoe Formation) plus the base of the Togur Formation, the foraminifera characterizing the *Recurvoides taimyrensis* JF9 Zone have been recovered, notably *Recurvoides taimyrensis, Recurvoides* sp. ind. *Kutsevella barrowensis* and *Trochammina* ex gr. *kisselmani* (Komissarenko 1989). In the Pliensbachian sections of western Siberia, ostracodes are rather rare and represented only by the index species of the *Ogmoconcha longula* JO2 Zone (Fig. 10).

The Togur Formation (stratigraphic analogue of the Kiterbyut Formation, lower part of the Lower Toarcian) occurs in the central regions of western Siberia and consists of black, sometimes bituminous, mudstones. The foraminiferal assemblages of the *Ammobaculites lobus–Saccammina inanis* JF11 Zone, an analogue of the northern Siberian lower Toarcian *Ammobaculites lobus–Trochammina kisselmani* JF11 Zone, occur in the Togur, Kiterbyut, the lowermost parts of the Novogodnyay, and the Nadoyakh Formations. Taxa present include *Ammodiscus glumaceus, Ammobaculites lobus, Saccammina inanis, Trochammina kisselmani, Globulina sibirica* and *Kutsevella* ex gr. *barrowensis.*

When the data are insufficient (specific facies or poor recovery from the core) to distinguish this foraminiferal zonation, foraminiferal biostratons of wider stratigraphic range have been established. At the base of the Upper Pliensbachian, the *Trochammina inusitata* JF2 Zone (Lower Pliensbachian–lower part of Upper Pliensbachian) has been recognized. The *Ammodiscus glumaceus* JF12 Zone is considered a biostratigraphic subdivision ranging from Lower Toarcian to Lower Aalenian (Fig. 10). However, in its lower part, there is a well-defined marker level: *Ammobaculites lobus–Saccammina inanis* JF11 Zone. The undifferentiated middle part of *Ammodiscus glumaceus* JF12 Zone can be correlated with the middle Siberian *Astacolus praefoliaceus–Lenticulina multa* JF12 Zone. At this level, in the Novogodnyay Formation and Nadoyakh Formation, rare *Ammobaculites praefoliaceus, Lenticulina* sp. ind. and *Ammodiscus glumaceus* occur. In the Kiterbyut Formation

and lowermost part of the Nadoyakh Formation the single ostracode species *Camptocythere mandelstami* (JO4 Zone) has been recognized (Fig. 10).

Barents Sea Region

There is much less information about the Pliensbachian–Toarcian microfaunas from the Barents Sea region. The oldest foraminiferal assemblages of Pliensbachian age have been described from mudstones occurring in the Wilhelm Island, Spitsbergen, area. This assemblage is represented by *Ammodiscus siliceus, Trochammina lapidosa, Glomospira* ex gr. *gordialis, Saccammina* sp., *Gaudryina* sp. and *Textularia* ex gr. *areoplecta* (Klubov 1965), which are characteristic of the *Trochammina lapidosa* JF4 Zone, upper part of the Upper Pliensbachian–lowermost Toarcian (Fig. 11). Diverse *Ammodiscus* spp. (Löfaldli & Nagy 1980) were recovered from the clayey silts of the Wilhelmøya Formation, Passet Member, dated as Upper Sinemurian–Toarcian (Kongsøya, Kong Karls Land). These deposits are overlain by Middle and Upper Jurassic sediments, often beginning with a layer of phosphorite concretions, which contain Toarcian and Aalenian ammonites (Pchelina 1965, 1967). The microfauna from the sandy silts of the upper part of the upper Tegetthoff Formation (Bell Island, Franz Josef Land) comprises the foraminifera *Ammodiscus siliceus, Trochammina lapidosa, Saccammina* sp., *Glomospira* ex gr. *gordialis, Recurvoides taimyrensis, Reophax metensis* and *Textularia areoplecta* (Fig. 6m; Fig. 8d, e), which are characteristic of the *Recurvoides taimyrensis* JF9 Zone.

In the Barents Sea region, in the overlying deposits of the lowermost Toarcian, no foraminifera have been found. In the central areas of the Barents Sea shelf, the rare ostracode *Camptocythere mandelstami* JO4 Zone has been recovered from ditch-cutting samples only. Impoverished foraminiferal assemblages comprising *Astacolus praefoliaceus* and *Dentalina* aff. *forta* from the *Astacolus praefoliaceus* JF12 Zone from the upper part of the Lower Toarcian (Fig. 11), have been recovered in well sections from the central areas of the Barents Sea shelf (Gramberg 1988; Basov *et al.* 1989).

Arctic Canada

In the northern Yukon and northern Richardson Mountains, only one occurrence of foraminifera (*Trochammina* sp. 5264 and *Trochammina* sp. 5271) has been described (Poulton

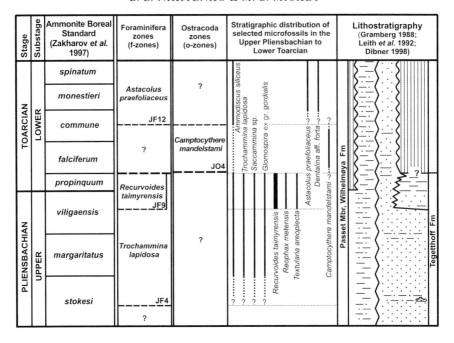

Fig. 11. Summary of the distribution of selected Upper Pliensbachian–Lower Toarcian foraminifera and ostracodes, Barents Sea area. For legend, see Figure 2.

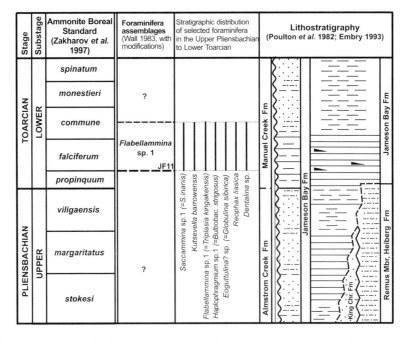

Fig. 12. Summary of the distribution of selected Upper Pliensbachian–Lower Toarcian foraminifera, Canadian Arctic. For legend, see Figure 2.

et al. 1982) from sandy silts of the Almstrom Creek Formation, dated as Late Pliensbachian by the occurrence of the ammonite *Amaltheus*. In the overlying silty clays and mudstones of the Manuel Creek Formation, a richer foraminiferal assemblage has been recovered (*Trochammina* sp. 5267, *Trochammina* sp. cf. *T. canningensis* (= *Ammoglobigerina canningensis*), *Ammodiscus* sp. cf. *A. orbis* (= *A. siliceus*), *Ammobaculites* sp. 5261 (= *A. lobus*), *Ammobaculites* sp. 4925 (= *Bulbobaculites strigosus*) and *Spiroplectammina* sp. 5273). This assemblage is most typical for the *Ammobaculites lobus–Trochammina kisselmani* JF11 Zone, which is based on the occurrences of these foraminifera and the ammonite *Dactylioceras* sp. (Poulton *et al.* 1982).

In sections from the Canadian Arctic archipelago, in the shales of the Jameson Bay Formation, Wall (1983) established the *Flabellammina* sp. assemblage, which has been dated as Toarcian. The foraminiferal assemblages, however, include *Saccammina* sp. 1 (= *S. inanis*), *Kutsevella barrowensis*, *Flabellammina* sp. 1 (= *Triplasia kingakensis*), *Haplophragmium* sp. 1 (= *Bulbobaculites strigosus*) and *Eoguttulina*? sp. (= *Globulina sibirica*). These are diagnostic of the northern Siberian *Ammobaculites lobus–Trochammina kisselmani* JF11 Zone, which is characteristic of the lower part of the Lower Toarcian (Fig. 12). Therefore, the stratigraphic range of the *Flabellammina* sp. assemblage can now be dated as the lower part of the Lower Toarcian (*falciferum* Ammonite Zone–lower part of the *commune* Ammonite Zone).

In the central part of the Canadian Arctic archipelago, Souaya (1976) established two foraminiferal zones based on ditch-cutting samples, namely *Ammodiscus* sp. cf. *A. rugosus* (Pliensbachian–?Toarcian) and *Ammodiscus* sp. cf. *A. baticus* (?Pliensbachian–lower part of the Bathonian), from sediments now envisaged to be Pliensbachian–Lower Aalenian. The foraminifera from these zones are characterized by similar assemblages comprising both Pliensbachian and Toarcian species, and taxa typical of the Middle and Upper Jurassic (*Ammodiscus thomsi, Flabellammina*? sp., *Ammobaculites venustus, A. vetusta, A. alaskensis, A. barrowensis, Gaudryina dyscrita, Haplophragmoides kingakensis, Kutsevella barrowensis, Trochammina* sp. cf. *T. sablei, Pseudobolivina* sp. C and *Astacolus ectypus*).

At present there are no published data on Pliensbachian and Toarcian ostracodes from Arctic Canada.

The Pliensbachian and Toarcian sediments from Arctic Canada and northern Siberia are rather similar (Figs 2, 3–5 & 12). For example, in the northern Yukon and northern Richardson Mountains, the Pliensbachian sandy silts of the Almstrom Creek Formation are overlain by Lower Toarcian clays and clayey siltstones of the lower part of the Manuel Creek Formation (Poulton *et al.* 1982). In the Canadian Arctic archipelago, the Lower Toarcian Jameson Bay Formation, sometimes containing bituminous clays, overlies the Pliensbachian sandy silts of the uppermost part of the Heiberg Formation (Embry 1993). A gradual change of Lower Pliensbachian siltstones and silty clays to Toarcian bituminous clays can only be recognized in the Pliensbachian–Toarcian part of the Jameson Bay Formation.

Arctic platform of Alaska

In northern Alaska, the Upper Pliensbachian is represented by the lower member of the Kingak Formation, comprising mudstones, interbedded with siltstones and sandstones (Fig. 2). Some sections, however, are characterized by mudstones or organic-rich mudstones with rare interbedded siltstones. The Lower Toarcian deposits of the lower member of the Kingak Formation are represented by bituminous mudstones, which in turn are overlain, and, in some cases, replaced by, alternating non-bituminous mudstones and siltstones (Mickey & Haga 1987).

In the northern regions of Arctic Alaska, the Pliensbachian–Toarcian deposits are recognized in many well sections. Micropalaeontological subdivision of these sediments is based on the analysis of conventional core and ditch cutting samples. At the base of Upper Pliensbachian section the *Trochammina inusitata–Turritellella volubilis* JF2 Zone (Upper Sinemurian–lower part of Upper Pliensbachian) is represented by an impoverished foraminiferal assemblage (*Ammodiscus siliceus, Trochammina inusitata, Turritellella volubilis, Spiroplectammina* sp. and *Marginulinopsis hatangensis*). In a few sections, this stratigraphic level is marked by an abundance of *Ammodiscus siliceus*, but it is limited to local sections and cannot be traced as widely as in eastern and western Siberia. The upper horizons of the Kingak Formation are characterized by foraminiferal assemblages of the *Annarginulina arctica–A. gerkei* JF7–JF8 Zone. Foraminifers are abundant and diverse in this part of section. They include *Trochammina lapidosa, Lenticulina gottingensis, Ichthyolaria lustrata, Pseudonodosaria pseudovulgata, Annarginulina gerkei, Citharina fallax, Saracenaria sublaevis, Kutsevella barrowensis* and *Marginulinopsis quadricostata* (Fig. 13).

Fig. 13. Summary of the distribution of selected Upper Pliensbachian–Lower Toarcian foraminifera, Arctic Platform of Alaska. For legend, see Fig. 2.

The *Recurvoides taimyrensis* JF9 Zone is represented by an impoverished foraminiferal composition. It is dominated by *Recurvoides taimyrensis*. Common taxa include *Kutsevella barrowensis, Saccammina* sp. 2 and *Textularia areoplecta*. In the lower part of this f-zone (JF9), foraminifera from the underlying *Anmarginulina arctica–A. gerkei* JF7–JF8 Zone become extinct (*Conorboides buliminoides, Pyrulinoides anabarensis* and *Verneuilinoides* ex gr. *pudica*). In the upper part of the *Recurvoides taimyrensis* JF9 Zone, the first Toarcian taxa, which are typical for the overlying Zone, are present (*Trochammina kisselmani, Triplasia kingakensis* and *Ammodiscus glumaceus*). At the boundary between the *Recurvoides taimyrensis* JF9 Zone and the *Ammobaculites lobus–Trochammina kisselmani* JF11 Zone there is a sharp change in the taxonomic composition of foraminiferal assemblages (Fig. 14). In some sections it was possible to recognize only the *Trochammina lapidosa* JF4 Zone characterized by a long stratigraphic range. This situation is caused by rare sample recovery and the specific facies. Foraminiferal assemblages of this zone are represented by *Trochammina lapidosa, Lenticulina gottingensis, Hyperammina odiosa, Ichthyolaria lustrata, Marginulina amica, Dentalina communis* and *Geinitzinita tenera* (Figs 13 & 14). Ostracode assemblages of the Upper Pliensbachian and Lower Toarcian (*Ogmoconcha longula* JO2 Zone) are rather sparse, comprising only a few taxa (*Ogmoconchella ornata* and *Nanacythere* ex gr. *costata*). At the boundary of the *Ogmoconcha longula* JO2 Zones and *Camptocythere mandelstami* JO4 Zones, the composition of the ostracodal assemblages completely alters (Fig. 14).

It should be noted that the Pliensbachian–Toarcian boundary is similarly characterized in the northern regions of Alaska, Siberia and the northeastern regions of Russia (Figs 2, 3–5, 13 & 14). For example, in some sections in the upper part of *Recurvoides taimyrensis* JF9 Zone the foraminiferal assemblages contain both Pliensbachian and Toarcian taxa, suggesting that this part of the section corresponds with the lower part of the Lower Toarcian. In several sections, it is supported by joint occurrences of the ammonite *Dactylioceras* aff. *D. tenuicostatum* and foraminifera in core samples (Tappan 1955). In other sections, foraminiferal assemblages of the *Recurvoides taimyrensis* JF9 Zone are represented by Pliensbachian taxa only, and the boundary with the overlying zone is very sharp. In this case, the lower zone of the Lower Toarcian has probably been eroded or was not deposited in the section.

The foraminiferal assemblages allow us to reliably identify the *Ammobaculites lobus–Trochammina kisselmani* JF11 Zone recovered from the bituminous mudstones of the lower member of the Kingak Formation. The foraminifera are dominated by *Trochammina kisselmani, Ammoglobigerina canningensis* and *Bulbobaculites strigosus* (Fig. 14). Common taxa are represented by *Triplasia kingakensis, Ammobaculites lobus, Evolutinella taimyrensis* and *Citharina hofkeri*. In the same sedimentary interval, the *Camptocythere mandelstami* JO4 Zone has been established and is characterized by abundant *Camptocythere mandelstami* and additional rare *Kinkelinella* sp. juv., *K.* ex gr. *sermoisensis* and *Paracypris* sp. 2.

The overlying part of the lower member of the Kingak Formation is comprised of siltstones and clayey siltstones. In this part of the section, the foraminifera characterizing the *Astacolus praefoliaceus–Lenticulina multa* JF12 Zone include the inceptions of *Astacolus praefoliaceus, Lenticulina toarcense, L. multa* and *Nodosaria pulchra*. Along with foraminifera, some ostracode species (*Camptocythere occalata* and *Ektyphocythere* cf. *debilis*) which are typical of the ostracode assemblage for the *Camptocythere occalata* JO6 Zone have been recovered (Fig. 14).

Biotic and abiotic events

In the Arctic basin and northwestern seas of western Europe, during the Late Pliensbachian–Early Toarcian, several simultaneous biotic and abiotic events have been recognized (Nikitenko & Shurygin 1994*b*; Little & Benton 1995; Hylton & Hart 1998). One of the most striking biotic events is the Early Toarcian microbiota crisis (mass extinction event) in the Northern Hemisphere.

The beginning of the Late Pliensbachian (*stokesi* chron to the beginning of the *margaritatus* chron) is characterized by a transgression of the Arctic basin (Fig. 15). The climate was warm and wet; coal deposits accumulated in many areas of the Northern Hemisphere (Ilyina 1985; Shurygin *et al.* 2000). In the Arctic palaeobasin, and palaeoseas of the northwestern regions of Western Europe, the taxonomic diversity of foraminifera and ostracode assemblages gradually increases. For example, three genera of ostracodes and 20 genera of foraminifera have been defined for the *stokesi* chron in the Arctic seas, while the *margaritatus* chron is characterized by four genera of ostracodes and 29 genera of foraminifera (Fig. 16). The transgression and climatic warming caused the

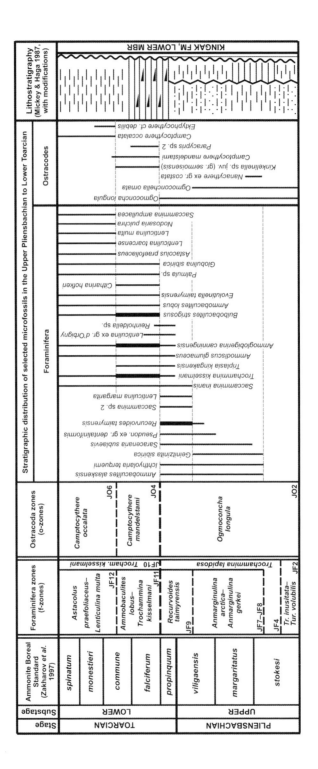

Fig. 14. Summary of the distribution of selected Upper Pliensbachian–Lower Toarcian foraminifera and ostracodes, Arctic Platform of Alaska.

invasion of a number of thermophilic migrant taxa (on both species and generic levels) in the microbenthos communities of the Arctic palaeoseas. Some foraminiferal species of the genera *Neobulimina, Saracenaria, Involutina, Ichthyolaria* and *Geinitzinita*, as well as possibly some ostracodal species of the genus *Nanacythere*, migrated from the west, while the foraminiferal genera *Grigelis, Pyrulinoides*, and *Astacolus* probably migrated from the Palaeopacific (Fig. 15). At that time, the palaeogeographical differentiation of the microbenthos characterizing different ecological (bionomical) zones was distinct. In the Late Pliensbachian, foraminiferal catenae with many elements (four to five) and ostracode catena with two elements were most typical for the northern Siberian seas. A catena is the lateral succession of interrelated communities on the bathymetric profile or slope extending from the palaeoshore toward the centre of the basin (Krasilov 1972, 1977; Tesakov 1978; Bogolepov 1983; Zakharov 1988; Nikitenko & Pospelova 1996).

The regressive stage of the Arctic palaeobasin began at the end of the *margaritatus* chron/the beginning of the *spinatum* chron. In association with a eustatic fall, a rather sharp cooling has been observed, denoted by the presence of glendonites in the northern regions of eastern Siberia (Kaplan 1976). At the same time, the climate gradually became arid (Zakharov 1994). The palaeobasins became more shallow, while the profile of the sea-bed changed. There was possibly a series of geographical barriers causing

restrictions. These events apparently caused changes in the current system, which resulted in the biotic connections with Western European seas being broken. However, the migration of microbenthos inside the Arctic Basin continued, denoted by the presence of the same taxa at similar stratigraphic levels in different Arctic regions (Fig. 15). Simultaneous eustatic fall, climatic cooling, change of sea-bed profile (and consequently changes of the current system) caused microbenthos depletion at the specific and generic levels, as well as dominance shifts in the Arctic microbenthos communities.

In the earliest Toarcian, a climatic warming (Ilyina 1985) took place in association with a major eustatic rise. Analysis of the microbenthos distribution at the Pliensbachian–Toarcian boundary suggests the absence of continuity between Pliensbachian and Toarcian microbenthos communities. At the base of the Lower Toarcian (*propinquum* Ammonite Zone), species and some genera of Arctic foraminifera were almost completely replaced, while some families disappeared (Fig. 15). The generic compositions of the ostracodes changed completely (Figs 15 & 17) and at that level in the Siberian and Western European seas the Healdidae disappeared (Arias 2000). During this crisis, the differentiation of the ecological zones of the benthos sharply reduced two- to three-element catena, and the biodiversity also decreased in individual elements of the catena.

A new stage in the development of microbenthos communities began at the *falciferum* chron. The taxonomic diversity, as well as the degree of differentiation of microbenthos associations and life-forms characterizing different ecological zones, gradually increased. During this stage, organic-rich black shales accumulated in the Arctic palaeobasins. Investigations of microcyclicity of the Lower Toarcian black shales indicate that the deposits at the boundaries of thin layers (2–5 mm) of organic-rich black shales were usually characterized by abundant monospecific communities of thin-shelled ostracodes with a well-developed system of pores and pore canals (i.e. *Camptocythere mandelstami*). In the deposits represented by the alternation of black layers with lighter grey clays, abundant and relatively diverse foraminiferal assemblages are recognized. The layers of black clays are characterized by rare eurybiotic *Ammodiscus* and *Saccammina* only. This feature of microbenthos distribution and structure in Lower Toarcian clays has been traced in numerous sections (Nikitenko 1994). It may be attributed to the alternation of periods of stagnant water and relatively well-aerated bot-

---

Fig. 15. Composite stratigraphic ranges of the Late Pliensbachian–Early Toarcian main microbenthic taxa from NE Siberia and NE Russia. Microbiotic and abiotic events. 1*, Zakharov (1994); 2*, Zakharov (1994), with modification; 3*, the model of mass extinction events adopted from Kauffman & Erwin (1995).
Ostracodes: 1, *Ogmoconcha*; 2, *Ogmoconchella*; 3, '*Mandelstamia*'; 4, *Nanacythere*; 5, *Kinkelinella*; 6, *Trachycythere*; 7, *Polycope*; 8, '*Monoceratina*'; 9, *Camptocythere*.
Foraminifera: 1, *Ammodiscus*; 2, *Glomospira*; 3, *Trochammina*; 4, *Astacolus*; 5, *Lenticulina*; 6, *Ammobaculites*; 7, *Reophax*; 8, *Hyperammina*; 9, *Saccammina*; 10, *Dentalina*; 11, *Citharina*; 12, *Spiroplectammina*; 13, *Geinitzinita*; 14, *Marginulina*; 15, *Gaudryina*; 16, *Ichthyolaria*; 17, *Nodosaria*; 18, *Marginulinopsis*; 19, *Hippocrepina*; 20, *Jaculella*; 21, *Frondiculinita*; 22, *Pseudonodosaria*; 23, *Involutina*; 24, *Conorboides*; 25, *Anmarginulina*; 26, *Neobulimina*; 27, *Grigelis*; 28, *Saracenaria*; 29, *Pyrulinoides*; 30, *Kutsevella*; 31, *Recurvoides*; 32, *Triplasia*; 33, *Reinholdella*; 34, *Globulina*; 35, *Palmula*; 36, *Cyclogyra*; 37, *Ammoglobigerina*; 38, *Bulbobaculites*; 39, *Evolutinella*.

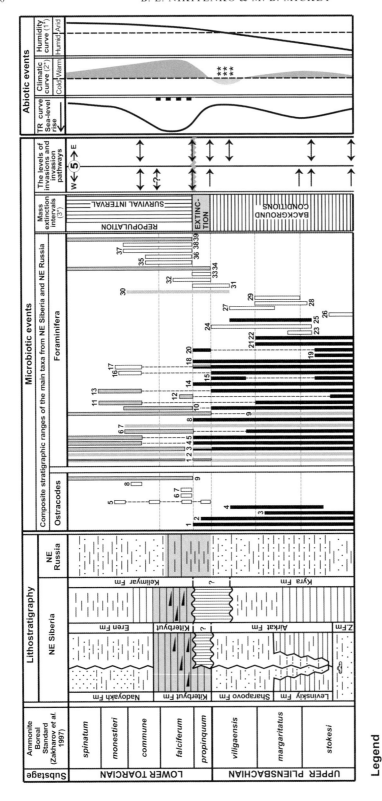

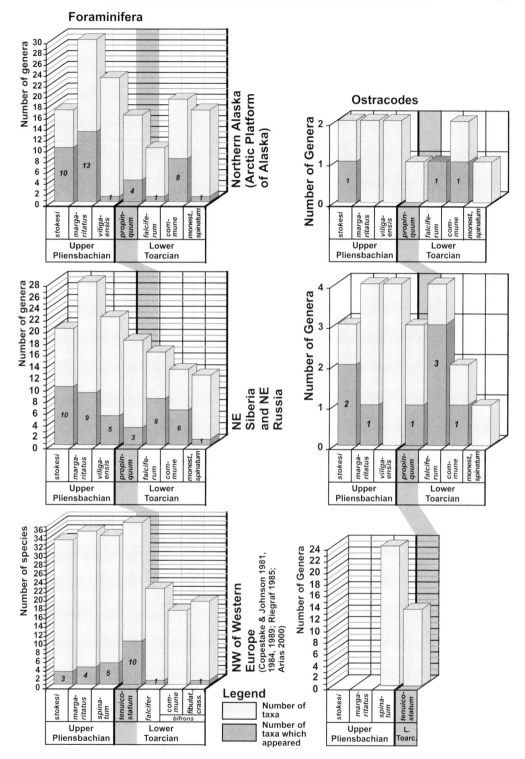

Fig. 16. Changes in taxonomic structure of foraminifera and ostracode associations

tom waters, as well as to periodic increases in the amount of organic material accumulating in the sedimentary basin.

During the post-crisis period there were reliable links between the microbenthos communities of the Arctic and Western European seas, caused by transgression and climatic warming. In the Arctic palaeobasin, this stage is characterized by periodic invasions of migrant taxa of both foraminifera (*Palmula, Cyclogyra* and *Nodosaria*) and ostracodes (*Trachycythere, Polycope* and *Kinkelinella*), which are widespread in the Toarcian Western European palaeoseas (Fig. 15). In Arctic palaeoseas, the Western European migrant taxa are generally rare, with no descendants. At the same time, some specific Arctic forms (for example, the ostracode genus *Camptocythere*) migrated to Western European seas, giving rise to new taxa (Triebel 1950; Bate & Coleman 1975).

The Early Toarcian microbiotic crisis was very sharp in both Arctic and Western European palaeobasins, and it was the most remarkable event of the Jurassic. For example, in the Arctic seas, the genera and families of the ostracodal communities were completely replaced by new taxa (Figs 15 & 17b). The species composition of foraminiferal assemblages changed considerably, while generic composition of foraminifera is characterized by partial changes. Many families disappeared (Fig. 17a). In the Western European seas (Fig. 16), the microbenthos crisis caused taxonomic changes generally on the species level among foraminifera and on the generic level among ostracodes (Fig. 16). In the Early Toarcian, the number of foraminifera and ostracodes was reduced by more than half (Copestake & Johnson 1981, 1984, 1989; Riegraf 1985; Arias 2000).

The regressive stage of the Arctic palaeobasin began in the middle of the *commune* chron, resulting in a differentiation of sedimentation conditions. Sandy silts accumulated in coastal areas of palaeobasins, while clayey silts were deposited in offshore areas. During this post-crisis period (an interval of recovery), the diversity of Arctic foraminifera was only a half of its level in Western European seas, and the difference between the ostracode diversity in the Arctic basin and European sea was even more sharp (Figs 15 & 16) (Copestake & Johnson 1981, 1984, 1989; Arias 2000). The taxonomic diversity of Arctic foraminiferal and ostracodal communities had gradually recovered by the Toarcian–Aalenian boundary. The model of Kauffman and Erwin (1995) for the basic structure of a mass extinction event holds for the Pliensbachian–Toarcian microbiotic event.

Palaeobiogeography

The comprehensive analysis of biotic and abiotic events and the reliable biostratigraphic data (ability to estimate isochronism or unisochronism of events) allow reliable palaeobiogeographical reconstructions. Very large biogeographical assemblages characterizing all the Jurassic are proposed on the basis of foraminiferal analysis (Gordon 1970; Basov 1983). On the one hand, for the Boreal Jurassic shelf assemblages, which are characteristic for the Boreal Zone, as well as for Tethyan Assemblages (for the Tethyan Zone) some biogeographical type assemblages of Jurassic foraminifera have been established: cyclamminiids–pavonitiniids (tropical zone), nodosariids–epistominiids (subtropical and temperate zone) and nodosariids–ammodisciids (subpolar zone) (Gordon 1970; Basov 1983). On the other hand, biogeographical maps for the Volgian stage were based on the analysis of the distribution of characteristic species of foraminifera (Ivanova 1973). Such studies are rare for the Jurassic ostracodes.

The traditional principles of palaeobiogeographical zonation (Saks *et al.* 1971; Saks 1972; Westermann 2000), such as definition of 'Realms' based on endemic family availability, as well as the definition of 'Provinces' based on the distribution of endemic genera, cannot be used for the microbenthos. In the Arctic palaeobasin, the microbenthos is generally characterized by foraminiferal and ostracode families and genera of rather wide geographical distribution (cosmopolitan) only. Analysis has been carried out using genera, because opinions on the classification of some species vary considerably in different publications, while the nomenclature of the genera is more standard.

Palaeobiogeographical studies should be based on abundance data, but they are not always available from the publications. In this case they can be substituted by presence/absence data, which are usually sufficient for large-scale palaeobiogeographical studies (Shi 1993; Liu *et al.* 1998). We performed multivariate analysis (Jaccard Cluster Analysis) on the micropalaeontological data obtained from the study of Upper Pliensbachian and Lower Toarcian sections from northwestern and eastern Siberia, northeastern Russia, Franz Josef Land and northern Alaska, as well as published data on northwestern Europe, the North Sea, the Barents Sea shelf and Arctic Canada (Klubov 1965; Norling 1972; Bate & Coleman 1975; Souaya 1976; Løfaldli & Nagy 1980; Copestake & Johnson

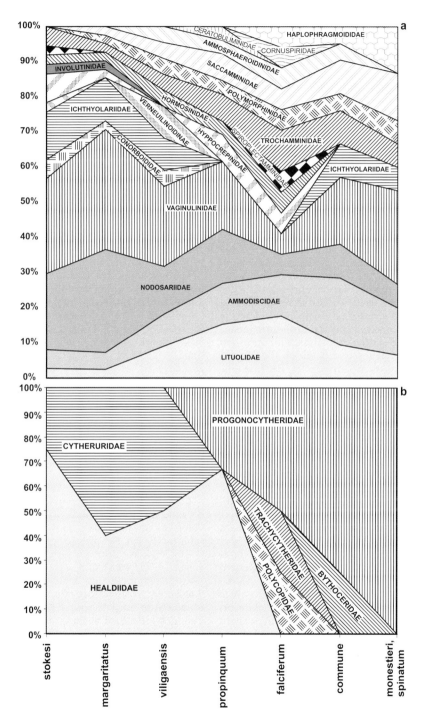

Fig. 17. Foraminifera (**a**) and ostracode (**b**) assemblage composition across the Pliensbachian–Toarcian boundary in northeastern Siberia and northeastern Russia.

1981, 1984, 1989; Poulton *et al*. 1982; Wall 1983; Ainsworth 1986, 1987; Basov *et al*. 1989; Malz & Nagy 1989; Dibner 1998). It also should be noted that the analysed data are unequal: the biostratigraphy of the Upper Pliensbachian and Lower Toarcian sections of different regions of the Northern Hemisphere were studied to different degrees. So, multivariate data on the Upper Pliensbachian and the Lower Toarcian have been used separately. Our studies of Upper Pliensbachian and Lower Toarcian foraminifera and ostracodes from northwestern and eastern Siberia, northern Alaska and Franz Josef Land include quantitative taxa proportions as well as the dynamics of taxonomic variation, community structure and other aspects, while, in publications devoted to the micropalaeontology of the Barents Sea shelf, Spitsbergen, the North Sea, northwestern Europe and Arctic Canada, these data were often lacking. Therefore, for palaeobiogeographical distribution of Late Pliensbachian and Early Toarcian foraminifera and ostracodes from these regions of the Arctic and northwestern Europe, presence/absence data have been used. The BioDiversity Professional program has been used to calculate the matrix and construct the dendrograms (McAleece *et al*. 1997). Cluster analysis with the group average link method and based on the Jaccard coefficient has been carried out. Because foraminifera and ostracodes react differently to environmental changes and represent different taxonomic groups, they have been analysed separately. This has allowed us to estimate and compare the results of the cluster analysis for these different groups of microfauna.

Based on these analyses, we identified the following biogeographical units for the Arctic and the northern area of the Boreal–Atlantic Realms: four foraminiferal provinces (northwestern Europe, North Sea, western Siberia–Canadian Arctic and eastern Siberia–northern Alaska provinces) for the Late Pliensbachian and Early Toarcian; four ostracodal provinces (northwestern Europe, North Sea, western Siberia and eastern Siberia–northern Alaska provinces) for the Late Pliensbachian; three ostracodal provinces (northwestern Europe, eastern Siberia–northern Alaska and western Siberia–Barents Sea provinces) for the Early Toarcian (Figs 18 & 19). The boundaries of the provinces and realms based on palaeogeographical distribution of different groups of microbenthos have changed their position during geological time. The North Sea region was apparently a transitional (ecotone) zone between Arctic and Boreal–Atlantic microbenthos associations (Figs 18 & 19).

Arctic palaeoseas may be divided into a number of ecological zones. In the northern Siberian and northern Alaskan seas, the Late Pliensbachian microfaunal communities were the richest and the most diverse among Early Jurassic microfaunal communities. During this time-frame, the palaeogeographical differentiation of microbenthos communities characterizing different ecological zones was distinct. In the Late Pliensbachian, in the northern Siberian seas (Fig. 20a) the foraminiferal catena commonly comprised many elements (four to five), while the ostracode catena were composed of only two elements.

The inner part of the upper sublittoral zone (Fig. 20a) was represented by nearly monospecific *Ammodiscus* communities, while *Saccammina, Glomospira* and some other taxa were rather rare (ecological zone F1). The agglutinated foraminiferal tests are often coarse grained. This zone is characterized by active hydrodynamics and unstable salinity.

The taxonomic diversity gradually increased with depth. For instance, in the outer part of the upper sublittoral zone (ecological zone F2), foraminifera are represented by abundant *Recurvoides* and numerous *Kutsevella, Saccammina* and *Glomospira*, while *Ammodiscus* and some other taxa are rarer. Sandy and silty grounds were settled by rare, but taxonomically diverse calcareous foraminifera, such as *Lenticulina, Astacolus, Marginulina, Nodosaria*, and *Ichthyolaria*. Large abundances of *Glomospira* in some areas of the palaeobasin suggest active hydrodynamic conditions, while high taxonomic diversity may indicate normal salinities. In the shallow-water offshore areas, ostracodes are rare and represented by only *Ogmoconcha* (Fig. 20a).

The maximum taxonomic diversity of microbenthos communities (Fig. 20a) has been observed in the inner part of the middle sublittoral zone. Near-shore areas are characterized by various calcareous foraminifera (*Anmarginulina, Pyrulinoides, Citharina* and *Conorboides*), although their assemblages are dominated by eurybiotic *Recurvoides* or *Trochammina* (ecological zone F3). Ostracodes are also more abundant in these areas.

Fig. 18. Palaeobiogeographical zonation of the Arctic Realm in the Late Pliensbachian on the basis of foraminifera (**a**) and on ostracodes (**b**), with dendrograms showing results of cluster analysis. (Base map after Golonka & Scotese (1995); palaeogeographical reconstructions after Bogolepov (1983), with modifications.)

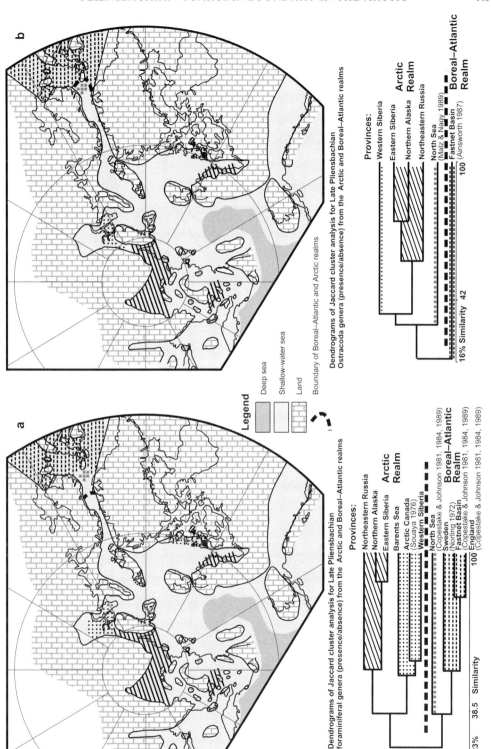

Fig. 18.

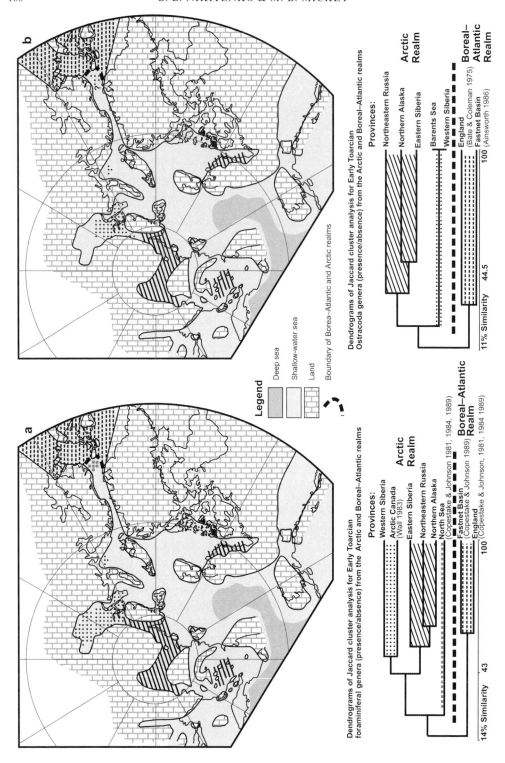

Fig. 19. Full caption on page 168.

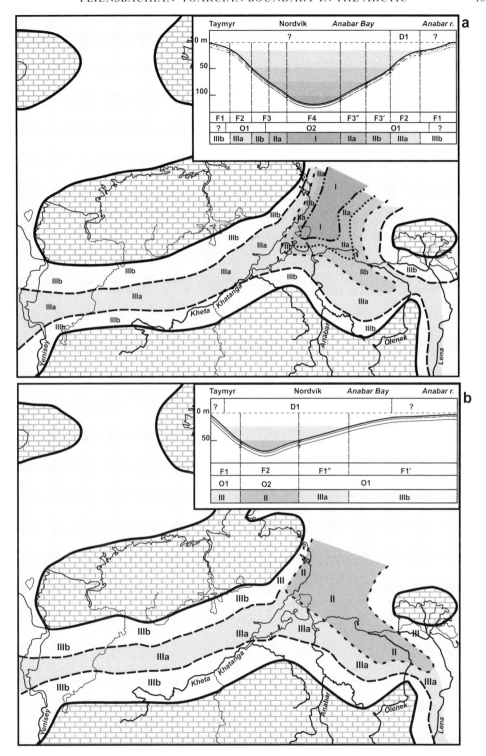

Fig. 20. Full caption on page 168.

In the outer part of the middle sublittoral zone (Fig. 20a) the taxonomic diversity of the microbenthos slightly decreases. These assemblages are dominated by calcareous foraminifera. The population density of *Lenticulina, Marginulina, Nodosaria, Pseudonodosaria, Geinitzinita* and *Planularia* increases, whereas agglutinated foraminifera are less abundant (ecological zone F3).

Foraminiferal communities of the lower sublittoral zone (Fig. 20a) are characterized by similar features, but they are less rich and diverse. This foraminiferal association lacks any dominant species and is characterized by a lower population density (ecological zone F4). They include typical eurybiotic taxa, such as *Trochammina, Dentalina, Astacolus* and *Pseudonodosaria*. The foraminifera are smaller and their tests are much thinner in comparison with the foraminifera of the middle sublittoral communities. The tests of agglutinating foraminifera are extremely fine grained.

The characteristic feature of the outer part of the middle sublittoral zone and the lower sublittoral zone is the diversity peak of ostracodes, *Ogmoconcha, Ogmoconchella, Nanacythere* and '*Mandelstamia*' (ecological zone O2).

During the Early Toarcian microbiotic crisis, differentiation of the microbenthos characterizing different ecological zones (two–three elements of a catena) as well as the diversity of lifeforms in the individual elements of the catena, decreased sharply (Fig. 20*b*). This new stage of the development of microbenthos communities began at the *falciferum* chron. The taxonomic diversity and the degree of differentiation of life-

Fig. 19. Palaeobiogeographical zonation of the Arctic Realm in the Early Toarcian on the basis of foraminifera (**a**) and on ostracodes (**b**), with dendrograms showing results of cluster analysis. (Base map after Golonka & Scotese (1995); palaeogeographical reconstructions after Bogolepov (1983), with modifications.)

form associations characterizing different ecological zones gradually increased.

Eurybiotic *Ammodiscus, Saccammina* and rare *Trochammina* are typical of microbenthos communities (Fig. 20b) of the inner part of the upper sublittoral zone (ecological zone F1). Geochemical data (Levchuk 1985) and the specific composition of the microfossils indicate the desalination of sea-water in this zone of the palaeobasin.

In the outer part of the upper sublittoral zone (Fig. 20b) foraminiferal assemblages are also dominated by *Trochammina* and *Ammobaculites*, while the number of *Ammodiscus* and *Saccammina* decreases, and *Bulbobaculites, Kutsevella* and *Triplasia* are rare (ecological zone F1). In this zone the ostracodes are represented only by *Camptocythere*.

The most diverse assemblages of foraminifera and ostracodes have been defined for the middle sublittoral zone (ecological zones F2 and O2). Foraminiferal communities (Fig. 20b) of this zone are dominated by *Trochammina, Triplasia* and *Ammobaculites* characterized by high population densities. *Spiroplectammina, Evolutinella, Kutsevella* and some other taxa are less abundant. Calcareous foraminiferal communities (*Palmula, Dentalina, Globulina* and *Cyclogyra*) are rather diverse, but their population density is low. Ostracodes are dominated by *Camptocythere mandelstami*, whereas *Kinkelinella, Trachycythere* and *Polycope* are rare (ecological zone O2). The carapaces of *Camptocythere mandelstami* are thin walled with well-developed pores and pore-canal systems. In all ecological zones of the Siberian palaeobasin, foraminiferal tests are usually very small and thin walled, suggesting unfavourable oxygen conditions at the beginning of the Early Toarcian.

In the second part of the Early Toarcian (the second part of the *commune* chron), the inner part of the upper sublittoral (Fig. 20b) zone was settled by rare specimens of *Ammodiscus, Saccammina* and *Glomospira* with small tests. The outer part of the upper sublittoral zone is

Fig. 20. The Yenisey–Lena marine basin in the Late Pliensbachian (**a**) and Early Toarcian (**b**), bathymetric profile, distribution of microbenthos and microphytoplankton ecological zones. III, upper sublittoral zone; II, middle sublittoral zone; I, lower sublittoral zone b, inner part; a, outer part. Community of microbenthos and associations of microphytoplankton in the Late Pliensbachian (**a**): Microphytoplankton associations (Nikitenko & Pospelova 1996): **D1**, *Nannoceratopsis*. The foraminiferal community: **F1**, *Ammodiscus–Saccammina*; **F2**, *Recurvoides–Kutsevella–Trochammina*; **F3**, *Trochammina–Lenticulina*; **F3″**, *Conorboides–Anmarginulina*; **F3′** *Trochammina–Pyrulinoides*; **F4**, *Astacolus–Anmarginulina*. The ostracode community: **O1**, *Ogmoconcha*; **O2**, *Ogmoconcha–Nanacythere*. Community of microbenthos and associations of microphytoplankton in the Early Toarcian (**b**): Microphytoplankton associations (Nikitenko & Pospelova 1996): **D1**, *Nannoceratopsis* The foraminiferal community: **F1**, *Trochammina–Kutsevella*; **F1′**, *Saccammina–Ammodiscus*; **F1″**, *Trochammina–Ammobaculites*; **F2**, *Trochammina–Triplasia*. The ostracode community: **O1**, *Camptocythere*; **O2**, *Camptocythere–Kinkelinella*.

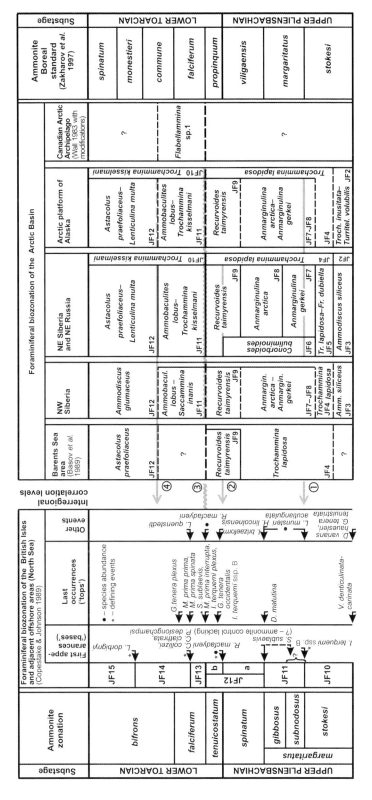

Fig. 21. The Circumboreal inter-regional correlation of the Upper Pliensbachian–Lower Toarcian based on foraminifera. Inter-regional correlation levels: 1, *Saracenaria sublaevis, Involutina liassica, Ichthyolaria terquemi, Grigelis apheilolocula. 2, Reinholdella pachyderma, Thurammina subfavosa. 3,* The level of the boreal crisis affecting the microbiota. Invasion of *Palmula deslongchampsi, Cyclogyra liasina.* Invasion in NW Europe of *Trochammina kisselmani, Ammoglobigerina canningensis, Haplophragmoides kingakensis. 4, Lenticulina multa, Astacolus praefoliaceus, Nodosaria pulchra, Palmula ex* gr. *tenuistriata.*

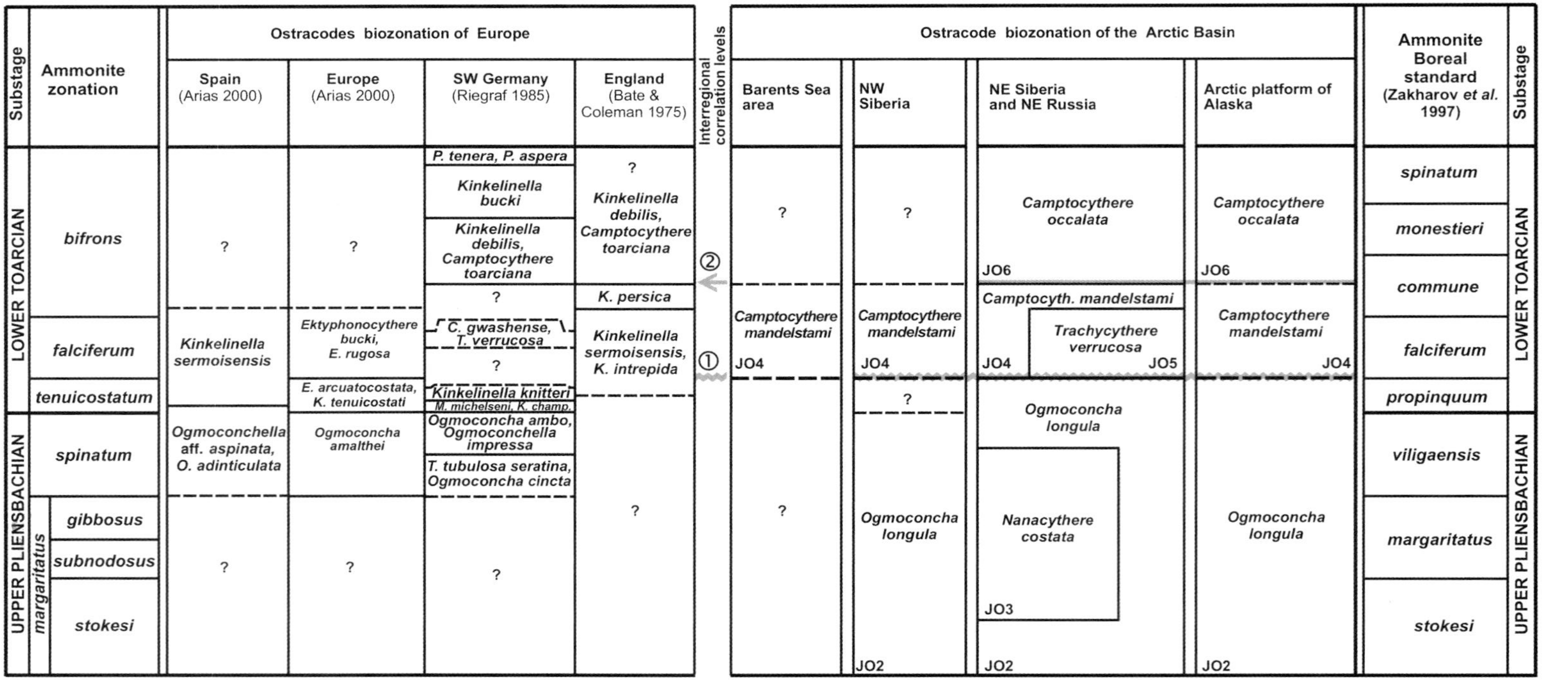

Fig. 22. The Circumboreal inter-regional correlation of the Upper Pliensbachian–Lower Toarcian based on ostracodes. Inter-regional correlation levels: 1, The level of the boreal crisis affecting the microbiota. Invasion of *Trachycythere verrucosa*, *Kinkelinella sermoisensis*, *Polycope pelta*. 2. Invasion of '*Monoceratina vulsa*', *Ektyphocythere* cf. *debilis*. Invasion in NW Europe of *Camptocythere toarciana* (= *C. occalata*).

characterized by rare *Lenticulina, Astacolus, Trochammina* and *Dentalina*. According to geochemical data (Levchuk 1985) and micro-fauna composition, the salinity of the water was unstable – ranging from normal-marine to brackish conditions.

The assemblages of the middle sublittoral zone are dominated by *Lenticulina* and *Astaco-lus*, while *Globulina, Ichthyolaria, Nodosaria, Dentalina, Citharina, Ammodiscus* and some other taxa are less abundant. The ostracode *Camptocythere* is typical of both the outer part of the upper sublittoral zone and the middle sublittoral zone (Fig. 20b). Geochemical data indicate normal salinity in this zone of the palaeobasin (Levchuk 1985).

Conclusions

The results of these investigations allow us to trace Lower Jurassic ostracode and foraminif-eral zonations developed from the northern regions of the eastern Siberia sections (Figs 3–5) over the whole Arctic basin: western Siberia (Fig. 10), NE Russia (Figs 3–5), Franz Josef Land (Fig. 11) and northern Alaska (Mickey *et al.* 1998) (Figs 13 & 14). Using published data, these zonal units or their analogues can be defined in Arctic Canada (Fig. 12) and the Barents Sea shelf (Wall 1983; Basov *et al.* 1989) (Fig. 11). Therefore, Lower Jurassic zonations based on foraminifera and ostracodes estab-lished for northern Siberia can be considered as an Arctic zonal standard (Figs 21 & 22). Moreover, several marker levels based on microfossils have been traced which allow us to correlate Arctic and Western European micro-fossil zonations of Lower and Middle Jurassic age (Figs 21 & 22).

The main abiotic and biotic events in the Late Pliensbachian and Early Toarcian of the Arctic Basin have been analysed. This allows us to conclude that a decrease of species and generic diversity of Arctic foraminifera and ostracodes began in the latest Pliensbachian, while in Western European palaeobasins the micro-benthos extinction began in the Toarcian.

The Early Toarcian microbiotic crisis in the Arctic was caused by several global events. At the end of the Late Pliensbachian there was a eustatic sea-level fall, climatic cooling, and changes of underwater topography. At the beginning of the Early Toarcian, there was climatic warming, a major eustatic rise, a change in the topography of the sea-bed, a change in the current system pattern and the development of anoxic environments. The alternation of these abiotic events during a short period of time resulted in a sharp decrease of microbiotic diversity followed by a new phase of develop-ment of microbenthos communities. The begin-ning of the *falciferum* chron is characterized by a very sharp change in the taxonomic composition of the microbenthos communities (Figs 15–17). The formation of black bituminous clays in Siberian palaeobasins, from the *falciferum* chron to the beginning of *commune* chron, correlates well with the second model of bituminous clay accumulation described by Hallam (1975). The deposits accumulated in a relatively shallow-water basin with a gently sloping sea-floor and the introduction of rather large quantities of organic material.

Mass extinction of microbenthos was simul-taneous in Arctic and Western European palaeo-seas and has been dated as Early Toarcian (*tenuicostatum* chron). The Early Toarcian microbiota crisis was distinct in both the Arctic and the Western European palaeobasins. For example, the genera and family composition of Arctic ostracodes completely changed, and 80% of the foraminiferal special disappeared with many families also disappearing altogether. In Western European palaeoseas, the taxonomic composition changed mainly at the species level among foraminifera and on the generic level among ostracodes (Fig. 16).

During the Late Pliensbachian and Early Toarcian there were permanent connections between the marine microbiota of the Arctic Palaeobasin, while Arctic and Western Eur-opean microbiota were linked only during short periods of eustatic sea-level rise and warming.

The comprehensive analysis of the biogeogra-phical distribution of Late Pliensbachian and Early Toarcian foraminifera and ostracodes, as well as Jaccard cluster analysis, allow us to define several biogeographical units within the Arctic and Boreal–Atlantic realms (Figs 18 & 19). The boundaries of provinces and realms based on the palaeogeographical distribution of ecological groups of microbenthos, as one would expect, change their position during geological time.

The authors are grateful to Dr E. B. Peschevitskaya for reading the manuscript and offering comments. We thank Dr N. R. Ainsworth, Dr A. B. Beaudoin and Dr J. H. Wall for their helpful and constructive discus-sions. The investigation has been carried out with the support of grants RFBR 00–05–65405 and 03–05–64391.

References

AINSWORTH, N. R. 1986. Toarcian and Aalenian Ostracoda from the Fastnet Basin, offshore

South-West Ireland. *Geological Survey of Ireland*, **3**, 277–366.

AINSWORTH, N. R. 1987. Pliensbachian Ostracoda from the Fastnet Basin, offshore Southwest Ireland. *Geological Survey of Ireland*, **4(1)**, 41–62.

ARIAS, C. 2000. The Pliensbachian–Toarcian boundary Ostracod biostratigraphy in the Cordillera Iberica, northeastern Spain. *Neues Jahrbuch für Geologie und Paläontologie Abhandlungen*, **216(2)**, 153–193.

AZBEL, A. Ya. & GRIGELIS, A. A. (eds) 1991. *Prakticheskoe Rukovodstvo po Mikrofaune SSSR. Tom. 5. Foraminifery Mezozoya. (Practical Manual on Microfauna of the USSR. Vol. 5. Mesozoic Foraminifers)*. Nedra, Leningrad, 5–373 (in Russian).

BASOV, V. A. 1983. Bentosnye foraminifery mezozoya Severnoy Atlantiki i ikh znachenie dlya Paleogeograficheskikh Rekonstruktcyj (Mesozoic benthic foraminifera of the Northern Atlantic and their significance for palaeogeographic reconstructions). *In*: ZAKHAROV, V. A. & NALNYAEVA, T. I. (eds) *Mezozoy Sovetskoy Arktiki (Mesozoic of Soviet Arctic Regions)*, Nauka, Novosibirsk, pp. 88–94 (in Russian).

BASOV, V. A., VASILENKO, L. V., SOKOLOV A. R. & YAKOVLEVA, S. P. 1989. Zonal'noe raschlenenie morskogo mezozoya Barentcevskogo bassejna (Zonal subdivision of the sea Mesozoic deposits of the Barents Sea). *In*: SOLOV'EV, V. A. (ed.) *Yarusnye i Zonal'nye Shkaly Boreal'nogo Mezozoya (Stage and Zonal Scales of the Boreal Mesozoic of the USSR)*. Nauka, Moscow, pp. 60–74 (in Russian).

BATE, R. H. & COLEMAN, B. E. 1975. Upper Lias Ostracoda from Rutland and Huntingdonshire. *Bulletin of the Geological Survey of Great Britain*, **55**, 1–41.

BERGQUIST, H. R. 1966. Micropaleontology of the Mesozoic rocks of northern Alaska. Exploration of naval petroleum reserve No. 4 and adjacent areas, Northern Alaska, 1944–53. Part. 2, Regional studies. *US Geological Survey, Professional Papers*. **302-D**, 93–227.

BOGOLEPOV, K. V. (ed.) 1983. *Paleogeographya Severa SSSR v Yurskom Periode (Paleogeography of the Northern USSR in the Jurassic)*. Nauka, Novosibirsk, pp. 3–190 (in Russian).

COPESTAKE, P. & JOHNSON, B. 1981. The Hettangian to Toarcian. *In*: JENKINS, D. G. & MURRAY, J. W. (eds) *Stratigraphical Atlas of Fossil Foraminifera*, Ellis Horwood, Chichester, pp. 81–105.

COPESTAKE, P. & JOHNSON, B. 1984. Lower Jurassic (Hettangian–Toarcian) foraminifera from the Mochras Borehole, North Wales (U.K.) and their application to a worldwide biozonation. *In*: OERTLI, H. J. (ed.) *Benthos'83. Second International Symposium Benthic Foraminifera, Pau, April 1983*, Elf-Aquitaine Pau, France, pp. 183–184.

COPESTAKE, P. & JOHNSON, B. 1989. The Hettangian to Toarcian (Lower Jurassic). *In*: JENKINS, D.G. & MURRAY, J.W. (eds) *Stratigraphical Atlas of Fossil Foraminifera. Second Edition*, Ellis Horwood, Chichester, pp. 126–270.

DIBNER, V. D. (ed.) 1998. *Geology of Franz Josef Land*. Oslo, Norsk Polarinstitutt, Meddelelse, **146**, 3–190.

EMBRY, A. F. 1993. Transgressive–regressive (TR) sequence analysis of the Jurassic succession of the Sverdrup Basin, Canadian Arctic Archipelago. *Canadian Journal of Earth Sciences*, **30**, 301–320.

GERKE, A. A. 1961. *Foraminifery Permskikh, Triasovikh i Leiasovykh Otlozheniy Neftenosnykh Rayonov Severa Central'noy Sibiri. (Foraminifera of Permian, Triassic and Liassic Deposits of the Oil-Bearing areas of the North of Central Siberia)*. Gostoptehizdat, Leningrad, pp. 3–579 (in Russian).

GLINSKIKH, L. A. 2001. Biostratigrafiya i mikrofauna nizhney i sredney yury Novoportovskoi ploshadi (Biostratigraphy and microfauna of Lower and Middle Jurassic of Novyi Port area). *Geologia, Geofizika i Razrabotka Neftyanyh Mestorozhdeniy (Geology, Geophysics and Reservoir Engineering)*, **10**, pp. 25–30 (in Russian).

GOLONKA, J. & SCOTESE C. R. 1995. Phanerozoic paleogeographic maps of Arctic margins. *In*: SIMAKOV, K. V. & THURSTON, D. K. (eds) *Proceedings of International Conference on Arctic Margins*, Magadan, Russia, pp. 1–16.

GORDON, W. A. 1970. Biostratigraphy of Jurassic foraminifera. *Bulletin of the Geological Society of America*, **81**, 1689–1704.

GRAMBERG, I. S. (ed.) 1988. Barentcevskaya shel'fovaya plita (Barents shelf plate). Nedra, Leningrad, 3–263, (in Russian).

HALLAM, A. 1975. *Jurassic Environments*. Cambridge University Press, Cambridge, pp. 3–229.

HALLAM, A. 1986. The Pliensbachian and Tithonian extinction events. *Nature*, **319**, 765–768.

HALLAM, A. & WIGNALL, P. B. 1999. Mass extinctions and sea-level changes. *Earth-Science Reviews*, **48**, 217–250

HARRIES, P. J. & LITTLE, C. T. S. 1999. The early Toarcian (Early Jurassic) and the Cenomanian–Turonian (Late Cretaceous) mass extinctions: similarities and contrasts *Palaeogeography, Palaeoclimatology, Palaeoecology*, **154**, 39–66.

HYLTON, M. D. & HART, M. B. 1998. Benthic Foraminiferal Response to Pliensbachian–Toarcian (Lower Jurassic) Sea-level Change and Oceanic Anoxia in NW Europe. World Wide Web Address: http://www.science.plym.ac.uk/departments/Geology/ResStaff/MHylton/publicat.htm#vncvr.

ILYINA, V. I. 1985. *Palinologiya Yury Sibiri. (Jurassic Palynology of Siberia)*. Nauka, Moscow, pp. 3–237 (in Russian).

IVANOVA, E. F. 1973. *Foraminirery Volzhskogo Veka Boreal'nykh Basseinov SSSR. (Foraminifera of Volgian Age of the Boreal Basins of the USSR)*. Nauka, Novosibirsk, pp. 3–139 (in Russian).

JENKYNS, H. C. 1985. The Early Toarcian and Cenomanian–Turonian anoxic events in Europe: comparisons and contrasts. *Geologische Rundschau*, **74**, 505–518.

JENKYNS, H. C. 1988. The early Toarcian (Jurassic) anoxic event: stratigraphic, sedimentary, and geochemical evidence. *American Journal of Science*, **288**, 101–151.

KAPLAN, M. E. 1976. *Litologiya Morskikh Mezozoiskikh Otlozheniy Severa Vostochnoy Sibiri. (Lithology of Mesozoic Marine Deposits of the North of East Siberia.)* Nedra, Leningrad, pp. 3–229, in Russian.

KAUFFMAN, E. G. & ERWIN, D. H. 1995. Surviving mass extinctions. *Geotimes*, **14**, 14–17.

KLUBOV, B. A. 1965. Triasovye i yurskie otlozheniya ostrova Wilhelma. (Triassic and Jurassic deposits of Wilhelm Island.) *In*: SOKOLOV, V. N. (ed.) *Materialy po Geologii Spitsbergen (Data on the Geology of Spitsbergen)*. Nauchno-issledovatelskiy Institut Geologii Arctiki, Leningrad, pp. 174–184, (in Russian).

KOMISSARENKO, V. K. 1989. Mikrofaunisticheskie repery zavodoukovskoy serii (Microfaunal marker levels in the Zavodoukovsk series). *In*: BRADUCHAN, YU. V. & PURTOVA, S. I. (eds) *Biostratigrafiya Osadochnogo Chehla Zapadno–Sibirskoy Ravniny. (Biostratigraphy of the Sedimentary Cover of the West Siberian Plain)*. ZapSibNIGNI, Tyumen, pp. 13–18 (in Russian).

KRASILOV, V. A. 1972. *Paleoekologiya Nazemnyh Rasteniy. Osnovnye Principy i Metody (Palaeoecology of Terrestrial Plants. Basic Principles and Methods)*. Far East Scientific Centre of the Academy of Sciences of the USSR, Vladivostok, pp. 5–208 (in Russian).

KRASILOV, V. A. 1977. *Evolutsiya i Biostratigrafiya (Evolution and Biostratigraphy)*. Nauka, Moscow, 3–254 (in Russian).

LEITH, T. L., WEISS, H. V. *ET AL.* 1992. Mesozoic hydrocarbon source-rocks of the Arctic region. *In*: VORREN, T. O., BERGSAGER, E., DAHLSTAMNES, Ø. A., HOLTER, O., JOHANSEN, B., LIE, E. & LUND, T. B. (eds) *Artic Geology and Petroleum Potential, Proceedings of the Norwegian Petroleum Society Conference, 15–17 August 1990*, Tromsø, Norway, Norwegian Petroleum Society, Special Publication, **2**, Elsevier, Amsterdam, pp. 1–25.

LEVCHUK, M. A. 1985. *Litologiya i Perspektivy Neftegazonosnosti Yurskikh Otlozheniy Enisey–Khatangskogo Progiba (Lithology and Oil and Gas Prospects of the Jurassic Deposits of the Yenisey–Khatanga Depression)*. Nauka, Novosibirsk, pp. 3–164 (in Russian).

LITTLE, C. T. S. & BENTON, M. J. 1995. Early Jurassic mass extinction: a global long-term event. *Geology*, **23**, 495–498.

LIU, C., HEINZE, M. & FÜRSICH, F. T. 1998. Bivalve provinces in the Proto-Atlantic and along the southern margin of the Tethys in the Jurassic. *Palaeogeography, Palaeoclimatology, Palaeoecology*, **137**, 127–151.

LØFALDLI, M. & NAGY, G. 1980. Foraminiferal stratigraphy of Jurassic deposits on Kongsoya, Svalbard. *Norsk Polarinstitutt, Skrifter*, **172**, 63–96.

MCALEECE, N., LAMBSHEAD, P. J. D., PATERSON, G.L.J. & GAGE, J.D. 1997. BioDiversity

Professional. http://www.nhm.ac.uk/zoology/bdpro.

MALZ, H. & NAGY, G. 1989. Lower Jurassic ostracoda from North Sea wells in the Norwegian Sector. *Courier Forschungsinstitut Senckenberg, Frankfurt am Main*, **113**, 61–75.

MICKEY, M. B. & HAGA, H. 1987. Jurassic–Neocomian biostratigraphy, North slope, Alaska. *In*: TAILLEUR, I. & WEIMER, P. (eds) *Alaskan North Slope Geology. Volume One*. The Pacific Section, Society of Economic Paleontologists and Mineralogists and the Alaska Geological Society, Anchorage, Alaska, pp. 397–404

MICKEY, M. B., NIKITENKO, B. & SHURYGIN, B. 1998. Petroliferous Upper Jurassic correlated across Western Siberia, Northern Alaska, Arctic Islands. *Oil and Gas Journal*, **96(50)**, 84–87.

NAGY, J. & JOHANSEN, H. O. 1991. Delta-influenced foraminiferal assemblages from the Jurassic (Toarcian–Bajocian) of the northern North Sea. *Micropaleontology*, **37(1)**, 1–40.

NIKITENKO, B. L. 1992. Zonal'naya shkala nizgney i sredney yury na severe Sibiri po foraminiferam (Foraminiferal zonal scale of Lower and Middle Jurassic of the northern regions of Siberia). *Geologia i Geofizika (Russian Geology and Geophysics)*, **1**, 3–14, in Russian.

NIKITENKO, B. L. 1994. Ranne- i sredneyurskie ostrakody severa Sibiri: osnovnye zakonomernosti evolyutcy i zonal'naya shkala (Early and Middle Jurassic Ostracoda of the northern region of Siberia: the main features of their evolution and zonal scale). *Stratigrafia. Geologicheskaya Korrelyatsia (Stratigraphy: Geological Correlation)*, **2(4)**, 38–55 (in Russian).

NIKITENKO, B. L. & POSPELOVA, V. Yu. 1996. Mikrobiota (bentos i fitoplankton) i biofacii v ranne- sredneyurskikh moryakh na severe Sibiri. (Microbiota (benthos and phytoplankton) and biofacies in Early and Middle Jurassic seas of Siberia). *In*: KANYGIN, A. V. (ed.) *Geodinamika i Evolutsia Zemli (Geodynamics and Evolution of the Earth)*. Publishing House of the Siberian Branch of the Russian Academy of Sciences, Novosibirsk, pp. 177–180 (in Russian).

NIKITENKO, B. L. & SHURYGIN, B. N. 1994*a*. The use of parallel biozonal scales for refined correlation in the Jurassic of the Boreal Realm. *In*: THURSTON, D. K. & FUJITA, K. (eds) *Proceedings 1992 International Conference on Arctic Margins, Anchorage, Alaska*. US Department of the Interior Minerals Management Service, Alaska Outer Continental Shelf Region, Anchorage, Alaska, pp. 33–38.

NIKITENKO, B. L. & SHURYGIN, B. N. 1994*b*. Lower Toarcian black shales and Pliensbachian–Toarcian crisis of the biota of Siberian paleoseas. *In*: THURSTON, D. K. & FUJITA, K. (eds) *Proceedings 1992 International Conference on Arctic Margins, Anchorage, Alaska*. US Department of the Interior Minerals Management Service, Alaska Outer Continental Shelf Region, Anchorage, Alaska, pp. 39–45.

NIKITENKO, B. L., SAP'ANIK, V. V. & GLINSKIKH, L. A. 2000. Ranne- sredneyurskie kompleksy foraminifer i ostracod severnoy i yuzhnoy okrain Zapadno–Sibirskoi ravniny. (Early and Middle Jurassic Foraminifera and Ostracoda assemblages from the northern and southern margins of the West Siberian Lowland). *Novosti Paleontologii i Stratigrafii. Prilozhenie k Zhurnalu Geologiya i Geofizika (News of Paleontology and Stratigraphy. Supplement to Journal Geologiya i Geofizika)*, **2–3**, 87–110 (in Russian).

NORLING, E. 1972. Jurassic stratigraphy and foraminifera of Western Scania, Southern Sweden. *Sveriges Geologiska Undersokning*, **46**, 1–120.

PCHELINA, T. M. 1965. Mezozoiskie otlozheniya raiona Van-Keilen-Fiorda (Zapadnyi Spitsbergen). (Mesozoic deposits of the Van Keulenfjorden area). *In*: SOKOLOV, V. N. (ed.) *Materialy po Geologii Spitsbergen. (Data on the Geology of Spitsbergen)*. Nauchno-issledovatelskiy Institut Geologii Arctiki, Leningrad, pp. 149–173 (in Russian).

PCHELINA, T. M. 1967. Stratigrafia i nekotorye osobennosti veschestvennogo sostava mezozoiskikh otlozheniy yuzhnykh i severnykh raionov Zapadnogo Spitsbergena. (Stratigraphy and peculiarities of the lithology of the Mesozoic deposits of the southern and northern areas of Western Spitsbergen). *In*: SOKOLOV, V. N. (ed.) *Materialy po Stratigrafii Spitsbergena (Data on the Stratigraphy of Spitsbergen)*. Nauchno-issledovatelskiy Institut Geologii Arctiki, Leningrad, pp. 121–158 (in Russian).

POULTON, T. P., LESKIW, K. & AUDRETSCH, A. 1982. Stratigraphy and microfossils of the Jurassic Bug Creek Group of Northern Richardson Mountains, Northern Yukon and adjacent Northwest Territories. *Geological Survey of Canada, Bulletin*, **325**, 1–137.

RIEGRAF, W. 1985. Microfauna, Biostratigraphie und Fazies im Unteren Toarcium Sudwestdeutschlands und Vergleiche mit benachbarten Gebieten. *Tubinger Micropalaontology*, **3**, 1–232.

RÖHL, H.-J., SCHMID-RÖHL, A., OSCHMANN, W., FRIMMEL, A. & SCHWARK, L. 2001. The Posidonia Shale (Lower Toarcian) of SW-Germany: an oxygen-depleted ecosystem controlled by sea level and palaeoclimate. *Palaeogeography, Palaeoclimatology, Palaeoecology*, **165**, 27–52.

SAKS, V. N. 1972. Nekotorye Obschie Voprosy Paleogeografii i Paleobiogeografii Mezozoiskoi ery. (Some Problems of the Palaeogeography and Palaeobiogeography of the Mesozoic). *In*: SAKS, V. N. (ed.) *Problemy Paleozoogeografii Mezozoya Sibiri (Problems of the Palaeozoogeography of the Siberian Mesozoic)*. Nauka, Moscow, pp. 5–18 (in Russian).

SAKS, V. N. (ed.) 1976. *Stratigrafia Yurskoi Sistemy Severa SSSR. (Stratigraphy of the Jurassic System of the North of the USSR)*. Nauka, Moscow, pp. 5–436 (in Russian).

SAKS, V. N., BASOV, V.A. & DAGYS, A. A. 1971. Paleozoogeografiya morey boreal'nogo poyasa v yure i neokome. (Palaeozoogeography of the Boreal seas in the Jurassic and Neocomian). *In*: SAKS, V. N. (ed.) *Problemy Obschey i Regional'noy Geologii (Problems of General and Regional Geology)*. Nauka, Novosibirsk, pp. 179–211 (in Russian).

SHI, G. R. 1993. Multivariate data analysis in palaeoecology and palaeobiogeography: a review. *Palaeogeography, Palaeoclimatology, Palaeoecology*, **105**, 199–234.

SHURYGIN, B. N., NIKITENKO, B. L. ET AL. 2000. *Stratigraphiya Neftegazonosnyh Basseynov Sibiri. Yurskaya Systema. (Stratigraphy of Oil and Gas Basins of Siberia. Jurassic System)*, Novosibirsk, Publishing House of Siberian Branch of Russian Academy of Sciences, Department 'Geo', 3–476, in Russian.

SOUAYA, F. G. 1976. Foraminifera of Sun-Gulf-Global Linckens Island well P-46, Arctic Archipelago, Canada. *Micropaleontology*, **22**, 249–306.

TAPPAN, H. 1955. Foraminifera from the Arctic Slope of Alaska. Part 2. Jurassic Foraminifera. *US Geological Survey, Professional Paper*, **236-B**, 21–90.

TESAKOV, Yu. I. 1978. *Tabulaty. Popuyatsionniy, Biocenotycheskiy i Biostratigraficheskiy Analiz (Tabulata. Populational, Biocoenosic and Biostratigraphic Analysis)*. Nauka, Moscow, pp. 3–262 (in Russian).

TRIEBEL, E. 1950. *Camptocythere*, eine neue Ostracoden-Gattung aus dem Dogger Norddeutschlands. *Senckenbergiana*, **31**, 197–208.

WALL, J. H. 1983. Jurassic and Cretaceous foraminiferal biostratigraphy in the Eastern Sverdrup Basin, Canadian Arctic Archipelago. *Bulletin of Canadian Petroleum Geology*, **31(4)**, 246–281.

WESTERMANN, G. E. G. 2000. Biochore classification and nomenclature in paleobiogeography: an attempt at order. *Palaeogeography, Palaeoclimatology, Palaeoecology*, **158**, 1–13.

ZAKHAROV, V. A. 1988. Paleoekologicheskie issledovaniya (Palaeoecological researches). *In*: MENNER, V. V. & MAKRIDIN, V. P. (eds) *Sovremennaya Paleontologiya. (New Palaeontology)*. Nedra, Moscow, pp. 369–400.

ZAKHAROV, V. A. 1994. Climatic fluctuations and other events in the Mesozoic for the Siberian Arctic. *In*: THURSTON, D. K. & FUJITA, K. (eds) *Proceedings International Conference on Arctic Margins, Anchorage, Alaska*. US Department of the Interior, Minerals Management Service, Alaska Outer Continental Shelf Region, Anchorage, Alaska, pp. 23–28.

ZAKHAROV, V. A., BOGOMOLOV, Yu. I. ET AL. 1997. Boreal zonal standard and biostratigraphy of the Siberian Mesozoic. *Russian Geology and Geophysics*, **38(5)**, 965–993.

Palynostratigraphy of the classic Portland and Purbeck sequences of Dorset, southern England, and the correlation of Jurassic–Cretaceous boundary beds in the Tethyan and Boreal realms

CHRIS O. HUNT

Geographical Sciences, University of Huddersfield, Queensgate, Huddersfield HD1 3DH, UK (e-mail: c.o.hunt@hud.ac.uk)

Abstract: Placement of the Jurassic–Cretaceous boundary and its correlation between the Tethyan and Boreal realms are still contentious. The distribution of stratigraphically significant dinoflagellate cysts in the Portland Stone and Purbeck formations of the Isle of Purbeck, Dorset, UK provides a basis for direct correlation between these sections and the type Berriasian in southeast France. The base of the Berriasian – and thus of the currently accepted Jurassic–Cretaceous boundary – most probably lies at the base of the Cypris Freestones in the Purbeck Formation. Miospore correlation between the Dorset sections and ammonite-bearing rocks in the Spilsby Province suggests that the base of the Cretaceous lies close to the base of the *Subcraspidites preplicomphalus* zone in the Boreal Realm.

The latest Jurassic and earliest Cretaceous were marked globally by low sea-levels and consequent provincialism of marine biota. European biotas are divided biogeographically into the southern Tethyan province and the northern Boreal province (Fig. 1). The distinctive nature of the biota in these provinces has necessitated the establishment of independent zonations and stage nomenclature.

In the Tethyan province, the terminal Jurassic stage has historically been known as the Tithonian, although no stratotype has been recognized. The basal Cretaceous stage is the Berriasian, with a stratotype and a provisionally agreed 'golden spike' at the base of bed 138 at Berrias in the Ardeche, France (Anon. 1975). The Berriasian stratotype is regarded as problematical because the underlying 'Tithonique' does not contain ammonites (Ogg & Lowrie 1986). The ammonite fauna at Berrias is comparatively localized and many correlations within Tithonian–Berriasian rocks in the Tethyan realm use calpionellids, but these planktonic microfossils are not widespread outside Tethyan limestone facies.

North of Tethys, provincialism of ammonite faunas is very marked close to the Jurassic–Cretaceous boundary. The terminal Jurassic stage is the Portlandian, with a basal stratotype in Dorset at Hounstout Cliff (Wimbledon & Cope 1978). The rocks overlying the type Portlandian, the Purbeck Formation, are mostly non-marine and thus lack ammonite faunas.

Thus 'Purbeckian', the earliest name for the following stage, was quickly discarded for stratigraphic purposes, although it is still used as a facies term.

Separate stratotypes were set up for the terminal Jurassic and basal Cretaceous stages in the rocks of the Russian Platform. Here the terminal Jurassic stage is the Volgian and the basal Cretaceous stage is the Ryazanian. Casey (1967) demonstrated the incompleteness of the type Volgian. It has become known that there is a discrepancy in age between the base of the Ryazanian and the base of the Berriasian (Wimbledon & Hunt 1983; Wimbledon 1995; Sey & Kalacheva 1997; Hoedemaeker 1999). Attempts to correlate between the various boundary successions are hampered by a general lack of strong biostratigraphic evidence; moreover, correlations based on events or sequence stratigraphy have not held up to close scrutiny (Ogg & Lowrie 1986).

In England, marine deposition was virtually continuous in the Portland–Wight Basin in Southern England during the Late Jurassic Kimmeridgian and Portlandian stages (Ainsworth *et al.* 1998), but no continuous fully marine sequence exists across the Jurassic–Cretaceous boundary. Townson (1975) and Coe (1996) suggested discontinuities in deposition during the Portlandian, but differed in their assessments of where these might be. Recent detailed logging of sections by Wimbledon (1980, 1986, 1995), Allen *et al.* (in press) and

From: BEAUDOIN, A.B. & HEAD, M.J. (eds) 2004. *The Palynology and Micropalaeontology of Boundaries.* Geological Society, London, Special Publications, **230**, 175–186. 0305-8719/04/$15 © The Geological Society of London 2004.

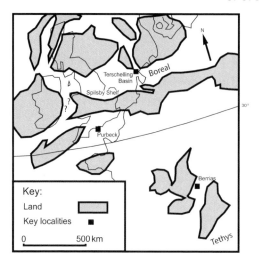

Fig. 1. Palaeogeography near the Jurassic–Cretaceous boundary, with key localities indicated (modified from Hawkes *et al.* 1998).

palaeoenvironmental work by Hunt (1987) do not, however, support the suggestion of widespread unconformities within these rocks. Fully marine sedimentation in the Portland–Wight Basin largely ended with the top of the Portland Stone Formation. Sedimentation in this basin was thereafter predominantly non-marine (Ainsworth *et al.* 1998), although interrupted by a series of marine incursions of varying magnitude (Hunt 1987).

A discontinuous and condensed Late Portlandian–Early Ryazanian depositional series was recognized by Casey (1973) in the Spilsby Shelf area of Eastern England. Casey's (1963, 1973) correlation of the Spilsby series with the later Portlandian and Lower Cretaceous rocks of the Portland–Wight Basin rested on two assumptions. The first was the apparent recognition of the Spilsby ammonite *Paracraspidites oppressus* in the Shrimp Bed at the very top of the Portland Stone Formation in Dorset. The second was the recognition of the Cinder Bed in the middle part of the Purbeck Beds as a marine event, equivalent to the base of the *Praetollia runctoni* zone in the Spilsby Shelf. According to Wimbledon (1985), the correlation of the Shrimp Bed with rocks in Eastern England is unreliable, because the specimens from Eastern England attributed to *Paracraspidites oppressus* by Casey (1973) are assignable to species of the *Titanites anguiformis, Kerberites kerberus* and *Kerberites okusensis* biozones. The ammonites in the Shrimp Bed in Dorset attributed by Casey (1973) to *Paracraspidites oppressus* are fragmentary and unattributable to any single species.

The Cinder Bed contains no age-diagnostic macrofossils, and Casey's (1963) correlation rested upon it marking a 'marine event' that could be matched with a supposed marine transgression in the Mid-Spilsby Nodule Bed. Later, Casey (1973) demonstrated that the Mid-Spilsby Nodule Bed was Late Ryazanian in age and the Cinder Bed was more loosely related to one of four possible 'marine events' in the Spilsby series. Nevertheless, several influential publications, including Wimbledon (1980), accepted the Cinder Bed as the base of the Ryazanian in Southern England. This correlation was questioned by Wimbledon & Hunt (1983).

A resolution of these issues is offered by marine palynomorphs in the Purbeck Formation (Wimbledon & Hunt 1983; Hunt 1987). In this paper the occurrence of stratigraphically significant dinoflagellate cysts (hereafter called dinocysts) is described from the Portland Stone of the Isle of Purbeck at St Aldhelm's Head Quarry (NGR SY964761: W2° 03′ 00″ 50° 35′ 05″ N) and St Aldhelm's Head (SY962754: W2° 03′ 12″ N50° 34′ 40″) and from the Purbeck Formation of Durlston Bay (NGR SZ035780 to SZ037785: W1° 57′ 02″ N50° 36′ 04″ to W1° 56′ 06″ N50° 36′ 20″) and Durlston Head (NGR SZ035772: W1° 57′ 03″ N50° 35′ 36″), in Dorset, England (Fig. 2). The dinocysts, together with magnetostratigraphy (Ogg *et al.* 1994), enable the position of the currently accepted Portlandian–Berriasian boundary in southern England to be identified. This work calibrates a miospore-based correlation by Abbink *et al.* (2001) of rocks in the Spilsby Province (which contain widely correlatable Boreal ammonites and dinocysts) with the Purbeck Formation (Hunt 1985).

The Portland Stone and Purbeck formations

The Portland Stone Formation consists of between 22 and 40 m of limestones, predominantly of shallow-water origin (Townson 1975). Norris (1965) described selected dinocysts from the Portland Stone Formation and Hunt (1987) described microplankton assemblages.

The Purbeck Formation consists of up to 120 m of limestones, shales and evaporites, of predominantly lagoonal origin. Details of the stratigraphy are given in Bristow (1857), with modern sedimentological interpretation provided, for example, by West (1975). Miospores of the Purbeck Formation were described by Norris (1969), Wimbledon & Hunt (1983) and Hunt (1985). Norris (1965) described selected dinocysts from the lower part of the Purbeck

Formation. Hunt (1987) described the strong facies control of dinocyst and acritarch assemblages. Although the Purbeck Formation is predominantly non-marine, a number of horizons contain marine dinocysts, oysters, *Protocardia, Corbula* and other marine taxa, notably the Hard Cockle Bed, Cinder Bed, Scallop Bed and Corbula Beds.

Materials and methods

This study is based on 10 productive samples from the Portland Stone Formation and 67 from the Purbeck Formation at a mean sample interval of just less than 2 m. The samples are placed in Figure 3 against bed-by-bed logging by Wimbledon (1995, and *in* Benton & Spenser 1995, fig. 7.14), from a datum in the highest bed exposed in the Purbeck Formation in Durlston Bay. The samples are the same as those used by Hunt (1987). Samples were processed using standard palynological techniques – HCl and then HF maceration, sieving on 10 μm nylon mesh, followed by swirling on a clock glass. Well over half the samples were limestones: in these and especially in the samples from the Portland Stone Formation, samples ranging up to 2 kg in weight were processed to ensure adequate palynomorph recovery. Where available, at least 250 palynomorphs were counted from each sample. Where material was sufficient, a further five slides were scanned from each sample to locate rare specimens. The data

were handled in Tilia, Tiliagraph and TGView. Dinocyst nomenclature follows Williams *et al.* (1998) and miospore terminology follows Hunt (1985).

Dinocyst biostratigraphy

Figure 3 shows the distribution of selected dinocysts in the Portland Stone and Purbeck formations in Dorset. The distribution of many taxa is extremely discontinuous and corresponds to a series of marine events (Hunt 1987). Most samples containing dinocysts are characterized by large numbers of long-running, ecologically generalist taxa such as *Mendicodinium groenlandicum, Barbatacysta pelionensis* and an unpublished *Gochteodinia* species. Stratigraphically significant taxa are generally present at less than 1% of the microplankton assemblage and thus are indicated on Fig. 3 as presences. The presence of recycled Carboniferous and Jurassic taxa in the Soft Cockle Beds, Corbula Beds, Upper Cypris Clays and Cypris Clays indicates that range-tops are potentially unreliable in these parts of the section. Range bases may have been delayed in appearance by the lack of suitable facies for marine dinoflagellates, but are inherently more reliable than range tops where recycling is apparent. Nevertheless, the distribution of taxa enables correlation with records from other localities. Key comparisons are with the work of Monteil (1992*a, b* and *in* Stover *et al.* 1996) and previously unpublished work by

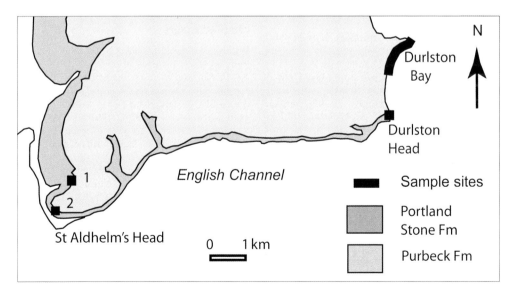

Fig. 2. The location of the studied sections in Dorset, England. Locality 1 is St Aldhelm's Head Quarry and locality 2 is St Aldhelm's Head cliff section.

the present author for the basal Cretaceous type section at Berrias, France.

Key range-top and range-base tie points with the Berriasian type section are shown in Figure 4. The base of the Berriasian, and thus of the Cretaceous, is marked in Bed 138 at Berrias by the range tops of *Dichadogonyaulax culmula* and *Senoniasphaera jurassica* and the range bases of *Warrenia californica* (Fig. 5a) and *Amphorula monteilii* (Fig. 6b). Other important range tops are *Amphorula monteilii* in bed 145, *Impletosphaeridium tribuliferum* in bed 146, *Egmontodinium polyphlacorum* in bed 148 and *Kleithriasphaeridium porosispinum* in bed 149. Other key appearance datums include *Dichadogonyaulax bensonii* in Bed 146 (Monteil *in* Stover *et al.* 1996, text-fig. 40) and *Cirrusphaera dissimilis* (Fig. 5b) in bed 144, *Kleithriasphaeridium fasciatum* and *Muderongia simplex* in bed 149.

By comparing events in the Berriasian type section with the Dorset sequence, it is suggested that the base of the Berriasian lies between the top of the Freestone Bed at St Aldhelms Head (the range top of *Kleithriasphaeridium porosispinum* and *Dichadogonyaulax culmula* and range base of *Amphorula monteilii* and *Cirrusphaera dissimilis*) and the base of the Cypris Freestones on St Aldhelm's Head (the range base of *Warrenia californica*). This is in broad agreement with correlations based on charophytes and ostracods (Blanc & Mojon 1996). The magnetostratigraphy of Ogg *et al.* (1994) is consistent with the base of the Cretaceous lying at the base of the Cypris Freestones.

The base of *Dichadogonyaulax bensonii* and the top of *Impletosphaeridium tribuliferum* in the Hard Cockle suggest correlation with bed 146 in the *Pseudosubplanites grandis* ammonite zone at Berrias, and again is approximately consistent with the magnetostratigraphy of Ogg *et al.* (1994). The incoming of *Kleithriasphaeridium fasciatum* and *Muderongia simplex* in the topmost Building Stones suggests correlation with bed 149, at the top of the *Subthurmannia subalpina* ammonite zone at Berrias and with the Upper Ryazanian *Scriniodinium pharo* dinocyst subzone (*Surites icenii* ammonite zone) in the North Sea and Spilsby Shelf. This is consistent with the magnetostratigraphy of Ogg *et al.* (1994). The incoming of *Pseudoceratium pelliferum* in bed 156 at Berrias near the top of the *Dalmasiceras dalmasi* ammonite zone suggests correlation with the *Pseudoceratium pelliferum* dinocyst subzone (*Peregrinoceras albidum* ammonite zone) in the North Sea (Davey 1982; Costa & Davey 1992).

Miospore biostratigraphy

The incoming of miospore taxa in Dorset (Hunt 1985) and the Terschelling Basin in the Spilsby Province facilitates close correlation between the two sections (Abbink *et al.* 2001). The range base of *Leptolepidites psarosus* in the Broken Beds Dorset provides a Late Portlandian tie-point with the *Subcraspidites primitivus* ammonite zone in the Spilsby province. The range base of *Apiculatisporis verbitskayae* (Fig. 6e) at the base of the Cypris Freestones enables correlation of the basal Berriasian to be made with the *Subcraspidites preplicomphalus* ammonite zone in the Spilsby province.

The range bases of *Matonisporites elegans* (Fig. 6d) and *Aequitriradites spinulosus* (Fig. 6c) in the Cherty Freshwater Beds suggest correlation with the upper part of the *Subcraspidites lamplughi* ammonite zone in the Terschelling Basin. 'Cretaceous' miospores, however, rise in the *Hectoroceras kochi* zone in the Terschelling Basin, but in Dorset very suddenly rise in the Cherty Freshwater Beds (Hunt 1985). This suggests that in Dorset the stratal equivalent to the *Praetollia runctoni* ammonite zone is missing (Abbink 2001). These correlations suggest that most of the upper Volgian should be attributed to the Cretaceous, with its base in the Boreal Realm lying close to the base of the *Subcraspidites preplicomphalus* ammonite zone and within the *Amphorula expiriatum* dinocyst subzone and equivalents (Fig. 7).

Provincialism and the interpretation of compiled ranges

Wimbledon & Hunt (1983) pointed out that there were no bivalves in common between the North Sea and Wessex basins during the latest Jurassic and earliest Cretaceous. It is clear from the results presented here that ranges of stratigraphically useful dinocyst taxa such as *Dichadogonyaulax culmula* are very different in Dorset and in the North Sea basin. Little comparison can be drawn between dinocyst floras in Dorset and the Boreal sequences reported by Duxbury (1977), Davey (1982), Birkelund *et al.* (1983), Piasecki (1984) and Heilmann-Clausen (1987) between the *Kerberites kerberus* and the *Surites icenii* ammonite zones. This is consistent with the two basins being completely isolated from one another during this interval. Only correlation using miospores (Abbink *et al.* 2001) links the Dorset sections, and thus Berrias, with the Boreal Realm during this time. Amalgamation of dinocyst ranges for the Wessex and North Sea basins (e.g. Davey 1979; Riding & Thomas 1992)

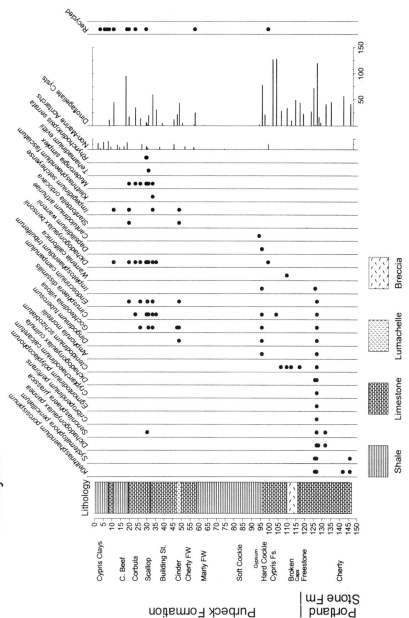

Fig. 3. Stratigraphic occurrence of selected dinocysts and acritarchs in a composite section of the Portland Stone and Purbeck formations in the Isle of Purbeck, Dorset. Depths in the section are metres below the highest exposed bed in the Purbeck Formation. Sections are: Durlston Bay 0–103 m, Durlston Head 103–116 m, Durlston Head 103–116 m, St Aldhelm's Head Quarry 117 m, St Aldhelm's Head Cliff 118–147 m.

Ammonite zone	Bed	Range tops	Range bases
Dalmasiceras dalmasi	156		Pseudoceratium pelliferum Phoberocysta neocomica
	155		
	154		
Berriasella privasensis	153		
	152		
	151		
	150		
Subthurmannia subalpina	149	Kleithriasphaeridium porosispinum	Kleithriasphaeridium fasciatum, Muderongia simplex
	148	Egmontodinium polyphlacorum	
	147		
Pseudosubplanites grandis	146	Impletosphaeridium tribuliferum	Dichadogonyaulax bensonii, Tehamadinium evitti
	145	Amphorula monteiliae	Endoscrinium campanula
Berriasella jacobi	144		Cirrusphaera dissimilis, Ctenidodinium elegantulum
	143		
	142		
	141		
	140		
	139		
	138	Dichadogonyaulax culmula, Senoniasphaera jurassica	Warrennia californica, Amphorula monteiliae

Fig. 4. Key range tops and range bases in the Berriasian type section (after Monteil 1992*a, b*; Monteil *in* Stover *et al.* 1996, text-fig. 40; and Hunt, unpublished data)

for this interval is potentially misleading if applied to either basin. There is still therefore a need for biostratigraphic schemes tied explicitly to rock units rather than to abstractions based on standard ammonite zonation, magnetic chrons or eustatic events for this period of isolation.

The utility of event-based correlations?

Correlations of non-biostratigraphically calibrated events based on magnetostratigraphy and sequence stratigraphy are subject to problems caused by parts of the stratigraphic column at any given locality – including supposedly widely visible, large-scale events – not being represented by rock or visible non-sequences. This is a particular problem in shallow-water shelf palaeoenvironments, such as at Berrias, where sedimentary evidence for non-sequences may not be evident. Attempts to force sequence-stratigraphic correlation on to shallow-water facies rocks where no strong biostratigraphic calibration is available are especially likely to be problematical. This is not only because of the probability of missing rock, but also because there is an extremely high probability that local tectonic or even sedimentary events will provide significant 'noise' to

confuse any eustatic signal. The biostratigraphic results set out in this paper are incompatible with the magnetostratigraphic correlations of Ogg *et al.* (1994) above the level of the Hard Cockle Beds. This is because of the considerable hiatus suggested by the biostratigraphic correlations at Berrias, and the smaller, later one in Dorset. Similarly, re-evaluation of the event correlations suggested by Hoedemaeker (1999) is required. Event-correlation only becomes reliable when calibrated with secure biostratigraphy.

Fig. 5. Selected stratigraphically significant dinocysts from the Purbeck Formation, all 1000 × Nomarski. For each specimen, the slide code is followed by an England Finder reference: (**a**) *Warrenia californica* Monteil, dorsal view showing two-plate precingular archeopyle: Intermarine Beds, Ladydown, Wardour, LD16.1, K41.1; (**b**) *Cirrusphaera dissimilis* Monteil, ventral view: Hard Cockle Bed, Durlston Bay, DB13.3, J35.4; (**c**) *Endoscrinium campanulum* (Gocht) Vozzhennikova, lateral view of hypocyst: Cinder Bed, Durlston Bay, DB2.3, D37.4; (**d**) *Gochteodinia villosa* (Vozzhennikova) Norris, lateral view of small specimen, showing archeopyle: Cinder Bed, Durlston Bay, DB2.3, O33.3.

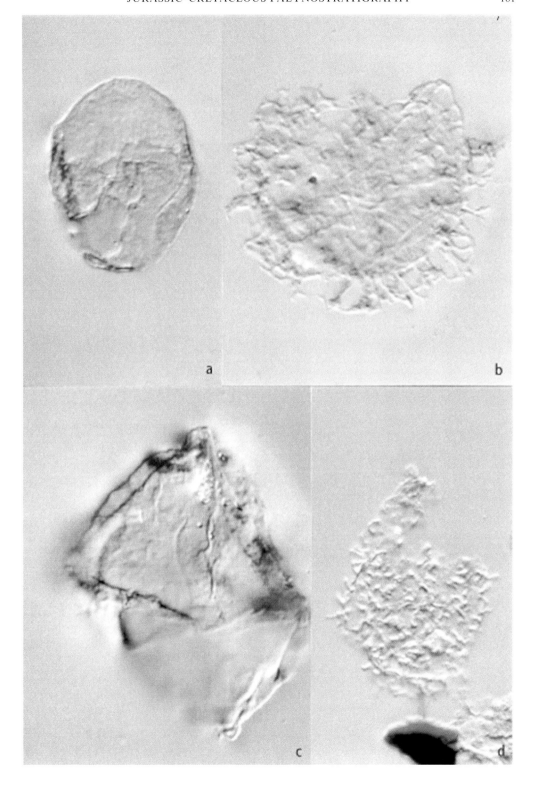

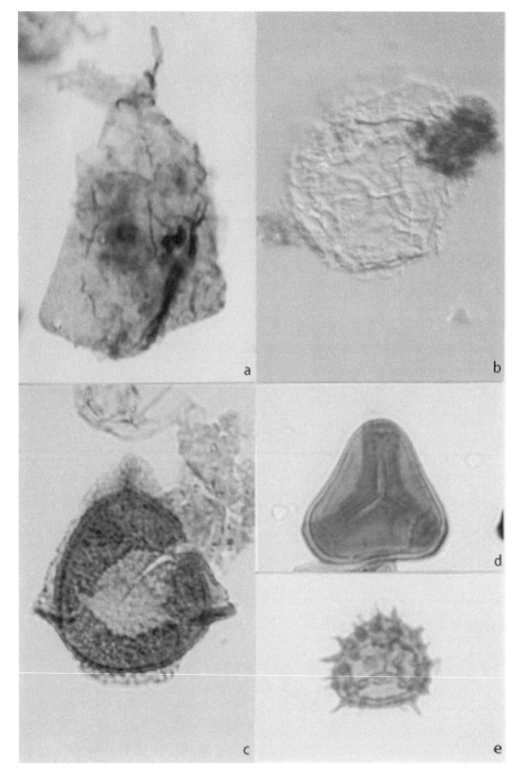

Age	Tethyan ammonites	Berrias	Dorset	Dorset spores (m) and ammonites (a)	Spilsby ammonites	North Sea dinocysts		
Berriasian	D. dalmasi	156 •	???	???	P. albidum	• P. pelliferum		
		155	Corbula	F. wongthaggiensis (m)	S. stenomphalus	S. pharo		
		154						
	B. privasensis	153						
		150						
	S. subalpina	147		M. elegans (m)	S. icenii	•		
		149 •	Intermarine					
	hiatus		Cinder		H. kochi ▲	R. thula		
			Cherty FW▲				G. villosa	
			hiatus		P. runctoni			
			Cherty FW▲		▲			
			Marly FW		S. lamplughi			
			Soft Cockle	A. verbitskayae (m)	S. preplicomphalus			
	P. grandis	146 •	Hd Cockle •					
		145	Cypris				A. expiriatum	
	B. jacobi	144	Freestones					
		138 •	• ▲		▲			
Portlandian (pars.)	'Tithonique'		Broken ▲	P. radiatus (m)	▲			
			Caps		S. primitivus			
			Shrimp					
			Freestone	T. anguiformis (a)	???			

Fig. 7. Correlation of key European sequences around the Jurassic–Cretaceous boundary (partly after Abbink *et al.* 2001). Dinocyst tie-points are indicated by a filled circle, and miospore tie-points by a filled triangle.

Conclusion

Relatively well-constrained dinocyst biostratigraphic tie-points enable correlation between the end of the Portlandian stage in Britain and the start of the Berriasian stage in Tethys. This correlation demonstrates the utility of the type Portlandian in Dorset as the terminal Jurassic stage and for the first time provides a good assessment of the position of the Tethyan – and thus global – Jurassic–Cretaceous boundary outside the area where this is already provided by the Tethyan ammonite and calpionellid zonations. The Late Portlandian–Early Berriasian sea in Southern England was an arm of Tethys and unconnected with the Boreal Ocean, as suggested Wimbledon & Hunt (1983), but the miospore correlations suggested by Abbink *et al.* (2001) bridge the gap between the disjunct Tethyan and Boreal zonations. At the Jurassic–Cretaceous boundary, palynology has the potential to resolve long-running uncertainties and constrain correlation.

Fig. 6. Selected stratigraphically significant dinocysts and miospores from the Purbeck Formation, all from Durlston Bay, all 1000 ×, **a, c–e** transmitted light; **b**, Nomarski. (a) *Cantulodinium arthuriae* Van Helden, ventral view showing archaeopyle: gypsum body in the Soft Cockle Beds, DB12.1, G26.3; (**b**) *Amphorula monteilii* Dodekova, lateral view of specimen with operculum partially detached: Hard Cockle Bed, DB13.3, L32.1; (**c**) *Aequitriradites spinulosus* (Cookson & Dettmann) Cookson & Dettmann, distal view showing well-developed hilum: Cherty Freshwater Beds, DB7.4, F44.1; (**d**) *Matonisporites elegans* Hunt, holotype, in apical view, Cherty Freshwater Beds, DB7.2, K33.3; (**e**) *Apiculatisporites verbitskayae* Dörhöfer, apical view: Cherty Freshwater Beds, DB7.4, B37.2.

It is a pleasure to acknowledge the supervision of C. Downie early in my study of the Dorset sections, and the encouragement and good advice of E. Spinner, K. Dorning and W. Wimbledon. K. Dorning is thanked for sample processing at Pallab Research, Sheffield and for much logistical support. This paper was substantially improved by a constructive review by W. Wimbledon, the referee's comments from R. Fensome and J. Riding, and editorial input from M. Head.

Appendix I: Listing of figured species with author citations

Dinocysts

Amphorula monteilii Dodekova 1994
Cantulodinium arthuriae Van Helden 1986
Cirrusphaera dissimilis Monteil 1992*a*
Endoscrinium campanulum (Gocht 1959) Vozzhennikova 1967
Gochteodinia villosa (Vozzhennikova 1967) Norris 1978
Warrenia californica Monteil 1992*a*

Miospores

Aequitriradites spinulosus (Cookson & Dettmann 1958) Cookson & Dettmann 1961
Apiculatisporites verbitskayae Dörhöfer 1979
Matonisporites elegans Hunt 1985

References

ABBINK, O. A., CALLOMON, J. H., RIDING, J. B., WILLIAMS, P. D. B. & WOLFARD, A. 2001 Biostratigraphy of Jurassic–Cretaceous boundary strata in the Terschelling Basin, The Netherlands. *Proceedings of the Yorkshire Geological Society*, **53**, 4, 275–302.

AINSWORTH, N. R., BRAHAM, W., GREGORY, F. J., JOHNSON, B. & KING, C. 1998. The lithostratigraphy of the latest Triassic to earliest Cretaceous of the English Channel and adjacent areas. *In*: UNDERHILL, J. R. (ed.) *Development, Evolution and Petroleum Geology of the Wessex Basin*. Geological Society, London, Special Publications, **133**, 103–164.

ALLEN, P., RADLEY, J. & WIMBLEDON, W. A. P. in press. *The Jurassic–Cretaceous Boundary Beds*. Geological Conservation Review Series.

ANON., 1975. *Colloque sur le Crétace Inferieur, Lyon (1973)*. Bureau de Récherches Géologiques et Minières, Mémoires, **86**, 1–393.

BENTON, M. J. & SPENSER, P. S. 1995 *Fossil Reptiles of Great Britain*. Chapman & Hall GCR Series, London.

BIRKELUND, T., CLAUSEN, C. K., HANSEN, H. N. & HOLM, L. 1983. The *Hectoroceras kochi* Zone (Ryazanian) in the North Sea Central Graben and remarks on the Late Cimmerian Unconformity. *Danmarks Geologische Undersøgelse Arbog 1982*, pp. 53–72.

BLANC, E. & MOJON, P.-O. 1996. Un paléokarst du Crétacé basal (Berriasien moyen) dans le Jura Suisse occidental (région de Bienne): corrélations avec les domains boreal et téthysien. *Cretaceous Research*, **17**, 403–418.

BRISTOW, H. W. 1857. Comparative sections of the Purbeck strata of Dorset: 1. Durlston Bay; 2 Worbarrow Bay; 3. Mewps Bay; 4 Ridgeway Hill, railway cutting. *Vertical Sections of the Geological Survey*, Sheet 22.

CASEY, R. 1963. The dawn of the Cretaceous Period in Britain. *Bulletin of the South-east Union of Scientific Societies*, **117**, 1–15.

CASEY, R. 1967. The position of the Middle Volgian in the English Jurassic. *Proceedings of the Geological Society, London*, **1640**, 246–247.

CASEY, R. 1973. The ammonite succession at the Jurassic–Cretaceous boundary in eastern England. *In*: RAWSON, P. F. & CASEY, R. (eds) *The Boreal Lower Cretaceous*. Geological Journal Special Issue, **5**, 193–266.

COE, A. L. 1996. Unconformities within the Portlandian Stage of the Wessex Basin and their sequence-stratigraphical significance. *In*: HESSELBO, S. P. & PARKINSON, D. N. (eds) *Sequence Stratigraphy in British Geology*. Geological Society, London, Special Publications, **103**, 109–144.

COSTA, L. & DAVEY, R. 1992. Dinoflagellate cysts of the Cretaceous System. *In*: POWELL, A. J. (ed.) *A Stratigraphic Index of Dinoflagellate Cysts*. Chapman & Hall, London, pp. 99–153.

DAVEY, R. 1979. The stratigraphic distribution of dinocysts in the Portlandian (latest Jurassic) to Barremian (Early Cretaceous) of northwest Europe. *American Association of Stratigraphic Palynologists Contributions Series*, **5B**, 48–81.

DAVEY, R. 1982. Dinocyst stratigraphy of the latest Jurassic to Early Cretaceous of the Haldager no. 1 borehole, Denmark. *Danmarks Geologiske Undersøgelse, Serie B*, **6**, 1–57.

DUXBURY, S. 1977. A palynostratigraphy of the Berriasian to Barremian of the Speeton Clay of Speeton, England. *Palaeontographica B*, **160**, 17–67.

HAWKES, P. W., FRASER, A. J. & EINCHCOMB, C. C. G. 1998. The tectono-stratigraphic development and exploration history of the Weald and Wessex basins, Southern England, UK. *In*: UNDERHILL, J. R. (ed.) *Development, Evolution and Petroleum Geology of the Wessex Basin*. Geological Society, London, Special Publications, **133**, 39–65.

HEILMANN-CLAUSEN, C. 1987. Lower Cretaceous dinoflagellate biostratigraphy in the Danish Central Trough. *Danmarks Geologiske Undersøgelse, Serie A*, **17**, 1–89.

HOEDEMAEKER, P. J. 1999. A Tethyan–Boreal correlation of pre-Aptian Cretaceous strata: correlating the uncorrelatables. *Geologica Carpathica*, **50(2)**, 101–124.

HUNT, C. O. 1985. Miospores from the Portland Stone Formation and the lower part of the Purbeck Formation (Upper Jurassic/Lower Cretaceous) from Dorset, England. *Pollen et Spores*, **27**, 419–451.

HUNT, C. O. 1987. Dinoflagellate cyst and acritarch assemblages in shallow-marine and marginal-marine carbonates: Portland Stone and Purbeck Formations (Upper Jurassic/Lower Cretaceous) of Southern England and Northern France. *In*: HART, M. B. (ed.) *The Micropalaeontology of Carbonate Environments.* Ellis Horwood, Chichester, pp. 208–225.

MONTEIL, E. 1992*a*. Quelques nouvelles especes-index de kystes de dinoflagelles (Tithonique–Valanginien) du sud-est de la France et de l'ouest de la Suisse. *Revue de Paléobiologie*, **11(1)**, 273–297.

MONTEIL, E. 1992*b*. Kystes de dinoflagelles index (Tithonique–Valanginien) du sud-est de la France. Proposition d'une nouvelle zonation palynologique. *Revue de Paléobiologie*, **11(1)**, 299–306.

NORRIS, G. 1965. Archaeopyle structures in Upper Jurassic dinoflagellates from South England. *New Zealand Journal of Geology and Geophysics*, **8**, 792–806.

NORRIS, G. 1969. Miospores from the Purbeck Beds and marine Upper Jurassic from southern England. *Palaeontology*, **12**, 574–620.

OGG, J. G. & LOWRIE, W. 1986 Magnetostratigraphy of the Jurassic–Cretaceous boundary. *Geology*, **14**, 547–550.

OGG, J. G., HANSENYAGER, R. W. II & WIMBLEDON, W. A. 1994 Jurassic–Cretaceous boundary: Portland–Purbeck magnetostratigraphy and possible correlation to the Tethyan faunal realm. *Geobios*, **MS 17**, 519–527.

PIASECKI, S. 1984. Dinoflagellate cyst stratigraphy of the Lower Cretaceous Jydegard Formation, Bornholm, Denmark. *Bulletin of the Geological Society of Denmark*, **32**, 154–161.

RIDING, J. & THOMAS, J. 1992 Dinoflagellate cysts of the Jurassic System. *In*: POWELL, A. J. (ed.) *A Stratigraphic Index of Dinoflagellate Cysts.* Chapman & Hall, London, pp. 7–97.

SEY, I. I. & KALACHEVA, E. D. 1997. Jurassic/Cretaceous boundary in the Boreal Realm (biostratigraphy and Boreal–Tethyan correlations). *International Subcommission on Jurassic Stratigraphy Newsletter*, **24**, 50–51.

STOVER, L. E., BRINKHUIS, H. *ET AL.* 1996. Mesozoic–Tertiary dinoflagellates, acritarchs and prasinophytes. *In*: JANSONIUS, J. & MCGREGOR, D.

C. (eds) *Palynology: Principles and Applications. Vol. 2.* American Association of Stratigraphic Palynologists' Foundation, Dallas, Texas, pp. 641–750.

TOWNSON, W. G. 1975. Lithostratigraphy and deposition in the type Portlandian. *Journal of the Geological Society, London*, **131**, 619–668.

WEST, I. M. 1975. Evaporite and associated sediment from the basal Purbeck Formation (Upper Jurassic) of Dorset, *Proceedings of the Geologists' Association*, **86**, 205–225.

WILLIAMS, G. L., LENTIN, J. K. & FENSOME, R. A. 1998. *The Lentin and Williams Index of Fossil Dinoflagellates: 1998 Edition.* American Association of Stratigraphic Palynologists Contributions Series, **34**.

WIMBLEDON, W. A. 1980. Portlandian. *In*: COPE, J. C. W., DUFF, K. L., PARSONS, C. F., TORRENS, M. S., WIMBLEDON, W. A. & WRIGHT, J. (eds) *A Correlation of Jurassic Rocks in the British Isles. Part Two: Middle and Upper Jurassic.* Special Reports of the Geological Society, London, **14**, 85–93.

WIMBLEDON, W. A. 1985 The Portlandian, the terminal Jurassic stage in the Boreal Realm. *In*: MICKKELSEN, E. (ed.) *International Symposium on Jurassic Stratigraphy, Erlangen, 1984, Volume II.* Geological Survey of Denmark, Copenhagen, pp. 533–549.

WIMBLEDON, W. A. 1986. Rythmic sedimentation in the Late Jurassic–Early Cretaceous. *Proceedings of the Dorset Natural History and Archaeological Society*, **108**, 127–133.

WIMBLEDON, W. A. 1995. *In*: CALLOMON, J. & COPE, J. C. W. The Jurassic Geology of Dorset. *In*: TAYLOR, P. *Field Geology of the British Jurassic.* Geological Society, London, pp. 51–104.

WIMBLEDON, W. A. & COPE, J. C. W. 1978. The ammonite faunas of the English Portland Beds and the zones of the Portlandian Stage. *Journal of the Geological Society, London*, **135(2)**, 183–190.

WIMBLEDON, W. A. & HUNT, C. O. 1983. The Portland–Purbeck junction (Portlandian–Berriasian) in the Weald, and correlation of latest Jurassic–early Cretaceous rocks in southern England. *Geological Magazine*, **120(3)**, 267–280.

The mid-Cenomanian non-sequence: a micropalaeontological detective story

MALCOLM B. HART

School of Earth, Ocean and Environmental Sciences, University of Plymouth, Drake Circus, Plymouth PL4 8AA, UK (e-mail: mhart@plymouth.ac.uk)

Abstract: The mid-Cenomanian non-sequence is described in terms of its stratigraphical position, regional impact and importance in Cenomanian stratigraphy. After its discovery in the site investigation for the Channel Tunnel and its location within the chalk succession of the Dover–Sangatte area, it has been traced throughout the United Kingdom and northern France. In stratigraphically complete successions it is coincident with the base of the *Rotalipora cushmani* Taxon Range Zone, although in many areas there is a major hiatus (= sequence boundary?) at this level. In more marginal successions, the non-sequence is characterized by the presence of reworked, phosphatized macrofossil assemblages in which the actual date of deposition can only be determined by the non-phosphatized macrofaunal elements or the microfossils extracted from the enclosing sediments. In Dorset/Devon and northern France the Cenomanian successions are condensed, and horizons with reworked macrofaunas have been investigated using a variety of micropalaeontological techniques (thin-sections, processed residues, acid reductions, etc.). In these areas the mid-Cenomanian non-sequence becomes one of the most important features of the succession and marks a major hiatus in many localities.

The mid-Cenomanian non-sequence was discovered in the 1960s during the site investigation work for the Channel Tunnel. At first it was envisaged that this break in the depositional history of the 'Lower Chalk' might cause problems during the construction phase of the project. In the event, most of the route of the tunnel was located stratigraphically below this level and it was only very close to the French end of the tunnel that any engineering work took place this high in the succession. The initial interest in the stratigraphy of the non-sequence was, therefore, replaced with more major engineering concerns at the Albian–Cenomanian boundary (see Hart 2000).

The discovery and subsequent assessment of the regional scale and importance of the mid-Cenomanian non-sequence is here documented for the first time. Following its discovery in the site investigation work, it was only incidental to the construction phase but, over the last 30 years, its importance and relevance to Cretaceous stratigraphy has been made clear by the subsequent research reported here.

Site investigation for the Channel Tunnel

The first mention of a cross-Channel 'fixed link' was in 1751, when Nicolas Desmaret, a French farmer, suggested that a causeway, bridge or tunnel should be constructed between France and Britain. The first serious proposal for a tunnel was made by Albert Mathieu-Favier in 1802, although an alternative proposal for the sinking of a submerged tube was made one year later by Tessier du Mottray. The worsening political situation between Britain and France over the next decades halted any further proposals and little, if any, further progress was made. It was in 1855 that the idea was resurrected by Thome de Gamond who, almost single-handed, began the geological mapping of the sea-floor between Calais and Dover. With the increasing development of the railways, Isambard Kingdom Brunel and Robert Stephenson both showed an interest in the idea of a tunnel. Royal support came from Prince Albert, who saw this as a way of saving Queen Victoria from the violent seasickness that she apparently suffered while travelling by ship!

In 1878 a French company began excavations near Sangatte while, in 1880, Sir Edward Watkin sank a shaft at Abbot's Cliff near Dover and tunnelled 800 m using a compressed-air tunnelling machine designed by Col. Frederick Beaumont. During these early attempts at construction there was growing political opposition to the whole concept of a 'fixed link' and all work was halted in 1883, by which time the French had dug 1800 m and the British had tunnelled over 2100 yards. The world wars of the twentieth century intervened and the only

From: BEAUDOIN, A.B. & HEAD, M.J. (eds) 2004. *The Palynology and Micropalaeontology of Boundaries.* Geological Society, London, Special Publications, **230**, 187–206. 0305-8719/04/$15 © The Geological Society of London 2004.

significant mention of the tunnel between the wars was in 1929. In that year, at a conference in Le Havre, Professor P. F. Kendall (an eminent mining and water engineer) presented a paper on the proposed tunnel under the English Channel. This interesting account (which was published in *The Naturalist* in October 1929) ended with the following statement.

It seems to me imperative that, if timely warning is to be given of approach to adverse conditions, a geologist with an intimate knowledge of the lithology and palaeontology of the Chalk should be in attendance at the tunnel works and should make a close examination of each length of excavation before the linings are put in place. This may mean a visit every day, and perhaps *twice* a day. He would thus be able to note any change of dip or of the texture of the Chalk and assist the engineers in the solution of the problems which arise. It may be advisable that the French and English geologists should examine in concert each other's section. I conclude with the earnest hope that in *my time* the breach of the last barrier of Chalk between the two headings and a handclasp between French and English workers will signalise a closer bond of friendship between the two nations.

While the handclasp did not occur in 'his time', this statement proved to be a remarkably accurate prediction of what actually occurred some 60 years later. Geologists on the UK side did visit the faces once or twice a day and (micro)-palaeontologists were present on both sides of the Channel (see Harris *et al.* 1996).

Eventually, in the 1950s, the Channel Tunnel Study Group embarked on a major geological survey of the strata between Dover (Fig.1) and Sangatte. David J. Carter (then at Imperial College, London University) was commissioned to produce a correlation of the chalk succession in the area using foraminifera. Such investigations had, by this time, become commonplace in the oil industry, but this was the first major engineering project to employ such methods. The direction of this investigation was greatly influenced by the work of Williams-Mitchell (1948), who had recently published the first foraminiferal zonation of the chalk in the UK. This seminal work has scarcely had the recognition it deserves, as many of the taxa (and the ranges that he described) are still used by micropalaeontologists working on the chalk foraminifera of NW Europe (see Hart *et al.*

1989). In the course of the 1958–1959 investigation, David Carter, almost single-handedly, investigated the onshore succession, as well as samples from both boreholes and drop-cores that were collected from the English Channel. In Bruckshaw *et al.* (1961) an outline zonation of the Middle Cretaceous succession was published, and this is reproduced in Figure 2.

The distribution of the foraminifera indicated in Figure 2 was not compared (at that time) to other regions of Europe (or elsewhere), because it was very much a 'local' zonation and, in any case, there was no real international standard against which to make comparisons. During the early 1960s, Carter continually updated his information on the fauna of the mid-Cretaceous succession in anticipation of further developments. Some of this work involved the formal identification of taxa that had previously been in open nomenclature. With the publication of Bandy's (1961) synthesis of the Cretaceous planktonic foraminifera, it became clear that the first appearance (and last appearance) of *Rotalipora cushmani* was of major importance and the slightly earlier appearance of *Rotalipora reicheli* was also significant. As Bandy's data came (mainly) from the USA, this was also one of the first examples of how the planktonic foraminifera could be used in inter-continental correlation.

In 1964–1965, the Channel Tunnel Study Group conducted a major investigation of the Dover–Sangatte area, with a large number of marine boreholes being added to those drilled in the earlier work. By this time, a number of possible tunnelling horizons had been excluded and the Lower Chalk (of Cenomanian age) had been identified as the preferred option. In this part of the succession (Fig. 3) the Lower Chalk (now the Grey Chalk Subgroup of the Chalk Group; see Mortimore *et al.* 2001) is characterized by alternations of grey chalk and dark grey marly chalk. There are no flints (cherts) at this level, and the optimum line of the tunnel was to be located above the obvious beds of the sponge *Exanthesis labrosus* (see Kennedy *in* McKerrow 1978, fig. 103) below the level of the *mid-Cenomanian non-sequence*.

When first identified, the mid-Cenomanian non-sequence was simply the base of the *Rotalipora cushmani* Taxon Range Zone. It was located within Zone 11 of the benthic zonation scheme (see Fig. 2; the appearance of *R. cushmani* [15] within the zone characterized by the lower part of the range of *Plectina cenomana* [17]). It was also known that, at the same point in the succession, there was a major change in the proportions of planktonic and

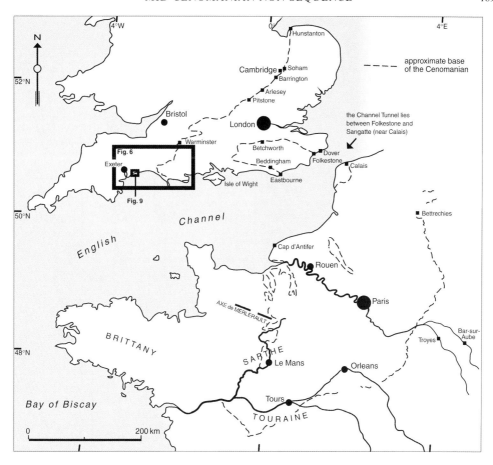

Fig. 1. Outline map of southern England and northern France showing the base of the Cenomanian and the localities discussed in the text. The locations of Figures 6 & 9 are indicated.

benthic taxa. Below the non-sequence relatively few planktonic individuals are found in the 500–250 μm size fraction, while immediately above the first appearance of *R. cushmani* there can be anything up to 60–70% of the fauna composed of planktonic taxa. The term 'non-sequence' was used because it appeared to most closely fit current definitions. See, for example, Allaby & Allaby (1990):

A minor break in a concordant succession of strata, representing a period during which either no deposition of sediment occurred or it was subsequently removed. Such periods may be of short duration and localized, but are not necessarily so. *Compare* diastem.

As work on the correlation of the marine boreholes progressed, it became clear that one of the most important relationships to understand was that between the Lower Chalk and the underlying Gault Clay Formation. This required both a detailed knowledge of the succession and of the microfauna and, as a result, this work was time-consuming (see details in Hart 2000). This meant that there were thousands of samples from the remainder of the Lower Chalk succession which, although less important, needed analysis and correlation. In order to accomplish this part of the work Carter looked to develop a rapid, but effective (and accurate), method of correlation. At this very point in time, Shaw (1964) published his book on *Time in Stratigraphy* and Carter immediately considered if this new form of 'graphical correlation' could be adapted to solve the problems of the tunnel. After lengthy discussions and experimentation, the new system was abandoned and a 'graphical' method adopted that used the planktonic:

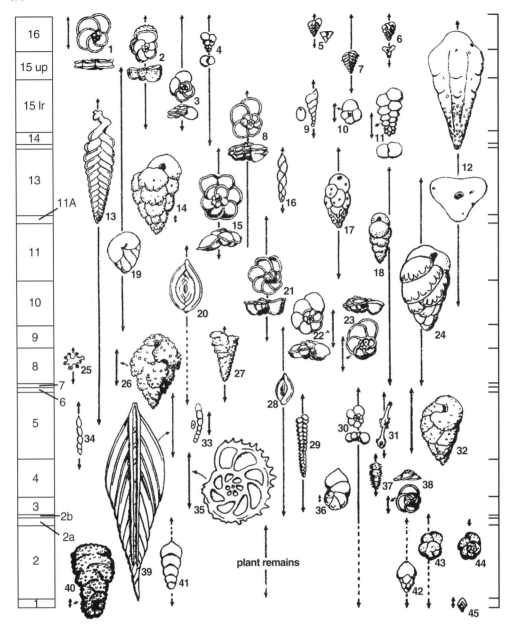

Fig. 2. The distribution of key species of foraminifera in the mid-Cretaceous succession of the area investigated during the 1958–1959 work of the Channel Tunnel Study Group (from Bruckshaw *et al.* 1961). The specific identification of the foraminifera indicated by numbers 1–45 is almost irrelevant, especially since many – at the time of publication – were in open nomenclature. Two species are, however, significant: 15, *Rotalipora cushmani*; 21, *Rotalipora reicheli*. Reproduced with permission of the Institution of Civil Engineers and Thomas Telford Publishing.

benthic ratios of suites of samples from adjacent boreholes. In some cases the stratigraphical information from adjacent boreholes was plotted on graphs and simple lines of correlation generated. This decision was based on the argument that graphical correlation establishes a 'standard' succession against which other successions are correlated. In the case of the

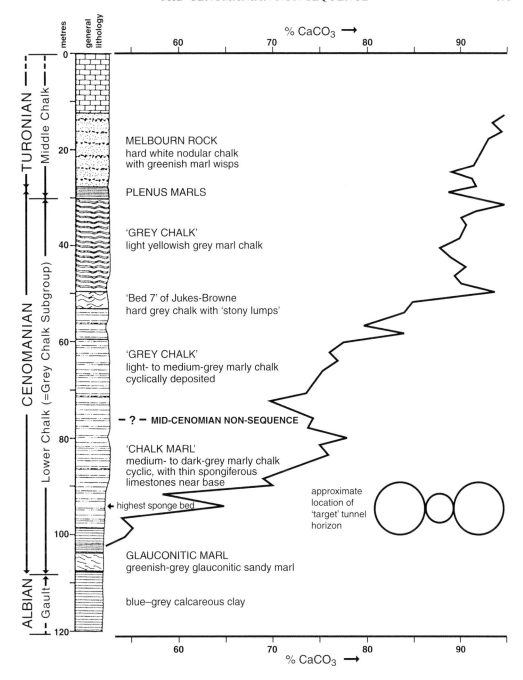

Fig. 3. The principal lithological features of the cross-Channel succession as recorded in a typical borehole from the UK side of the Channel. The graph indicates the increasing calcium carbonate content of the chalk; after Hart (1992). The lithostratigraphical nomenclature has changed recently (see Mortimore *et al.* 2001 for a full review), but some of the 'informal' names are still used here.

Channel Tunnel the correlation required was not against a 'standard', but along the line of the tunnel – from borehole to borehole. Using relatively simple planktonic:benthic ratios, backed up by zonal determinations, Carter settled on a graphical method of correlation, some of the data for which could be gathered by less trained personnel. Using the 500–250 µm grain-size fraction (in which the majority of adult foraminifera will be found) it is possible to count the numbers of planktonic (surface-water dwelling) foraminifera and benthic (substrate-dwelling) foraminifera. While this is fully acknowledged as rather an imprecise methodology to employ if one was undertaking a detailed palaeoecological analysis, this planktonic:benthic ratio (or P:B ratio) does produce a striking pattern (Fig. 4). The zonal scheme shown in Figure 4 is that used by Carter & Hart (1977) in their stratigraphical work in Southern England and is basically the same zonation that was later used by Hart *et al.* (1989). The P:B ratio plot shows two very distinctive features: a major non-sequence in the middle of the succession (between zones 11i and 11ii) and a major peak in the occurrence of *Rotalipora cushmani* which was later named the 'c-line' in correlation charts. The mid-Cenomanian non-sequence was identified by:

- an abrupt increase in the percentage of planktonic foraminifera recorded in the samples;
- the first appearance of *Rotalipora cushmani*, although rare specimens of the related *Rotalipora montsalvensis* are found below this level; and
- the extinction of *Favusella washitensis*: its last appearance being in the chalk/marl rhythms immediately below the non-sequence.

The non-sequence (or P/B break in the work of Paul *et al.* 1994) is located just above the *Orbirhynchia mantelliana* Band (Kennedy 1969), which lies a short distance below the marked change in lithology from chalk/marl rhythms to more massive beds of chalk separated by thin marl seams. The P:B ratio plots for all the boreholes across the Channel contain many features in common, and several of the most distinctive events were used to generate a correlation along the length of the tunnel (Fig. 5). Using this methodology it was possible to use these correlation lines to generate an accurate cross-section from Folkestone/Dover to Sangatte. When these data were assembled it became clear that the 'c-line' provided a valuable datum and that, below this level, the mid-Cenomanian non-sequence (MCNS) was seen to cross-cut many of the correlation lines (see Fig. 5). The MCNS was identified, therefore, as more than a minor faunal or sedimentary break, i.e. a clearly marked regional event. Although the planktonic:benthic ratio cannot

really be used as a means of calculating water depth (in absolute terms) it is clear that the marked increase in planktonic taxa indicates a relatively major sea-level shift (see Hart & Bailey 1979).

Regional significance of the MCNS

In autumn 1965, just as the final stages of the Channel Tunnel Site Investigation were coming to a close, the author and R. J. H. Hiscock (a fellow student) were dispatched to north Dorset (Figs 1 & 6) to investigate the Lower Chalk successions in a more marginal setting. All of these localities are very small, isolated and exceptionally difficult to locate. They cannot be found without the use of 1:50 000 Ordnance Survey maps. Unfortunately, such detailed work is required if the subtle changes in the Cenomanian succession are to be determined in this region (see Kennedy 1970; Drummond 1970; Carter & Hart 1977; Hart 1994). The area in question lies between Shillingstone and Buckland, and includes localities (with grid references) at:

- Stour Bank, near Shillingstone (ST. 846 106);
- Okeford Fitzpaine (ST. 805 105);
- Stoke Wake (ST. 763 067);
- Dorsetshire Gap (ST. 742 033); and
- Buckland Newton (ST. 703 051).

At the first two locations (Fig. 6; 'star-shaped' symbols), the base of the chalk appears to be in a 'normal' Glauconitic Marl, typical of localities all over Southern and SE England. At Stoke Wake (Fig. 6; 'sunburst' symbol) there is a marked erosion surface cutting into the Upper Greensand with a 'bouldery' basal bed to the chalk succession. No phosphatized fossils are recorded (Kennedy 1970, p. 624). The lowermost part of the chalk succession (Fig. 7) is faintly glauconitic but this dies out rapidly up-section. The chalk just above the base of the succession contains large numbers of planktonic foraminifera and appears to be just above the MCNS. At other localities immediately to the west (Dorsetshire Gap and Buckland Newton; Fig. 6; 'cross' symbols) a phosphatic Basement Bed (Kennedy 1970, pp. 625–629) appears which contains a variety of macrofossils preserved in both light- and dark-coloured phosphate. There is an admixture of macrofaunal elements, indicating significant reworking. The top of the Upper Greensand is eroded and shows evidence of both phosphatization and glauconitization. The microfauna indicates a level well above the MCNS, up to Zone 11ii (11A on Fig. 2) or 12 of

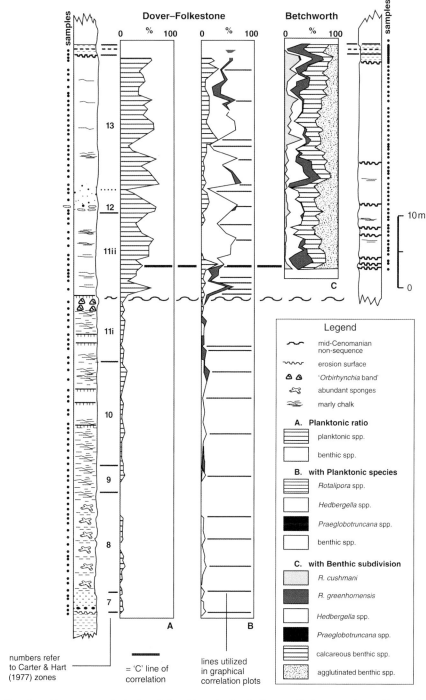

Fig. 4. Zonation, bio-events and planktonic:benthic ratio for the Lower Chalk succession at Dover: borehole P.000 was located just inside Dover Harbour (Fig. 1). The zones are those used by Carter & Hart (1977). Graph A shows the rare P:B ratio plot, while Graph B has the planktonic component broken down into generic groupings. Graph C shows the succession at Betchworth, Surrey (Fig. 1), with the benthic component subdivided into agglutinated taxa and calcareous taxa. The numbers adjacent to the lithological column for the Dover succession are the foraminiferal zones of Carter & Hart (1977).

the benthic zonation. At all other localities west of this area the base of the chalk becomes progressively younger until, at Membury (6 km NW of Axminster), the glauconitic chalks resting on the underlying strata are of latest Cenomanian age (Hart 1970; Hart 1975; Carter & Hart 1977; Mortimore *et al.* 2001, pp. 133–137).

The place where the MCNS cuts on to the top of the Upper Greensand in North Dorset, therefore, is marked by a major change in the characteristics of the 'Chalk Basement Bed'. The acceptance that the base of the chalk was diachronous across southern and SW England (Hancock 1969; Hart 1970; Drummond 1970; Kennedy 1970; Carter & Hart 1977; and subsequent research summarized in Mortimore *et al.* 2001) was an important step in our understanding of mid-Cretaceous stratigraphy in the UK. It also brought the understanding of the MCNS to a wider audience.

Correlation using planktonic:benthic ratio graphs

Using the methodology shown in Figure 4, Hart (1970) and Carter & Hart (1977) demonstrated the utility of the planktonic:benthic ratio counts by generating a correlation (Fig. 4) from Dover to Betchworth (immediately east of Dorking, Surrey). The Betchworth succession was sampled at a very close spacing, and the graph produced from the faunal data is very similar to that at Dover. The base of the quarry was, unfortunately, just about the level of the 'c-line' of correlation and, while a peak in the counts of *R. cushmani* is recorded, one cannot be certain that it is a coeval horizon. Some of the peaks in the *R. cushmani* distribution are quite clearly comparable, although it is noticeable that *Praeglobotruncana* species are more abundant in the Surrey succession. Betchworth is approximately 110 km from Dover – more than twice the distance across the English Channel shown in Figure 5.

At the same time as the correlation with Betchworth was being generated, Hart (1970) attempted to correlate the Lower Chalk successions at Eastbourne, Culver Cliff (Isle of Wight) and Compton Bay (Isle of Wight) with that recorded at Dover. In the first instance this was designed to link up with the successions studied in north Dorset. Sampling of the three successions was undertaken at 1-m intervals (approximately) and the prepared residues were investigated for both benthic and planktonic foraminifera. The resulting graphs (Fig. 8) clearly identify the MCNS (between Zones 11i

and 11ii), although the 'c-line' – so prominent at Dover and across the English Channel towards Sangatte – can only be identified with some difficulty. Why should the planktonic:benthic ratio plots look so different?

The cross-Channel correlation was based on boreholes located approximately 1 km apart (or even closer), and the total distance was only 42 km. The four successions shown in Figure 8 cover a total distance of over 200 km, and it is not surprising that, over this distance, differences are apparent. The sampling interval was not identical to that at Dover (or at Betchworth), and it is known that within chalk/marl rhythms there is a variation within the fauna (Leary & Hart 1992). In comparing the planktonic:benthic ratios, it is evident that:

- the closer the sampling interval (e.g. Dover), the greater the variability;
- the planktonic foraminifera are, generally, more abundant at Dover and Eastbourne;
- *Rotalipora* spp. are more abundant at Dover and Eastbourne; and
- the MCNS is clearly located above the *O. mantelliana* horizon at all locations.

Murray (1976) argues that the abundance and maximum size of planktonic foraminifera decreases across the continental shelf away from the present-day continental edge. The data from the successions across Southern England suggest that the Compton Bay succession, which was deposited nearer to the 'Cornubian Island' (Hart 1999) records fewer planktonic foraminifera than successions in other parts of the basin. The Cenomanian successions of the Goban Spur (DSDP Leg 80) which were deposited adjacent to the edge of the continental shelf do contain an abundant, and large-sized, planktonic fauna (Leary & Hart 1989), in agreement with Murray's model.

The correlation shown in Figure 8 confirms that the MCNS is a major feature of the Cenomanian succession. Later work by Paul *et al.* (1994) also reported the presence of the MCNS (= P/B Break) in the Folkestone, Southerham (Sussex), Culver Cliff (Isle of Wight) and Speeton (Yorkshire) successions.

Fig. 5. The correlation of Borehole P.000 (Dover) with three selected boreholes drilled at marine sites along the route of the tunnel. The 'c-line' has been used as a datum for the correlation, which uses some of the bio-events identified in Figure 4. The succession on the French coast (right-hand column) is based on the work of Robaszynski *et al.* (1980). GM marks the Glauconitic Marl at the base of the chalk succession.

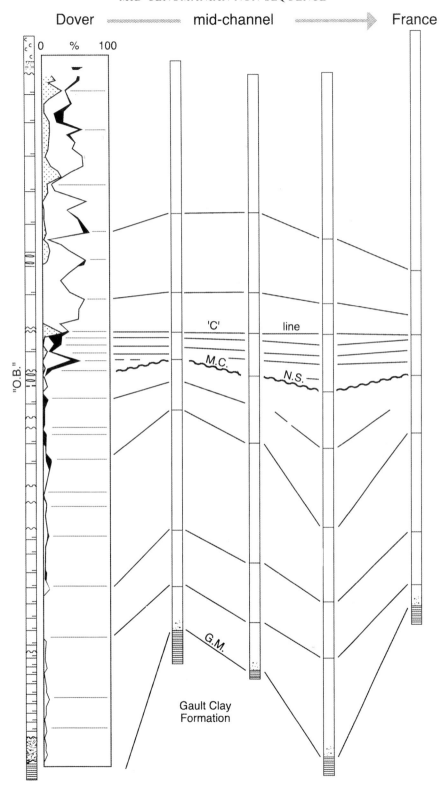

Dover ═══════ mid-channel ═══════▶ France

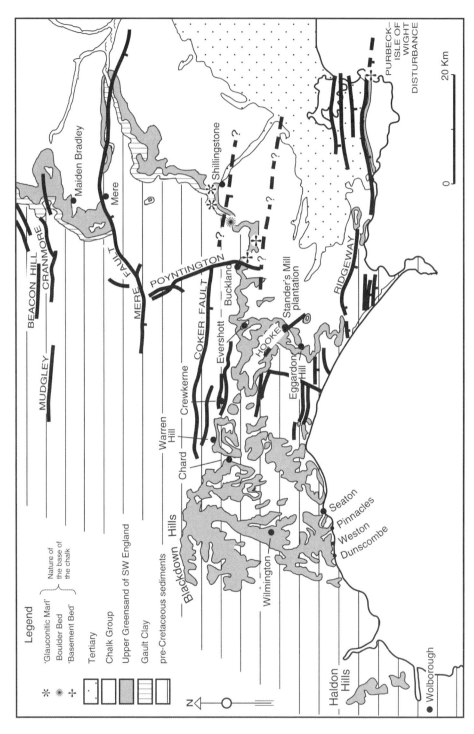

Fig. 6. Outline geological map of Dorset, east Devon, south Somerset and SW Wiltshire (based on the maps of the British Geological Survey). Additionally, the map shows the major faults identified by Chadwick (1986) and Jenkyns & Senior (1991), which may have been active in the early to mid-Cretaceous. The nature of the base of the chalk is indicated for a few key locations that are mentioned in the text.

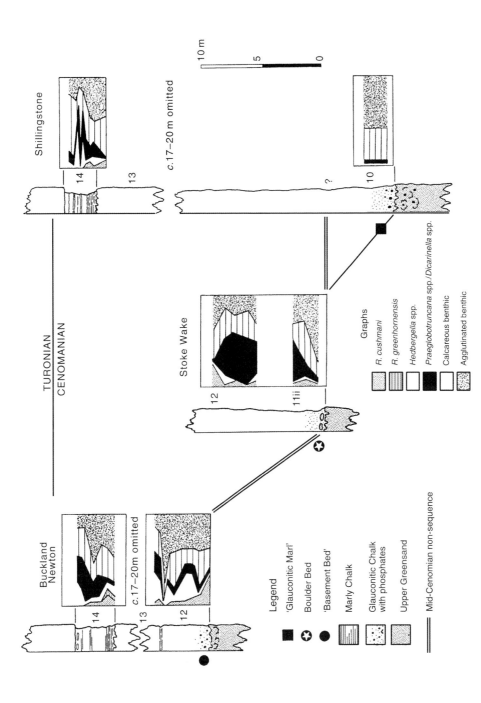

Fig. 7. The base of the chalk at three locations (see Fig. 6) in mid-Dorset. Zone 14 is equivalent to the Plenus Marls. The datum used for the construction of the diagram is the extinction of *Rotalipora cushmani*. Data modified from Hart (1994).

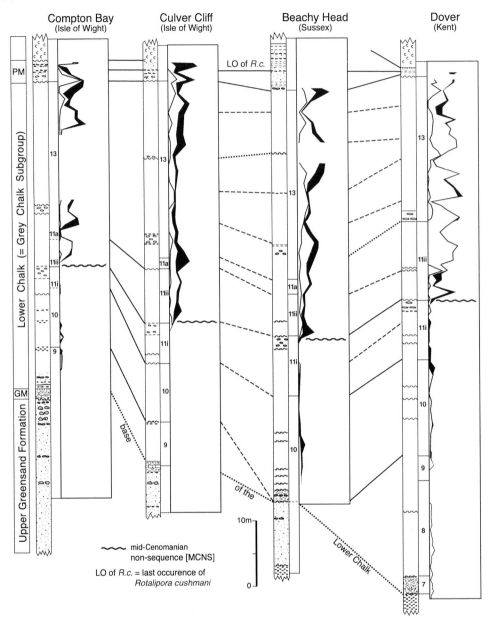

Fig. 8. Correlation of the Lower Chalk succession at Dover, Eastbourne (Sussex), Culver Cliff (Isle of Wight) and Compton Bay (Isle of Wight). The ornament in the planktonic:benthic graphs is the same as that used in Figures 4 & 5.

In Dorset, Somerset and east Devon, the MCNS was confirmed (Hart 1970; Carter & Hart 1977) in the majority of successions, with the base of the chalk becoming progressively younger in the successions already discussed. In addition, it was also recorded at Warren Hill (between Chard and Crewkerne), Snowdon Hill (Chard) and – finally – at Membury (Hart 1975) where the chalk succession was recognized as being of Turonian age, rather than Cenomanian. This conclusion has been supported by Mortimore *et al.* (2001).

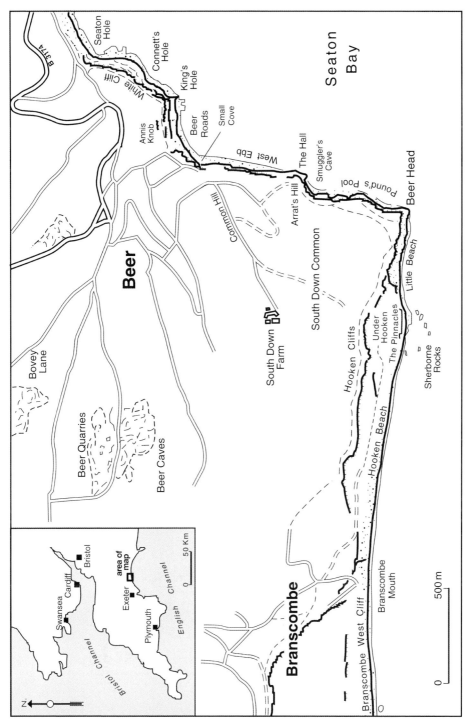

Fig. 9. Locality map for the mid-Cretaceous successions in the vicinity of Beer, SE Devon. The Pinnacles succession shown in Figure 10 was collected from a fallen block (since removed by cliff falls and coastal erosion) that was on the beach below the Pinnacles to the west of Beer Head. The same succession is still available in the Hooken Cliffs immediately inland of the Pinnacles, although this succession is rather difficult to access.

Marginal facies of the Anglo-Paris Basin

In SW Dorset and east Devon and in the western part of the Paris Basin (Maine, Sarthe, etc.) there are more arenaceous facies that were, generally, deposited in much shallower-water environments. In the Beer area (Figs 1 & 9), the Cenomanian succession is represented by a succession of thin, sandy limestones (Meyer 1874; Jukes-Browne & Hill 1903; Smith 1957, 1961, 1965; Drummond 1970; Hart 1970; Kennedy 1970; Carter & Hart 1977; Jarvis & Woodroof 1984; Jarvis & Tocher 1987; Jarvis et al. 1988; Robaszynski et al. 1998). Within these limestones the processing methods used on the marly chalks of southern England (the solvent method of Brasier 1980) were totally inappropriate and three alternative techniques were employed:

- thin sections – on which counts could not be made;
- hydrochloric acid reductions – the residues of which had to be studied underwater because drying the resultant fauna caused them to disintegrate. The planktonic foraminifera were only preserved as glauconitic chamber infillings, which are very difficult to identify to species level; and
- crushed underwater with a pestle and mortar – the residues of which could be counted with some degree of confidence, although only low numbers of foraminifera were recorded. This may make the results a little less reliable than samples where over 500 specimens in the 500–250 μm size fraction would normally be counted and where all size fractions would be inspected for species content.

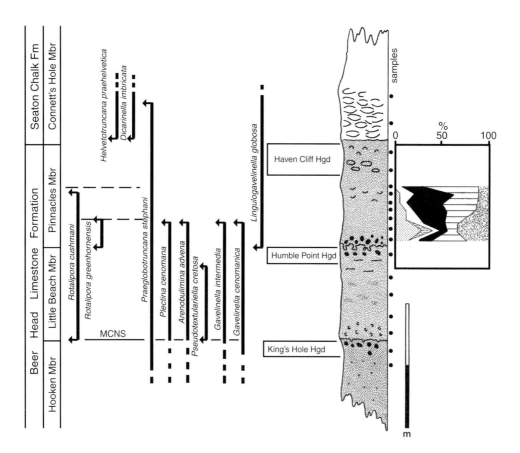

Fig. 10. The Beer Head Limestone Formation recorded from a fallen block below the Pinnacles (ST.220 879), west of Beer Head (see Fig. 9). The ornamentation in the planktonic:benthic graph is the same as that used in Figures 4 & 7. The MCNS is indicated, as are the distinctive extinction levels of *R. cushmani* and *R. greenhornensis*.

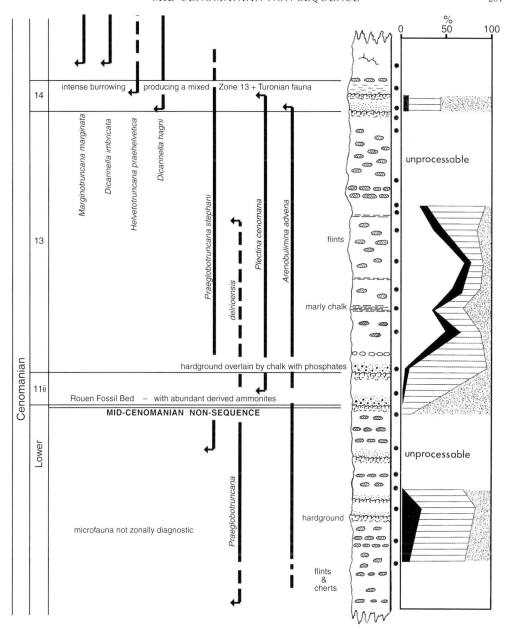

Fig. 11. The Cenomanian succession of the Cap d'Antifer cliffs (Seine Maritime, France; see Fig. 1), together with the ranges of some key foraminifera. The ornamentation in the planktonic:benthic graph is the same as that used in Figures 4 & 7. Note the absence of *Rotalipora* spp. in this succession, despite the abundance of planktonic foraminifera. As most of these are species of *Hedbergella*, this is probably a restriction caused by the shallow water in that environment at the time of deposition.

Within the Beer Head Limestone Formation (Jarvis & Woodroof 1984) there are a number of important hardgrounds separating the individual beds of limestone (members). Three of these hardgrounds (Hgd) are shown in Figure 10: the King's Hole Hardground, the Humble Point Hardground and the Haven Cliff Hardground. Bed C of Jukes-Browne & Hill (1903)

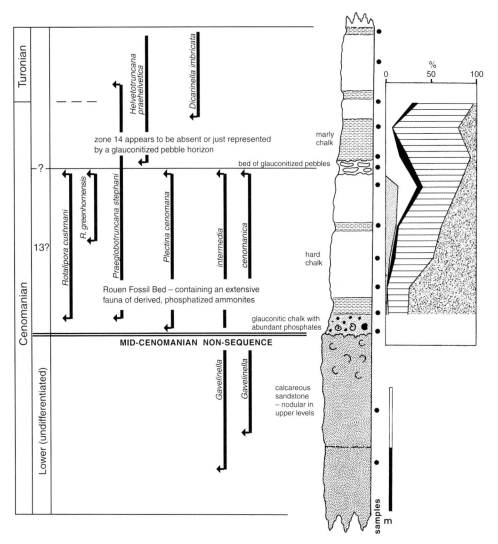

Fig. 12. The Cenomanian succession of the Côte Ste Catherine (Rouen; see Fig. 1) section. The ornamentation in the planktonic:benthic ratio graph is that used in Figs 4 & 7. Note the prominent feature identified as the 'Rouen Fossil Bed'.

and Smith (1957) was renamed the Pinnacles Member (of the Beer Head Limestone Formation) by Jarvis & Woodroof (1984). Despite the problems of sample preparation, the Pinnacles Member has yielded a reasonable microfauna, including the extinction of *R. greenhornensis* and *R. cushmani* in precisely the same relationship seen in the Dover succession. If anything, *R. greenhornensis* appears to be slightly more abundant in the Devon succession, and this could be due to either the proximity to the developing Atlantic Ocean, or the more robust nature of the test (reducing breakage during

processing). The fauna of Bed B (= Little Beach Member) is less distinctive, with only a few long-ranging taxa being recorded. The planktonic foraminifera are very rare (glauconitic moulds only) but include *R. cushmani* and *Praeglobotruncana stephani*. Below the King's Hole Hardground Bed A2 (= Hooken Member) the fauna is essentially composed of agglutinated foraminifera and a few long-ranging forms of the calcareous benthic genus *Gavelinella* – none of which can be used to identify any particular zone within the Cenomanian. The mid-Cenomanian non-sequence is located below Bed B, being represented by the surface above the King's Hole Hardground (see also Robaszynski *et al.* 1998, figs 12 and 14).

When the same techniques were adopted in an investigation of the Seine Maritime coast at Cap d'Antifer (Figs 1 & 11) and at the famous Côte Ste Catherine section in Rouen (Figs 1 & 12) similar faunas were recovered. In some cases, counts are possible, while in other parts of the succession the samples are almost impossible to process by other than thin-section or acid reduction. In this area the 'Rouen 2' hardground (Juignet & Breton 1992; Robaszynski *et al.* 1998) is the local correlative of the mid-Cenomanian non-sequence. For further discussion, see Juignet (1970), Carter & Hart (1977) and Robaszynski *et al.* (1998).

In the sand-dominated successions of Maine, northern France, to the north and NE of Le Mans, the only succession in which good foraminiferal assemblages at this level have been investigated is the old quarry at Les Aulnais, near Théligny (Juignet & Breton 1992). In this succession the bed of phosphatized fossils that are found in the glauconitic chalks of the basal Craie de Théligny rest on a resistant calcareous sandstone which is reminiscent of the Eggardon Grit of SW England (see Drummond 1970; Kennedy 1970; Carter & Hart 1977). The faunal relationships are almost identical to the Eggardon Hill succession, and the base of the Craie de Théligny appears to rest on the mid-Cenomanian non-sequence.

Summary

The mid-Cenomanian non-sequence is, in near-complete successions, simply the base of the zone of *Rotalipora cushmani*. When traced laterally it was soon recognized that there is a hiatus at this level, and that in many places there is evidence of missing strata both above and below the non-sequence; in places it is clearly marking an unconformity. The sudden increase in planktonic foraminifera above the non-sequence appears to indicate a major change in water depth at this level because the overlying strata are characterized by 'floods' of keeled planktonic foraminifera. Following the methodology of Emery & Myers (1996, fig. 6.14), such 'floods' may record maximum flooding surfaces and, in 1997a, Hart suggested that the 'c-line' of correlation (Fig. 4) might be a maximum flooding surface and that the MCNS was, potentially, a sequence boundary. It is also evident that, in marginal areas (e.g. Dorset and Devon) the MCNS is also a 'transgressive surface'. This suggestion was not followed by Robaszynski *et* *al.* (1998), although subsequent communication with the lead author of that paper has indicated that it had been prepared some time in advance of final publication. More recently, Gale (pers. com.) has indicated that the MCNS may be a sequence boundary and, in a recent compilation based in the Cauvery Basin, Gale *et al.* (2002) have recognized additional sequences within the Cenomanian succession.

There are inherent difficulties in the application of sequence stratigraphy to deeper-water carbonate environments such as the chalk of NW Europe. Sequence stratigraphy was developed in siliciclastic successions, and relies on the identification of exposed surfaces, palaeosols, ravinement surfaces, influx of detrital sediments, etc. Hancock (1989) has made extensive use of nodular chalks and hardgrounds in his models of sea-level change in the chalk succession: taking each hardground as marking the end of a period of relative sea-level fall. That hardgrounds are important is not in dispute, but their association with more marginal successions has been taken, by some, to indicate shallower-water conditions. Gale (1996) has summarized some of the characteristic indicators of sea-level change in the chalk succession although (Gale 1996, p. 185) he does highlight some of the problems associated with this type of analysis. In a review based on the successions in SW England, Hart (1997*b*) has also considered the problems caused by sediment production being controlled by biotic changes in the surface waters rather than sediment supply from neighbouring landmasses (as would be the case in 'classic' sequence stratigraphy). It is apparent that in many of the chalk successions in the UK the influx of deeper-water dwelling planktonic foraminifera provides an indication of increased habitable water column (= an increase in water depth over the shelf). Figure 13 shows a model of the distribution of both planktonic and benthic foraminifera within an idealized sequence (based on the Emery & Myers 1996, fig. 6.14 model). While the sediment response shown in this figure is that of a siliciclastic setting, the faunal changes would be the same (or similar) in a chalk environment. The dramatic change in the planktonic:benthic ratio recorded at the MCNS clearly records a significant change in water depth (= habitable water column) over the shelf area of the Anglo-Paris Basin and elsewhere (see Eicher 1969*a*, *b*; Carter & Hart 1977, fig. 11).

As a sequence boundary, and an important 'non-sequence' in the context of this paper, this break in deposition forms a major feature in marginal successions where the hiatus is that

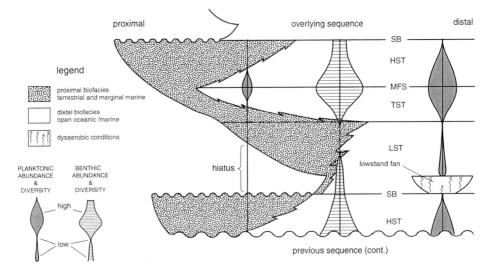

Fig. 13. Schematic interpretation of the distribution of foraminifera in an idealized sequence (adapted from Emery & Myers 1996, fig. 6.14). As this model is based on a siliciclastic succession, it can only be applied to a carbonate succession with caution (see text for discussion).

much greater. It can be identified also in many other parts of the world, including the Western Interior Sea-way of the USA (Eicher 1969a, b; Carter & Hart 1977), the Cauvery Basin, India (Tewari 1996; Hart et al. 2001), the Sergipe Basin, Brazil (Koutsoukos & Hart 1990, fig. 2) and the Carnarvon Basin, Western Australia (Haig 2002, p. 58). A major 'non-sequence' in the mid-Cenomanian has also been reported by Campbell (2003) from the Bathurst Island Group, offshore Northern Australia.

The author acknowledges the help of a wide range of colleagues, both in the UK and abroad. D. J. Carter is particularly thanked for the part that he played in generating many of the ideas presented here and for being such an able mentor. J. Abraham provided the final versions of the diagrams and is thanked for his valuable assistance.

References

ALLABY, A. & ALLABY, M. (eds) 1990. *The Concise Oxford Dictionary of Earth Sciences.* Oxford University Press, Oxford, 410 pp.

BANDY, O. L. 1961. Cretaceous planktonic foraminiferal zonation. *Micropaleontology*, **13**, 1–31.

BRASIER, M. D. 1980. *Microfossils*, Chapman & Hall, London, 193 pp.

BRUCKSHAW, J. M., GOGUEL, J., HARDING, H. J. B. & MALCOR, R. 1961. The work of the Channel Tunnel Study Group 1958–1960. *Proceedings of the Institution of Civil Engineers*, **18**, 149–178.

CAMPBELL, R. J. 2003. *Calcareous nannofossil and foraminiferal analysis of the Middle to Upper Cretaceous Bathurst Island Group, Northern Bonaparte Basin and Darwin Shelf, Northern Australia.* Unpublished Ph.D. thesis, University of Western Australia, Perth.

CARTER, D. J. & HART, M. B. 1977. Aspects of mid-Cretaceous stratigraphical micropalaeontology. *Bulletin of the British Museum, Natural History (Geology)*, **29**, 1–135.

CHADWICK, R. A. 1986. Extension tectonics in the Wessex Basin, southern England. *Journal of the Geological Society*, **143**, 465–488.

DRUMMOND, P. V. O. 1970. The Mid-Dorset Swell. Evidence of Albian–Cenomanian movements in Wessex. *Proceedings of the Geologists' Association*, **81**, 679–714.

EICHER, D. L. 1969a. Palaeobathymetry of Cretaceous Greenhorn Sea in Eastern Colorado. *American Association of Petroleum Geologists, Bulletin*, **53**, 1075–1090.

EICHER, D. L. 1969b. Cenomanian and Turonian planktonic foraminifera from the western interior of the United States. *In*: BRILL, E. J. (ed.) *Proceedings of the First International Conference on Planktonic Microfossils, Geneva, 1967*, Leiden, **2**, 163–174

EMERY, D. & MYERS, K. J. 1996. *Sequence Stratigraphy*, Blackwell Science, Oxford, 297 pp.

GALE, A. S. 1996. Turonian correlation and sequence stratigraphy of the Chalk in southern England. *In*: HESSELBO, S. P. & PARKINSON, D. N. (eds), *Sequence Stratigraphy in British Geology*, Geological Society, London, Special Publications, **103**, 177–195.

GALE, A. S., HARDENBOL, J., HATHWAY, B., KENNEDY, W. J., YOUNG, J. R. & PHANSALKAR, V. 2002. Global correlation of Cenomanian (Upper Cretaceous) sequences: evidence for Milankovitch control on sea level. *Geology*, **30**, 291–294.

HAIG, D. W. 2002. *Post-Conference Field Excursion Guidebook: Perth to Shark Bay*. Forams 2002, International Symposium on foraminifera, University of Western Australia, Perth, Australia, February 2002, 120 pp.

HANCOCK, J. M. 1969. Transgression of the Cretaceous sea in south-west England. *Proceedings of the Ussher Society*, **2**, 61–83.

HANCOCK, J. M. 1989. Sea-level changes in the British region during the Late Cretaceous. *Proceedings of the Geologists' Association*, **100**, 565–594.

HARRIS, C. S., HART, M. B. & WOOD, C. J. 1996. A revised stratigraphy. *In*: HARRIS, C. S., HART, M. B., VARLEY, P. M. & WARREN, C. D. (eds) *Engineering Geology of the Channel Tunnel*, Thomas Telford, London, 398–420.

HART, M. B. 1970. *The distribution of Foraminiferida in the Albian and Cenomanian of S. W. England*. Unpublished Ph.D. thesis, University of London.

HART, M. B. 1975. Microfaunal analysis of the Membury chalk succession. *Proceedings of the Ussher Society*, **3**, 271–279.

HART, M. B. 1992. The geology and micropalaeontology of the Channel Tunnel. *Geology Today*, **July–August**, 137–141.

HART, M. B. 1994. The mid-Dorset Swell; a re-assessment. *Proceedings of the Ussher Society*, **8**, 308–312.

HART, M. B. 1997a. Foraminifera of the United Kingdom chalk succession; role in correlation and sequence stratigraphy of the Cenomanian–Turonian. *Annales de Société Géologique du Nord*, **5** (2me série), 159–166.

HART, M. B. 1997b. The application of micropalaeontology to sequence stratigraphy; an example from the chalk succession of South-West England. *Proceedings of the Ussher Society*, **9**, 158–163.

HART, M. B. 1999. The Cornubian Island. *Report and Transactions of the Devonshire Association for the Advancement of Science*, **131**, 27–47.

HART, M. B. 2000. Foraminifera, sequence stratigraphy and regional correlation; an example from the uppermost Albian of Southern England. *Revue de Micropaléontologie*, **43**, 27–45.

HART, M. B. & BAILEY, H. W. 1979. The distribution of the planktonic foraminiferida in the mid-Cretaceous of NW Europe. *Aspekte der Kreide Europas, IUGS Series A*, **6**, 527–542.

HART, M. B., BAILEY, H. W., CRITTENDEN, S., FLETCHER, B. N., PRICE, R. J. & SWIECICKI, A. 1989. Cretaceous. *In*: JENKINS, D. G. & MURRAY, J. W. (eds), *Stratigraphical Atlas of Fossil Foraminifera*, British Micropalaeontological Society Series, Ellis Horwood, Chichester, pp. 273–371.

HART, M. B., JOSHI, A. & WATKINSON, M. P. 2001. Mid-Late Cretaceous stratigraphy of the Cauvery Basin and the development of the Eastern Indian Ocean. *Journal of the Geological Society of India*, **58**, 217–229.

JARVIS, I. & TOCHER, B. A. 1987. Field Meeting: the Cretaceous of SE Devon, 14–16 March 1986. *Proceedings of the Geologists' Association*, **98**, 51–66.

JARVIS, I. & WOODROOF, P. B. 1984. Stratigraphy of the Cenomanian and basal Turonian (Upper Cretaceous) between Branscombe and Seaton, SE Devon, England. *Proceedings of the Geologists' Association*, **95**, 193–215.

JARVIS, I., CARSON, G. A., HART, M. B., LEARY, P. N. & TOCHER, B. A. 1988. The Cenomanian–Turonian (late Cretaceous) anoxic event in SW England: evidence from Hooken Cliffs, near Beer, SE Devon. *Newsletters on Stratigraphy*, **18**, 147–164.

JENKYNS, H. C. & SENIOR, J. R. 1991. Geological evidence for intra-Jurassic faulting in the Wessex Basin and its margins. *Journal of the Geological Society*, **148**, 245–260.

JUIGNET, P. 1970. Précisions stratigraphiques et sédimentologiques sur le Cénomanien du Pays de Caux entre Saint-Jouin-Bruneval et le Cap d'Antifer (Seine Maritime). *Bulletin, Bureau Recherche Géologie et Minières, Paris, 2me Série*, **1**, 11–15.

JUIGNET, P. & BRETON, G. 1992. Mid-Cretaceous sequence stratigraphy and sedimentary cyclicity in the western Paris Basin. *Palaeogeography, Palaeoclimatology, Palaeoecology*, **91**, 197–218.

JUKES-BROWNE, A. J. & HILL, W. 1903. *The Cretaceous Rocks of Britain Vol. 2 – The Lower and Middle Chalk of England*. Memoir of the Geological Survey of the UK, London, HMSO, 568 pp.

KENDALL, P. F. 1929. The proposed tunnel under La Manche. *The Naturalist*, October 1st, 1929, no pagination [reprinted by A. Brown & Sons Ltd., London, 327–332].

KENNEDY, W. J. 1969. The correlation of the Lower Chalk of south-east England. *Proceedings of the Geologists' Association*, **80**, 459–560.

KENNEDY, W. J. 1970. A correlation of the uppermost Albian and the Cenomanian of South-West England. *Proceedings of the Geologists' Association*, **81**, 613–677.

KOUTSOUKOS, E. A. M. & HART, M. B. 1990. Cretaceous foraminiferal morphogroup distribution patterns, palaeocommunities and trophic structures: a case study from the Sergipe Basin, Brazil. *Transactions of the Royal Society of Edinburgh: Earth Sciences*, **81**, 221–246.

LEARY, P. N. & HART, M. B. 1989. The use of the ontogeny of deep water dwelling planktonic foraminifera to assess basin morphology, the development of water masses, eustasy and the position of the oxygen minimum zone in the water column. *Mesozoic Research*, **2**, 67–74.

LEARY, P. N. & HART, M. B. 1992. The benthonic foraminiferal response to changing substrate in Cenomanian (Cretaceous) rhythms induced by orbitally-forced surface water productivity. *Journal of Micropalaeontology*, **11**, 107–111.

McKERROW, W. S. (ed.) 1978. *The Ecology of Fossils*, Duckworth, London, 384 pp.

MEYER, C. J. A. 1874. On the Cretaceous rocks of Beer Head and the adjacent cliff sections, and on the relative horizons therein of the Warminster and Blackdown fossiliferous deposits. *Quarterly Journal of the Geological Society, London*, **30**, 369–393.

MORTIMORE, R. N., WOOD, C. J. & GALLOIS, R. W. 2001. *British Upper Cretaceous Stratigraphy*, Geological Conservation Review Series, No. 23, 558 pp., Joint Nature Conservation Committee, Peterborough.

MURRAY, J. W. 1976. A method of determining proximity of marginal seas to an ocean. *Marine Geology*, **22**, 103–119.

PAUL, C. R. C., MITCHELL, S. P., MARSHALL, J. D., LEARY, P. N., GALE, A. S., DUANE, A. M. & DITCHFIELD, P. W. 1994. Palaeoceanographic events in the Middle Cenomanian of Northwest Europe. *Cretaceous Research*, **15**, 707–738.

ROBASZYNSKI, F., AMEDRO, F., FOUCHER, J. C., GASPARD, D., MAGNIEZ-JANNIN, F., MANIVIT, H. & SORNAY, J. 1980. Synthèse biostratigraphique de l'Aptien au Santonien du Boulonnais à partir de sept groupes Paléontologiques: Foraminifères, Nannoplancton, Dinoflagellés et Macrofaunes. *Revue de Micropaléontologie*, **22**, 1–323.

ROBASZYNSKI, F., GALE, A., JUIGNET, P., AMEDRO, F. & HARDENBOL, J. 1998. Sequence stratigraphy in the Upper Cretaceous Series of the Anglo-Paris Basin: exemplified by the Cenomanian Stage. *In*: DE GRACIANSKY, P.-C. HARDENBOL, J., JACQUIUN, T. & VAIL, P. R. (eds), *Mesozoic and Cenozoic Sequence Stratigraphy of European Basins*, SEPM, Special Publication No. **60**, 363–386.

SHAW, A. B. 1964. *Time in Stratigraphy*, McGraw-Hill, New York, 365 pp.

SMITH, W. E. 1957. The Cenomanian Limestone of the Beer District, south Devon. *Proceedings of the Geologists' Association*, **68**, 115–135.

SMITH, W. E. 1961. The Cenomanian deposits of south-east Devonshire. The Cenomanian Limestone and contiguous deposits west of Beer. *Proceedings of the Geologists' Association*, **72**, 91–134.

SMITH, W. E. 1965. The Cenomanian deposits of south-east Devonshire. The Cenomanian Limestone east of Seaton. *Proceedings of the Geologists' Association*, **76**, 121–136.

TEWARI, A. 1996. *The Middle to Late Cretaceous microbiostratigraphy (foraminifera) and lithostratigraphy of the Cauvery Basin, Southeast India*. Unpublished Ph.D. thesis, University of Plymouth, UK.

WILLIAMS-MITCHELL, E. 1948. The zonal value of foraminifera in the Chalk of England. *Proceedings of the Geologists' Association*, **59**, 91–112.

Chronostratigraphy of proposed Turonian–Coniacian (Upper Cretaceous) stage boundary stratotypes: Salzgitter-Salder, Germany, and Wagon Mound, New Mexico, USA

PAUL J. SIKORA[1][*], RICHARD W. HOWE[1,4], ANDREW S. GALE[2] & JEFFREY A. STEIN[3]

[1]*Energy and Geoscience Institute, The University of Utah, 423 Wakara Way, Suite 300, Salt Lake City, UT, 84108, USA (e-mail: psikora@egi.utah.edu; rhowe@egi.utah.edu)*
[2]*Department of Palaeontology, The Natural History Museum, Cromwell Road, London, SW7 5BD, UK (e-mail: asg@mailserver.nhm.ac.uk)*
[3]*BP America, 501 WestLake Park Blvd, P.O. Box 3092, Houston, TX, 77253, USA (e-mail: SteinStop@aol.com)*
[4]*Correspondence: Geoscience Australia, GPO Box 378, Canberra 2601, ACT, Australia (e-mail: Richard.Howe@ga.gov.au)*

Abstract: A knowledgeable choice for a stage boundary stratotype is dependent upon obtaining high-resolution stratigraphic data. Detailed analyses conducted for the two potential Turonian–Coniacian stage boundary stratotypes that were considered at the Second Cretaceous Stage Boundary Symposium provide both positive and negative insights for consideration. The Salzgitter-Salder Quarry in central Germany (which was recommended by the symposium) contains abundant bivalve fossils, including the recommended boundary datum: the lowest occurrence of the inoceramid bivalve *Cremnoceramus deformis erectus*. Foraminifera are also abundant, but extensive diagenetic recrystallization seriously degrades nannofossil and palynomorph recovery and limits the potential of the section for stable isotope stratigraphy and radiometric dating. Furthermore, palaeoenvironmental analysis indicates that much of the Salzgitter stage boundary interval has resulted from allochthonous sedimentation, indicating that the well-developed lithological cyclicity between limestone and marlstone that occurs in the section is largely autocyclic. The orbital cyclostratigraphic potential of the section is therefore also in question.

The Wagon Mound outcrop in northeastern New Mexico, USA, has good recovery and biostratigraphic control for all three microfossil groups, but the base of *C. deformis erectus* occurs above the section, by definition placing the section entirely in the Upper Turonian. Well-preserved ammonites and inoceramid bivalves are also recoverable in over half of this section. Facies have not been recrystallized and represent continuous autochthonous sedimentation with sharply defined lithological cyclicity between limestone/marlstone couplets on a fine stratigraphic scale. In addition, a number of bentonites with proven datability occur in the section. Thus the bio- and chemostratigraphic dating potential, as well as the radiometric dating potential, of the section are good. However, much of the section is composed of carbonaceous, dysoxic facies with abnormal marine micro- and macrofossil assemblages, limiting study of the stratigraphic or palaeoecological trends leading up to the boundary.

The absence of the datum at Wagon Mound is puzzling, because microfossil biostratigraphy suggests that the section is substantially coeval with the Salzgitter-Salder section. The *C. deformis erectus* datum may thus be diachronous. Until the suitability of the recommended boundary datum is addressed, a reasoned choice of a section for the boundary stratotype is not possible. In any case, the absence of *C. deformis erectus* and the abnormal facies in the lower part of the Wagon Mound section, and the extensive diagenesis and partly allochthonous nature of the Salzgitter-Salder section, are serious enough problems to warrant rejection of both sections as stratotypes.

At the Second International Symposium on Cretaceous Stage Boundaries, held in Brussels, Belgium, in September 1995, two sections were proposed as potential stratotypes for the Turonian–Coniacian boundary: the Wagon Mound (Fig. 1) outcrop section in New Mexico, USA,

From: BEAUDOIN, A.B. & HEAD, M.J. (eds) 2004. *The Palynology and Micropalaeontology of Boundaries.* Geological Society, London, Special Publications, **230**, 207–242. 0305-8719/04/$15 © The Geological Society of London 2004.

and the Salzgitter-Salder quarry section (Fig. 2), in Lower Saxony, Germany (Kauffman *et al.* 1996). Ideally, a stratotype section should be stratigraphically complete, with well-preserved and abundant macro- and microfossils, and have well-documented macro- and microfossil biostratigraphy.

The macrofossil biostratigraphy of the Wagon Mound section is documented in Walaszczyk & Cobban (2000) and in this study, and that of the Salzgitter-Salder section is documented in Wood *et al.* (1984) and Kauffman *et al.* (1996). The event that the Brussels Symposium recommended for defining the Turonian–Coniacian boundary is the lowest occurrence (LO) of the inoceramid bivalve *Cremnoceramus rotundatus (sensu* Tröger *non* Fiede), which was reported by Kauffman *et al.* (1996) to be present in both of the potential stratotypes. *Cremnoceramus rotun-*

datus was considered by Walaszczyk & Cobban (2000) to be a junior synonym of *C. deformis erectus* (Meek), which is followed in this study.

Global correlation to stage stratotypes and their boundaries is often based on microfossil biostratigraphy, because many sections (particularly deep-marine sections) have poor macrofossil assemblages. Macrofossils are also more susceptible to geographical and climatic endemism than microfossils and, because many macrofossils are benthic, they are often strongly facies-controlled in distribution. Once a stratotype section is well correlated to microfossil biostratigraphy, its practical stratigraphic utility is greatly enhanced, because it can be defined in a much wider range of marine facies, and from a greater variety of sample types, such as drill cuttings, from which macrofossil recovery is generally very poor.

Fig. 1. Location of the Wagon Mound outcrop.

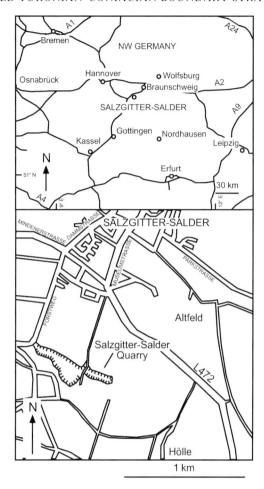

Fig. 2. Location of the Salzgitter-Salder outcrop.

Neither of the potential stratotype sections considered has a published microfossil biostratigraphy – limiting their potential for global correlation. The main aim of this study is to document the foraminiferal, calcareous nannofossil and marine palynomorph biostratigraphy of the two sections, and to use these events to correlate the Turonian–Coniacian boundary as defined by macrofossils. Unfortunately, based on the resulting correlation, it is not possible to recommend either section as a good Turonian–Coniacian stratotype, before serious chronostratigraphic problems are resolved.

Materials and methods

This study is based on outcrop samples collected from the Wagon Mound and Salzgitter-Salder sections. The Wagon Mound section (36° 01.39′ N 104° 41.85′ W, WGS84 sphaeroid) is located in NE New Mexico in a road cut along Interstate Highway 25, approximately 1 km NE of the town of Wagon Mound (Fig. 1), at mile marker 389. A 20-m section of limestones, marls, sandstones and shales of the Carlile and Niobrara Formations is well exposed in outcrop (Fig. 3), with horizontal bedding. The Salzgitter-Salder section (52° 07.55′ N 10° 19.80′ E, WGS84 sphaeroid) occurs in a partially abandoned quarry in Lower Saxony, central Germany, approximately 500 m south of the town of Salzgitter-Salder (Fig. 2). According to Kauffman *et al.* (1996), 260 m of limestones and marls are exposed in the walls of the quarry. This study concentrates on a 9.82-m section across the proposed Turonian–Coniacian boundary, as defined by the recommended boundary datum, the lowest occurrence of *Cremnoceramus deformis erectus* (Fig. 4). Bedding in the quarry dips to the north at approximately 70°. Illegal

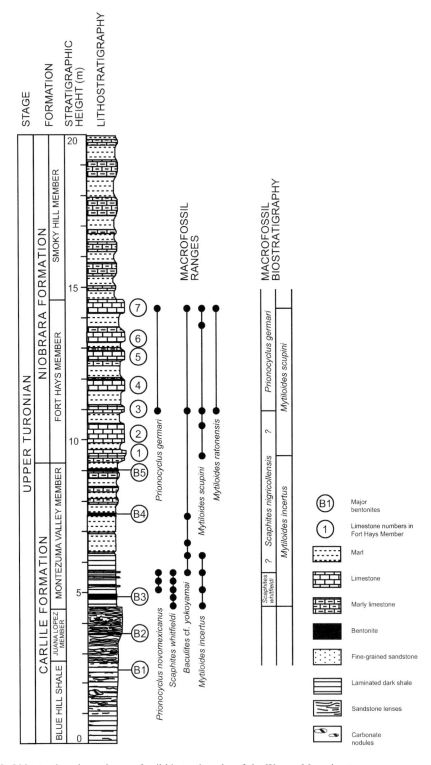

Fig. 3. Lithostratigraphy and macrofossil biostratigraphy of the Wagon Mound outcrop.

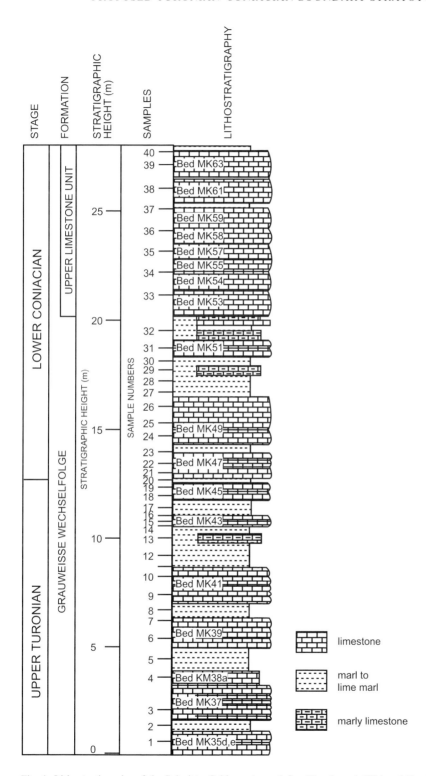

Fig. 4. Lithostratigraphy of the Salzgitter-Salder outcrop (after Wood *et al.* 1984 and Kauffman *et al.* 1996).

quarrying of limestone has greatly changed the appearance of the outcrop, which can be seen by comparing the photograph in fig. 3 of Kauffman *et al.* (1996) and Fig. 5 in this study.

Samples were processed for foraminifera, using standard preparation techniques, which include the boiling and disaggregation of samples in a solution of water, Calgon, and detergent, and then washing the resulting slurry through a 75-μm mesh sieve. The >75-μm sand fractions were then collected on filter paper in a Buchner funnel, dried, and stored. For indurated limestones that could not be washed, standard petrographic thin-sections were prepared, and examined using a transmitted light microscope. All sand fractions were selectively picked for planktonic foraminifera and biostratigraphically important benthic foraminifera, and representative specimens were mounted on slides. Well-preserved foraminiferal specimens were digitally imaged using a Phillips 505 Scanning Electron Microscope (SEM), having been sputter coated for eight minutes with gold at 20–30 mÅ.

For nannofossils, smear slides were prepared using standard techniques (see Bown & Young

1998). A small amount of fresh rock was scraped on to a coverslip and then smeared evenly with a wet toothpick. The coverslip was then dried on a hotplate, before being glued to a glass slide using Norland 61 optical adhesive. Nannofossil slides were examined at 1250 × magnification, using a Zeiss Universal cross-polarizing microscope, and taxa were recorded semi-quantitatively. Digital images of the nannofossils were captured using a Sony DSC-S75 3.2 megapixel digital camera mounted on the light microscope.

Palynological analyses were performed on a select subset of samples, using standard maceration and slide preparation techniques. Staining was used to highlight specimens.

Lithostratigraphy

Wagon Mound

The Wagon Mound section (Figs 3 & 6) exposes a conformable contact between the Carlile and Niobrara formations. Across the Western Interior Basin, this contact is more usually marked by a major unconformity, indicative of a large drop in sea-level (e.g. Elder & Kirkland 1993; Leckie

Fig. 5. Photograph of the Turonian–Coniacian boundary interval in the Salzgitter-Salder section.

Fig. 6. Photograph of the Wagon Mound outcrop. Bentonites B1 and B2 are shown.

et al. 1997). Only in the basinal deposits of south-central Colorado and northeastern New Mexico does the section become continuous (Laferriere 1987).

Approximately 9.8 m of the upper Carlile Formation is exposed, comprising three members: the Blue Hill Member, the Juana Lopez Calcarenite Member and the Montezuma Valley Shale Member (the 'Unnamed Shale' Member of Laferriere 1987), from oldest to youngest, respectively (Fig. 3). The lower shale, assigned to the Blue Hill Member, is about 3.1 m thick and is largely covered at Wagon Mound by talus, but several gully washes along the base of the outcrop have eroded through the talus and provide fresh exposures. The Blue Hill Member is a black to dark-grey, pyritic, slightly to very calcareous, laminated claystone containing chips of inoceramid bivalves and numerous, thin (<0.01 m) layers of fine sandstone. Often lenticular and sometimes showing current ripples, the sandstone layers contain small fragments and isolated prisms of inoceramid bivalves. Some of the sandstone bases are bioturbated by a 2 mm diameter trace. The upper 1 m of the unit is more calcareous overall, and contains sparse, large,

lenticular (0.2 × 1.0 m) septarian Fe-calcite concretions. This more calcareous interval is also marked by a prominent (0.04 m) yellow bentonite (B1 in Fig. 3) 0.55 m beneath the top of the member. The Blue Hill Member is marked by low-diversity, high-abundance assemblages of both macrofossils and microfossils, that increase in absolute abundance up-section.

The Juana Lopez Member is approximately 1.8 m thick at Wagon Mound. The unit is marked by complex interbedding of thin calcarenite and sandy, inoceramid limestone (Fig. 7a), dark-grey shale and bedded, rippled and, rarely, bioturbated fine-grained sandstone (Fig. 7b). The upper part of the sandstone layers is marked by hummocky cross-stratification. A thin (10 cm), yellow bentonite (B2 in Fig. 3) occurs near the middle of the member. The Juana Lopez Member is quite indurated and forms a prominent ledge in outcrop (Fig. 8).

The uppermost part of the Carlile Formation at Wagon Mound is comprised of 4.8 m of calcareous claystone/shale, previously known informally as the Unnamed Shale member (Laferriere 1987), but correlated by ammonite stratigraphy in this study to the Montezuma

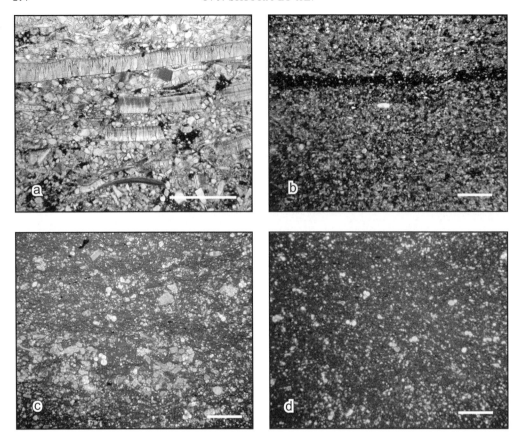

Fig. 7. Thin-section photos of the main indurated lithologies present in the Wagon Mound section. (**a**) limestone from the upper Juana Lopez Member, 4.55 m, composed of sandy inoceramid packstone; (**b**) well-sorted, fine-grained quartz sandstone from the middle Juana Lopez Member (3.20 m), with thin, organic-rich muddy laminae; (**c**) typical limestone from the Fort Hays Member, first limestone at 9.85 m, showing densely fossiliferous, bioturbated wackestone with abundant macrofossil debris and planktonic foraminifera; (**d**) typical limestone from the Smoky Hill Member, ninth limestone at 16.45 m, showing intensely bioturbated, organic-rich wackestone with abundant planktonic foraminifera and very fine-grained macrofossil debris (bar = 1 mm).

Valley Member of the Mancos Shale in the Four Corners region (Leckie *et al.* 1997). The lower 1.8 m is composed of carbonaceous, poorly to moderately calcareous, black claystone that contains abundant inoceramids, ammonites and fish debris. This lower section weathers very easily, requiring extensive trenching to obtain fresh samples. The upper 3.0 m of the Montezuma Valley Member is marked by much more calcareous, extensively bioturbated, dark-grey shale/marlstone that is poorly fossiliferous for macrofossils, but contains abundant micro-fossils. The upper section is more resistant to weathering than the lower portion of the unit, resulting in a pronounced break in outcrop slope (Fig. 9). The Montezuma Valley Member con-tains three bentonites, the thickest in the lower portion of the section (0.14 m) whereas the other

two occur in the more calcareous upper part (B3, B4 and B5, respectively, in Fig. 3).

The Carlile Formation is conformably over-lain by 5.35 m of the Fort Hays Member of the Niobrara Formation. The Fort Hays Member is composed of sharply defined couplets of hard, micritic limestone (0.2 to 0.6 m thick) and medium- to dark-grey marlstone (0.3 m to 0.6 m thick; Figs 3 & 9). The limestone interbeds make up the greatest thickness of the section, which is the primary lithological criterion defin-ing the Fort Hays Member. The limestone is consistent in lithology throughout: very fossili-ferous, extensively bioturbated wackestone marked by abundant planktonic foraminifera, few to frequent benthic species and common to abundant inoceramid and/or echinoid debris (Fig. 7c). Macrofossil debris visible to the naked

Fig. 8. Oblique photograph of the Wagon Mound outcrop, showing the prominent ledge formed by the Juana Lopez Member.

eye is quite rare, however. The limestone is very clean, with little clay, and well indurated. The intervening beds vary in clay content between a calcareous claystone and marlstone, although the former is most common. Relatively soft lithologically, the claystone/marlstone samples completely disaggregate during foraminiferal processing, to yield washed residues composed completely of macrofossil debris and foraminifera. Subsidiary mineral constituents such as pyrite are extremely rare.

The Smoky Hill Member of the Niobrara Formation conformably overlies the Fort Hays Member. The analysed Smoky Hill Member section is approximately 10.6 m thick at Wagon Mound, with an additional 1.5 m of thermally altered section underlying the Cenozoic basalt capping the outcrop (Fig. 10). As in the Fort Hays Member, the Smoky Hill Member is composed of extensively bioturbated limestone/claystone couplets with very rare macroscopic macrofossils. However, in the Smoky Hill Member, the couplets are more irregularly spaced and less sharply delineated, and calcareous claystone composes most of the section

thickness (Fig. 3). Limestone beds in the Smoky Hill Member comprise very fossiliferous wackestone marked by abundant planktonic foraminifera, few to frequent benthic foraminifera and common to abundant macrofossil debris (Fig. 7d). They contain little clay, and are very indurated. Macrofossil debris is even finer grained than in the Fort Hays Member and is almost entirely composed of inoceramid and other indeterminate mollusc fragments, with only very rare echinoderm debris. The Smoky Hill Member is also much more organic-rich (Fig. 7d). The claystone layers, as in the Fort Hays Member section, yield residues almost completely composed of macrofossil debris and foraminifera. However, rare to frequent pyrite is consistently present, and no marlstone is noted.

Salzgitter-Salder

The Turonian–Coniacian boundary occurs in the upper part of the Salzgitter-Salder section in the Grauweisse Wechselfolge Formation, which is composed of discrete, thickening-upwards marlstone/limestone couplets (Wood *et al.*

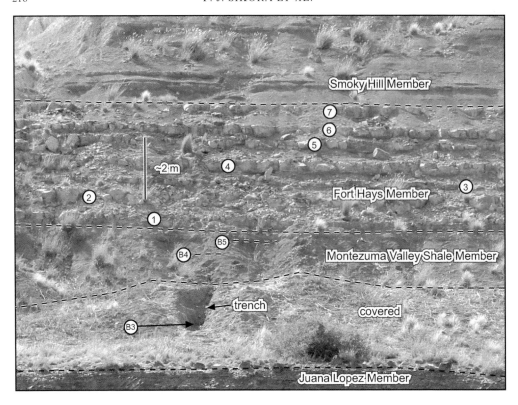

Fig. 9. Photograph of the Montezuma Valley Shale and Fort Hays Member at Wagon Mound. Bentonites B3–B5 and limestone beds 1–7 are shown.

1984). Nearly 30 m of section were analysed for this study, beginning at 14.6 m below the recommended boundary datum (the LO of *Cremnoceramus deformis erectus*) and continuing to 15.2 m above the boundary. The upper 6.8 m of the studied interval (i.e. from 23.0 to 29.8 m) are predominantly limestone, with much less frequent, thinner and more sporadic marlstone layers than in the lower Grauweisse Wechselfolge Formation. This upper interval is referred to informally in local stratigraphy as the Upper Limestone Unit (Fig. 4). The studied section is richly fossiliferous, especially in inoceramid bivalves, echinoids and foraminifera. However, ammonites are rare, and extensive diagenetic recrystallization results in poor recovery of nannofossils and palynomorphs. Fresh exposures of marlstone beds are dark grey and relatively indurated. However, the marlstone disaggregates well upon washing, yielding abundant foraminifera in free specimen.

The limestone beds of the Salzgitter section are dark to medium grey, extensively recrystallized and very indurated. Thin-section examination reveals that many of these limestone layers are calcisphere wackestone, with little or no evidence of bioturbation (Fig. 11a).

Palaeontology

Foraminifera

Wagon Mound. Microfossil recovery in the Wagon Mound section is generally very good. The most abundant and/or biostratigraphically significant foraminiferal species are illustrated on Figs 12 to 16. Only near the base of the Blue Hill Member and in most of the Juana Lopez Member does recovery become poor. Both planktonic and benthic foraminifera from the Blue Hill Shale generally increase in abundance up-section. Their diversity is low, and, in the lower portion of the outcrop of the member they are present as near-monospecific assemblages. However, in the more calcareous upper part of the member, foraminiferal diversity rises for both planktonic and benthic species. Nevertheless, both abundance and diversity remain much lower than that which characterizes the Niobrara section.

Fig. 10. Photograph of the Smoky Hill Member at Wagon Mound.

Preservation of foraminifera in the Blue Hill Shale ranges from very poor (due to dissolution) to good. Following similar trends as abundance and diversity, preservation improves up-section in the unit. Macrofossil debris is abundant, but composed largely of bivalve debris derived from a low-diversity assemblage dominated by *Mytiloides* (Kauffman *et al.* 1994). However, occasional ammonites occur in the upper, more calcareous section.

Foraminiferal recovery in the Juana Lopez Member is generally poor. The claystone/marlstone layers of the lower portion of the unit yield abundant inoceramid debris and other indeterminate mollusc fragments, but only infrequent benthic foraminifera and extremely infrequent planktonic species (small *Hedbergella* and *Whiteinella*). The fossil content of the well-cemented calcarenite in the middle of the unit is very poor. However, occasional discontinuous muddy laminae contain very fine-grained macro-

fossil debris and occasional benthic and planktonic foraminifera (Fig. 7b). The calcarenite is too indurated to yield free microfossil specimens, requiring study in thin-section.

Macrofossils are abundant in the limestone beds of the Juana Lopez Member, although predominantly composed of small, indeterminate fragments of inoceramids, other molluscs and echinoid debris. Occasional ammonite moulds are also present. Echinoderm debris is most common in the cleanest limestone layers, whereas inoceramid debris is dominant in the more argillaceous limestone at the top of the unit. Foraminifera are largely composed of rare to frequent planktonic species, mainly heterohelicids, although diversity increases in the uppermost part of the unit. Benthic foraminifera are extremely rare. The induration of the Juana Lopez Member limestone beds usually permits study of microfossils only in thin-section. However, the uppermost part of the interval becomes

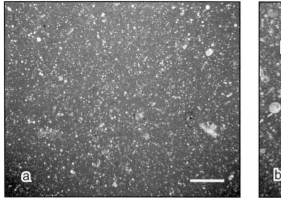
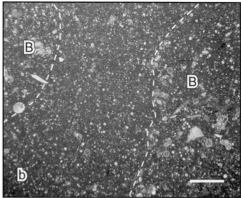
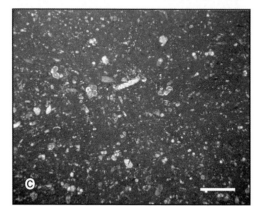

Fig. 11. Thin-section photos of limestone beds from the Salzgitter-Salder outcrop, illustrating the three main depositional facies. (**a**) massive calcisphere wackestone from 3.2 m, indicative of calciturbidites or fine-grained debris flows; (**b**) burrowed foraminiferal, calcisphere wackestone from 27.2 m, burrow infill (**B**) characterized by common planktonic foraminifera and fine-grained macrofossil debris, indicating more intermittent sediment flow deposition mixing with interbedded autochthonous material via bioturbation; (**c**) autochthonous pelagic wackestone from 12.0 m, rich in planktonic foraminifera and fine-grained macrofossil debris (bar = 1 mm).

more argillaceous as part of a gradational contact with the overlying Montezuma Valley Shale. The uppermost limestone yields frequent free specimens of foraminifera by washing. However, preservation is poor, due to fragmentation and recrystallization.

The Montezuma Valley Shale of the Carlile Formation contains abundant, diverse and well-preserved inoceramid bivalves and ammonites throughout the poorly exposed lower section. Planktonic foraminifera are abundant, but poorly preserved, while benthic foraminifera are frequent, mainly comprising *Planulina* spp. and agglutinated taxa. Fine-grained macrofossil debris is uncommon. In the more calcareous upper portion, planktonic foraminifera become even more abundant, but diversity remains low, with dominance by heterohelicids and *White-inella*. Benthic foraminifera are rare or absent,

fine-grained inoceramid debris becomes abundant, and there is an influx of echinoderm debris as well. The macrofossil debris is almost entirely

Fig. 12. Foraminifera. All bars equal 100 μm. (**a & b**) *Haplophragmoides gilberti*, (**a**) dorsal view, (**b**) edge view, Blue Hill Member, Carlile Formation, Wagon Mound outcrop, 1.2 m; (**c**) *Eggerellina mariae*, Salzgitter-Salder, 18.9 m; (**d–f**) *Globorotalites micheliana*, (**d**) dorsal view, (**e**) edge view, (**f**) ventral view, Salzgitter-Salder, 19.8 m; (**g–i**) *Pseudoparella*? *ripleyensis*, (**g**) dorsal view, (**h**) edge view, (**i**) ventral view, Salzgitter-Salder, 16.2 m; (**j–l**) *Valvulineria infrequens*, (**j**) dorsal view, (**k**) edge view, (**l**) ventral view, Fort Hays Member, Niobrara Formation, Wagon Mound outcrop, 9.5 m; (**m–o**) *Anomalinoides talaria*, (**m**) dorsal view, (**n**) edge view, (**o**) ventral view, Fort Hays Member, Niobrara Formation, Wagon Mound outcrop, 9.1 m.

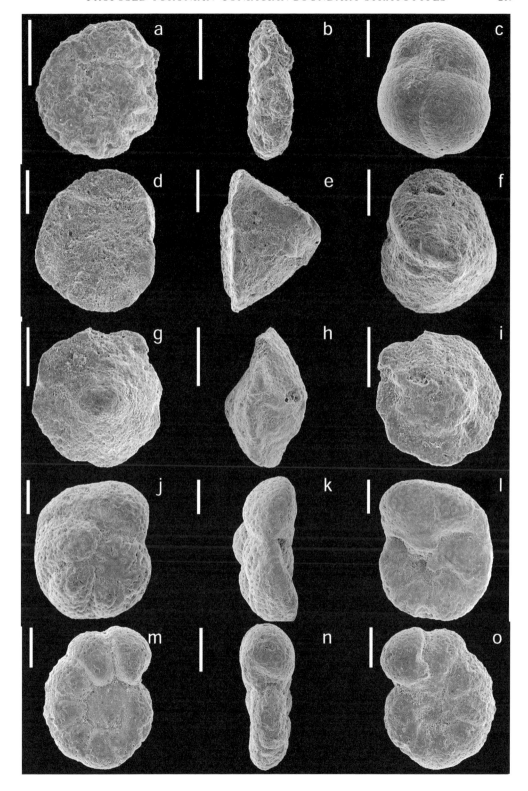

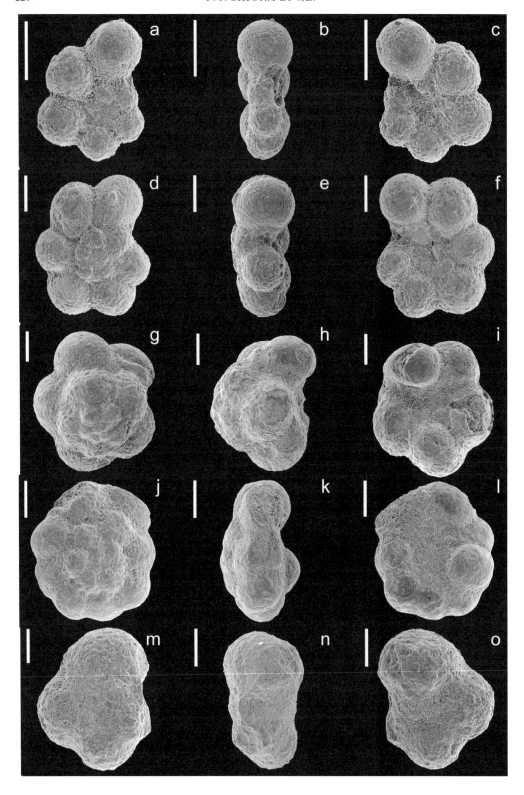

present as sand- and silt-sized fragments, reflecting intense bioturbation. Although much more common, the planktonic foraminifera from throughout the Montezuma Valley Shale are similar in species composition to those noted from the limestone beds in the uppermost part of the Juana Lopez Member.

Abundant foraminifera and fine-grained macrofossil debris characterize both limestone and claystone of the Fort Hays Member of the Niobrara Formation (Fig. 7c), with little variation in microfossil composition. The limestone is very indurated, however, and can only be studied in thin-section. Although microfossil composition is similar to the upper Montezuma Valley Shale, the Fort Hays Member is distinguished by an increase in planktonic foraminiferal diversity, especially amongst keeled species, and a marked rise in the abundance of echinoid debris and benthic foraminifera. Preservation of Fort Hays Member foraminifera ranges from fair to good. Although silt and sand-sized macrofossil fragments are often abundant in the Fort Hays Member, whole specimens are very rare, either as unaltered shell material or as moulds.

The planktonic foraminifera of the lower 2.3 m of the Smoky Hill Member are similar in species composition to those of the upper Fort Hays Member, but species of *Whiteinella* become dominant, with less-common keeled taxa. Fine-grained inoceramid debris remains abundant, but echinoderm debris is nearly absent, as are benthic foraminifera. The middle 5.0 m of the studied Smoky Hill Member section is marked by less dominance of *Whiteinella*, with higher species diversity among planktonic foraminifera and an influx of a common, diverse assemblage of large nodosariid benthic foraminifera. The abundance of inoceramid debris declines upwards. Finally, in the upper 2.3 m of the studied Smoky Hill Member section, keeled planktonic foraminifera become dominant, with the highest abundance of *Dicarinella* noted in the Niobrara section. Among benthic species,

nodosariids decline in favour of agglutinated taxa, mainly ataxophragmiids. Inoceramid debris is infrequent. Preservation of foraminifera is in general good throughout the Smoky Hill Member section. As with the Fort Hays Member, limestone beds require study in thin-section (Fig. 7d), and no major difference is noted in microfossil composition between limestone and claystone layers.

Salzgitter-Salder. The marlstone beds of the Salzgitter-Salder outcrop yield abundant planktonic foraminifera in free specimen, with fair to good preservation. Fine-grained bivalve and echinoderm debris is also abundant, and whole specimens of these macrofossils are common in the outcrop. Benthic foraminiferal abundance ranges from frequent to abundant. Planktonic foraminifera dominated by non-keeled species (mainly *Whiteinella*) are prevalent in the lowest part of the studied section (Fig. 4) from 0.0 to 11.7 m, although *Archaeoglobigerina cretacea* is also common. Benthic foraminifera are common, but are composed of an unusual assemblage of *Arenobulimina* and diverse *Gavelinella* species mixed with deep-water siliceous agglutinated taxa, mainly ammodiscids.

From 11.7 m to the base of the Coniacian at 14.6 m (as marked by the recommended boundary marker: the LO of the bivalve *Cremnoceramus deformis erectus*), planktonic foraminifera become dominated by keeled species: mainly *Marginotruncana* spp. Among benthic foraminifera, gavelinellids become dominant. Siliceous agglutinated taxa become rare and sporadic in distribution. The section immediately above the boundary, from 15.1 to 17.9 m is characterized by an abrupt turnover in planktonic foraminiferal composition, with extreme dominance by *Whiteinella* and rapid decline of keeled species (nearly absent from 16.8 m through 17.9 m). Benthic foraminiferal composition becomes mixed again, with a return of frequent *Arenobulimina* and deep-water siliceous taxa. However, beginning at 18.9 m, keeled planktonic foraminifera begin a rapid rise in abundance, and benthic foraminifera again become dominated by gavelinellids. By 21.6 m, keeled planktonic species are again dominant, whereas benthic foraminiferal diversity reaches a maximum.

Unlike the Niobrara section at Wagon Mound, the Salzgitter limestone beds have a markedly different microfossil composition to that of the marlstone. The limestone is predominantly calcisphere wackestone, whereas calcispheres are either rare or absent in the

Fig. 13. All bars equal 100 μm. (**a–c**) *Hastigerinoides subdigitata*, (**a**) dorsal view, (**b**) edge view, (**c**) ventral view, Juana Lopez Member, Carlile Formation, Wagon Mound outcrop, 4.2 m; (**d–f**) *Whiteinella aprica*, (**d**) dorsal view, (**e**) edge view, (**f**) ventral view, Fort Hays Member, Niobrara Formation, Wagon Mound outcrop, 6.1 m; (**g–i**) *Whiteinella paradubia*, (**g**) dorsal view, (**h**) edge view, (**i**) ventral view, Salzgitter-Salder, 18.9 m; (**j–l**) *Anaticinella multiloculata*, (**j**) dorsal view, (**k**) edge view, (**l**) ventral view, Salzgitter-Salder, 1.8 m; (**m–o**) *Archaeoglobigerina blowi*, (**m**) dorsal view, (**n**) edge view, (**o**) ventral view, Salzgitter-Salder, 19.2 m.

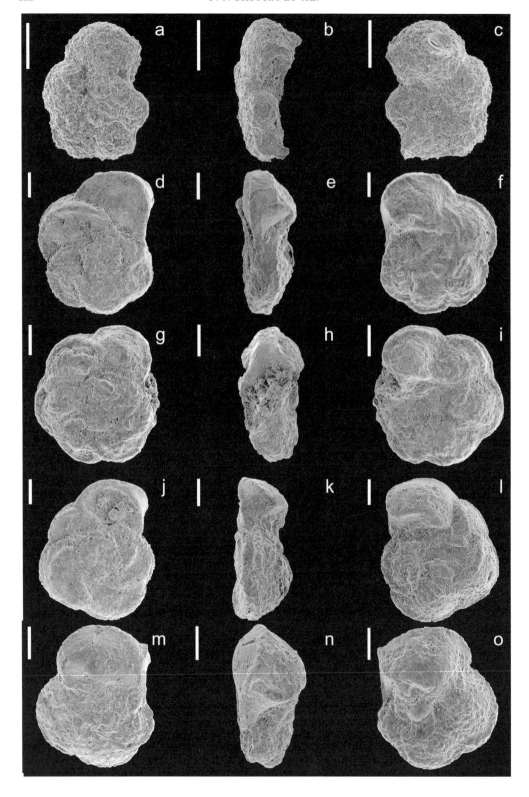

marlstone washed residues. The calcisphere wackestone frequently displays a massive texture, with little evidence of bioturbation (Fig. 11a). Also common are calcisphere limestone with a higher planktonic foraminiferal content and rare burrows, indicative of mixing of different layers by bioturbation (Fig. 11b). The rarest type of limestone at Salzgitter-Salder is foraminiferal wackestone in which calcispheres are rare (Fig. 11c). There is no obvious pattern in the distribution of these carbonate facies in the studied interval.

Calcareous nannofossils

Wagon Mound. Calcareous nannofossil abundance varies from very low (with some samples barren) to moderate, with generally poor to moderate preservation. Significant nannofossil species are illustrated on Figures 17 & 18. The lower part of the Wagon Mound section (0 to 5.76 m), comprising the Blue Hill Member, the Juana Lopez Member and the Montezuma Valley Shale, contains an unusual Upper Turonian to lowermost Coniacian assemblage composed of diverse, moderately to well-preserved holococcoliths. This assemblage decreases in abundance in the Montezuma Valley Shale between 5.26 and 6.40 m, and is absent from the overlying Niobrara Formation section. The holococcolith assemblage includes rare *Bifidalithus geminicatillus*, rare *Calculites* cf. *anfractus*, common *Saepiovirgata biferula*, and four undescribed species, two of which are common (these species will be described in a separate publication by RWH). The assemblage also contains an undescribed placolith.

The presence of *B. geminicatillus* and *S. biferula* is surprising, because Varol (1991) described both of these species from the Campanian of the North Sea. The specimens of *S. biferula* observed in this study are about

half the size of the holotype (although larger specimens similar in size to the holotype occur very rarely in the Santonian and Campanian of the Niobrara Chalk from western Kansas in unpublished work by R. W. Howe), but appear otherwise identical. Also surprising is the presence of *C.* cf. *anfractus*, similar to a species described from the Cenomanian of the North Sea by Jakubowski (1986).

The previous North Sea distribution of all three species indicates that they have strong cool-surface-water ('Boreal') affinities. Their presence in the Upper Turonian Wagon Mound section therefore suggests a strong Boreal affinity for the Western Interior Seaway at this time, probably associated with much cooler surface waters than those indicated by both nannofossils and planktonic foraminifera in the overlying Fort Hays Member and Smoky Hill Member. Upper Cretaceous intervals with diverse holococcoliths are relatively rare (e.g. Campanian holococcoliths described from the Gulf of Mexico by Risatti (1973) and Wind & Wise (1978)) and the Wagon Mound section provides a rare insight into the Turonian–Coniacian history of this poorly understood coccolith group.

The overall nannofossil assemblage in the Blue Hill Member and Juana Lopez Member exhibits very low abundance and poor preservation. The assemblage is dominated by the above-mentioned holococcoliths and *Watznaueria barnesae*, with less-common *Prediscosphaera cretacea*, *Gartnerago obliquum*, *Tranolithus* spp., and *Eiffellithus* spp. Species richness varies from 10 to 22 species, with barren samples at 4.40 m, 5.76 m and 8.20 m. The disparity in preservation and abundance between the holococcoliths and heterococcoliths in this interval is difficult to explain. It suggests that the environment at the time of deposition was favourable for holococcoliths, but not heterococcoliths, and that the heterococcoliths may have been penecontemporaneously reworked.

Nannofossil assemblages in the Fort Hays and Smoky Hill Members of the Niobrara Formation are richer and better preserved than those of the underlying Carlile Formation. Abundance is low to moderate, with poor to moderate preservation. Species richness varies from 13 to 40 species, with most samples having between 20 and 35 species. The assemblages are dominated by *Watznaueria barnesae*, with lesser abundances of *Eiffellithus* spp., *Gartnerago obliquum*, *Lithraphidites carniolensis*, *Prediscosphaera cretacea*, *Retecapsa* spp., *Tranolithus* species, and indeterminate small *Zeugrhabdotus* spp.

Fig. 14. All bars equal 100 μm. (**a–c**) *Falsotruncana douglasi*, (**a**) dorsal view, (**b**) edge view, (**c**) ventral view, Juana Lopez Member, Carlile Formation, Wagon Mound outcrop, 2.4 m; (**d–f**) *Marginotruncana paraconcavata*, (**d**) dorsal view, (**e**) edge view, (**f**) ventral view, Fort Hays Member, Niobrara Formation, Wagon Mound outcrop, 9.5 m; (**g–i**) *Marginotruncana paraventricosa*, (**g**) dorsal view, (**h**) edge view, (**i**) ventral view, Salzgitter-Salder, 5.6 m; (**j–l**) *Dicarinella concavata*, (**j**) dorsal view, (**k**) edge view, (**l**) ventral view, Smoky Hill Member, Niobrara Formation, Wagon Mound outcrop, 14.1 m; (**m–o**) *Dicarinella primitiva*, (**m**) dorsal view, (**n**) edge view, (**o**) ventral view, Fort Hays Member, Niobrara Formation, Wagon Mound outcrop, 9.5 m.

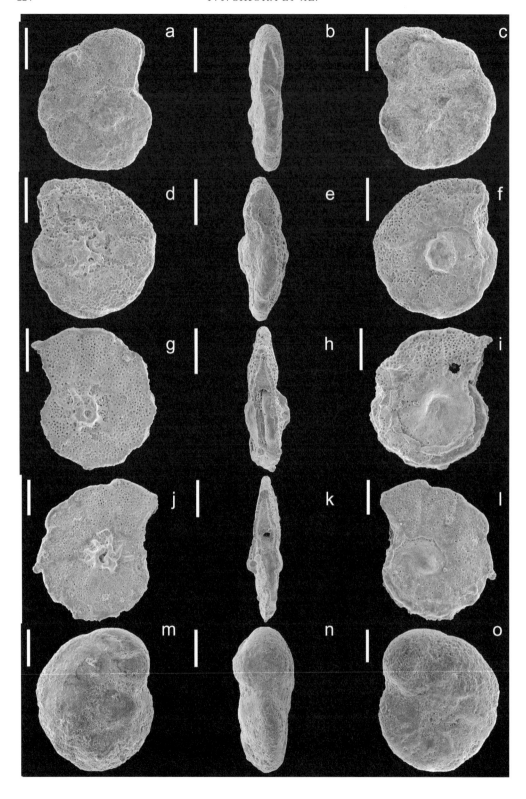

Nannofossils are consistently rare to very rare and poorly preserved throughout the Salzgitter-Salder section, making meaningful biostratigraphic zonation very difficult. Lees (pers. comm. 2003) records relatively abundant and diverse nannofossil assemblages from this section, so it is likely that her processing methods were more suited to the lithology. Marlstone layers have slightly higher species richness and abundance than the limestone beds. Species richness varies from one to 37 species, with most samples having 10 or less taxa, and only four of 40 samples having 20 or more species. The assemblages are dominated by *Watznaueria barnesae*, with lesser abundances of *Eiffellithus* spp., *Gartnerago obliquum*, *Lithraphidites carniolensis*, *Prediscosphaera cretacea*, *Retecapsa* spp., *Tranolithus* spp., and *Zeugrhabdotus bicrescenticus*.

Marine palynomorphs

Wagon Mound. Dinoflagellate cyst recovery is largely limited to the claystone and marlstone beds in both sections. Even within these strata, the recovery and assemblage composition is variable – probably the result of a combination of outcrop weathering, diagenesis and palaeoenvironment. In the Wagon Mound section, an LO of *Dinogymnium albertii* in the sample at 2.2 m indicates a latest Turonian age. At the base of the measured section (0.0 m) within the Blue Hill Member there are rare specimens of *Oligosphaeridium totum totum*, whose highest stratigraphic occurrence (HO) is characteristic of the Upper Turonian. The species composition of the dinoflagellate assemblage changes substantially within the Juana Lopez Member. Whereas the Blue Hill Member and Juana Lopez Member assemblages features a marked cool surface-water affinity 'Boreal' component (e.g. *Chatangiella* spp.),

these forms are much rarer in the Niobrara Formation, where they are replaced by species with more warm surface-water 'Tethyan' distributions (e.g. *Xiphophoridium*). Moderate diversity and the absence of deep-water taxa such as *Pterodinium* spp. indicate open marine shelf depositional conditions.

Salzgitter-Salder. In the Salzgitter-Salder outcrop, most of the palynomorphs recovered were derived from a more restricted palaeoenvironment. Much of the Turonian section is characterized by a low-diversity dinoflagellate assemblage strongly dominated by the species *Palaeohystrichophora infusorioides*, typical of very shallow-water and possibly restricted depositional conditions (Bottjer & Stein 1994). However, a few samples from the Turonian section yield somewhat higher diversity, more open shelf assemblages, indicating more normal marine hemipelagic deposition. The sample at 13.4 m yields moderately diverse species that include the Turonian indexes *Florentinia clavigera* (HO) and *Oligosphaeridium totum totum* (HO, as at Wagon Mound). Unfortunately, the latest Turonian datum, the LO of *Dinogymnium albertii* that occurred at Wagon Mound, was not observed in the Salzgitter-Salder section, probably due to palaeoenvironmental exclusion. Dinoflagellate recovery is also variable in the Lower Coniacian interval, varying from nearly monospecific recovery of *P. infusorioides* to high-diversity high-abundance events that include relatively abundant deep-water taxa (i.e. *Pterodinium* spp.). In general, dinoflagellate diversity is higher in the Coniacian, indicating more hemipelagic, open marine conditions. The assemblage from 21.6 m is particularly diverse, and yields several important Lower Coniacian markers. Most notable is the occurrence of *Pervosphaeridium*

Fig. 15. All bars equal 100 μm. (**a–c**) *Planulina kansasensis*, (**a**) dorsal view, (**b**) edge view, (**c**) ventral view, Smoky Hill Member, Niobrara Formation, Wagon Mound outcrop, 14.1 m; (**d–f**) *Gavelinella petita*, (**d**) dorsal view showing highly limbate and raised sutures on the early whorls and the early part of the ultimate whorl, (**e**) edge view, note relatively high trochospire and very thickened, imperforate periphery, (**f**) ventral view exhibiting prominent umbilical boss, Blue Hill Member, Carlile Formation, Wagon Mound outcrop, 0.4 m; (**g–i**) *Gavelinella petita* transitional to *Planulina texana*, (**g**) dorsal view showing highly raised and limbate sutures restricted to early whorls; (**h**) edge view showing much reduced trochospire height and less-thickened periphery, (**i**) ventral view with reduced umbilical boss, Blue Hill Member, Carlile Formation, Wagon Mound outcrop, 1.2 m; (**j–l**) *Planulina texana s.s.*, (**j**) dorsal view showing raised sutures restricted to early whorls and developed only near the spiral suture, and a final whorl with slightly limbate to slightly depressed sutures, (**k**) edge view showing extremely low trochospire, the much reduced height of the raised dorsal sutures and a further reduction in the thickness of the imperforate periphery, (**l**) ventral view showing much reduced umbilical boss, Blue Hill Member, Carlile Formation, Wagon Mound outcrop, 1.4 m; (**m–o**) *Lingulogavelinella* cf. *vombensis* (Brotzen) *sensu* Hart *et al.* (1989), (**m**) dorsal view, (**n**) edge view, (**o**) ventral view, Salzgitter-Salder outcrop, 13.1 m

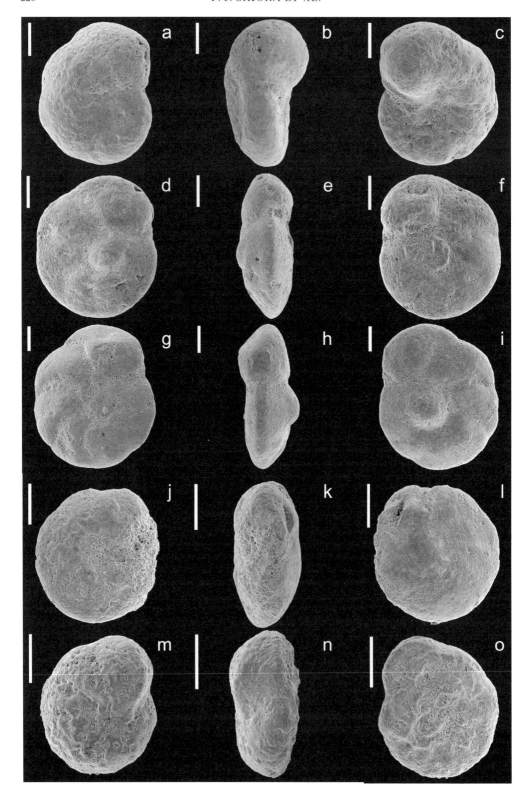

Fig. 16. All bars equal 100 μm. (**a–c**) *Gavelinella daini*, (**a**) dorsal view, (**b**) edge view, (**c**) ventral view, Salzgitter-Salder, 1.8 m; (**d–f**) *Gavelinella menneri*, (**d**) dorsal view, (**e**) edge view, (**f**) ventral view, Salzgitter-Salder, 8.4 m; (**g–i**) *Gavelinellopsis tourainensis*, (**g**) dorsal view, (**h**) edge view, (**i**) ventral view, Salzgitter-Salder, 15.5 m; (**j–l**) *Stensioina granulata levis*, (**j**) dorsal view, (**k**) edge view, (**l**) ventral view, Salzgitter-Salder, 11.7 m; (**m–o**) *Stensioina granulata kelleri*, (**m**) dorsal view, (**n**) edge view, (**o**) ventral view, Salzgitter-Salder, 13.1 m.

truncigerum (absent at Wagon Mound) that provides a useful Lower Coniacian LO. Other age-diagnostic taxa include *Endoscrinium campanula* and *Dapsilidinium laminaspinosum* – both taxa with a HO in the Lower Coniacian.

Chronostratigraphy

The Turonian–Coniacian boundary at Salzgitter-Salder is set on the boundary datum recommended at the Second International Symposium

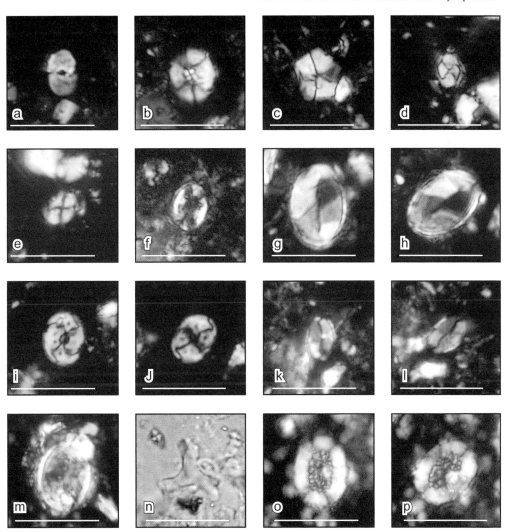

Fig. 17. All bars equal 10 μm. (**a**) *Bifidalithus geminicatillus*, Wagon Mound, 1.85 m; (**b**) *Biscutum* sp. D, Wagon Mound, 0.85 m; (**c**) *Braarudosphaera regularis*, Wagon Mound, 0.85 m; (**d & e**) *Calculites* cf. *C. anfractus*, Wagon Mound, 6.50 m; (**f**) *Eiffellithus eximius*, Wagon Mound, 1.85 m; (**g & h**) Holococcolith sp. B, Wagon Mound, 1.85 m; (**i & j**) Holococcolith sp. C, Wagon Mound, 0.85 m; (**k & l**) Holococcolith sp. E, Wagon Mound, 0.35 m; (**m**) *Kamptnerius magnificus*, Wagon Mound, 25.15 m; (**n**) *Marthasterites furcatus*, Wagon Mound, 24.65 m; (**o & p**) *Miravetesina ficula*, Wagon Mound, 25.15 m.

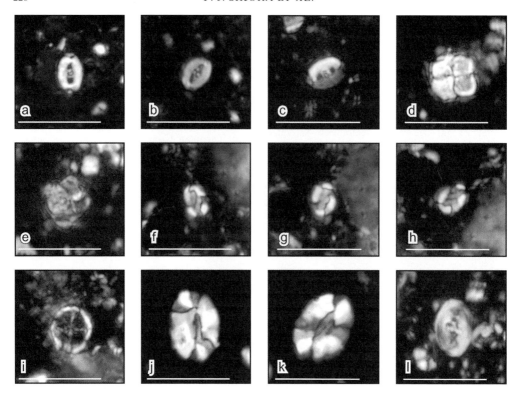

Fig. 18. All bars equal 10 μm. (**a** & **b**) *Pharus* sp. A, Wagon Mound, 0.35 m; (**c**) *Pharus* sp. A, Wagon Mound, 0.35 m; (**d** & **e**) *Quadrum intermedium*, Wagon Mound, 3.35 m; (**f** & **h**) *Saepiovirgata biferula*, Wagon Mound, 0.35 m; (**i**) *Stoverius achylosus*, Wagon Mound, 1.85 m; (**j** & **k**) *Tortolithus carteri* sp. nov. Wagon Mound, 4.75 m; (**l**) *Zeugrhabdotus biperforatus*, Wagon Mound, 25.15 m.

on Cretaceous Stage Boundaries: the lowest occurrence of the bivalve *Cremnoceramus rotundatus* (Kauffman *et al.* 1996), which has since been synonymized with *C. deformis erectus* (Walaszczyk & Cobban 2000). This study has identified several microfossil and/or nannofossil biostratigraphic events that are associated with the boundary datum that may serve as stratigraphic proxies (Fig. 19). As noted by Walaszczyk & Cobban (2000), contrary to Kauffman *et al.* (1996), *C. deformis erectus* is not present in the Wagon Mound section – making the entire section Turonian. Walaszczyk & Cobban (2000) record the base of *C. deformis erectus* in the upper part of the nearby Springer section (about 35 km north of Wagon Mound on highway I-25, near the town of Springer), which is partially equivalent to the Wagon Mound section, but ranges stratigraphically higher. The LO of *C. deformis erectus* is said to occur in the Springer section at a level approximately 10 m above the top of the Wagon Mound section (Fig. 19).

This absence of *Cremnoceramus deformis erectus* in the Wagon Mound section is confirmed by frequent occurrences of the ammonite *Prionocyclus germari* in the Fort Hays Member of the Niobrara Formation. This taxon has been extensively used throughout the Western Interior as an Upper Turonian stratigraphic index (Kennedy *et al.* 2001) that precedes the stratigraphic range of *C. deformis erectus* (Walaszczyk & Cobban 2000). However, the relative biostratigraphy of planktonic foraminifera and marine palynomorphs indicates a substantial stratigraphic equivalence of the Wagon Mound and Salzgitter-Salder sections (Fig. 19). As such, a major discrepancy exists between the correlations based upon macrofossils and those based upon microfossils between the two sections. This raises questions about the global synchroneity of the LO of *C. deformis erectus*.

Wagon Mound

The ammonite succession of the Upper Turonian to Lower Coniacian in the southern part of the Western Interior Basin has been well described (Cobban 1951; Kennedy *et al.* 2001).

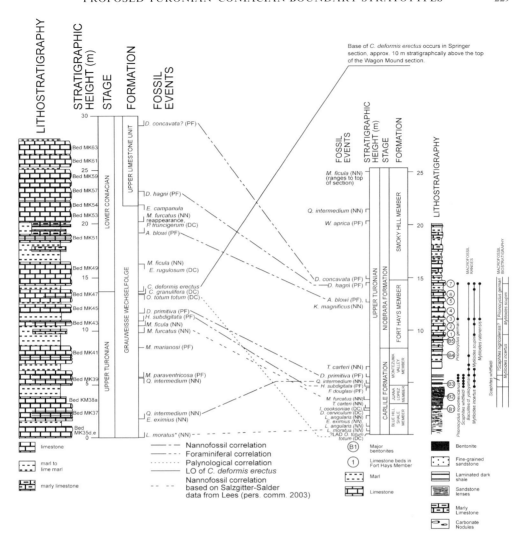

Fig. 19. Correlation of lithostratigraphy and the principal biostratigraphic datums noted from the Salzgitter-Salder and Wagon Mound sections. The location of the recommended boundary datum (LO of *C. deformis erectus*) in the Salzgitter-Salder section is contrasted with its inferred position 10 m above the top of the Wagon Mound section. We consider that nannofossils in the samples that we examined are too rare and sporadic in the Salzgitter-Salder section for reliable correlation. **DC**, dinoflagellates; **NN**, nannofossils; **PF**, planktonic foraminifera; *, datum occurs at base of section.

A series of biostratigraphic zones have been erected, based upon the relatively short ranges of mostly endemic species belonging to the genera *Prionocyclus, Scaphites* and *Forresteria*. In addition, Walaszczyk & Cobban (2000) have established a detailed inoceramid zonation, with which they were able to partially zone the Wagon Mound section. We have re-collected ammonites and inoceramids from the Wagon Mound section (Fig. 19), and our specimens were identified by Dr William Cobban of the

United States Geological Survey in Denver, Colorado. The resulting macrofossil zonation indicates that the Carlile Formation and Fort Hays Member of the Niobrara Formation in the Wagon Mound section fall entirely within the Upper Turonian.

Abundant, mostly fragmentary, specimens of *Scaphites whitfieldi* occur in the basal 1.15 m of the Montezuma Valley Shale, and rarely in the highest 0.1 m of the underlying Juana Lopez Member. Also present in this interval are rarer specimens of *Prionocyclus novomexicanus* and *Baculites* cf. *yokoyamai*. The Upper Turonian *S. whitfieldi* zone is indicated. The upper part of the Montezuma Valley Shale and the basal two limestones and intervening marlstones of the Fort Hays Member are largely barren of whole macrofossils, except for the 7.15-m level in the lower Fort Hays Member. From this level are recovered abundant, but badly preserved, specimens of *B.* cf. *yokoyamai* (Fig. 3). The middle and upper parts of the Fort Hays Member yield infrequent specimens of *Prionocyclus germari* at about 11.0 m and 14.5 m in the section. This is the zonal index of the uppermost Turonian *P. germari* Zone of the Western Interior (Kennedy *et al.* 2001). The species is also known from Germany (Kaufmann *et al.* 1996) and the Czech Republic (Cech 1987), where it ranges up to and just above the so-called *Didymotis* II event that marks the top Turonian and is immediately beneath the LO of *Cremnoceramus deformis erectus*. The Fort Hays Member also yields the inoceramids *Mytiloides scupini* and *M. ratonensis* that are indicative of the Upper, but not uppermost, Turonian (Walaszczyk & Cobban 2000).

Thus the previously proposed Turonian–Coniacian boundary level at Wagon Mound (Kaufmann *et al.* 1996) actually occurs near the base of the *P. germari* Zone, which is widely accepted to be of Late Turonian age (e.g. Kennedy *et al.* 2001). Together with the inoceramid zonation of the section by Walaszczyk & Cobban (2000), this precludes any further discussion of Wagon Mound as a Turonian–Coniacian boundary stratotype if the current recommended boundary datum is adopted (i.e. *C. deformis erectus*). Rather, based upon macrofossils, the Fort Hays Member falls entirely within the *P. germari* and *M. scupini* Zones of latest Turonian age. A Coniacian inoceramid fauna, including *C. deformis erectus*, first occurs in the higher part of the Smoky Hill Member at Springer, New Mexico, at a level equivalent to about 10 m above the top of the Wagon Mound outcrop.

Stratigraphy at the Wagon Mound section is complicated by palaeoenvironmental factors. Planktonic foraminiferal recovery in the Blue Hill Member increases from none in the basal sample to frequent in the less-carbonaceous upper interval, but diversity and preservation remain poor throughout. Planktonic foraminifera provide no useful datums, comprising a nearly monospecific assemblage of *Heterohelix globulosa*, with the only other species noted being *Hedbergella implicata* and *H. lata*. Benthic foraminifera are dominated by an informally named species, '*Anomalina* W', used widely as a Turonian HO by the petroleum industry in the subsurface section across the Gulf of Mexico. This taxon is synonymous with the published taxon *Gavelinella petita* (Lundquist 2000; also see Taxonomic Notes, below). *Gavelinella petita* forms a near-monospecific assemblage in the lower part of the Blue Hill Member at Wagon Mound, and then declines sharply in abundance in the upper part of the unit, with a HO at 1.2 m in the section. From 1.0 to 1.2 m, *G. petita* co-occurs with specimens that appear transitional in morphology between it and the widespread (in the Western Interior and Gulf Coast basins) benthic taxon *Planulina texana* (Fig. 15j–l; also see Taxonomic Notes, below). At 1.4 m, *P. texana sensu stricto* has its LO. It is probable that *P. texana* was derived from *G. petita*, with the rapid morphological transition recorded in the section from 1.0 to 1.2 m possibly representing a punctuated evolutionary event. The only other foraminiferal biostratigraphic event of note in the Blue Hill Member is the LO of the endemic benthic species *Planulina kansasensis* at 1.0 m.

The poorly preserved, low-abundance nannofossil assemblages in the Blue Hill Member (with the exception of the unusual holococcolith assemblage described above) make precise biostratigraphic zonation difficult. The presence of *Eiffellithus eximius* and *Lithastrinus moratus* (*L. septenarius* of many authors) in the absence of *Marthasterites furcatus* suggests a Late Turonian age for the Blue Hill Member. The presence of very rare *Lilliasterites angularis* in the Blue Hill Member also supports a Late Turonian age (Stradner & Steinmetz 1984), as does the presence of a single specimen of *Stoverius achylosus* at 0.35 m – a species with an Upper Turonian HO (Burnett 1998 and J. A. Bergen, unpubl. data).

Although the Blue Hill Member is carbonaceous: a lithology usually favourable to palynomorph recovery, dinoflagellates are either very rare or absent in the unit. Weathering may be the cause, but the Blue Hill Member did yield well-preserved calcareous microfossils, including some very prone to dissolution, such as holococcoliths. The dinoflagellate *Oligosphaeridium totum totum*, occurring at the base of the measured section, is known to have an Upper Turonian HO (Williams *et al.* 1993). Near the top of the unit, at 2.2 m there are also two other datums indicative of the uppermost Turonian: the LO of *Dinogymnium albertii* and the LO of *Isabelidinium cooksoniae* (Fig. 19).

In contrast to the Blue Hill Member, the overlying Juana Lopez Member is an example of an unfavourable lithology for microfossil recovery (recrystallized calcarenite) that none-theless yields a number of important biostratigraphic datums (Fig. 19). Among planktonic foraminifera, long-ranging species remain dominant, especially *Heterohelix globulosa*, but also less common species of *Hedbergella* and *Whiteinella*. However, in more argillaceous limestone at the top of the unit there are rare stratigraphic indexes, including the keeled Upper Turonian index *Falsotruncana douglasi*, with a HO at 4.55 m, and an influx of *Hastigerinoides* species (i.e. *H. subdigitata* and *H. watersi*) at 4.75 m. Historically, the lowest stratigraphic occurrence of species of *Hastiger-inoides* has been used in Western Interior sections to mark the base of the Coniacian (Frerichs *et al.* 1977), but *H. subdigitata* has been reported from Turonian strata (Eicher and Worstell 1970). The LO of *Marthasterites furcatus* occurs at 3.35 m in the Juana Lopez Member – an event often used to approximate the Turonian–Coniacian boundary. However, Lees (pers. comm. 2003) has shown that the LO of *M. furcatus* is highly variable stratigraphi-cally, occurring as low as the middle Turonian.

A very similar relative succession of plank-tonic foraminiferal and palynomorph biostrati-graphic datums correlates the LO of *Cremnoceramus deformis erectus* in the Salzgit-ter-Salder section to a level within the Wagon Mound outcrop, even though the inoceramid datum is absent in the latter (Fig. 19). The equivalent level falls between the LO of *Dicar-inella primitiva*, at 5.26 m in the Montezuma Valley Member of the Carlile Formation, and the LO of *Archaeoglobigerina blowi*, at 12.75 m in the lower part of the Fort Hays Member of the Niobrara Formation. These planktonic foraminiferal datums and others common to both sections (e.g. the LO of *Dicarinella concavata*) were long considered to be Coniacian datums (e.g. Caron 1985), but were then calibrated to the Turonian of Tunisia in the definitive study of Robaszynski *et al.* (1990). Nevertheless, regardless of the stage calibration, the relative microfossil biostratigraphy indicates that the Wagon Mound and Salzgitter-Salder sections are largely coeval. This directly contra-dicts the placement of the boundary in the Wagon Mound section based on macrofossil stratigraphy, suggesting the possibility that the LO of *C. deformis erectus* is not synchronous between the Salzgitter-Salder and Wagon Mound sections.

The abundant and diverse foraminiferal and nannofossil assemblages of the Fort Hays and Smoky Hill members of the Niobrara Forma-tion are characterized by a well-defined succes-sion of biostratigraphic datums (Fig. 19). For planktonic foraminifera, the principal events include:

The LO of *Archaeoglobigerina blowi* in the middle Fort Hays Member at 12.75 m

The HO of *Dicarinella hagni* in the upper Fort Hays Member at 14.55 m

The LO of *Dicarinella concavata* at the base of the Smoky Hill Member at 14.90 m

In addition, a number of benthic foraminiferal datums are noted:

The LO of *Eouvigerina gracilis* in the lower Fort Hays Member at 10.35 m

The LO of *Valvulineria infrequens* in the middle Fort Hays Member at 11.75 m

The LO of *Palmula pilulata* in the upper Fort Hays Member at 12.75 m

The LO of *Neoflabellina suturalis* in the upper Fort Hays Member at 14.35 m

The LO of *Dorothia smokyensis* in the upper Fort Hays Member at 14.35 m

No significant nannofossil or palynomorph datums occur within the Niobrara section.

Salzgitter-Salder

Foraminiferal biostratigraphic control is gener-ally good, but complicated by the radical change in biofacies between the marlstone and limestone beds within the stacked couplets (Fig. 4). The dominance of calcispheres in most of the lime-stone, accompanied by a large drop in plank-tonic foraminiferal abundance, probably explains why most biostratigraphic datums fall within marlstone beds. As such, the stratigraphic position of foraminiferal datums (Fig. 19) is probably partially controlled by palaeoenviron-ment. However, because most of the limestone/marlstone couplets are less than 1 m in thickness, the effect on stratigraphic placement is probably minor.

The Upper Turonian section analysed by this study is much more pelagic-rich than the carbonaceous shale and calcarenite that com-poses this interval at Wagon Mound. However, almost no Turonian-restricted species are noted. The sole exception is the occurrence of *Margin-otruncana marianosi* at 8.4 m. The most noticeable biostratigraphic event in the Upper Tur-onian interval, however, is a strong influx of the seldom-described planktonic foraminifer *Mar-ginotruncana paraventricosa* at 5.6 m, a bio-horizon that has been noted regionally (Brauti-gam 1962). The Coniacian section is marked by a similar succession of datums as those that characterized the Wagon Mound section. The interval analysed at Salzgitter-Salder does not penetrate as far into the Coniacian as the Wagon Mound interval – possibly reaching only to the LO of *Dicarinella concavata*, questionably iden-tified from a limestone thin-section at 29.2 m. The total list of planktonic foraminiferal datums follows, with events also occurring in the Wagon Mound section marked by (*).

Influx of *Marginotruncana paraventricosa* at 5.6 m

Presence of *Marginotruncana marianosi* at 8.4 m

LO of *Hastigerinoides subdigitata* at 10.9 m*

LO of *Dicarinella primitiva* at 11.7 m*

LO of *Archaeoglobigerina blowi* at 19.2 m*

HO of *Dicarinella hagni* at 23.0 m*

LO of *Dicarinella concavata?* at 29.2 m*

In addition, the Salzgitter-Salder section con-tains a diverse assemblage of benthic foramini-fera, many of which have been used as biostratigraphic indices in the North Sea and UK chalk succession or in the Gulf of Mexico. One of the most obvious of these events is the LO of the informally described species *Lingulogave-linella* cf. *vombensis* (Brotzen) *sensu* Hart *et al.* (1989, pl. 7.19, pp. 352–353), a datum indicative of the base of the Coniacian in the UK chalk. This species has also been noted as approximating the Turonian–Coniacian boundary in the Shakh–Bogota section of the northern Mangyshlak area of Kazakhstan (Naidin *et al.* 1984). Other important North Sea area markers include sub-species of *Stensioina granulata* long used as stratigraphic indices in northwest Europe (e.g. Koch 1977). In Salzgitter-Salder, these include *S. granulata levis* and *S. granulata kelleri* that may also occur near the boundary in western Kazakh-stan, described as *Stensioina* sp. ex gr. *S. granulata* (Naidin *et al.* 1984). A summary of benthic foraminiferal events follows:

LO of *Praebulimina reussi* at 5.6 m

LO of *Globorotalites subconica* at 7.8 m

LO of *Eouvigerina gracilis* at 8.4 m*

LO of *Gavelinopsis tourainensis* at 10.9 m

LO of *Heterostomella austinana* at 10.9 m

LO of *Stensioina granulata kelleri* at 11.7 m

LO of *Lingulogavelinella* cf. *vombensis* (Brot-zen) *sensu* Hart *et al.* 1989 at 13.1 m

LO of *Osangularia whitei* at 14.6 m

HO of *Stensioina granulata kelleri* at 17.9 m

HO of *Stensioina granulata levis* at 20.2 m

Calcareous nannofossil preservation is so poor and abundance is so low in our samples from the Salzgitter-Salder section, that any kind of accurate biostratigraphy is impossible. A general Late Turonian to Early Coniacian age is indicated for the section by the LO of *Lithastrinus moratus* (*L. septenarius* of many authors) at 8.40 m, the HO of *Miravetesina ficula* at 10.40 m, the HO of *Marthasterites furcatus* at 20.20 m, and the absence of *Micula decussata* from the section.

Microfloral biostratigraphy in the Salzgitter-Salder section is relatively poor, due to the extensive diagenesis. Although marine palyno-morphs are characterized by low diversity, nevertheless several important biostratigraphic datums are noted. These include the Upper Turonian HO of *Oligosphaeridium totum totum* at 13.4 m (also noted in the Blue Hill Member at Wagon Mound) and the Lower Coniacian LO of *Pervosphaeridium truncigerum* at 21.6 m.

The recommended boundary datum, the LO of the bivalve *Cremnoceramus deformis erectus*, occurs at 14.6 m, a boundary placement also supported by the HO of the dinoflagellate *Oligo-sphaeridium totum totum* at 13.4 m. Several planktonic foraminiferal datums are also asso-ciated with the stage boundary and occur in the same order as in the Wagon Mound section, including (from lowest to highest occurrence): the LO of *Hastigerinoides subdigitata*, the LO of *Dicarinella primitiva*, the HO of *Dicarinella hagni* and the LO of *Archaeoglobigerina blowi* (Fig. 19). Historically, several Salzgitter-Salder benthic foraminiferal datums that occur below the defined stage boundary have been used to mark the base of the Coniacian, and include the LO of the northwest European datum *Gavelinopsis tourainensis*, and the LO of Gulf of Mexico datum *Heterostomella austinana*. In addition, the LO of the European Coniacian index *Lingulogavelinella* cf. *vombensis* (Brotzen) *sensu* Hart *et al.* (1989) occurs at 13.4 m (Fig. 19).

All these microfossil 'boundary' indexes fall within 4 m of the *C. deformis erectus* datum in the Salzgitter-Salder section, indicating that the European occurrence of this event would serve as a boundary datum that did not substantially change the micropalaeontological definition of the Turonian–Coniacian stage boundary. However, the lack of a similar congruence between microfossil and macrofossil datums in the Wagon Mound section presents an unresolved discrepancy.

Palaeoenvironment

Wagon Mound

In general, the Carlile Formation is indicative of depositional environments unfavorable for calcareous microfossils. The very low-diversity assemblages characteristic of the black, pyritic Blue Hill Member (Fig. 3) clearly indicate a dysoxic and restricted depositional environment, a facies that is quite extensive in the Lower to Middle Turonian of the Western Interior Basin and the Gulf of Mexico coast (e.g. Kump and Slingerland 1999). The benthic foraminifer *Gavelinella petita* was a taxon well adapted to such a palaeoenvironment, and it dominates the deeper-water eutrophic Turonian facies of the Gulf of Mexico and the central axis of the Western Interior sea-way. Surface water conditions were abnormal, with planktonic foraminifera dominated by *Heterohelix globulosa* and lesser amounts of *Hedbergella* species. One possible cause for the unusual pelagic assemblage and the stratified water column indicated by the benthic assemblage would be the dominance of a relatively cool, lower-salinity and low-density surface water mass. Modelling of precipitation and evaporation rates for the Western Interior sea-way at this time has indicated that it may have been a net exporter of fresh water – similar to the modern Black Sea (Slingerland *et al.* 1996). In addition, the unusual nannofossil assemblage that occurs in the more calcareous portion of the Blue Hill Member indicates cool surface water conditions. These nannofossils had a distinct affinity for cool 'Boreal' water masses, indicating southward flow of a colder, denser, northern water mass into the Wagon Mound area. Regardless of the cause of this stratified water column, the less-carbonaceous facies of the upper part of the Blue Hill Member at Wagon Mound indicate a time during which this stratification was breaking down, with progressively higher oxygenation levels in the bottom water. A likely cause for this palaeoenvironmental change was a major

sea-level drop in the Middle Turonian (Hardenbol *et al.* 1998) causing a drop in pelagic productivity as well as a basinward shift of any oxygen-minimum zone. We hypothesize that the quick termination of widespread dysoxic environments led to a punctuated evolutionary event whereby *Gavelinella petita* evolved to *Planulina texana*, a more generalist species that subsequently dominated open-marine facies across the Western Interior Basin and Gulf of Mexico shelf from the Coniacian to Campanian (Cushman 1946).

The eustatic drop is reflected at Wagon Mound by regressive facies culminating in the Juana Lopez Member (Fig. 3). The lower portion of the Juana Lopez Member is largely composed of tightly cemented, calcareous quartz sandstone and calcarenite, indicative of extensively reworked sediments deposited well above storm-wave base and possibly above normal-wave base. This interval represents the maximum marine regression. Microfossils within this layer are limited to thin, discontinuous muddy laminae and are composed of very small nodosariid benthic taxa and unidentifiable fragments of planktonic species (Fig. 20a). These muddy laminae are probably indicative of ephemeral deeper-water conditions associated with storm surge events. The uppermost portion of the Juana Lopez Member at Wagon Mound (4.00–4.75 m) is largely composed of sandy, inoceramid packstone (Fig. 7a) with few to frequent foraminifera. This facies represents the beginning of a transgression, with deeper-water depositional conditions below normal-, but above storm-wave base. The storm deposits are marked by a complex lithofacies of grain- and mud-supported laminae, including mud-draped ripples (Fig. 20b).

The transgression continues with deposition of the shallow-marine facies of the Montezuma Valley Shale. The poorly calcareous, carbonaceous shale of the lower portion of the unit is indicative of quiet, open-marine, yet relatively turbid and nearshore deposition that gradually gave way to clearer, deeper-water, inner-shelf palaeoenvironments represented by the very calcareous shale and marlstone of the upper Montezuma Valley Shale. Nannofossil and palynomorph assemblages indicate continuation of cool surface water conditions during lower Montezuma Valley Shale time, but there is a sharp decline in higher latitude taxa in the upper Montezuma Valley Shale. The regressive facies preserved in the Wagon Mound section (i.e. the upper Blue Hill Member through middle Juana Lopez Member), as well as the basal transgressive facies of the upper Juana Lopez Member

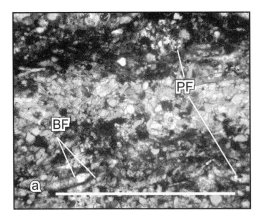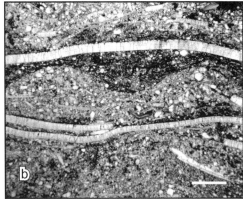

Fig. 20. Thin-section photos showing depositional details of the Juana Lopez Member; (**a**) close-up of muddy laminae in fine-grained sandstone at 3.20 m, showing very small nodosariid benthic foraminifera (**Bf**) and planktonic foraminiferal fragments (**Pf**), indicating deposition during ephemeral storm surges; (**b**) complex lamination in limestone from 4.55 m, showing mud-draped ripples composed of quartz silt and very fine-grained macrofossil debris, indicating storm deposits of the basal transgressive sequence (bar = 1 mm).

through Montezuma Valley Shale, are absent across much of the Western Interior Basin to the north and east of the Wagon Mound area (Laferriere 1987). This extensive unconformity indicates the large magnitude of the terminal Turonian eustatic fall.

The transgression continues with deposition of the Fort Hays Member of the Niobrara Formation. The lower 2.5 m of the Fort Hays Member is indicative of open-marine, middle-shelf facies, dominated by non-keeled foraminifera and with rare benthic taxa composed principally of nodosariids. This represents deposition in only slightly deeper water than the upper Montezuma Valley Shale facies. The culmination of the transgression is represented by the upper part of the Fort Hays Member from 12.35 m to 14.85 m. A major influx occurs of diverse, keeled planktonic species and a more diverse assemblage of benthic foraminifera composed of gavelinellids, nodosariids and buliminids. Middle to inner-outer shelf, normal-marine, mesotrophic conditions are indicated. An exception to this palaeoenvironment is provided by the marlstone at 13.40 m that indicates ephemeral development of an oxygen minimum zone associated with high pelagic productivity. A sharp drop in planktonic abundance and diversity characterizes the sample, with an assemblage dominated by shallow-water dwellers such as *Heterohelix globulosa* and tiny species of *Hedbergella* that indicate exclusion of planktonic fauna from the lower photic zone. Benthic foraminifera are abundant, but strongly dominated by the very compressed species

Planulina kansasensis – a probable low-oxygen opportunist. This discrete dysoxic layer may mark the time of maximum flooding during the transgression.

The lower 2.3 m of the Smoky Hill Member section are indicative of regressive, more argillaceous facies corresponding with a pulse of the Sevier Orogeny to the west. Keeled planktonic species are much less common than in the upper Fort Hays Member, and benthic foraminifera become very rare. A relatively turbid water column and more rapid sedimentation rates are indicated, but palaeobathymetry is indeterminate, due to the rarity of benthic species. The middle 5.0 m of the Smoky Hill Member section are marked by an increase in keeled planktonic foraminifera and overall species diversity, as well as by a diverse nodosariid benthic foraminiferal assemblage. Such an assemblage is characteristic of less-turbid conditions on an open-marine middle shelf, possibly indicating an increase in local sea-level that displaced terrestrial sediment sources landward. This transgression continued with deposition of the upper 2.3 m of the analysed Smoky Hill Member section marked by abundant keeled planktonic taxa, especially species of *Dicarinella*, as well as ataxophragmiid agglutinated benthic foraminifera, indicating normal-marine, outer-shelf palaeobathymetry with a strong warm surface-water 'Tethyan' influence. The limestone beds of the Smoky Hill Member are similar in composition to those of the Fort Hays Member, although lower in species diversity and more carbonaceous (Fig. 7d), and benthic foraminifera are more common than in the Smoky Hill Member claystone beds, indicating lower sedimentation rates and less turbidity. These intervals of carbonate deposition may be indicative of short-term climatic changes to more arid conditions, leading to decreased erosion on land.

Salzgitter-Salder

This section provides less evidence of major sea-level fluctuations relative to the Wagon Mound section. An unusual mix of benthic foraminifera characterizes the marlstone of the lower part of the section (0.0–11.7 m). Deep-water, siliceous agglutinates are frequent: mainly species of *Glomospira* and *Ammodiscus*, but also including rarer taxa such as *Caudammina ovulum* and *Kalamopsis grzybowskii*. More common than these basinal species are taxa characteristic of outer-shelf to uppermost-slope palaeobathymetry, principally species of *Gavelinella* and *Gyroidinoides*, and ataxophragmiid agglutinated taxa. Finally, also common are shallower shelf indicators: mainly species of *Arenobulimina* agglutinated benthic foraminifera and abundant echinoid debris. Such a palaeobathymetric mixture of assemblages is indicative of allochthonous microfossils and deposition at least in part by sediment flows. This hypothesis is supported by the composition of dinoflagellates from this interval: generally a very low-diversity assemblage dominated by *Palaeohystrichophora infusorioides*, indicative of restricted, shallow-marine facies and downslope transport. Furthermore, thin-section examination of the limestone layers interbedded with the marlstone of this lower section reveal massive calcisphere wackestone, quite different from the foraminiferal assemblage recovered from the marlstone (Fig. 11a). 'Calcisphere' is a general term used to describe a mix of calcareous dinoflagellates and reproductive cysts from benthic calcareous algae (e.g. dasyclads) that predominate in near-shore carbonate facies. It therefore appears that the limestone layers represent sediment flow deposits (e.g. calciturbidites) and that even the marlstone beds contain a large allochthonous component.

The marlstone beds in the overlying interval from 12.0–14.3 m indicate deposition during a more quiescent period in which down-gradient sediment transport abated. Benthic foraminiferal diversity drops as the outer-shelf/upper-slope assemblage, dominated by gavelinellids, comes to make up most of the benthic foraminifera. It is likely that this assemblage is indicative of the *in situ* palaeobathymetry of the entire analysed interval. The shallower-water

components noted from the lower section are allochthonous, and the deep-water siliceous agglutinated foraminifera may have been opportunists taking advantage of a benthic environment that was frequently disturbed by sediment flows – a phenomenon noted in modern slope environments (Kaminski 1985). This hypothesis is also supported by palynological analysis, which shows a marked increase in dinoflagellate diversity to a more normal, open-marine assemblage. Also, thin-section analysis of the limestone beds from this part of the section reveal the only carbonate facies in the Salzgitter-Salder section indicative of entirely autochthonous deposition, i.e. heavily bioturbated, planktonic-foraminiferal wackestone (Fig. 11c).

The Lower Coniacian interval from 14.6 to 17.9 m is marked by two major changes from the underlying quiescent section: a turnover in planktonic foraminiferal composition, and the return of allochthonous beds. The planktonic foraminifera of the 12.0–14.3 m section are dominated by keeled species, mainly of the genus *Marginotruncana*, but also with consistently present *Dicarinella* taxa. The fauna of the Lower Coniacian section, however, is marked by a sharp decline in the abundance of keeled species and dominance of large *Whiteinella* taxa, mainly *W. paradubia* and *W. aprica*. This assemblage is more 'Boreal' in aspect – similar to the species composition noted in basinal, Coniacian North Sea chalk (Sikora *et al.* 1999).

The incursion of a cold-water mass into the Salzgitter area at this time is not likely to have been due to global climatic change, because the Early Coniacian was a time of warming relative to the cooler Late Turonian (see Wagon Mound discussion, above). It is more likely to have been a regional palaeoceanographic event, possibly related to local tectonic movement. This hypothesis is supported by the coincident resumption of allochthonous sedimentation, possibly triggered by seismic disturbances. Calcisphere wackestone once again characterizes limestone beds, and benthic foraminifera recovered from the marlstone again show a mix of shallower- and deeper-water species, with the dominant gavelinellid assemblage. Also, as in the allochthonous interval at the bottom of the section (0.0–11.7 m), palynomorph abundance and diversity plummets in this Coniacian section – again featuring dominance by *Palaeohystrichophora infusorioides*.

The overlying interval from 18.9 to 23.0 m is characteristic of another quiescent period of deposition dominated by autochthonous sedimentation. Dominated by marlstone, the section contains benthic foraminifera once again largely composed of the gavelinellid assemblage. Keeled planktonic foraminifera also dominate the pelagic assemblage, indicating either a warming of surface water and/or local flooding event. In addition, this interval is marked by the most diverse and deep-water dinoflagellate cyst assemblage recovered in the analysed section. 'Boreal' cool surface-water affinity dinocyst taxa (i.e. *Chatangiella* spp.) are a major component of the deep-water assemblage, suggesting that a flooding event is the more likely scenario.

Finally, the uppermost part of the studied interval from the Upper Limestone Unit (24.3–29.8 m) is dominated by calcisphere wackestone and thin, more poorly developed marlstone. Although marked by common calcispheres, the limestone beds from this unit have a high planktonic foraminiferal content (Fig. 11b), possibly indicating less frequent and thinner allochthonous intervals (dominated by calcispheres) that were subsequently mixed with autochthonous deposits through bioturbation.

Comparative stratigraphy

In general, no scientific decision is made entirely without non-scientific bias, and the choice of a section stratotype certainly is no exception to this rule. A stratotype is often chosen more for which outcrop has had the greatest degree of investment of time and expenditure than for its relative scientific merit. Varying degrees of chauvinism, both subdiscipline and national, also often play a role. Nevertheless, a well-chosen stratotype will serve as a valuable tool for consistent stratigraphic research, with indirect ramifications throughout all the geosciences that are dependent upon reliable age correlation. Such a choice should therefore be taken very seriously and not made in haste. We believe that in addition to the more technical criteria for stratotype selection (such as accessibility, permanence, etc.), a good boundary stratotype section should clearly exhibit advantages in three more empirical areas.

Definition of the boundary datum

Certainly, one of the foremost traits that a boundary stratotype section should have is a well-defined level for the recommended boundary datum. The LO of the bivalve *Cremnoceramus deformis erectus* has been well defined in the Salzgitter-Salder section, occurring commonly from its LO at 14.6 m and then easily found further up-section. In contrast, the *C. deformis erectus* datum is absent from the

Wagon Mound outcrop, despite the presence of an abundant bivalve assemblage. However, microfossil relative biostratigraphy indicates that the Salzgitter-Salder and Wagon Mound outcrops are largely coeval and that the *C. deformis erectus* datum in Germany is equivalent to a level in the Wagon Mound section that substantially predates its Western Interior LO. This discrepancy may indicate that the inoceramid datum is globally diachronous – certainly not an impossibility for a fossil of a benthic organism. However, the European and Western Interior macrofossil biostratigraphy for the Turonian–Coniacian has been intercalibrated using several additional ammonite and inoceramid datums, and is very persuasive (Walaszczyk & Cobban 2000). This macrofossil calibration indicates that the Wagon Mound section in its entirety is stratigraphically lower than the measured Salzgitter-Salder section of the present study. Therefore, in order to validate the microfossil correlation, it appears that not only the LO of *Cremnoceramus deformis erectus*, but also that of several other well-studied bivalves and ammonites, would have to be diachronous, while maintaining the same relative order of events. While this would certainly be unlikely, the same can be said of the microfossil datums. The relative stratigraphic order of these events is quite similar between the two stratotype candidates. This biostratigraphy is also the basis of many years of research, and is at least equally persuasive, especially when considering the much more widespread distribution upon which the microfossil biostratigraphy is based. In order to maintain isochroneity between the *C. deformis erectus* datums in the Salzgitter-Salder and New Mexico sections, several microfossil datums will need to be diachronous, while maintaining the same relative order of events. Although it is true that many of these microfossil datums are now considered to occur well within the Turonian, this stage calibration is largely based upon much of the same macrofossil biostratigraphy (Robaszynski *et al.* 1990) that conflicts with the microfossil datums in this study. It would be somewhat circular in reasoning to assess possible diachroneity in a macrofossil zonation based upon microfossil stage calibrations that resulted from that same macrofossil stratigraphy.

Fossil recovery

Both sections have serious deficiencies in fossil recovery. The Blue Hill Member at Wagon Mound is fairly thin, and is either poorly fossiliferous or characterized by near-monospecific assemblages for both microfossils and macrofossils. Recovery improves considerably in the Juana Lopez Member and lower Montezuma Valley Member, with frequent to common bivalves and ammonites, and rich calcareous microfossil assemblages in the upper Montezuma Valley Shale and Niobrara Formation intervals. Nevertheless, the lack of a normal open-marine section in the Blue Hill and Juana Lopez Members is a serious drawback – obscuring or preventing the study of evolutionary, palaeoecological and stratigraphic trends of the latest Turonian.

In contrast, the Salzgitter-Salder section has a very fossiliferous, normal open-marine, Upper Turonian section that is more than 20 m thick and is underlain by a well-developed Middle Turonian section. The problem with fossil recovery in this section is not facies or lack of exposure: it is diagenesis. Although planktonic foraminifera are generally common and diverse, nannofossil assemblages are depauperate and poorly preserved due to recrystallization. Palynomorph recovery is not as severely affected, but recovery is seriously degraded in certain intervals, especially in the limestone beds. For high-resolution stratigraphic correlation to a stratotype, use of multidisciplinary proxies provides the best results. One type of microfossil may exhibit stratigraphic truncation due to environmental exclusion or diagenesis that will not affect another group. If diagenesis allows only one group to be used for correlation, palaeoecological truncation of stratigraphic ranges may go unrecognized. For the Salzgitter-Salder section, however, widespread global correlation to other intervals will probably rely mainly upon planktonic foraminifera alone. In contrast, for the Wagon Mound section and overlying intervals, a multidisciplinary integration of all three major microfossil groups is feasible to define the stage boundary and the entire Coniacian section.

Independent absolute age dating

Another key aspect of a stratotype section is the potential for age dating independent of biostratigraphy. For a Turonian–Coniacian section, three applicable methods are radiometric dating, orbital cyclicity and stable isotopic signature. No information on stable isotopes is currently available for either section, but the extensive diagenetic alteration of the Salzgitter-Salder section would be likely to have a detrimental affect on retrieving primary isotopic values. For radiometric dating, both sections possess a number of bentonite layers. Dating has been attempted for Salzgitter-Salder bentonites, but no useful results were obtained, because of diagenetic alteration (S. Voigt, pers. comm. 2002). Wagon Mound bentonites have not been dated previously, but the thicker bentonite in the Juana Lopez Member (B1 in Fig. 3) was dated by Obradovich (1993) in a nearby section and yielded an $^{40}Ar/^{39}Ar$ date (90.21 ± 0.72 Ma, i.e. Late Turonian) only slightly older than obtained for this level by the current study. Encouraged by this result, we have collected several bentonite samples from Wagon Mound for $^{40}Ar/^{39}Ar$ analyses that are currently ongoing.

For cycle stratigraphy, both the Grauweisse Wechselfolge section at Salzgitter-Salder and the Niobrara Formation at Wagon Mound exhibit well-defined cyclicity, with numerous lime/marl couplets on a fine stratigraphic scale. By combining cycle analysis with radiometric dates (that could allow the derivation of an absolute age duration of the section), the cycles may be shown to be orbitally controlled. If so, all datums within the section may be able to be placed within a precessional order of age resolution (approximately 20 000 years). We have collected samples from Wagon Mound at every 10 cm for cycle analysis, with measurements currently under way for both carbonate content and magnetic susceptibility. The results will be presented in a subsequent paper. For Salzgitter-Salder, however, cyclostratigraphic dating is much less feasible. The poor likelihood of obtaining any radiometric dates from the section prevents an absolute age determination of its duration, making recognition of orbital periodicities more speculative (i.e. having to rely on defining a hierarchy of periodicities and seeing if the ratios match those of the principal orbital cycles). Even if periodicities can be defined, it is unlikely that they will be orbitally derived. The great majority of the limestone beds in the Salzgitter-Salder section are at least partially and often totally allochthonous. In the lower and middle portion of the analysed section, this was also often true for the marlstone layers. This need not be an impediment to biostratigraphy. The derivation of the allochthonous component was probably from penecontemporaneous down-gradient movement of sediment flows – events instantaneous in geological time. However, it does indicate that much, if not all, of the lithological cyclicity noted in the section is autocyclic, not orbital. The potential for cyclostratigraphic dating of the Salzgitter-Salder section is therefore very poor.

Which section should we choose?

An adequate resolution of the discrepancy between the microfossil and macrofossil biostratigraphy for the Wagon Mound and Salzgitter-Salder sections will require further study by both microfossil and macrofossil palaeontologists. Until this discrepancy is resolved, or until a new datum is selected, we believe that a discussion of the relative merits of the Wagon Mound and Salzgitter-Salder sections (or any other outcrop) as a stage boundary stratotype is largely moot. Nevertheless, the question of boundary datum aside, this detailed palaeontological study of the Wagon Mound and Salzgitter-Salder sections has revealed both definite merits and serious deficiencies of both for use as boundary stratotype sections.

At Wagon Mound the uppermost Juana Lopez through Smokey Hill section contains a rich assemblage of macrofossils and microfossils with a succession of well-defined datums. A multidisciplinary integration of microfossils from all three major groups can be used as stratigraphic proxies to correlate the section to a wide range of marine settings and sample types. The section is characterized by a succession of inoceramid bivalves and ammonites that allows correlation to Western Interior macrofossil zonations. The radiometric dating potential of the section is good (and soon to be evaluated), and the autochthonous Niobrara section shows excellent, high-resolution cyclostratigraphy that may allow absolute dating on a precessional level of resolution. However, the poor fossil content of much of the Carlile Formation section, and its limited exposure at Wagon Mound, prevent study of many palaeontological trends near the end of the Turonian.

The Salzgitter-Salder section is also very fossiliferous for macrofossils, as well as foraminifera. It provides a normal marine section for both the Turonian and Coniacian section, not just immediately below and above the boundary, but extending down-section into the Middle Turonian and up-section well into the Coniacian. The LO of *Cremnoceramus deformis erectus* is well defined, with the species abundant from its LO and up section. However, the extensive diagenetic alteration (recrystallization) of the section has serious repercussions. Nannofossil recovery is poor, and palynomorph distribution is sporadic with highly variable recovery. Thus, a multidisciplinary integration of microfossils from all three major groups that can be used as stratigraphic proxies to correlate the section to a wide range of different localities could not be achieved here. Microfossil correlation will be heavily dependent upon planktonic foraminifera. Furthermore, the recrystallization of bentonites in the section prevents reliable radiometric dating. Successful cyclostratigraphic absolute age calibration of the section is also unlikely, because palaeoenvironmental analysis indicates that most of the limestone beds and many of the marlstone layers are allochthonous deposits. The lithological cycles noted in the outcrop are therefore autocyclic in nature, reflecting local palaeoceanographic and tectonic controls.

Together with the discrepancy between microfossil and macrofossil biostratigraphy, we raise these issues not to incite needless contention, but to try to ensure selection of the best boundary stratotype possible. We are confident that the Turonian–Coniacian palaeontological community will be able to quickly resolve these issues and select a boundary stratotype and datum that best serves stratigraphy and geoscience as a whole.

Taxonomic notes

Benthic foraminifera (PJS)

Gavelinella petita (Carsey)

Fig. 15d–f

Description: Test, compressed, small, coarsely perforate, low trochospire, biconvex to rarely concavo-convex, the dorsal side being higher; 10–12 chambers in the final whorl, increasing regularly in size; dorsally evolute with sutures on earlier whorls and early chambers of the last whorl very limbate and strongly raised, sometimes fusing into a small, central umbo, sutures of later chambers on last whorl becoming flush, limbate to very slightly depressed; ventrally involute with small, but prominent central boss, sutures flush and limbate, sometimes very slightly raised near the boss; periphery subangular with a greatly thickened imperforate ridge; aperture extending from the umbilical boss to the peripheral ridge, covered by poorly developed flaps extending from the last few chambers. *Remarks:* This taxon has been long known to biostratigraphers in the petroleum industry by the informal designation '*Anomalina* W' and widely used as a top Turonian HO. In his doctoral dissertation, Lundquist (2000) identified this taxon as equivalent to *Gavelinella petita* (Carsey) from analysis of the type specimen. Tappan (1940) had declared Carsey's species to be invalid because the drawing of the type specimen was mistakenly of a 'cristallarian test'. Based upon Carsey's original description, she then synonymized the taxon with her new species, *Gavelinella plummerae* (Tappan). However, Lundquist (2000) stated that the type specimen was mistakenly thought by Tappan to be a 'cristallarian', due to poor preservation, and was actually a gavelinellid equivalent to '*Anomalina* W'. Carsey's short type description also did not note the raised dorsal sutures because of the poor preservation, leading to Tappan's synonymy with *G. plummerae*. The confused status of *Gavelinella petita* may yet necessitate suppression and erection of a new species, but, until the matter can be investigated further, the usage of Lundquist (2000) is followed here.

Transition to Planulina texana: Gavelinella petita bears similarity to the well-known species *Planulina texana* (Carsey). However, this widely distributed species of the Coniacian to Santonian Western Interior and Gulf of Mexico differs from *G. petita* by being more compressed, with a much lower trochospire; differing in the nature of the dorsal sutures, being strongly limbate only between the chambers of the earliest whorls and even then much less raised than those of *G. petita*, whereas in all of the final whorl, are only slightly limbate, flush to even slightly depressed; by having a much less thickened, imperforate margin; and, by having a much less well-developed umbilical boss (Fig. 15 j–l).

In a very thin interval of the Blue Hill Member of the Carlile Formation in the Wagon Mound outcrop (1.2 to 1.4 m), common specimens transitional to the two taxa occur (Fig. 15 g–i). These transitional specimens are intermediate between *G. petita* and *P. texana* in the height of the trochospire, the robustness of the umbilical boss, and thickness of the imperforate periphery. The raised dorsal sutures are just as raised and limbate on the chambers of the earlier whorls as in *G. petita*, but less developed on the earliest chambers of the last whorl. However, the sutures of the early chambers of the last whorl are still more prominent than those of the last whorl in *P. texana*. The HO for *G. petita s.s.* occurs at the top of this transitional zone at 1.2 m in the Wagon Mound section. The LO for *P. texana s.s.* occurs just above the top of the zone at 1.4 m. It thus appears that this narrow zone represents a rare recording of a punctuated evolutionary event, whereby *G. petita* quickly gave rise to *P. texana*, perhaps in response to the rapid disappearance of widespread dysoxic palaeoenvironments at this time.

Calcareous nannofossils (James A. Bergen[*] and R. W. Howe)

Tortolithus carteri Bergen & Howe sp. nov.
Fig. 18j & k

Watznaueria virginica (*auct. non* Bukry 1969). Bralower & Bergen 1998, p. 76.
Tortolithus caistorensis (*auct. non* Crux 1982). Burnett, 1998, p. 313, pl. 6.9, fig. 21.

Diagnosis: A brightly birefringent species of *Tortolithus*.

Description (light microscope): A small to large, normally elliptical murolith. The rim appears to be bicyclic. The outer rim cycle is very narrow and faintly birefringent. The broad inner rim cycle is brightly birefringent (first-order white to orange) and is constructed of a low number (16–22) of relatively large, imbricated elements. The inner rim cycle sutures are oblique and its elements are raised distally at their inner terminations to form a narrow 'lip' around the central area margin. The central area is relatively narrow and filled by a plate constructed of a single-element cycle of elements. The central area elements are less birefringent than the rim, and are bisected by a prominent longitudinal suture. Small perforations may be present between the junctures of the central area elements and the inner rim margin. A distal projection has not been observed. Length varies from 4 to 8 μm.

Etymology: Named in honour of palaeontologist Joseph G. Carter from the University of North Carolina, Chapel Hill.

Type: Holotype, Fig. 18j & k. Deposited in the collections of Geoscience Australia, Canberra, under the GA sample number 1441001. Type locality is the Wagon Mound section, New Mexico, USA.

Occurrence: This species is restricted to the Upper Turonian and Coniacian in the Western Interior of the US, Southern England, and the North Sea. Its lowest occurrence is below that of *Micula decussata* within Zone CC13. Its highest occurrence occurs 20 metres below the terminal Coniacian in the Whitecliff section in the Isle of Wight and defines the top of Zone KN27 of Bergen & Sikora (1999) in the North Sea.

Discussion: Burnett (1998) illustrated a brightly birefringent Coniacian specimen identified as *Tortolithus caistorensis* Crux and extended the range of that species from the Campanian down into the Coniacian. *T. caistorensis*, although

[*]BP America, 501 Westlake Park Blvd, PO Box 3092, Houston, TX 77253, USA.

having a distal shield construction similar to *T. carteri*, is entirely faintly birefringent and restricted to the Campanian. Its central elements are also raised above the distal rim surface. Electron photomicrographs of *Tortolithus virginica* (Bukry) seem virtually indistinguishable from Coniacian specimens of *T. carteri* observed under the light microscope. However, the original specimens of *T. virginica* illustrated by Bukry (1969) were recovered from the basal Campanian (Taylor Marl) of the Waxahachie section in SE Texas and are very small. JAB has re-examined this section and observed small specimens with the light microscope that are faintly birefringent and have the ultrastructure of *T. virginica*. This species also has its lowest occurrence at the base of the Campanian at this locality within the uppermost Austin chalk. Specimens of the brightly birefringent species, *Tortolithus carteri*, have only been recovered from Upper Turonian and Lower Coniacian sections in the Western Interior (US), England, and the North Sea. The species is very small near the base of its stratigraphic range in the Upper Turonian and Lower Coniacian, but became larger during the Upper Coniacian. *Tortolithus carteri* is distinguished from other species of *Tortolithus* by its bright birefringent rim (often first-order yellow to orange) and has an older stratigraphic occurrence.

We thank BP Exploration Ltd for the generous research and development grant provided to the Energy & Geoscience Institute from which this study was funded. We also thank BP and Conoco Inc. for waiving their rights to confidentiality to data previously generated for them by EGI that was instrumental in the success of this study. We are grateful to S. Voigt of the University of Cologne for her generosity and stratigraphic expertise in guiding our field collection at the Salzgitter-Salder section. We are also grateful to W. Cobban of the USGS in Denver for his time and great skill in the identification of the ammonites and inoceramids that we collected from the Wagon Mound section. Finally, our thanks are due to R. Scott, J. Kennedy and J. Hancock for thoughtful discussions that resulted in an improved report of our investigations.

References

BERGEN, J. A. & SIKORA, P. J. 1999. Microfossil diachronism in southern Norwegian North Sea chalks: Valhall and Hod fields. *In*: JONES, R. W. & SIMMONS, M. D. (eds) *Biostratigraphy in Production and Development Geology*. Geological Society, London, UK, pp. 85–111.

BOTTJER, R. J. & STEIN, J. A. 1994. Relationship of stratigraphic traps to submarine unconformities; examples from the Tocito Sandstone, San Juan Basin, New Mexico and Colorado. *In*: DOLSON, J. C., HENDRICKS, M. L. & WESCOTT, W. A. (eds) *Unconformity-related Hydrocarbons in Sedimentary Sequences; Guidebook for Petroleum Exploration and Exploitation in Clastic and Carbonate Sediments*. Rocky Mountain Association of Geologists, Denver, CO, USA, pp. 81–208.

BOWN, P. R. & YOUNG, J. R. 1998. Techniques. *In*: BOWN, P. R. (ed.) *Calcareous Nannofossil Biostratigraphy*. Chapman & Hall, London, UK, pp. 16–28.

BRALOWER, T. & BERGEN, J. A. 1998. Cenomanian–Santonian calcareous nannofossil biostratigraphy of a transect of cores drilled across the Western Interior Seaway. *In*: DEAN, W. E. & ARTHUR, M. A. (eds) *Stratigraphy and Palaeoenvironments of the Cretaceous Western Interior Seaway, USA*. Society of Economic Paleontologists and Mineralogists, Concepts in Sedimentology and Paleontology, **6**, 59–77.

BRAUTIGAM, F. 1962. *Zür stratigraphie und Palaontologie des Cenomans und Turons im nordwestlichen Harzland*. Thesis TH, Braunschweig, 261 pp.

BUKRY, D. 1969. Upper Cretaceous coccoliths from Texas and Europe. *The University of Kansas Paleontological Contributions*, **Article 51 (Protista 2)**, 1–79.

BURNETT, J. A. 1998. Upper Cretaceous. *In*: BOWN, P. R. (ed.) *Calcareous Nannofossil Biostratigraphy*. Chapman & Hall, London, UK, pp. 132–199.

CARON, M. 1985. Cretaceous planktic foraminifera. *In*: BOLLI, H. M., SAUNDERS, J. B. & PERCH-NIELSEN, K. (eds) *Plankton Stratigraphy*. Cambridge University Press, New York, USA, pp. 17–86.

CARSEY, D. O., 1926. Foraminifera of the Cretaceous of Central Texas. *Texas University Bulletin*, **2612**, 48.

CECH, S. 1987. Upper Cretaceous Didymotis Events from Bohemia. *In*: WIEDMANN, J. (ed.) *Cretaceous of Western Tethys*, pp. 657–676.

COBBAN, W. A. 1951. Colorado Shale of central and northwestern Montana and equivalent rocks of Black Hills. *Bulletin of the American Association of Petroleum Geologists*, **35**, 2170–2198.

CRUX, J. A., 1982. Upper Cretaceous (Cenomanian to Campanian) calcareous nannofossils. In: LORD, A. R. (ed.) *A Stratigraphical Index of Calcareous Nannofossils*, British Micropalaeontological Society Series, Ellis Horwood Limited, Chichester, UK, pp. 81–135.

CUSHMAN, J. A. 1946. Upper Cretaceous Foraminifera of the Gulf Coastal region of the United States and adjacent areas. *United States Geological Survey Professional Papers*, **206**, 241 pp.

EICHER, D. L. and WORSTELL, P. 1970. Cenomanian and Turonian foraminifera from the Great Plains, United States. *Micropaleontology*, **16(3)**, 269–324.

ELDER, W. P. and KIRKLAND, J. I. 1993. Cretaceous paleogeography of the Colorado Plateau and adjacent areas. *In*: MORALES, M. (ed.) Aspects of Mesozoic geology and paleontology of the Colorado Plateau. *Museum of Northern Arizona Bulletin*, **59**, 129–151.

FRERICHS, W. E., POKRAS, E. M. & EVETTS, M. J. 1977. The genus *Hastigerinoides* and its significance in the biostratigraphy of the Western

Interior. *Journal of Foraminiferal Research*, **7(2)**, 149–156.

HARDENBOL, J., THIERRY, J., FARLEY, M. B., JACQUIN, T., DE GRACIANSKY, P.-C. and VAIL, P. R. 1998. Cretaceous sequence chronostratigraphy. *In*: DE GRACIANSKY, P.-C., HARDENBOL, J., JACQUIN, T. & VAIL, P. R. (eds) *Mesozoic and Cenozoic Sequence Chronostratigraphic Framework of European Basins*. Society of Economic Mineralogists and Paleontologists Special Publications, Tulsa, OK, **60**, Chart 4.

HART, M. B., BAILEY, H. W., CRITTENDEN, S., FLETCHER, B. N., PRICE, R. & SWIECICKI, A. 1989. Cretaceous. *In*: JENKINS, D. G. & MURRAY, J. W. (eds) *Stratigraphical Atlas of Fossil Foraminifera, Second Edition*. Ellis Horwood, Chichester, UK, pp. 273–371.

JAKUBOWSKI, M. 1986. New calcareous nannofossil taxa from the Lower Cretaceous of the North Sea. *International Nannoplankton Association Newsletter*, **8**, 38–42.

KAMINSKI, M. A. 1985. Evidence for control of abyssal agglutinated foraminiferal community structure by substrate disturbance: results from the Hebble area. *Marine Geology*, **66**, 113–131.

KAUFFMAN, E. G., KENNEDY, W. J. & WOOD, C. J. 1996. The Coniacian stage and substage boundaries. *In*: RAWSON, P. F., DHONDT, J. M., HANCOCK, J. M. & KENNEDY, W. J. (eds), Proceedings 'Second International Symposium on Cretaceous Stage Boundaries' Brussels, 8–16 September 1995. *Bulletin de l'Institut Royal des Sciences Naturelles de Belgique*, **66(supplement)**, 81–94.

KAUFFMAN, E. G., SAGEMAN, B. B., KIRKLAND, J. I., ELDER, W. P., HARRIES, P. J. & VILLAMIL, T. 1994. Molluscan biostratigraphy of the Cretaceous Western Interior Basin, North America. *In*: CALDWELL, W. G. E. & KAUFFMAN, E. G. (eds), *Evolution of the Western Interior Basin*. Geological Association of Canada, Special Paper, **39**, 397–434.

KENNEDY, W. J., COBBAN, W. A. & LANDMAN, N. H. 2001. A revision of the Turonian members of the subfamily Collignoniceratinae from the United States Western Interior and Texas. *Bulletin of the American Museum of Natural History*, **267**, 140 pp.

KOCH, W. 1977. Biostratigraphie in der Oberkreide und Taxonomie von Foraminiferen. *Geologisches Jahrbuch, Reihe A*, **38(2)**, 11–123.

KUMP, L. R. and SLINGERLAND, R. L. 1999. Circulation and stratification of the early Turonian Western Interior Seaway: sensitivity of a variety of forcings. *Geological Society of America Special Paper*, **332**, 181–190.

LAFERRIERE, A. P. 1987. Cyclic sedimentation in the Fort Hays Member, Niobrara Formation (Upper Cretaceous) in northeastern New Mexico and southeastern Colorado. *New Mexico Geological Society Guidebook, 38th Field Conference, NE New Mexico*, New Mexico Geological Society, Sante Fe, NM, pp. 249–254.

LECKIE, R. M., KIRKLAND, J. I. & ELDER, W. P. 1997. Stratigraphic framework and correlation of a principal reference section of the Mancos Shale (Upper Cretaceous), Mesa Verde, Colorado. *New Mexico Geological Society Guidebook, 48th Field Conference, Mesozoic Geology and Paleontology of the Four Corners Region*, pp. 163–216.

LUNDQUIST, J. J. 2000. *Foraminiferal biostratigraphic and palaeoceanographic analysis of the Eagle Ford, Austin, and Lower Taylor Groups (Middle Cenomanian through Lower Campanian) of Central Texas*, The University of Texas at Austin, Doctoral Dissertation, 545 pp.

NAIDIN, D. P., BENYAMOVSKY, V. N. & KOPAEVICH, L. F. 1984. *Methods of Transgression and Regression Study Exemplified by Late Cretaceous Basins of West Kazakhstan*. Moscow University Press, Moscow, Russia (in Russian) 162 pp.

OBRADOVICH, J. D. 1993. A Cretaceous time scale. *In*: CALDWELL, W. G. E. & KAUFFMAN, E. G. (eds) *Evolution of the Western Interior Basin*. Geological Association of Canada, Special Papers, **39**, pp. 379–396.

RISATTI, J. B. 1973. Nannoplankton biostratigraphy of the Bluffport Marl–Lower Prairie Bluff Chalk interval (Upper Cretaceous) in Mississippi. *In*: SMITH, L. A. & HARDENBOL, J. (eds) *Proceedings of the Symposium on Calcareous Nannofossils*. Gulf Coast Section, Society of Economic Paleontologists and Mineralogists, pp. 8–57.

ROBASZYNSKI, F., CARON, M. ET AL. 1990. A tentative integrated stratigraphy in the Turonian of central Tunisia: formations, zones and sequential stratigraphy in the Kalaat Senan area. *Bulletin Centres Recherche Exploration et Production, Société Nationale Elf Aquitaine*, **14**, 214–384.

SIKORA, P. J., BERGEN, J. A. & FARMER, C. L. 1999. Chalk palaeoenvironments and depositional model, Valhall–Hod fields, southern Norwegian North Sea. *In*: JONES, R. W. & SIMMONS, M. D. (eds) *Biostratigraphy in Production and Development Geology*, Geological Society London, Special Publications, **152**, 113–137.

SLINGERLAND, R. L., KUMP, L. R., ARTHUR, M. A., SAGEMAN, B. B. & BARRON, E. J. 1996. Estuarine circulation in the Turonian western Interior Seaway of North America. *Geological Society of America Bulletin*, **10(8)**, 941–952.

STRADNER, H. & STEINMETZ, J. 1984. Cretaceous calcareous nannofossils from the Angola Basin, Deep Sea Drilling Project Site 530. *Initial Reports of the Deep Sea Drilling Project*, **75**, 565–649.

TAPPAN, H. 1940. Foraminifera from the Grayson formation of northern Texas. *Journal of Palaeontology*, **14**, p. 124.

VAROL, O. 1991. New Cretaceous and Tertiary calcareous nannofossils. *Neues Jahrbuch für Geologie und Paläontologie, Abhandlungen*, **182**, 211–237.

WALASZCZYK, I. & COBBAN W. A. 2000. Inoceramid faunas and biostratigraphy of the Upper Turonian–Lower Coniacian of the Western Interior of the United States. *Special Papers in Palaeontology*, **64**, The Palaeontological Association, London, UK, 118 pp.

WILLIAMS, G. L., STOVER, L. E. & KIDSON, E. J. 1993. Morphology and stratigraphic ranges of selected Mesozoic–Cenozoic dinoflagellate taxa in the northern hemisphere. *Geological Survey of Canada Paper*, **92–10**, 1–137.

WIND, F. H. & WISE, S. W. 1978. Mesozoic holococcoliths. *Geology*, **6**, 140–142.

WOOD, C. J., ERNST, G. and RASEMANN, G. 1984. The Turonian–Coniacian stage boundary in Lower Saxony (Germany) and adjacent areas: the Salzgitter-Salder Quarry as a proposed international standard section. *Bulletin of the Geological Society of Denmark*, **33**, 225–238.

The palynological record across the Cretaceous–Tertiary boundary in differing palaeogeographical settings from the southern Pyrenees, Spain

M. T. FERNÁNDEZ-MARRÓN[1], N. LÓPEZ-MARTÍNEZ[1],
J. F. FONOLLÁ-OCETE[1] & M. F. VALLE-HERNÁNDEZ[2]

[1]*Dept./UEI Paleontología, Universidad Complutense/CSIC, Facultad C. Geológicas, 28040 Madrid, Spain (e-mail: emarron@geo.ucm.es)*
[2]*Area Paleontología, Facultad Ciencias, Universidad de Salamanca, 37008 Salamanca, Spain*

Abstract: North American and Pacific spore-pollen records show a major extinction event at the Cretaceous–Tertiary (K–T) boundary, and abrupt changes are similarly found in many marine organisms world-wide. In contrast, records from the Old World reveal little evidence of terrestrial vegetational change across the boundary. In order to improve the characterization of changes across the K–T boundary, palynological assemblages from two sections in the southern Pyrenees have been evaluated. The abundance and diversity of trilete fern spores are high in Maastrichtian samples and show a statistically significant decrease during the Danian. The 'fern spike' of low-diversity spores found elsewhere is not recorded in the Pyrenean region. Minor replacements of taxa across the K–T boundary are also noted, as well as an increase in inaperturate gymnosperm pollen in the Danian. Comparing our two examined sections with one another reveals important differences in angiosperm pollen composition.

Dramatic floral changes have been documented across the Cretaceous–Tertiary (K–T) boundary in the North American and Pacific records. Here, a major extinction event in the plant record, and a sudden, brief increase in fern abundance (the 'fern spike'), have been correlated with an iridium anomaly related to an extraterrestrial impact at the boundary (Johnson *et al.* 2000; Vajda *et al.* 2001, and references therein). However, the palynological record in the Old World has not yet shown any appreciable changes during this critical period, which hinders the detection of the K–T boundary. Until now, some of the best-documented continuous sections dated by biostratigraphy and magnetostratigraphy across the K–T boundary in Europe and Africa have failed to show any significant palynological changes (Méon 1990, 1991; Médus *et al.* 1988, 1992; López-Martínez *et al.* 1999; Mayr *et al.* 1999). This lack of a clear palynological K–T boundary in the Old World contrasts with the abrupt change observed in the fossil record of many protists (coccoliths, planktonic foraminifera) and metazoans (molluscs, sharks and reptiles).

In the Pyrenean Basin, a thick succession of red beds characterizes the Tremp Formation, which dates from Late Cretaceous to Early Tertiary. Within this succession Ashraf & Erben (1986) recorded an impoverishment of plant species, which they interpreted as representing the palynological K–T boundary. However, biostratigraphic and magnetostratigraphic dating subsequently demonstrated an older age for this interval – at around the Campanian–Maastrichtian transition (*sensu* Gradstein *et al.* 1995; López-Martínez *et al.* 1999; Ardèvol *et al.* 2000; López-Martínez *et al.* 2001). A decrease in plant diversity is recorded in other Old World regions (Stets *et al.* 1996; Markevitch *et al.* 2000), but this event can be correlated better with the Campanian–Maastrichtian transition than with the K–T boundary. Therefore, no regional events in the Old World Late Cretaceous palynological succession have yet been demonstrably correlated with this boundary.

The apparently smooth transition across the K–T boundary in the palynological record of the Old World may be due to incomplete sampling or to palaeoenvironmental factors. We have therefore studied the palynological record across the boundary in the south central Pyrenees (Spain) by comparing two sections about 50 km apart in differing palaeogeographical settings:

(1) The Fontllonga section (Lleida, Catalonia) representing upper estuarine deposits with a

From: BEAUDOIN, A.B. & HEAD, M.J. (eds) 2004. *The Palynology and Micropalaeontology of Boundaries.* Geological Society, London, Special Publications, **230**, 243–255. 0305-8719/04/$15 © The Geological Society of London 2004.

sedimentation rate between 10 and 100 m Ma^{-1} near the K–T boundary (Alvarez-Sierra *et al.* 1994; López-Martínez *et al.* 1998*a*; Mayr *et al.* 1999).

(2) The Campo section (Huesca, Aragón), a highly expanded stratigraphic section of marine platform deposits with a sedimentation rate up to 200 m Ma^{-1} (López-Martínez *et al.* 1998*b*; Ardèvol *et al.* 2000; Fernández-Marrón *et al.* 2000).

Correlating two palynological successions across the K–T boundary from the same region but representing different palaeogeographical settings should help to detect the palaeoenvironmental, climatic and evolutionary factors that affected the plant fossil record during this critical interval.

Geological setting

The south central Pyrenees (Spain) contain a rich geological record across the Cretaceous–Tertiary transition, represented by marine and non-marine deposits from the Aren and Tremp Formations (Fig. 1). Middle Campanian to Palaeocene deposits exceeding 2000 m in thickness are preserved in excellent outcrops. The Aren Formation consists of biocalcarenitic and hybrid sandstones from nearshore environments, intercalated with offshore marls and turbidite deposits basinwards (i.e. westwards); its age ranges from Mid-Campanian to Late Maastrichtian. The Tremp Formation consists of red beds and peritidal limestones deposited in coastal and continental settings. The middle part of the formation contains the K–T boundary; its lower part intercalates with the Aren Formation (Ardèvol *et al.* 2000; López-Martínez *et al.* 2001).

The Fontllonga and Campo sections are situated in the South Pyrenean Central Unit, which is a complex allochthonous tectonic slab formed by a detached Mesozoic cover thrust over the foreland Ebro Basin. The South Pyrenean Central Unit is made up of several thrust sheets, which have noticeably shortened the original distance between sections. The Fontllonga and the Campo sections are separated by the Montsec thrust anticline (Fig. 1), whose shortening effect has been estimated at least about 17 km (Ardèvol *et al.* 2000).

The Fontllonga section (41° 58′ N, 0° 51′ E), situated on the Ager syncline at Lleida, is located within the Sierras Marginales thrust sheet, which consists of Jurassic, Upper Cretaceous and Palaeogene limestones and sandstones overlying Upper Triassic gypsum. The Tremp

Formation here consists of about 700 m of Campanian to Palaeocene red beds, interpreted as transitional marine/non-marine sediments (paralic deposits) formed in peritidal and upper estuarine palaeoenvironments. Mixed marine and freshwater influence within this red bed succession is attested by tidal sedimentary structures (sigmoidal cross-stratification, mud drapes), remains of marine organisms (the cyanobacterium *Girvanella*, marine dinoflagellates, and the rays *Igdabatis* and *Rhombodus*) and marine bioclastic components within the sandstones (red algae, marine molluscs), remains of terrestrial and lacustrine organisms (dinosaur eggshells, continental ostracodes and molluscs) and isotopic composition (Álvarez-Sierra *et al.* 1994; López-Martínez *et al.* 1998*a*; Mayr *et al.* 1999).

The Campo section (42° 23′ N and 0° 24′ E) is located in the Cotiella thrust sheet, formed by Upper Cretaceous and Palaeogene platform limestones, slope breccias, marls and turbidites. Campanian and Maastrichtian deposits here reach more than 2000 m in thickness, formed by turbidites and marls in the lower part, and deltaic sandstones and shelfal calcarenites in the upper part. The overlying red beds equivalent to the lower Tremp Formation consist of a 60-m thick interval comprising red mudstones and sandstones with minor intercalations of black shales and dolostones (Eichenseer 1988; Robador *et al.* 1990). This section is situated in a basinward position relative to Fontllonga. The marine origin of the Campo red beds is attested by the presence of non-reworked dinoflagellates, micro- and macroforaminifera (*Laffiteina bibensis*), authochthonous rudists and a drifted ammonite shell (*Pachydiscus gollevillensis*).

The Cretaceous–Tertiary boundary

The Cretaceous–Tertiary boundary has been located within the middle of the Tremp Formation in the south central Pyrenees, using biostratigraphy (foraminifera, charophytes, rudists, ammonites, vertebrates), magnetostratigraphy and chemostratigraphy. In the Fontllonga section, the K–T boundary occurs within a 1- to 3-m thick lutite interval near the top of a thick sandstone unit correlated with Chron C29r (Galbrun *et al.* 1993). Dinosaur remains are common below this interval but disappear just above it, where a $\delta^{13}C$ isotopic anomaly indicates a marked change in organic productivity. Vertebrate remains allow this geochemical anomaly to be placed in the earliest Palaeocene (López-Martínez *et al.* 1998a, 1999).

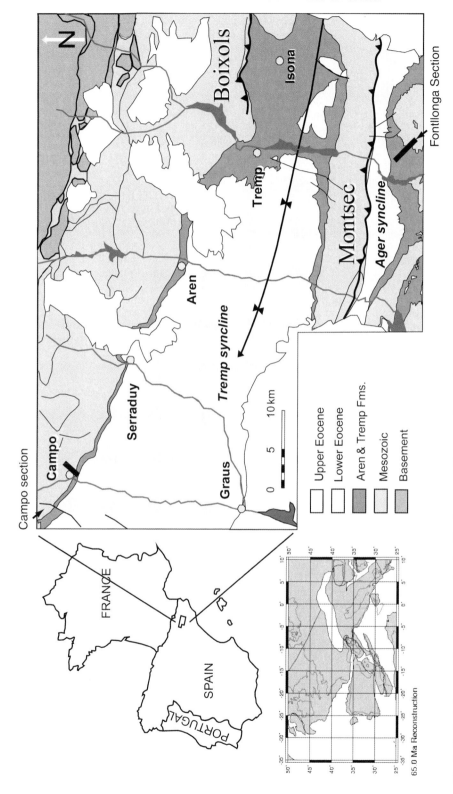

Fig. 1. Geological map of the studied area showing Fontllonga and Campo sections and a palaeogeographical map for the uppermost Maastrichtian–lowermost Palaeocene interval. Plate reconstruction according to http://www.odsn.de/odsn/services/paleomap/adv_map.html.

In the Campo section, stable isotopic analyses have not yet revealed a $\delta^{13}C$ isotopic anomaly related to the K–T boundary. Preliminary magnetostratigraphic analyses have shown reversed polarity in the uppermost 30 m of the Aren Sandstone and in the 60-m thick lower Tremp Formation (Galbrun *et al.* in press) that is compatible with Chron C29r containing this boundary. Biostratigraphic interpretation relies on the presence of the benthic foraminiferid *Laffiteina bibensis* in the middle part of the red beds. This species has been interpreted as being earliest Palaeocene in age, by Serra-Kiel *et al.* (1998), who used it as a marker for their lowermost Tertiary SBZ-1 biozone. However, in the Campo section this species is associated with rudists and ammonites, which confirms its Cretaceous age as deduced in other regions (Eichenseer 1988; Loeblich & Tappan 1988; López-Martínez *et al.* 1998*b*). Palaeocene charophyte taxa are reported just above the uppermost rudist- and ammonite-bearing level (Y. Tambareau, pers. comm.). The foraminiferid *Laffiteina bibensis* is observed until approximately 55 m above the base of the Tremp Formation (Fig. 2). Therefore, the K–T boundary in the Campo section can be placed above the highest occurrence of rudists, ammonites and dinosaurs and below the massive carbonate Unit 3 of Danian age, correlated to the middle part of the Tremp Formation and to the Salarons Formation (Eichenseer 1988; Robador *et al.* 1990; Fig. 2). Lithostratigraphic correlation indicates that the K–T boundary can probably be placed within the lower 10 m of this 16-m thick interval, which corresponds with a reversed magnetic polarity interval (Galbrun *et al.* in press; O. Oms, pers. comm.).

In continental sections from the Old World, no iridium anomaly has yet been associated with a K–T boundary level as determined by biostratigraphic methods. The Fontllonga and Campo sections are among the best-calibrated Old World continental sections for this critical period. Although hiatuses across the K–T boundary interval cannot be excluded, they are not likely in either section: the critical interval in both sections lies within a thick reversed magnetic interval correlated with Chron C29r. In the Fontllonga section, the stratigraphic interval correlated with Chron C29r is 35.8 m thick, whereas in the Campo section it exceeds 38 m. The K–T boundary interval in the Fontllonga section is situated within a detrital unit whose sedimentation rate is estimated at about 50 m/Ma^{-1}. The uppermost part of the Chron C29r interval, which is of Tertiary age, corresponds to a limestone unit with palaeosols,

indicating a strong drop in sedimentation rate. For this reason, the K–T boundary lies near the top of the Chron C29r interval in this section (Fig. 2).

The Campo section does not yet have a clearly delimited Chron C29r interval. A hiatus is expected to be present in the Danian part of the section (above CP-13 sample, Fig. 2) because the normal polarity chrons C29n and C28n are lacking.

Palynology

This study analyses data statistically from nine samples of the Fontllonga section (two samples from López-Martínez *et al.*, 1999; six samples from Mayr *et al.*, 1999; and the newly analysed sample #31) and six samples of the Campo section (all newly analysed). Indices employed are the abundance (number of specimens) and diversity (number of species) of spores relative to the total spore–pollen assemblage, excluding fungi. The indices are treated as percentages. Spores include bryophytes, lycopods and ferns; whereas pollen includes gymnosperms and angiosperms. The total number of spores and pollen counted per sample ranges between 29 and 632 specimens (average of 185) for our samples and those of López-Martínez *et al.* (1999), and between 90 and 270 specimens (average of 162) for those of Mayr *et al.* (1999). The data for each sample are given in Tables 1 to 3 and in Figure 3.

Fontllonga section

The Fontllonga section has been repeatedly sampled for palynology in order to detect changes in the floral composition across the K–T boundary (Médus *et al.* 1988, 1992; López-Martínez *et al.* 1999; Mayr *et al.* 1999). The Fontllonga palynological record includes samples from the boundary interval studied by Médus *et al.* (1988), two samples embracing the boundary studied by López-Martínez *et al.* (1999, samples F#32 and F#36) and six samples studied by Mayr *et al.* (1999), three of them from the Maastrichtian (CH-21, CH-25 and CH-26) and three from the Lower Danian (CH-16, CH-27 and CH-20). Mayr *et al.* (1999) included another Danian sample from the neighbouring Figuerola section. These previous studies show only small, fluctuating changes in the palynological succession across the K–T boundary.

In our study we included another palynological assemblage dated as Late Maastrichtian (sample F#31); additional intermediate samples were prepared but did not contain palyno-

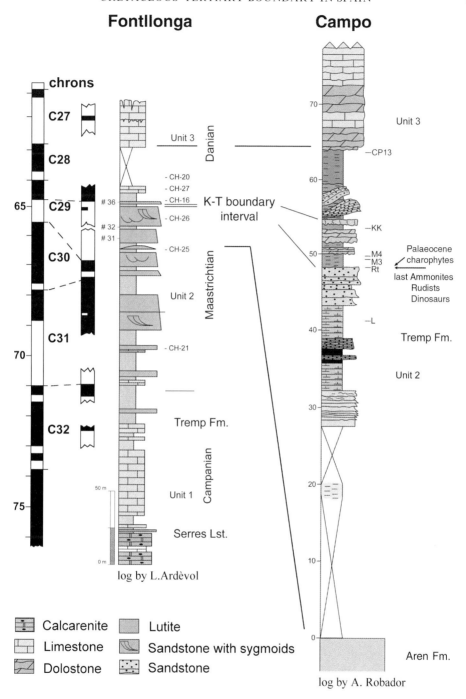

Fig. 2. The position of palynological samples evaluated in the present study. Left, Fontllonga stratigraphic section showing palaeomagnetic polarity and proposed correlation (Galbrun *et al.* 1993; López-Martínez *et al.* 1998*a*; and Mayr *et al.* 1999). Sample #31 is from the present study, samples #32 and #36 are from López-Martínez *et al.* (1999), and samples CH-16 to CH-27 are from Mayr *et al.* (1999). Right, Campo stratigraphic section corresponding mostly with a reversed polarity chron assumed to be C29r. Lines of correlation to the Fontllonga section are based on sequence stratigraphy and biostratigraphy (Robador *et al.* 1990; Ardevol *et al.* 2000).

Table 1. *Comparison of spore frequency (species diversity and relative abundance) in palynomorph assemblages below and above the K–T boundary in the Fontllonga section.*

Fontllonga section	Diversity (%)			Abundance (%)			No. of samples
	Max.	Mean	Min.	Max.	Mean	Min.	
Uppermost Maastrichtian	66.7	50.5	40.0	78.7	54.8	30.1	6
Lowermost Danian	50.0	43.1	36.4	48.0	37.0	28.5	4
t-test probability		16.4% (–)			7.3% (–)		

Data from López-Martínez *et al.* (1999), Mayr *et al.* (1999) and new data from this work (see Table 3). (–) not statistically significant.

morphs. The positions of all samples statistically analysed in this paper for the Fontllonga section are shown in Figure 2.

Spores are the main component of the three palynomorph assemblages, and are generally large trilete types: psilate *Leiotriletes* spp. and *Cyathidites* spp., ornamented and thick-walled *Lycopodiumsporites* sp., *Matthesisporites plurituberosus* Döring, *Polypodiaceoisporites* spp. and *Echinatisporis* spp., as well as cingulate *Patellasporites* sp. and taeniate *Cicatricosisporites* sp. spores. The flora was thus dominated by lycopods and ferns, mainly from the Schizaceae, Gleichenidaceae, Cyatheaceae and Polypodiaceae families. Thick-walled spores reach 90–94% of the spore assemblage, indicating the strong influence of locally developed fern forests.

The spores *Biretisporites potoniaei* Delcourt & Sprumont, *Matthesisporites plurituberosus* Döring and *Trilites tuberculiformis* (Cookson) Dettman, proposed as Cretaceous markers by Asraf & Erben (1986), appear in our Cretaceous assemblage F#31 from Fontllonga. However, Mayr *et al.* (1999) also reported these species from Danian samples in the Fontllonga area.

The predominance of spore diversity and abundance over pollen is particularly high in the Cretaceous samples, although the difference is not large (Fig. 3). Mayr *et al.* (1999) also reported an increase in trilete spore abundance and diversity within the uppermost Maastrichtian in the Fontllonga section, and interpreted this dominance as indicative of environmental change across the K–T boundary. When all samples are considered, the palynomorph assemblages below this boundary actually show an overall dominance in spores samples above the boundary, but the difference is not statistically significant (a 7% probability of a null hypothesis remains; see Table 1). Both spore diversity and abundance decrease across the K–T boundary, but the difference in the Fontllonga samples is too low and the overlap too high to be significant as a biostratigraphic boundary criterion.

In the Fontllonga section, those samples containing the highest spore abundance (F#32 and CH-25, 71–78%) are very close to the K–T boundary but are not the closest. Older Campanian and Maastrichtian samples from other Pyrenean areas show even higher spore ratios in the palynomorph assemblages, reaching as much as 85.3% diversity and 88.4% abundance (De Porta *et al.* 1985; Ashraf & Erben 1986;

Table 2. *Comparison of spore frequency (species diversity and relative abundance) in palynomorph assemblages across the K–T boundary for the combined Fontllonga and Campo sections.*

Fontllonga and Campo sections	Diversity (%)			Abundance (%)			No. of samples
	Max.	Mean	Min.	Max.	Mean	Min.	
Uppermost Maastrichtian and K–T boundary interval	74.6	58.6	40.0	80.8	61.6	30.1	11
Lowermost Danian	50.0	44.5	36.4	48.1	37.3	28.5	5
t-test probability		3.5%*			0.07%[†]		

Data from López-Martínez *et al.* (1999), Mayr *et al.* (1999), Fernández-Marrón *et al.* (2000) and new data from this work (see Table 3).
*Statistically significant.
[†]Highly significant.

Table 3. *Counts of palynological taxa and specimens from the Fontllonga and Campo sections.*

	Fontllonga									Campo					
	CH21*	CH25*	#31	#32	CH26*	#36	CH16*	CH27*	CH20*	L	Rt	M3	M4	14kk	CP13
Diversity (taxa)	14	21	58	40	18	44	22	23	17	56	19	51	59	26	22
Spores	7	14	27	20	9	16	11	9	8	35	11	29	44	18	11
(trilete)	(6)	(13)	(23)	(18)	(9)	(14)	(9)	(9)	(6)	(33)	(11)	(24)	(43)	(18)	(10)
Gymnosperms	2	2	6	4	2	6	2	1	1	6	3	7	5	4	7
(inaperturate pollen)	(0)	(1)	(1)	(2)	(1)	(3)	(1)	(1)	(1)	(4)	(2)	(5)	(2)	(1)	(4)
Angiosperms	5	5	25	16	9	22	9	13	8	15	5	15	10	4	4
(Normapolles)	(1)	(1)	(8)	(5)	(2)	(6)	(2)	(4)	(3)	(2)	(1)	(1)	(1)	(0)	(0)
Abundance	93	239	91	552	128	632	142	270	96	80	29	82	90	64	39
Spores	28	188	40	396	68	304	41	80	38	55	17	51	71	50	15
(trilete)	(28)	(177)	(34)	(378)	(61)	(287)	(36)	(78)	(34)	(53)	(17)	(45)	(70)	(50)	(14)
Gymnosperms	20	17	15	46	4	76	18	21	25	9	6	11	8	7	18
(inaperturate pollen)	(0)	(12)	(2)	(8)	(1)	(19)	(17)	(18)	(25)	(7)	(3)	(9)	(4)	(1)	(11)
Angiosperms	45	34	36	110	56	252	83	165	33	16	6	20	11	7	6
(Normapolles)	(2)	(12)	(18)	(95)	(15)	(114)	(12)	(18)	(8)	(2)	(1)	(1)	(1)	(0)	(0)

Counts for those samples indicated by an asterisk (*) are calculated from Mayr *et al.* (1999, tables 1 and 2) excluding fungal and algal remains and dinoflagellate cysts.

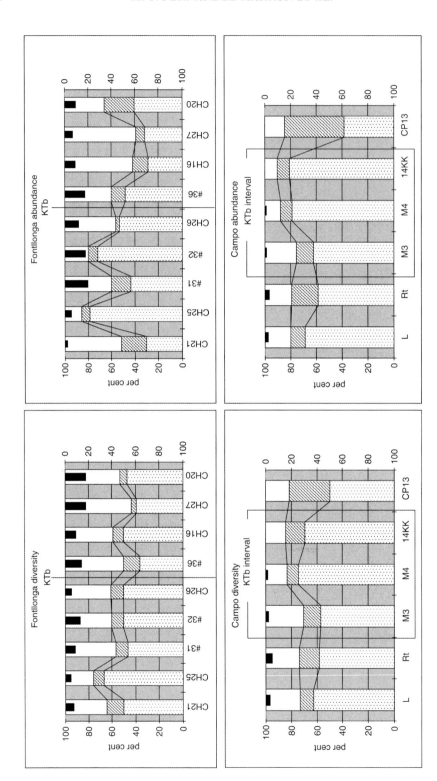

Fig. 3. Diagrams showing spore and pollen abundance and diversity. Spores, dotted; gymnosperm pollen, hatched; angiosperm pollen, white; Normapolles, black, inversely scaled.

Médus *et al.* 1988). Therefore, during latest Cretaceous times, the Pyrenean region was already dominated by ferns, which increases the difficulty in detecting a fern spike similar to those reported for North America and New Zealand just above the K–T boundary (Fleming & Nichols 1990; Vajda *et al.* 2001).

Gymnosperms are a minor component of the palynomorph assemblages in the Fontllonga section, reaching about 10% of the total diversity and abundance. Cupressaceae–Taxodiaceae and Cycadaceae are the main components, the Pinaceae being extremely rare both in uppermost Cretaceous and Palaeocene samples. Samples studied by Mayr *et al.* (1999) around the K–T boundary in the Fontllonga section also show a very similar gymnosperm ratio and composition. A proposed increase in Pinaceae abundance after the boundary as a biostratigraphic criterion in the Fontllonga section (Médus *et al.* 1992) can therefore be excluded. The frequency of bisaccate pollen is often related to taphonomic factors, and in marine samples is extremely sensitive to the distance of the sample location from shore.

The pollen composition in the Fontllonga section shows a major angiosperm component, reaching more than 40% of the total spore–pollen assemblage. A diverse angiosperm flora includes: *Tricolpopollenites* sp., *Polycolpites* sp., *Rugulitriporites* sp., *Subtriporopollenites* sp., *Triporopollenites* spp., *Polyporopollenites* sp., *Triatriopollenites* sp., etc. The Normapolles group (*Trudopollis* sp., *Vacuopollis* sp., *Semioculopollis* sp., *Nudopollis* sp.) is an important component, comprising about 12% of the total assemblage diversity and 18% of the abundance, although Mayr *et al.* (1999) reported a lower Normapolles abundance and diversity (lower than 10%). The Normapolles *Pseudoromeinipollenites* cf. *paleocenicus* occurs only in Tertiary samples from Fontllonga, according to our results and those of Mayr *et al.* (1999). This species may be characteristic of the European Tertiary and different from Cretaceous forms attributed to the same genus by Médus (1986) and Médus *et al.* (1988).

Campo section

In order to obtain the highest resolution record possible across the K–T boundary, the more expanded Campo section has been chosen to explore the palynological pattern of plant change. Chron C29r containing the boundary may here span more than 90 m in thickness, compared with around 50 m in the Fontllonga section. Moreover, the grey–black shale and clay-dominated deposits of the K–T transition in the Campo section are more favourable to continuous deposition and palynomorph preservation than in the Fontllonga section, where an amalgamation of channel sandstones correlated to Chron C29r presumably contain stratigraphic hiatuses.

The red-bed interval in the Campo section has yielded six significant palynological assemblages among the numerous studied samples. Two (samples L and Rt) correspond with the uppermost Maastrichtian levels containing *Laffiteina bibensis*, rudists and ammonites; three samples above them (M3, M4 and KK) correspond to a 10-m thick interval where the K–T boundary can probably be situated; and the highest analysed sample (CP-13) is considered Tertiary in age because of its close proximity to the Danian limestone unit (Fig. 2).

The total diversity in the Campo samples is similar to that in Fontllonga (an average of about 40 v. 47 taxa per sample), in spite of fewer specimens counted (66 v. 425 average specimens per sample respectively). However, the variance between samples is much more important in the Campo section (standard deviation 18.4 v. 9.4). The dominance of spores over pollen in the Campo samples, both in diversity (50% spore taxa on average) and abundance (65% spore specimens on average), is even stronger than in the Fontllonga section (44% and 54% respectively) (Fig. 3). We note the lack of cingulate and teniate spores in Campo, which are present in Fontllonga.

The trilete spore species *Biretisporites potoniei* Delcourt & Sprumont, *Cyathidites minor* Couper, *Lycopodiumsporites austroclavatidites* (Cookson) Potonié, *Matthesisporites plurituberosus* Döring and *Polypodiaceoisporites potoniei* (Potonié & Gelletich) Kedves, which are restricted to the Maastrichtian according to Asraf & Erben (1986), occur in the lowermost five spore assemblages analysed from the Campo section and are absent from the Danian sample CP-13. However, three of these taxa are reported by Mayr *et al.* (1999) in the Danian samples from Fontllonga (see above). More sampling is necessary to confirm that at least two of these forms were extinct after the K–T boundary.

The previously noted increased spore–pollen ratio below the K–T boundary at Fontllonga is also seen in assemblages from the K–T boundary interval in the Campo section, which may be chronologically closer to the boundary than those from the Fontllonga section (Fernández-Marrón *et al.* 2000). The Upper Maastrichtian L and Rt assemblages reach around 60–70% in spore diversity and abundance; the spore ratio noticeably rises in the M4 and KK samples (around 70–75% diversity and 80% abundance), and decreases to 40–50% in the Danian CP-13 assemblage.

Gymnosperms are hardly more abundant in the Campo assemblages than in those of Fontllonga. We record three to seven taxa per sample with 9–20% average abundance. Only the Danian sample CP-13 shows a massive presence of gymnosperms, mainly *Inaperturopollenites* sp. (up to 32% diversity and 46% abundance, Fig. 3). This pollen form is present in all samples as well as *Araucariacites* sp. and pollen related to the Cycadophyta. Bisaccate pollen are rare. In all of the Campo samples, angiosperms are poor, both in diversity (average 22%) and abundance (17%), in relation to the total spore–pollen assemblage (Fig. 3). The pollen genus *Subtriporopollenites* which is represented by several species, together with *Triatriopollenites* sp. and *Polycolpites* sp., are the only significant components, whereas the Normapolles presence is insignificant (average 2% diversity and less than 1% abundance). Hence, the angiosperm pollen frequency from the Campo succession differs strongly from that of Fontllonga, this difference being statistically highly significant in both diversity and abundance (null hypothesis probability $p = 0.0002$ and $p = 0.002$ respectively, according to the t-test).

Both angiosperm and Normapolles frequencies decrease upwards in the Campo palynological succession, although the numbers of specimens counted in the youngest samples are not yet large enough to be conclusive. The extraordinarily low percentage of Normapolles in the Campo samples (less than 1% of about 400 counted specimens) seems related to a very low representation of angiosperms, and not to a replacement by modern-type angiosperms which is a long-term trend across the Cretaceous–Tertiary transition (López-Martínez *et al.* 1999). However, the Normapolles decline needs to be fully validated before being considered a reliable signal (see below).

Comparison between sections

When palynological samples from both the Fontllonga and Campo sections are considered together, the observed changes in spore–pollen ratio across the K–T boundary show a consistent pattern. The difference in spore–pollen ratio becomes reinforced and statistically significant or highly significant (Table 2). On average, the spore–pollen ratio across the K–T boundary falls from 59% diversity and 62% abundance, to 45% diversity and 37% abundance. Sample CP-

13 from Campo closely fits the ratio of Tertiary samples from the well-dated Fontllonga section, which supports its Danian age. The three samples from the Campo K–T boundary interval are similar to those from the Cretaceous, although the boundary itself cannot yet be confidently placed in relation to them.

The spore occurrence pattern in the Campo section shows good correlation between diversity and abundance peaks (correlation coefficient $r = 0.93$), indeed a much better correlation than at Fontllonga ($r = 0.58$) and also better than at other Pyrenean localities (La Posa and Coll de Nargó, $r = 0.87$) (calculated from data in De Porta *et al.* 1985 and Ashraf & Erben 1986). In contrast, the North American fern spike shows a high spore abundance with low diversity (Tschudy *et al.* 1984). The two New Zealand sections which document the fern spike differ, but both show a relatively high spore diversity, that includes both ground and tree ferns, for a duration of 30 000 years (Vajda *et al.* 2001).

The unusual composition of gymnosperms from the Campo Tertiary sample shows some similarities with a Danian sample from the Figuerola section, near Fontllonga, in having an unusually high abundance of inaperturate pollen (Mayr *et al.* 1999). The New Zealand record also documents a gymnosperm-rich period during the Early Danian, lasting more than 1 Ma after the fern spike and revealed by dominance of the conifer pollen *Phyllocladidites* (Vajda *et al.* 2001).

In contrast to the relatively rich and diverse angiosperms characterizing the Fontllonga assemblages, with Normapolles pollen comprising about half of the specimens, the low representation of Normapolles and other angiosperm pollen close to the K–T boundary in the Campo section could be considered a palaeoenvironmental signal, indicating a regressive step in the vegetation successional sequence. The frequency of angiosperms is usually a rather consistent indicator in palynological composition. However, the Normapolles frequency in other Pyrenean palynological studies seems to be highly unstable when comparing data from different authors for the same localities. For example, our Normapolles frequences in the Fontllonga samples (17–19% of a total of 1700 spores and pollen) are significantly higher than those for the same part of the section studied by Mayr *et al.* (1999) (5–11% of up to 1455 spores and pollen), in spite of good general agreement between both palynological studies. Also in La Posa grey marl samples (latest Campanian, lower Tremp Formation, Isona, Lleida), the Normapolles reach around 20% of species diversity according to De Porta *et al.* (1985), but only 1.4% according to Ashraf & Erben (1986). These differences cannot be explained by random sampling effects or palaeoenvironmental factors, since the samples came from the same parts of the same section. The possibility that preparation techniques may affect the Normapolles frequency is another factor that needs to be studied. Meanwhile, we do not consider the Normapolles frequency to be a reliable signal in our analysis.

Conclusions

Palynological changes across the K–T boundary in the south central Pyrenees have been portrayed in previous studies as following a smooth transition, with minor vegetational fluctuations linked to local palaeoenvironmental factors. We have re-evaluated a previously published palynological succession from the best time-constrained section, at Fontllonga, and have analysed an additional sample. New palynological data have also been collected from the highly expanded Campo section, situated in a more paralic environment and a palaeogeographical position more distal relative to the shoreline.

Our results lead to a better characterization of the palynological K–T boundary. The most noticeable pattern in plant changes across this boundary in the Pyrenean realm is the increase in trilete spores during the latest Maastrichtian and K–T boundary interval assemblages, and its decrease in the Danian assemblages. In our study, this pattern previously observed in the Fontllonga sections and in some localities in the south of France (Médus *et al.* 1988; López-Martínez *et al.* 1999; Mayr *et al.* 1999; Fernández-Marrón *et al.* 2000) has been reinforced by showing that this difference is statistically highly significant, and by verifying the same pattern in the highly expanded Campo section. In the Pyrenees, a long interval, from uppermost Maastrichtian to the K–T boundary interval, is characterised by taxonomically diverse as well as abundant trilete spores. This contrasts with the short-duration fern-spike at the K–T boundary in North America and New Zealand, where an abrupt increase in ferns represents a low-diversity assemblage comprising the monolete form genus *Laevigatosporites* or the trilete form genus *Cyathidites*, respectively (Sweet *et al.* 1999; Vajda *et al.* 2001). It is therefore likely that the fern increase in our study is driven by different causal mechanisms from those of the fern spike in North America and New Zealand.

There are no noticeable extinctions across the K–T boundary in the studied sections. Several biostratigraphic criteria previously proposed for delimiting the boundary need to be modified or rejected. The spore species *Cyathidites minor* Couper, *Lycopodiumsporites austroclavatidites* (Cookson) Potonié, and *Polypodiaceoisporites potoniei* (Potonié & Gelletich) Kedves are recorded below and above the K–T boundary, whereas *Biretisporites potoniei* Delcourt & Sprumont, *Matthesisporites plurituberosus* Döring and *Trilites tuberculiformis* (Cookson) Dettman, which are only found in our Cretaceous assemblages, have nevertheless been reported from Danian samples by Mayr *et al.* (1999). All these species were proposed as Cretaceous markers by Asraf & Erben (1986). An increase in bisaccate pollen after the K–T boundary is not observed and its fluctuations are not recommended as biostratigraphic criterion (Médus *et al.* 1992). The decrease in Normapolles abundance around the boundary (López-Martínez *et al.* 1999) is also a flawed criterion, since its fluctuations are based on unstable observations. *Pseudoromeinipollenites* cf. *paleocenicus*, if distinguishable from its Cretaceous relatives, would be a biostratigraphically significant newcomer after the K–T boundary.

The increase in frequency of spores across the K–T boundary is better marked in the Campo section, where two fern-rich samples from the K–T boundary interval show extremely low proportions of angiosperm pollen. Following this increase in spores, two Tertiary samples from both sections show an unusual abundance in inaperturate gymnosperm pollen. This pattern in the palynological succession across the K–T boundary is similar to that from other regions where a fern spike has been documented. This correlation would imply that the youngest spore-rich samples from Campo could already correspond with the earliest Tertiary. This hypothesis can be tested by geochemical analyses across this palynologically constrained K–T boundary interval.

Funds were provided by projects PB98-0813 and BTE2002-01430 of the Spanish Ministerio de Educación and Ministerio de Ciencia & Tecnología. We acknowledge the help of project members from Barcelona (UAB), Bilbao (UPV), Madrid (UCM), Rome (La Sapienzia) and Salamanca Universities, the Spanish Geological Survey (IGME), Institut d'Estudis Ilerdencs (IEI), Geoplay (Tremp, Lleida) and the villagers of Pallars Jussà (Catalonia) and Ribagorza (Aragón). We are also grateful to D. J. Nichols (US Geological Survey, Denver) and A. Sweet (Geological Survey of Canada, Calgary) for their helpful reviews of the manuscript, and especially to M. J. Head (Depart-

ment of Geography, University of Cambridge) for his
very careful editorial work.

References

ALVAREZ-SIERRA, M. A., ARRIBAS, M. E. *ET AL.*
1994. *El límite Cretácico–Terciario en la sección de
Fontllonga (Cuenca de Ager, provincia de Lérida).*
II Congreso GET Jaca, Comunicaciones, pp. 23–
26.

ARDEVOL, L., KLIMOWITZ, J., MALAGÓN, J. &
NAGTEGAAL, P. J. C. 2000. Depositional
sequence response to foreland deformation in
the Upper Cretaceous of Southern Pyrenees,
Spain. *Bulletin of the American Association of
Petroleum Geologists*, **84**, 566–587.

ASHRAF, A. R. & ERBEN, H. K. 1986. Palynologische
Untersuchungen an der Kreide/Tertiar-Grenze
west-mediterraner Regionen. *Palaeontographica
B*, **200**, 111–163.

DE PORTA, J., KEDVES, M., SOLÉ DE PORTA, N. &
CIVIS, J. 1985. Palinología del Maastrichtiense del
barranco de la Posa (Lérida, España). Problemá-
tica regional. *Revista d'Investigacions Geologiques*,
40, 5–28.

EICHENSEER, H. 1988. Facies geology of late Maastrichtian to early Eocene coastal to shallow
marine sediments, Tremp–Graus basin, NE
Spain. Ph.D. Thesis, University of Tübingen,
237 pp.

FERNÁNDEZ MARRÓN, M. T., FONOLLÁ OCETE, J.
F., VALLE HERNÁNDEZ, M. F., ROBADOR, A. &
LÓPEZ MARTINEZ, N. 2000. Asociaciones espor-
opolínicas del Transito Cretácico–Terciario en la
Sección de Campo, Cuenca de Tremp-Graus
(Huesca). *In: XIII Simposio de la Asociación de
Palinólogos en Lengua Española*, Cartagena, Libro
de Resúmenes, pp. 195–196.

FLEMING, R. F. & NICHOLS, D. J. 1990. Fern-spore
abundance anomaly at the Cretaceous–Tertiary
boundary: a regional bioevent in western North
America. *In*: KAUFFMAN, E. G. & WALLISER,
O. H. (eds) *Extinction Events in Earth History*,
Springer-Verlag, Berlin, Heidelberg, pp. 347–
349.

GALBRUN, B., FEIST, M., COLOMBO, F., ROCCHIA, R.
& TAMBAREAU, Y. 1993. Magnetostratigraphy
and biostratigraphy of Cretaceous–Tertiary con-
tinental deposits, Ager basin, province of Lerida,
Spain. *Palaeogeography, Palaeoclimatology,
Palaeoecology*, **102**, 41–52.

GALBRUN, B., OZAWA, S., SAMSO, J. M., HOTTIN-
GER, FEIST, M., ROBIN, E., ROCCHIA, R. &
TAMBAREAU, L. (in press). About the age of
Laffiteina bibensis Marie in the Garumnian facies
of the Campo section (central South Pyrenean
zone): Biostratigraphical, magnetostratigraphical
studies and iridium anomaly prospects. *Dela
Opera*, Ljubljana.

GRADSTEIN, F. M., AGTERBERG, F. P., OGG, J. G.,
HARDENBOL, J., VAN VEEN, P., THIERRY, J.
HUANG, Z. 1995. A Triassic, Jurassic and
Cretaceous time scale. *In*: BERGGREN, W. A.,
KENT, D. V., AUBRY, M.P. & HARDENBOL, J.

(eds) *Geochronology, Time Scales and Global
Stratigraphic Correlation.* SEPM (Society for
Sedimentary Geology), Special Publication, **54**,
95–126.

JOHNSON, K., NICHOLS, D., LABANDEIRA, C. &
PEARSON, D. 2000. Devastation of terrestrial
ecosystems at the K–T boundary in North
America: the first calibrated record of plant and
animal response to the Chicxulub impact, *In:
Catastrophic Events and Mass Extinctions:
Impacts and Beyond*, Catastrophic Events Con-
ference, Vienna, Austria, 2000, pp. 85–86.

LOEBLICH, A. & TAPPAN, H. 1988. *Foraminiferal
Genera and their Classification.* Van Nostrand
Reinhold. New York.

LÓPEZ-MARTÍNEZ, N., ARDEVOL, L., ARRIBAS, M.
E., CIVIS, J. & GONZALEZ DELGADO, J. A. 1998*a*.
The geological record in non-marine environ-
ments around the K/T boundary (Tremp Forma-
tion, Spain). *Bulletin Société Geologique de
France*, **169(1)**, 11–20.

LÓPEZ-MARTÍNEZ, N., CANUDO, I. *ET AL.* 2001. New
dinosaur sites correlated with Upper Maastrichtian pelagic deposits in the Spanish Pyrenees:
implications for the dinosaur extinction pattern in
Europe. *Cretaceous Research*, **22**, 41–61.

LÓPEZ-MARTÍNEZ, N., CIVIS, J. *ET AL.* 1998*b*. El
límite Cretácico-Terciario en la sección de Campo
(Cuenca de Tremp-Graus, Pirineos Sur-Cen-
trales). Sedimentología, micropaleontología e isó-
topos estables de C y O. *In*: XIV Jornadas de
Paleontología, Tenerife, Libro de Resúmenes, pp.
105–107.

LÓPEZ-MARTÍNEZ, N., FERNÁNDEZ MARRÓN, T. &
VALLE, M. F. 1999. The succession of vertebrates
and plants across the Cretaceous–Tertiary Boundary in the Tremp Formation, Ager valley (South-
Central Pyrenees, Spain). *Geobios*, **32(4)**, 617–627.

MARKEVITCH, V. S., BUGDAEVA, E. V. & BOLOTSKY,
Y. L. 2000. Palynological evidence of vegetational
change and dinosaur extinction in the Amur
region. *Paleontological Journal*, **34(1)**, 50–53.

MAYR, C., THÜMMLER, B., WINDMAIER, G., ALTEN-
BACH, A. V., KÖLER, H. & TIEDEMANN, R. 1999.
New data about the Maastrichtian/Danian transi-
tion in the Southern Pyrenees (Ager Basin,
Catalonia, Spain). *Revista Española de Micro-
paleontología*, **31**, 357–368.

MÉDUS, J. 1986. Paléogéographie et systématique du
genre *Pseudoromeinipollenites* au Crétacé supér-
ieur. *Actas de Palinología*, 321–325.

MÉDUS, J., COLOMBO, F. & DURAND, J. P. 1992.
Pollen and spore assemblages of the uppermost
Cretaceous continental formations of south-east-
ern France and north-eastern Spain. *Cretaceous
Research*, **13**, 119–132.

MÉDUS, J., FEIST, M. *ET AL.* 1988. Prospects for
recognition of the palynological Cretaceous/Ter-
tiary boundary and an iridium anomaly in
nonmarine facies of the eastern Spanish Pyrenees:
a preliminary report. *Newsletters in Stratigraphy*,
18, 123–138.

MÉON, H. 1990. Palynologic studies of Cretaceous–
Tertiary interval at El Kef outcrop, northwestern

Tunisia: paleogeographic implications. *Review of Palaeobotany and Palynology*, **65**, 85–94.

MÉON, H. 1991. Études sporopolliniques à la limite Crétacé-Tertiaire. La coupe du Kef (Tunisie Nord-Occidentale) étude systématique, stratigraphie, paléogéographie et évolution climatique. *Palaeontographica B*, **223**, 107–168.

ROBADOR, A., SAMSÓ, J. M, SERRA-KIEL, J. & TOSQUELLA, J. 1990 Introduction in the Early Paleogene of the South Pyrenean Basin. IGCP Project 286. *In: Field Trip Guidebook. ITGE.* 159 pp.

SERRA-KIEL, J., HOTTINGER, L. *ET AL.* 1998. Larger foraminiferal biostratigraphy of the Tethyan Paleocene and Eocene. *Bulletin Société Géologique de France*, **169**, 281–299.

STETS, J., ASHRAF, A.-R. *ET AL.* 1996. The Cretaceous–Tertiary boundary in the Nanxiong basin (continental facies, Southern China). *In*:

McLEOD, N. & KELLER G. (eds) *Cretaceous–Tertiary Mass Extinctions. Biotic and Environmental Changes.* Norton, pp. 349–371.

SWEET, A. R., BRAMAN, D. R. & LERBEKMO, J. F. 1999. Sequential palynological changes across the composite Cretaceous–Tertiary (K–T) boundary claystone and contiguous strata, western Canada and Montana, U.S.A. *Canadian Journal of Earth Sciences*, **36**, 743–768.

TSCHUDY, R. H., PILLMORE, C. L., ORTH, C. J., GILMORE, J. S. & KNIGHT, J. D. 1984. Disruption of the terrestrial plant ecosystem at the Cretaceous–Tertiary boundary, Western Interior. *Science*, **225**, 1030–1032.

VAJDA, V., RAINE, J. I. & HOLLIS, C. J. 2001. Indication of global deforestation at the Cretaceous–Tertiary boundary by New Zealand Fern Spike. *Science*, **294**, 1700–1702.

Dinoflagellate cyst record of the deep-sea Cretaceous–Tertiary boundary at Uzgruň, Carpathian Mountains, Czech Republic

PRZEMYSŁAW GEDL

Institute of Geological Sciences, Polish Academy of Sciences, Senacka 1, 31–002, Kraków, Poland (e-mail: ndgedl@cyf-kr.edu.pl)

Abstract: The record of organic-walled dinoflagellate cysts in deep-sea facies across the Cretaceous–Tertiary boundary is poorly known. A detailed study of uppermost Maastrichtian–lowermost Danian Tethyan deep-sea flysch sediments deposited below the carbonate compensation depth at Uzgruň, in the Czech Republic, has yielded numerous and relatively well-preserved dinoflagellate cysts. Their distribution allows the Cretaceous–Tertiary boundary to be placed within a 73 cm interval, within which an iridium anomaly occurs. Assemblages show no major shifts within the boundary interval, but gradual changes were recorded that possibly relate to sea-level fluctuations and/or nutrient availability. High concentrations of peridinioids appear to indicate upwelling in this part of the Tethys near the Cretaceous–Tertiary boundary. The presence of thermophilic dinoflagellate cysts throughout the section points to a stable, warm-temperate to subtropical climate during the latest Maastrichtian and earliest Danian. Events, such as the *Areoligera* sp. acme, *Manumiella seelandica* acme and the *Spinidinium* sp. acme, known from other Cretaceous–Tertiary boundary sections around the world, were recognized within the studied material.

The causes, effects and scale of biotic change that began at the end of the Cretaceous remain controversial. A bolide impact (e.g. Alvarez *et al.* 1980), increased volcanic activity (e.g. McLean 1985), and palaeoclimatic changes of various kinds are frequently cited as causes of the Cretaceous–Tertiary (K–T) boundary event. Such events would have caused changes in surface-water chemistry (Hansen 1990), climatic cooling (e.g. Romein & Smit 1981; Perch-Nielsen *et al.* 1982), sea-level fluctuations (e.g. Keller *et al.* 1993) and a decrease in surface ocean productivity (e.g. Keller & Lindinger 1989). There is also debate over the scale and rate of biota extinction. Raup & Sepkoski (1984, 1986) claimed rapid mass mortality at the boundary, whereas Keller *et al.* (1993) and MacLeod (1996) postulated a protracted turnover. MacLeod also suggested that the incompleteness of the sedimentological record often explained the sharp extinction pattern observed. According to MacLeod *et al.* (1997), only the calcareous nannoplankton suffered sudden widespread extinction, whereas other fossil groups underwent stepwise extinction or crossed the K–T boundary unscathed.

Organic-walled dinoflagellate cysts (hereafter 'dinocysts') are one of the fossil groups that crossed the K–T boundary without significant change (e.g. Habib *et al.* 1992). Although dinocysts show a gradual decline in species richness in the latest Maastrichtian, only a few species are believed to have become extinct at or close to the boundary. Moreover, no abrupt increase in species diversity has been observed for the Early Palaeocene (Brinkhuis & Zachariasse 1988; Stover *et al.* 1996). Most of the K–T boundary sections examined for dinocysts represent inshore facies (e.g. Firth 1987; Brinkhuis & Schiøler 1996). In contrast, the Soláň Formation exposed at Uzgruň represents deep-sea flysch sediments deposited below the carbonate compensation depth (CCD) in the northeastern part of the Tethyan realm (Bubík *et al.* 1999). Dinocysts found in this stratigraphically continuous Maastrichtian–Danian section therefore provide new information on the Cretaceous–Tertiary boundary event. In these deep-water hemipelagic deposits, the autochthonous (oceanic) component of the dinocyst assemblages may be compared directly with cysts transported to this site by turbidite currents from the shelf.

Geological setting

The Soláň Formation exposed at the Uzgruň exposure in the Moravian Carpathians belongs to the Rača Zone of the Magura Nappe. The Magura Nappe is the largest and southernmost tectonic unit of the Flysch Carpathians (Fig. 1a).

From: BEAUDOIN, A.B. & HEAD, M.J. (eds) 2004. *The Palynology and Micropalaeontology of Boundaries.* Geological Society, London, Special Publications, **230**, 257–273. 0305-8719/04/$15 © The Geological Society of London 2004.

It includes Lower Cretaceous through Lower Oligocene deposits – mainly of turbidite character. Older deposits, beginning with the Lower Jurassic, are tectonically incorporated into the Pieniny Klippen Belt (e.g. Birkenmajer 1977). The Magura Nappe is divided on the basis of lithofacies into the Siary (northernmost), the Rača, the Bystrica, and the Krynica (southernmost) zones. Within these zones there is a general increase of coarse-grained deposits southwards (Birkenmajer & Oszczypko 1989). The Rača Zone is characterized by the common presence of fine-grained deposits.

The Soláň Formation, of Senonian through Palaeocene age, is developed as a thin-, or occasionally, medium-bedded flysch. Sandstone layers rarely exceed 10 cm in thickness, although sandstone layers more than 1 m thick do also occur. Dark-coloured, greenish-grey calcareous or non-calcareous silty claystones form the tops of turbidite cycles. Non-calcareous claystones (representing hemipelagic deposits), pelocarbonates and turbiditic limestones occur infrequently. The formation passes upwards into the Beloveža Formation (Bubík *et al.* 1999).

According to Bubík *et al.* (1999), the Soláň Formation was deposited in a deep-sea environment below the carbonate compensation depth (CCD). This is indicated by the lack of carbonates, and by the exclusively agglutinated foraminifera in the hemipelagites. The Soláň Formation is thought to have been deposited as distal turbidite sediments in a lower fan to abyssal plain setting.

Material

The studied section is about 16 m long and exposed as a continuous outcrop on the right (eastern) bank of an unnamed brook in the vicinity of the Slovak–Czech boundary-control point at Uzgruň (near the road between Velké Karlovice and Makov; Fig. 1). The strata dip steeply at an angle of 45–55° south. This section was designated as a potential Cretaceous–Tertiary boundary section by Bubík *et al.* (1999), who studied the foraminifera, radiolarians and calcareous nannoplankton from the Soláň Formation. The results of these studies did not precisely identify the position of the boundary. Slightly enriched iridium contents of between 0.06 and 0.09 ppb in three turbiditic samples (19E21, 19E23 and 19E25) were found during further studies. The enrichments were interpreted as representing reworking of the iridium anomaly layer associated with the K–T boundary (Bubík *et al.* 2002).

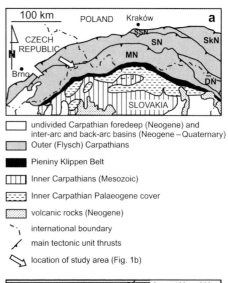

undivided Carpathian foredeep (Neogene) and inter-arc and back-arc basins (Neogene – Quaternary)

Outer (Flysch) Carpathians

Pieniny Klippen Belt

Inner Carpathians (Mesozoic)

Inner Carpathian Palaeogene cover

volcanic rocks (Neogene)

international boundary

main tectonic unit thrusts

location of study area (Fig. 1b)

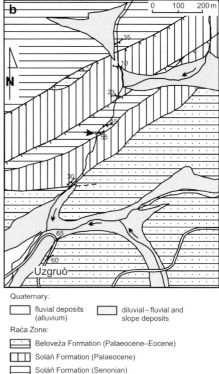

Quaternary:

fluvial deposits (alluvium)

diluvial – fluvial and slope deposits

Rača Zone:

Beloveža Formation (Palaeocene–Eocene)

Soláň Formation (Palaeocene)

Soláň Formation (Senonian)

tectonic thrust

30⟋ dip (in degrees) and strike of strata

roads

stream

studied section

Fig. 1. Location of the investigated section: (**a**) simplified tectonic map of the Western Carpathians (after Lexa *et al.* 2000); MN, Magura Nappe; SN, Silesian Nappe; SSN, Sub-Silesian Nappe; SkN, Skole Nappe; DN, Dukla Nappe; (**b**) geology of the Uzgruň area (after Bubík *et al.* 1999).

For the present study, 42 samples were taken from a 9-m thick interval of the section (Fig. 2). Samples were often taken at intervals as small as 1–2 cm in order to examine how lithological changes reflect changes in palynofacies and dinocyst assemblages. Fourteen samples were taken over 50-cm interval of the putative K–T boundary (Fig. 2). The fine-grained lithologies sampled were: pelocarbonates (19A1, 19C3), marly limestones (20C1, 20D1), calcareous turbidite claystones (19B1, 19C1, 19E), non-calcareous turbidite claystones (20B3, 20C2, 20E2, 19E1, 19E21, 19E23, 19E25, 19E27, 19E28, 19E4, 19F02, 19F06, 19F4, 19F6), non-calcareous hemipelagic claystones and clays (20B5, 20B6, 20C3, 20D3, 20E3, 19A, 19B2, 19C2, 19D1, 19D2, 19E2, 19E24, 19E26, 19E29, 19E3, 19E31, 19F01, 19F, 19F2, 19F5, 19F7).

Methods

Each sample, consisting of between 20 and 30 g of cleaned and crushed rock, was subjected to standard palynological procedures, including 38% hydrochloric acid (HCl) treatment, 40% hydrofluoric acid (HF) treatment, heavy-liquid ($ZnCl_2 + HCl$; density 2.0 g/cm^3) separation, ultrasound for 10–15 s and sieving at 15 μm on a nylon mesh. Two microscope slides were made from each sample, using glycerine jelly as a mounting medium.

Palynomorphs and phytoclasts were counted up to a total of 500 specimens, after which dinocysts continued to be counted until the entire slide had been enumerated (their frequency is shown in Fig. 3). The second slide was then scanned for additional dinocyst taxa. Dinocyst nomenclature follows Williams *et al.* (1998). The rock samples, palynological residues and slides are all stored in the collection of the Institute of Geological Sciences, Polish Academy of Sciences, Kraków.

Results

All samples from the Uzgruň section yielded rich palynological material consisting of terrestrial (land plant remains, including cuticles, opaque phytoclasts, pollen grains, spores, etc.) and marine elements. The latter are represented almost exclusively by dinocysts, comprising at least 116 taxa (Figs 3–5). An alphabetical species list of dinocyst taxa is provided in Appendix I. Rare foraminiferal organic linings are present. The ratio of terrestrial to marine elements varies distinctly between samples, reflecting their lithology. The palynofacies of samples taken from the turbidite layers is

dominated by terrestrial elements represented mainly by cuticles and sporomorphs. Opaque phytoclasts and dinocysts dominate samples from the hemipelagic deposits.

The dinocyst assemblages are also related to the lithology. Turbidite samples contain poorly preserved but abundant and taxonomically diverse dinocysts, with such taxa as *Spiniferites, Areoligera, Cerodinium* and the so-called 'round-browns' (possibly endocysts of *Trithyrodinium*) occurring frequently. Less-diverse but better-preserved dinocysts are found in the hemipelagic deposits. *Impagidinium*- and *Pterodinium*-rich assemblages with a few specimens of *Codoniella campanulata* occur here. In several hemipelagic samples (especially the pelocarbonates), an increase in frequency of an undetermined peridinioid dinocyst (Peridinioid sp. 1) is documented.

A few taxa occur frequently in almost all samples: *Spiniferites ramosus s.l.*, Peridinioid sp. 1, *Pterodinium cingulatum, Heterosphaeridium* sp. and *Areoligera medusettiformis*. Several other taxa, although present in the majority of samples, are infrequent: *Hystrichosphaeridium tubiferum, Cerodinium diebelii, Palaeotetradinium silicorum, Trithyrodinium* sp. and *Rottnestia* aff. *borussica*. Taxa that are frequent in some samples, but absent in others, are: *Manumiella seelandica, Senegalinium* sp. and *Spinidinium* sp. (Fig. 3). Most dinocyst taxa in the Uzgruň section are infrequent; they often occur as single specimens per sample, or may occur only once in the section.

Several dinocyst taxa from Uzgruň section are presumed to be recycled. These are taxa with known pre-Late Maastrichtian last appearances: e.g. *Chatangiella* spp., *Cannosphaeropsis utinensis* and *Coronifera oceanica* (e.g. Costa & Davey 1992). They occur in turbidites and hemipelagic sediments. No differences in state of preservation are observed among the forms treated as recycled and those believed to be *in situ*.

Position of the K–T boundary in the Uzgruň section

Dinocyst assemblages from the K–T boundary interval have been studied in many sections world-wide, both in low and high latitudes (e.g. Benson 1976; Hansen 1979; De Coninck & Smit 1982; Hultberg 1985; Firth 1987; Brinkhuis & Leereveld 1988; Brinkhuis & Zachariasse 1988; Kuhn & Kirsch 1992; Srivastava 1994; Elliot *et al.* 1994; Askin & Jacobson 1996; Nøhr-Hansen & Dam 1997). These studies permit a global evaluation of dinocyst distribution across the K–

P. GEDL

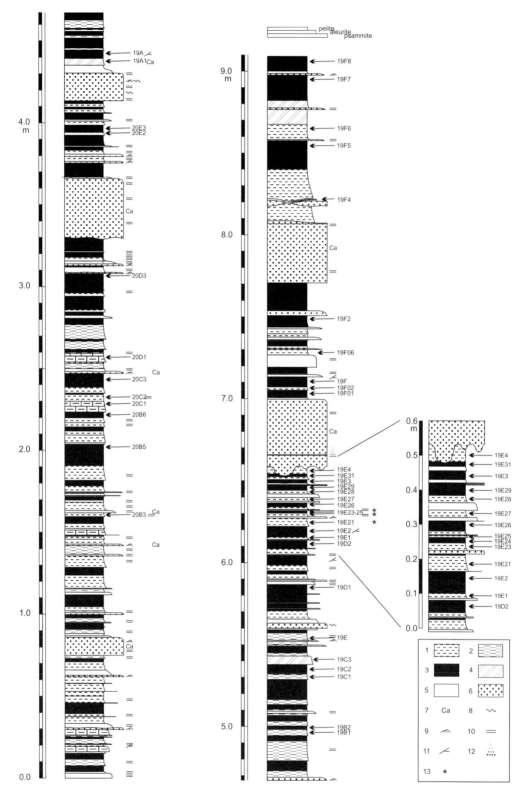

T boundary. No dinocyst mass extinction has been observed at the boundary (e.g. Brinkhuis & Zachariasse 1988). Rather, a species-diversity maximum in the Campanian–Maastrichtian is followed by an apparently gradual decline into the Early Palaeocene (Stover *et al.* 1996). Only a few global last appearance events have been recognized across the boundary. The dinocyst first appearance events at the boundary or in the Early Danian, although more numerous, are not comparable with the evolutionary radiation pattern of Early Palaeocene calcareous nanno-plankton.

The last appearances of *Dinogymnium* and related taxa (e.g. *Alisogymnium*) are dinocyst events associated with the K–T boundary. The last appearance of *Palynodinium grallator* was originally believed to coincide with this bound-ary (e.g. Powell 1992). Subsequent authors (e.g. Habib *et al.* 1996; Nøhr-Hansen & Dam 1997; Brinkhuis *et al.* 1998; Dam *et al.* 1998; Hern-green *et al.* 1998) have demonstrated that the last appearance of *Palynodinium grallator* is in the earliest Danian (basal part of the planktonic foraminiferal Zone P1a).

Membranilarnacia? tenella, Senoniasphaera inornata, Damassadinium californicum and *Car-patella cornuta* are among those dinocysts that appear for the first time in the Early Danian. It was previously believed that *S. inornata, D. californicum* and *C. cornuta* had an almost simultaneous first appearance at the K–T boundary (e.g. Hansen 1977). Later studies (e.g. Habib 1994; Habib *et al.* 1996; Brinkhuis *et al.* 1998) showed that only *S. inornata* first appears at this boundary. Both *D. californicum* and *C. cornuta* appear for the first time much later, in planktonic foraminiferal zones Pα or P1a. Brinkhuis & Schiøler (1996) suggested diachronous first appearances of these two taxa, the earliest being in low latitudes.

The basal part of the Uzgruň section, between samples 20B3 and 19D1, represents uppermost Maastrichtian, as indicated by the presence of *Disphaerogena carposphaeropsis* and *Palynodi-nium grallator* and the genera *Dinogymnium* and *Amphigymnium. Disphaerogena carposphaeropsis* is known to appear for the first time in the latest

Maastrichtian (e.g. Benson 1976; Brinkhuis & Zachariasse 1988; Moshkovitz & Habib 1993; Habib 1994; Nøhr-Hansen & Dam 1997). *Dinogymnium acuminatum* has its highest occur-rence in sample 19D1. Representatives of the genus *Dinogymnium* do not cross the K–T boundary (e.g. Stover *et al.* 1996), although some authors have recorded scattered specimens in lowermost Danian deposits (e.g. Brinkhuis & Zachariasse 1988). *Amphigymnium* sp. was found in two samples below 19D1 (Fig. 3); a single specimen of this genus in sample 19F is presumably recycled.

Carpatella cornuta, the first typical Danian species found in the studied material, has its lowest occurrence in sample 19E4 (Fig. 6). This sample is therefore regarded as the lowest documented Danian sample. However, the low-est global occurrence of *C. cornuta* is slightly above the K–T boundary (Brinkhuis *et al.* 1998). Therefore, the interval between sample 19E4 and 19F6 might be correlated with Lower Danian planktonic foraminiferal zone Pα or with the bottom part of P1a, since *Palynodinium grallator* has its highest occurrence in sample 19F6. Single specimens of *Adnatosphaeridium buccinum* were found in samples 19E23 and 19E25. This species was believed to be restricted to the Cretaceous, but is now known to also occur in the Lower Danian (e.g. Herngreen *et al.* 1998).

The precise position of the K–T boundary in the Uzgruň section, as based on dinocysts, remains uncertain within the 19D1–19E4 inter-val (Fig. 6). Geochemical data suggest its position coincides with sample 19E21 where the lowest slightly enriched iridium content was identified. Thus, the K–T boundary would be placed *c.* 35 cm below the lowest occurrence of *Carpatella cornuta*, and *c.* 38 cm above the highest occurrence of *Dinogymnium acuminatum* (Fig. 6).

Interpretation of palaeoenvironmental changes across the K–T boundary at Uzgruň

The Uzgruň section represents flysch sedimenta-tion consisting of turbiditic rhythms of relatively coarse-grained clastic material at the base, and fining upwards. A thin layer of hemipelagic/pelagic clay usually occurs at the top of each rhythm. Turbiditic material typically originates from the more proximal parts of a flysch basin, e.g. from outer shelf and slope environments, whereas hemipelagic deposits represent mainly autochthonous background sedimentation. Dinocyst assemblages reflect these different provenances (Fig. 7). Oceanic dinocysts (*Impa-*

Fig. 2. Lithological column of the Uzgruň section (after Bubík, unpubl.): 1, non-calcareous turbidite claystones; 2, calcareous turbidite claystones; 3, non-calcareous hemipelagic claystones and clays; 4, pelo-carbonates; 5, turbidite siltstones; 6, sandstones; 7, calcareous; 8, convoluted lamination; 9, ripples; 10, parallel lamination; 11, *Chondrites* sp.; 12, graded bedding; 13, iridium anomaly.

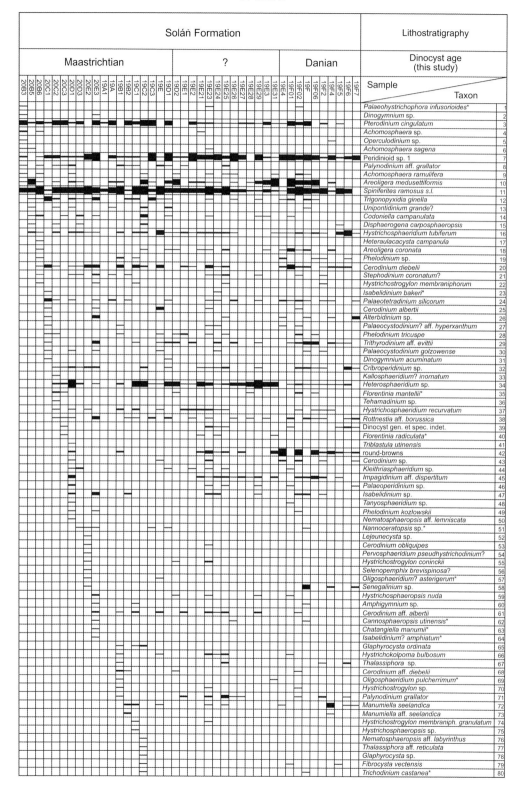

gidinium and *Pterodinium*) show the highest frequencies in hemipelagic samples. They are absent or rare in most of the turbidites. These genera occur across the K–T boundary and do not show any major peaks. An indistinct tendency towards a gradual up-section decrease in the *Impagidinium–Pterodinium* group can be detected (Fig. 7), and may be taken to indicate sea-level fall. This trend is more pronounced if *Codoniella campanulata* is included in the oceanic group (this species occurs in the studied material almost exclusively in hemipelagic samples). It constitutes up to 3–5% of the dinocyst assemblage in the lower part of the section, becoming almost absent upwards. The same tendency is clearly visible if the dinocyst distribution only in hemipelagic samples is taken into account (Fig. 8b). A general decline in the number of representatives of *Spiniferites* and *Achomosphaera*, which likewise might be related to sea-level fall, is also recognizable in turbiditic (Fig. 8a) and hemipelagic samples (Fig. 8b).

Representatives of *Areoligera* (mainly *A. medusettiformis*), a genus often associated with inshore environments (e.g. Brinkhuis 1994), show the highest frequencies in hemipelagic samples just below and above the lowest occurrence of *Carpatella cornuta* (Fig. 7 & Fig. 8b). This might indicate less-open oceanic conditions in the earliest Danian possibly related to a long-term sea-level fall from the latest Maastrichtian into the earliest Danian.

The up-section decrease in oceanic species (which are associated with oligotrophic waters) (Dale 1996) may also imply changes in surface waters related to a gradual increase in nutrient availability. The negative correlation of the oceanic *Impagidinium–Pterodinium* group curve with that of Peridinioid sp. 1 is particularly evident (Fig. 8b). Peridinioid sp. 1 (an undetermined species possibly related to *Senegalinium* or *Alterbidinium*) is the most frequent representative of the peridinialeans, whose mass occurrence in oceanic waters suggests a distinct increase in

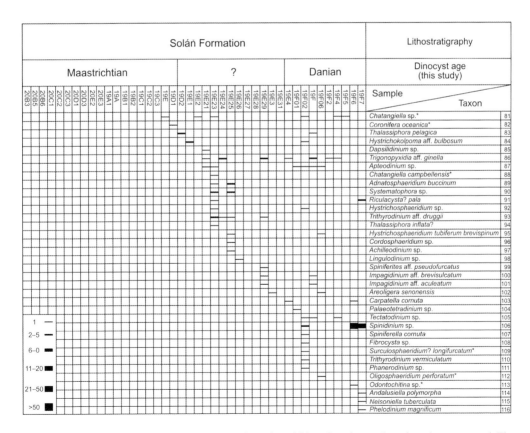

Fig. 3. Distribution of dinocysts in the Uzgruň section. Line widths reflect the number of specimens counted. The inferred age is based on dinocysts (this study, Fig. 6). Taxa considered to be recycled are identified with an asterisk (*).

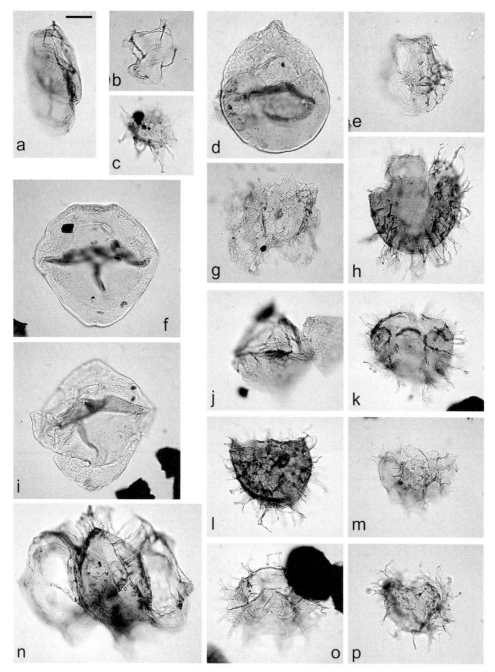

Fig. 4. Selected dinocysts from the Uzgruň section. The scale bar in (**a**) represents 15 μm and refers to all other photomicrographs. Slide code and England Finder references are given. (**a**) *Hystrichosphaeropsis nuda*, Uzgr20E3, H27/3–4; (**b**) *Adnatosphaeridium buccinum* – operculum, Uzgr19E23a, H50/1; (**c**) *Hystrichokolpoma bulbosum*, Uzgr19E23a, U37/3; (**d**) *Nelsoniella tuberculata*, Uzgr19F7, D48; (**e**) *Hystrichostrogylon coninckii*, Uzgr20E2, R39/1–2; (**f & i**) *Manumiella seelandica*, Uzgr19F4, H45/2; Uzgr19C1, L51/4; (**g**) *Riculacysta*? *pala*, Uzgr19E23a, V49/2; (**h**) *Areoligera medusettiformis*, Uzgr20B5, T36; (**j**) *Carpatella cornuta*, Uzgr19E4, O50/1–3; (**k**) *Areoligera coronata*, Uzgr19D1, T36; (**l**) *Heterosphaeridium* sp., Uzgr20C3, H38/1; (**m & p**) *Palynodinium* aff. *grallator*, Uzgr19E1, M33; Uzgr19B2, H32/3; (**n**) *Disphaerogena carposphaeropsis*, Uzgr20B5, U46/3–4; (**o**) *Palynodinium grallator*, Uzgr19E1, H32/1.

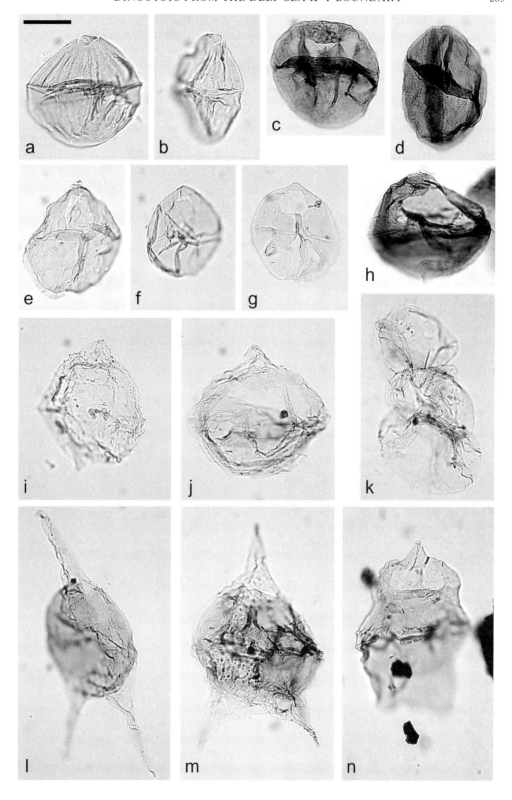

nutrient availability (e.g. Biffi & Grignani 1983). A frequency peak of the *Impagidinium–Pterodinium* group in sample 19B2 is followed by a gradual decline, starting with sample 19C2. In the same sample, Peridinioid sp. 1 is present as single specimen only. It begins to dominate in the superjacent sample 19C3 (almost 50% of dinocyst assemblage), becoming the most frequent species in hemipelagic samples up to 19E29 (Fig. 8b). The Peridinioid sp. 1 acme is the most pronounced event in the dinocyst record close to the K–T boundary in the Uzgruň section. Upwelling seems to be the most plausible explanation of this phenomenon, since there is no increase in peridinioids within adjacent turbiditic samples, and the palynofacies of the hemipelagic samples shows no increase in terrigenous palynomorphs that would be expected if river influx was responsible for the introduction of nutrients. Was the postulated upwelling related to the K–T event? Probably not, since the Peridinioid sp. 1 acme begins in sample 19C3, i.e. *c.* 45 cm below the highest occurrence of *Dinogymnium acuminatum* and *c.* 85 cm below the lowest iridium anomaly.

Among the other dinocyst events recorded in the Uzgruň section, none seems to be associated with the K–T event. Two acmes of *Manumiella seelandica*, a species commonly found around the boundary (e.g. Askin & Jacobson 1996), occur below and above the K–T boundary interval (Figs 7 & 8). A distinct frequency peak of *Heterosphaeridium* occurs below the lowest occurrence of *Carpatella cornuta* but above the iridium anomalies (Figs 7 & 8b). The significance of this acme is unknown because of the lack of palaeoenvironmental information on *Heterosphaeridium*.

No distinct signs of climatic change across the K–T boundary in the Uzgruň section were recognized. *Cerodinium* spp. and *Trithyrodinium* spp. (including the 'round-browns', probably endocysts of *Trithyrodinium* sp.) occur throughout the section, without marked fluctuations. The genus *Cerodinium* belongs to the tropical to subtropical McIntyre suite, and *Trithyrodinium evittii* was included in the warm temperate Williams suite by Lentin & Williams (1980). *Trithyrodinium* spp. were also found in the Upper Cretaceous strata of Morocco (Rauscher & Doubinger 1982), and Colombia and Venezuela (Yepes 2001). The constant presence of these tropical taxa in the Uzgruň section indicates rather stable and warm surface waters in the Magura Basin, consistent with the warm temperate or subtropical climate that prevailed here during the latest Maastrichtian and earliest Danian.

Comparison

Some dinocyst events recorded in the present study show similarity with those from other localities, and presumably reflect comparable palaeoenvironmental events associated with the K–T boundary.

An acme of Peridinioid sp. 1 in the Uzgruň section, interpreted as a result of upwelling, possibly correlates with peaks of *Senegalinium* species in other K–T sections. Peaks of *Senegalinium* found in West Greenland were interpreted by Nøhr-Hansen & Dam (1997) as a reflection of increased nutrient availability caused by upwelling linked to a transgressive phase. Similar peaks of *Senegalinium* specimens, although variously positioned in relation to the K–T boundary, were found in California (Drugg 1967), Tunisia (Brinkhuis & Zachariasse 1988) and Seymour Island, Antarctica (Elliot *et al.* 1994; Askin & Jacobson 1996).

Acmes of *Manumiella seelandica* in the uppermost Maastrichtian strata in the Uzgruň section are known elsewhere from several sections (e.g. Hultberg 1986; Firth 1987; Askin & Jacobson 1996; Smit & Brinkhuis 1996; Nøhr-Hansen & Dam 1997). This species has two abundance peaks at Uzgruň (Fig. 7). The almost monospecific *Manumiella seelandica* assemblages were interpreted by Hultberg (1986) as result of low-salinity or even brackish environments.

The abundance of *Areoligera* specimens in samples from the upper part of the section (Figs 3 & 7) resembles a similar event described by Hultberg (1985) from Scandinavia. Kuhn & Kirsch (1992) found representatives of *Areoligera* to dominate assemblages from the K–T boundary section in Austria.

Another characteristic dinocyst event is an acme of *Spinidinium* recognized above the K–T

Fig. 5. Selected dinocysts from the Uzgruň section. Scale bar in (**a**) represents 25 μm and refers to all other photomicrographs. Slide code and England Finder references are given. (**a**) *Amphigymnium* sp., Uzgr20E3, K48/2; (**b**) *Dinogymnium acuminatum*, Uzgr20C1, N48/2–4; (**c, d & h**) 'round-browns', possibly endocysts of *Trithyrodinium* sp., Uzgr19F2, E48; Uzgr19E23a, L36/1; Uzgr19F02a, P34/2; (**e–g**) Peridinioid sp. 1, Uzgr19E29, M29/3–4, cavate specimen; Uzgr19E26a, H36/3, endocyst; Uzgr19E29, F41/2–4, endocyst; (**i**) *Spinidinium* sp., Uzgr19F6, F51/1–2; (**j**) *Trithyrodinium* aff. *evittii*, Uzgr19Fc, O42/3–4; (**k**) *Codoniella campanulata*, Uzgr20B6, G37; (**l**) *Cerodinium diebelii*, Uzgr19B1, G30/2; (**m**) *Cerodinium albertii*, Uzgr19E23a, O51/2; (**n**) *Chatangiella campbellensis*, Uzgr19E23a, D49/2.

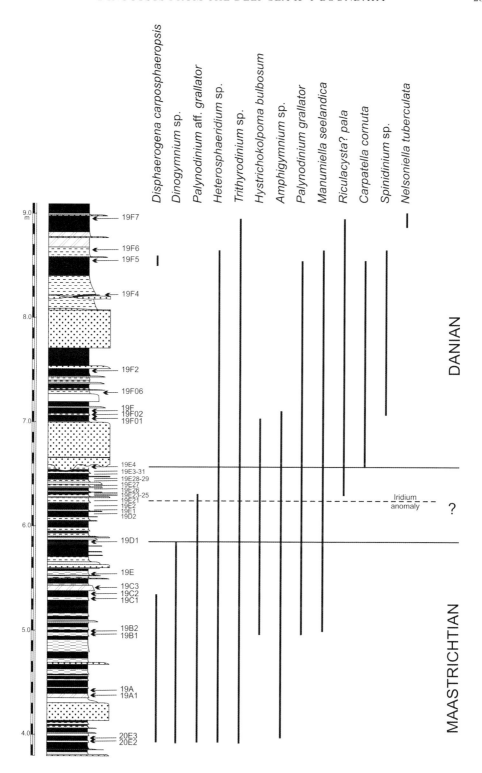

Fig. 6. Ranges of selected dinocysts in the Uzgruň section and the inferred age based on dinocysts.

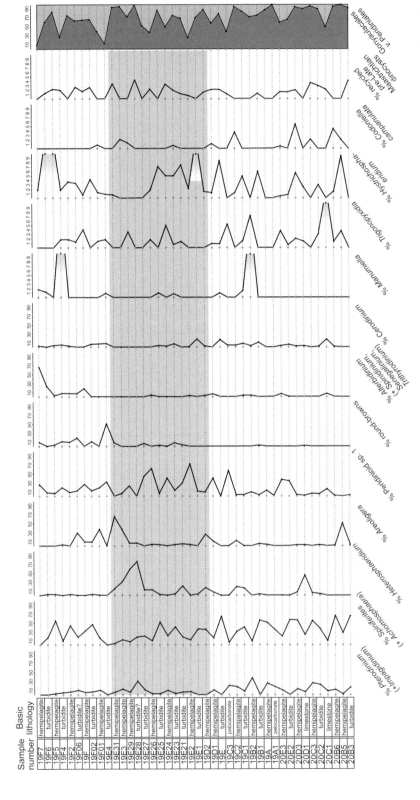

Fig. 7. Distribution of selected dinocyst groups and the ratio of Gonyaulacales v. Peridiniales in the Uzgruň section. The shaded area refers to the K–T boundary interval as inferred from dinocysts.

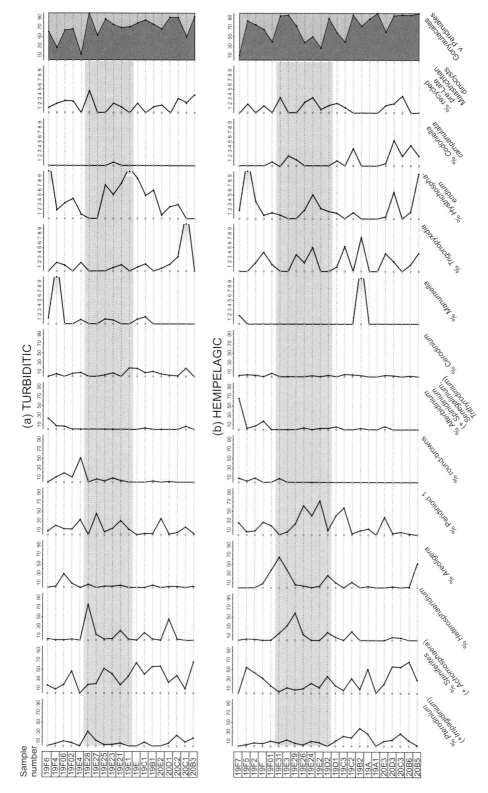

Fig. 8. Distribution of selected dinocyst groups and the ratio of Gonyaulacales v. Peridiniales in the Uzgruň section in (**a**) turbiditic and (**b**) hemipelagic samples. The shaded area refers to the K–T boundary interval, as inferred from dinocysts.

boundary at Uzgruň. The frequent occurrence of this genus, often in almost monospecific assemblages, was noted for the Danian of Seymour Island, West Antarctica by Askin (1988a, b). The first appearance of *Spinidinium densispinatum* in the Early Danian is mentioned by Brinkhuis & Zachariasse (1988) as being among the most important dinocyst events in the earliest Danian world-wide.

The continuous presence of *Trithyrodinium* spp. in uppermost Maastrichtian and lowermost Danian deposits at Uzgruň (no complete *Trithyrodinium evittii* was found in the Uzgruň section, but the 'round-browns' resemble the endocyst of *T. evittii*, and the species determined as *Trithyrodinium* aff. *evittii* differs from *T. evittii* only by its thinner endocyst wall) recalls the occurrence of this genus in other K–T sections. Nøhr-Hansen & Dam (1997) found acmes of *Trithyrodinium fragile* (later treated as a junior synonym of *T. evittii*, a Tethyan species, according to Nøhr-Hansen & Dam 1999) in lowermost Danian deposits of West Greenland. A short-term occurrence of *Trithyrodinium evittii* above the K–T boundary was also documented from Antarctica by Askin (1988a). This species was also found in a similar stratigraphic position in the USA (Drugg 1967; Firth 1987) and New Zealand (Strong *et al.* 1995).

Conclusions

These are as follows:

(1) The dinocyst record of the deep-sea Uzgruň succession, Moravian Carpathians, allows identification of the K–T boundary within a 73-cm interval in which an iridium anomaly has been found. The highest occurrence of the Maastrichtian species *Dinogymnium acuminatum* is 38 cm below the iridium anomaly, whereas the lowest occurrence of the Danian *Carpatella cornuta* is 35 cm above it. Between these two datums, there are no dinocyst events of biostratigraphic significance.

(2) The quantitative and qualitative changes in dinocyst assemblages at Uzgruň reflect lithologies in the section. Turbiditic samples have increased frequencies of often poorly preserved nearshore dinocysts (e.g. *Cerodinium* species), whereas hemipelagic samples contain frequent oceanic species (*Impagidinium–Pterodinium* group and *Codoniella campanulata*).

(3) No significant changes in the dinocyst assemblages were observed around the K–T boundary in the studied section. How-

ever, a gradual sea-level fall and/or increased nutrient supply were presumably responsible for a gradual up-section decrease in the frequency of oceanic taxa.

(4) The acme of Peridinioid sp. 1 near to the K–T boundary interval presumably signifies increased nutrient supply, and implies upwelling in the Magura Basin at this time.

(5) The continuous presence of *Cerodinium* spp. and *Trithyrodinium* spp. throughout the section suggests that surface waters were warm and stable across the boundary.

(6) Dinocyst events, such as the *Areoligera* sp. acme, *Manumiella seelandica* acme and the *Spinidinium* sp. acme, known from other K–T boundary sections around the world, were recognized within the studied material.

I would like to thank M. Bubík (Czech Geological Survey, Brno) for encouraging me to undertake this study, and for assistance with sample collecting and manuscript preparation. K. Birkenmajer (Institute of Geological Sciences, Polish Academy of Sciences, Kraków) kindly read the manuscript and suggested improvements. Critical remarks and linguistic correction by M. J. Head, G. L. Williams and H. Brinkhuis, significantly improved the manuscript. This study is part of a multidisciplinary project embracing the Palaeocene boundaries in the Magura/Nappe, led by M. Bubík (Grant Agency of the Czech Republic project no. 205/00/218: 'Paleocene boundary events in the Magura Flysch in Moravia').

Appendix

An alphabetical listing of dinocyst taxa found in the Uzgruň section is provided below. Full taxonomic citations are given in Williams *et al.* (1998). Taxa considered to be recycled are identified with an asterisk (*). Numbers in parentheses refer to Figure 3, followed by reference to the appropriate photomicrographs in Figures 4 and 5.

Achilleodinium sp. (97)
Achomosphaera ramulifera (9)
Achomosphaera sagena (6)
Achomosphaera sp. (4)
Adnatosphaeridium buccinum (89; Fig. 4b)
Alterbidinium sp. (26)
Amphigymnium sp. (60; Fig. 5a)
Andalusiella polymorpha (114)
Apteodinium sp. (87)
Areoligera coronata (18; Fig. 4k)
Areoligera medusettiformis (102)
*Cannosphaeropsis utinensis** (62)
Carpatella cornuta (103; Fig. 4j)
Cerodinium albertii (25; Fig. 5m)
Cerodinium aff. *albertii* (61)
Cerodinium diebelii (20; Fig. 5f)
Cerodinium aff. *diebelii* (68)

Cerodinium obliquipes (53)
Cerodinium sp. (43)
*Chatangiella campbellensis** (88; Fig. 5n)
*Chatangiella manumii** (63)
Chatangiella sp.* (81)
Codoniella campanulata (14; Fig. 5k)
Cordosphaeridium sp. (96)
*Coronifera oceanica** (82)
Cribroperidinium sp. (32)
Dapsilidinium sp. (85)
Dinocyst gen. *et* spec. indet. (39)
Dinogymnium acuminatum (31; Fig. 5k)
Dinogymnium sp. (2)
Disphaerogena carposphaeropsis (15; Fig. 4n)
Fibrocysta vectensis (79)
Fibrocysta sp. (108)
*Florentinia mantellii** (35)
*Florentinia radiculata** (40)
Glaphyrocysta ordinata (65)
Glaphyrocysta sp. (78)
Heteraulacacysta campanula (17)
Heterosphaeridium sp. (34; Fig. 4f)
Hystrichokolpoma bulbosum (66; Fig. 4c)
Hystrichokolpoma aff. *bulbosum* (84)
Hystrichosphaeridium recurvatum (37)
Hystrichosphaeridium tubiferum (16)
Hystrichosphaeridium tubiferum subsp. *brevispinum* (95)
Hystrichosphaeridium sp. (92)
Hystrichosphaeropsis nuda (59)
Hystrichosphaeropsis sp. (75)
Hystrichostrogylon coninckii (55; Fig. 4)
Hystrichostrogylon membraniphorum (22)
Hystrichostrogylon membraniphorum subsp. *granulatum* (74)
Hystrichostrogylon sp. (70)
Impagidinium aff. *aculeatum* (101)
Impagidinium aff. *brevisulcatum* (100)
Impagidinium aff. *dispertitum* (45)
Isabelidinium? *amphiatum** (64)
*Isabelidinium bakeri** (23)
Isabelidinium sp. (47)
Kallosphaeridium? *inornatum* (33)
Kleithriasphaeridium sp. (44)
Lejeunecysta sp. (52)
Lingulodinium sp. (98)
Manumiella seelandica (72; Fig. 4f, i)
Manumiella aff. *seelandica* (73)
Nannoceratopsis sp.* (51)
Nelsoniella tuberculata (115; Fig. 4d)
Nematosphaeropsis aff. *labyrinthus* (76)
Nematosphaeropsis aff. *lemniscata* (50)
Odontochitina sp.* (113)
Oligosphaeridium? *asterigerum** (57)
*Oligosphaeridium perforatum** (112)
*Oligosphaeridium pulcherrimum** (69)
Operculodinium sp. (5)
Palaeocystodinium golzowense (30)
Palaeocystodinium? aff. *hyperxanthum* (27)
*Palaeohystrichophora infusorioides** (1)
Palaeoperidinium sp. (46)
Palaeotetradinium silicorum (24)
Palaeotetradinium sp. (104)
Palynodinium grallator (71; Fig. 4o)

Palynodinium aff. *grallator* (8; Fig. 4m & p)
Peridinioid sp. 1 (7; Fig. 5e–g)
Pervosphaeridium pseudhystrichodinium? (54)
Phanerodinium sp. (111)
Phelodinium kozlowskii (49)
Phelodinium magnificum (116)
Phelodinium tricuspe (28)
Phelodinium sp. (19)
Pterodinium cingulatum (3)
Riculacysta? *pala* (91; Fig. 4g)
Rottnestia aff. *borussica* (42; Fig. 5c, d & h)
Selenopemphix brevispinosa? (56)
Senegalinium sp. (58)
Spinidinium sp. (106)
Spiniferella cornuta (107)
Spiniferites aff. *pseudofurcatus* (99)
Spiniferites ramosus s.l. (11)
Stephodinium coronatum? (21)
Surculosphaeridium? *longifurcatum** (109)
Systematophora sp. (90)
Tanyosphaeridium sp. (48)
Tectatodinium sp. (105)
Tehamadinium sp. (36)
Thalassiphora inflata? (94)
Thalassiphora pelagica (83)
Thalassiphora aff. *reticulata* (77)
Thalassiphora sp. (67)
Triblastula utinensis (41)
*Trichodinium castanea** (80)
Trigonopyxidia ginella (12)
Trigonopyxidia aff. *ginella* (86)
Trithyrodinium aff. *druggii* (93)
Trithyrodinium aff. *evittii* (29; Fig. 5j)
Trithyrodinium vermiculatum (110)
Unipontidinium grande? (13)

References

ALVAREZ, L. W., ALVAREZ, W., ASARO, F. & MICHEL, H. 1980. Extraterrestrial cause for the Cretaceous–Tertiary extinction. *Science*, **208**, 1095–1108.

ASKIN, R. A. 1988*a*. Campanian to Paleocene palynological succession of Seymour and adjacent islands, northeastern Antarctic Peninsula. *Geological Society of America, Memoir*, **169**, 131–153.

ASKIN, R. A. 1988*b*. The palynological record across the Cretaceous/Tertiary transition on Seymour Island, Antarctica. *Geological Society of America, Memoirs*, **169**, 155–162.

ASKIN, R. A. & JACOBSON, S. R. 1996. Palynological change across the Cretaceous–Tertiary boundary on Seymour Island, Antarctica: environmental and depositional factors. *In*: MACLEOD, N. & KELLER, G. (eds) *Cretaceous–Tertiary Mass Extinctions: Biotic and Environmental changes*. W. W. Norton, New York, pp. 7–25.

BENSON, D. G. 1976. Dinoflagellate taxonomy and biostratigraphy at the Cretaceous–Tertiary boundary, Round Bay, Maryland. *Tulane Studies in Geology and Paleontology*, **12**, 169–233.

BIFFI, U. & Grignani, D. 1983. Peridinioid dinoflagellate cysts from the Oligocene of the Niger Delta, Nigeria. *Micropaleontology*, **29**, 126–145.

BIRKENMAJER, K. 1977. Jurassic and Cretaceous lithostratigraphic units of the Pieniny Klippen Belt, Carpathians, Poland. *Studia Geologica Polonica*, **45**, 3–159.

BIRKENMAJER, K. & OSZCZYPKO, N. 1989. Cretaceous and Palaeogene lithostratigraphic units of the Magura Nappe, Krynica Subunit, Carpathians. *Annales Societatis Geologorum Poloniae*, **59**, 145–181.

BRINKHUIS, H. 1994. Late Eocene to Early Oligocene dinoflagellate cysts from the Priabonian type-area (Northeast Italy): biostratigraphy and paleoenvironmental interpretation. *Palaeogeography, Palaeoclimatology, Palaeoecology*, **107**, 121–163.

BRINKHUIS, H. & LEEREVELD, H. 1988. Dinoflagellate cysts from the Cretaceous/Tertiary boundary sequence of El Kef, northwest Tunisia. *Review of Palaeobotany and Palynology*, **56**, 5–19.

BRINKHUIS, H. & SCHIØLER, P. 1996. Palynology of the Geulhemmerberg Cretaceous/Tertiary boundary section (Limburg, SE Netherlands). *Geologie en Mijnbouw*, **75**, 193–213.

BRINKHUIS, H. & ZACHARIASSE, W. J. 1988. Dinoflagellate cysts, sea level changes and planktonic foraminifers across the K/T boundary at El Haria, Northwest Tunisia. *Marine Micropaleontology*, **13**, 153–191.

BRINKHUIS, H., BUJAK, J. P., SMIT, J., VERSTEEGH, G. J. M. & VISSCHER, H. 1998. Dinoflagellate-based sea surface temperature reconstructions across the Cretaceous–Tertiary boundary. *Palaeogeography, Palaeoclimatology, Palaeoecology*, **141**, 67–84.

BUBÍK, M., ADAMOVÁ, M. *ET AL.* 2002. Results of the investigations at the Cretaceous/Tertiary boundary in the Magura Flysch near Uzgruň. *Geologické výzkumy na Moravě a ve Slezsku v roce 2001*, **8**, 42–52.

BUBÍK, M., BĄK, M. & ŠVÁBENICKÁ, L. 1999. Biostratigraphy of the Maastrichtian to Paleocene distal flysch sediments of the Rača Unit in the Uzgruň section (Magura group of nappes, Czech Republic). *Geologica Carpathica*, **50**, 33–48.

COSTA, L. I. & DAVEY, R. J. 1992. Dinoflagellate cysts of the Cretaceous System. *In*: POWELL, A. J. (ed.) *A Stratigraphic Index of Dinoflagellate Cysts*. British Micropalaeontological Society Publication Series. Chapman & Hall, London, pp. 99–154.

DALE, B. 1996. Dinoflagellate cyst ecology: modelling and geological applications. *In*: JANSONIUS, J. & MCGREGOR, D. C. (eds) *Palynology: Principles and Applications*, Vol. 3. American Association of Stratigraphic Palynologists Foundation, Dallas, Texas, pp. 1249–1275.

DAM, G., NØHR-HANSEN, H. & KENNEDY, W. J. 1998. The northernmost marine Cretaceous–Tertiary boundary section: Nuussuaq, West Greenland. *Geology of Greenland Survey Bulletin*, **180**, 138–144.

DE CONINCK, J. & SMIT, J. 1982. Marine organic-walled microfossils at the Cretaceous–Tertiary boundary in the Barranco del Gredero (S.E. Spain). *Geologie en Mijnbouw*, **61**, 173–178.

DRUGG, W. S. 1967. Palynology of the Upper Moreno Formation (Late Cretaceous–Paleocene) Escarpado Canyon, California. *Palaeontographica*, **B120**, 1–71.

ELLIOT, D. H., ASKIN, R. A., KYTE, F. T. & ZINSMEISTER, W. J. 1994. Iridium and dinocysts at the Cretaceous–Tertiary boundary on Seymour Island, Antarctica: implication for the K–T event. *Geology*, **22**, 675–678.

FIRTH, J. V. 1987. Dinoflagellate biostratigraphy of the Maastrichtian to Danian interval in the U.S. Geological Survey Albany Core, Georgia, USA. *Palynology*, **11**, 199–216.

HABIB, D. 1994. Biostratigraphic evidence of the KT boundary in the eastern Gulf coastal plain north of the Chicxulub Crater. *Lunar and Planetary Institute Contributions*, **825**, 45–46.

HABIB, D., MOSHKOVITZ, S. & KRAMER, C. 1992. Dinoflagellate and calcareous nannofossil response to sea-level changes in Cretaceous–Tertiary boundary sections. *Geology*, **20**, 165–168.

HABIB, D., OLSSON, R. K., LIU, C. & MOSHKOVITZ, S. 1996. High-resolution biostratigraphy of sea-level low, biotic extinction, and chaotic sedimentation at the Cretaceous–Tertiary boundary in Alabama, north of the Chicxulub crater. *In*: RYDER, G., FASTOVSKY, D. & GARTNER, S. (eds). *The Cretaceous–Tertiary Event and Other Catastrophes in Earth History*. Geological Society of America, Special Papers, **307**, 243–252.

HANSEN, H. J. 1990. Diachronous extinctions at the K/T boundary; a scenario. *Geological Society of America, Special Papers*, **247**, 417–423.

HANSEN, J. M. 1977. Dinoflagellate stratigraphy and echinoid distribution in Upper Maastrichtian and Danian deposits from Denmark. *Geological Society of Denmark, Bulletin*, **26**, 1–26.

HANSEN, J. M., 1979. Dinoflagellate zonation around the boundary. *In*: BIRKELUND, T. & BROMLEY, R. G. (eds) *Cretaceous–Tertiary Boundary Events Symposium: I. The Maastrichtian and Danian of Denmark*. University of Copenhagen, pp. 136–141.

HERNGREEN, G. F. W., SCHUURMAN, H. A. H. M., VERBEEK, J. W., BRINKHUIS, H., BURNETT, J. A., FELDER, W. M. & KEDVES, M. 1998. Biostratigraphy of Cretaceous/Tertiary boundary strata in the Curfs quarry, the Netherlands. *Mededelingen, Nederlands Instituut voor Toegepaste Geowetenschappen TNO*, **61**, 3–57.

HULTBERG, S. 1985. *Dinoflagellate studies of the Upper Maastrichtian and Danian in southern Scandinavia*. Ph.D. thesis, Department of Geology, University of Stockholm, Stockholm, pp. 1–189.

HULTBERG, S. U. 1986. Danian dinoflagellate zonation, the C–T boundary and the stratigraphical position of the fish clay in southern Scandinavia. *Journal of Micropalaeontology*, **5**, 37–47.

KELLER, G. & LINDINGER, M. 1989. Stable isotope, TOC and CaCO$_3$ record across the Cretaceous/Tertiary boundary at El Kef, Tunisia. *Palaeogeography, Palaeoclimatology, Palaeoecology*, **73**, 243–265.

KELLER, G., BARRERA, E., SCHMITZ, B. & MATTSON, E. 1993. Gradual mass extinction, species survivorship, and long-term environmental changes across the Cretaceous–Tertiary boundary in high latitudes. *Geological Society of America, Bulletin*, **105**, 979–997.

KUHN, W. & KIRSCH, K.-H. 1992. Ein Kreide/Tertiär-Grenzprofil aus dem Helvetikum nördlich von Salzburg (Österreich). *Mitteilungen der Bayerischen Staatssamlung für Paläontologie und historische Geologie*, **32**, 23–35.

LENTIN, J. K. & WILLIAMS, G. L. 1980. Dinoflagellate provincialism with emphasis on Campanian peridiniaceans. *American Association of Stratigraphic Palynologists, Contributions Series*, **7**, 1–47.

LEXA, J., BEZÁK, V., ELECKO, M., MELLO, M., POLÁK, M., POTFAJ, M. & VOZÁR, J. 2000. *Geological Map of Western Carpathians and Adjacent Areas*. Ministry of the Environment of Slovak Republic, Geological Survey of Slovak Republic, Bratislava.

MCLEAN, D. M. 1985. Deccan Traps mantle degassing in the terminal Cretaceous marine extinctions. *Cretaceous Research*, **6**, 235–259.

MACLEOD, N. 1996. Stratigraphical completeness and planktonic foraminiferal survivorship across the Cretaceous–Tertiary (K/T) boundary. *In*: MOGUILEVSKY, A. & WHATLEY, R. (eds) *Microfossils and Oceanic Environments*. University of Wales, Aberystwyth, pp. 327–353.

MACLEOD, N., RAWSON, P. F. ET AL. 1997. The Cretaceous–Tertiary biotic transition. *Journal of the Geological Society, London*, **154**, 265–292.

MOSHKOVITZ, S. & HABIB, D. 1993. Calcareous nannofossil and dinoflagellate stratigraphy of the Cretaceous–Tertiary boundary, Alabama and Georgia. *Micropaleontology*, **39**, 167–191.

NØHR-HANSEN, H. & DAM, G. 1997. Palynology and sedimentology across a new marine Cretaceous–Tertiary boundary section on Nuussuaq, West Greenland. *Geology*, **25**, 851–854.

NØHR-HANSEN, H. & DAM, G. 1999. *Trithyrodinium evittii* Drugg 1967 and *T. fragile* Davey 1969: an artificial split of one dinoflagellate cyst species – stratigraphic and palaeoenvironmental importance. *Grana*, **38**, 125–133.

PERCH-NIELSEN, K., MCKENZIE, J. & HE, Q. 1982. Biostratigraphy and isotope stratigraphy and the catastrophic extinction of calcareous nannoplankton at the Cretaceous/Tertiary boundary. *Geological Society of America, Special Papers*, **190**, 353–371.

POWELL, A. J. 1992. Dinoflagellate cysts of the Tertiary System. *In*: POWELL, A. J. (ed.) *A Stratigraphic Index of Dinoflagellate Cysts*. British Micropalaeontological Society Publication Series. Chapman & Hall, London, pp. 155–249.

RAUP, D. M. & SEPKOSKI, J. J., Jr 1984. Periodicity of extinctions in the geological past. *Natural Academy of Sciences, Proceedings*, **81**, 801–805.

RAUP, D. M. & SEPKOSKI, J. J., Jr 1986. Periodic extinction of families and genera. *Science*, **231**, 833–836.

RAUSCHER, R. & DOUBINGER, J. 1982. Les dinokystes du Maestrichtien Phosphaté au Maroc. *Sciences Géologiques*, **35**, 97–116.

ROMEIN, A. J. T. & SMIT, J. 1981. The Cretaceous/Tertiary boundary: calcareous nannofossils and stable isotopes. *Paleontology, Proceedings*, **B84**, 295–314.

SMIT, J. & BRINKHUIS, H. 1996. The Geulhemmerberg Cretaceous/Tertiary boundary section (Maastrichtian type area, SE Netherlands); summary of results and a scenario of events. *Geologie en Mijnbouw*, **75**, 283–293.

SRIVASTAVA, S. K. 1994. Palynology of the Cretaceous–Tertiary boundary in the Scollard Formation of Alberta, Canada, and global KTB events. *Review of Palaeobotany and Palynology*, **83**, 137–158.

STOVER, L. E., BRINKHUIS, H. ET AL. 1996. Mesozoic–Tertiary dinoflagellates, acritarchs and prasinophytes. *In*: JANSONIUS, J. & MCGREGOR, D. C. (eds) *Palynology: Principles and Applications*, **2**. American Association of Stratigraphic Palynologists Foundation, Dallas, Texas, pp. 641–750.

STRONG, C. P., HOLLIS, C. J. & WILSON, G. J. 1995. Foraminiferal, radiolarian, and dinoflagellate biostratigraphy of Late Cretaceous to middle Eocene pelagic sediments (Muzzle Group), Mead Stream, Marlborough, New Zealand. *New Zealand Journal of Geology and Geophysics*, **38**, 171–212.

WILLIAMS, G. L., LENTIN, J. K. & FENSOME, R. A. 1998. The Lentin and Williams index of fossil dinoflagellates, 1998 edition. *American Association of Stratigraphic Palynologists, Contributions Series*, **28**, 1–856.

YEPES, O. 2001. Maastrichtian–Danian dinoflagellate cyst biostratigraphy and biogeography from two equatorial sections in Colombia and Venezuela. *Palynology*, **25**, 217–249.

Upper Palaeocene and Lower Eocene interval in the Dieppe–Hampshire Basin: biostratigraphic analysis based on pyritized diatoms

Y. VAN EETVELDE[1] & C. DUPUIS[2]

[1]Département de Géologie, Facultés Universitaires Notre-Dame de la Paix, rue Grafé 2, B-5000 (Namur), Belgium (e-mail: yoann.vaneetvelde@fundp.ac.be)
[2]Géologie fondamentale et appliquée, Faculté Polytechnique de Mons, rue de Houdain, 9, B-7000 (Mons), Belgium (e-mail: christian.dupuis@hydro.fpms.ac.be)

Abstract: Assemblages of brackish and marine pyritized diatoms have been examined from Thanetian and Ypresian sediments in the Dieppe–Hampshire Basin. Two sites were studied: the borehole of Saint-Josse and sections at Ailly, both located in northern France. Pyritized diatoms are preserved in the deposits by epigenesis or as internal moulds by the growth of pyrite crystals in internal cavities. In both sites studied, most groups of *in situ* microfossils (e.g. dinoflagellates, foraminifera, nannoplankton) were extremely rare or absent, in contrast to pyritized diatoms, which showed good recovery, thereby proving their utility across this interval. The Palaeocene–Eocene boundary referred to this study is the official boundary defined by the Carbon Isotope Excursion. This is recorded in both sites studied. Diatom assemblages change character through the stratigraphic sequence, with three major diatom assemblages being defined which provide a key reference marker for the Palaeocene–Eocene boundary sediments from the Dieppe–Hampshire Basin. The first assemblage, D1, is characterized by the abundance peak of *Coscinodiscus morsianus* var. *moelleri* and *Coscinodiscus morsianus* var. *morsianus*. This assemblage is recorded in Thanetian and Lower Sparnacian facies. The second assemblage, D2, is defined by the abundance peak of *Fenestrella antiqua*, the downhole occurrence of *Coscinodiscus morsianus* sp., and a great diversity of circular diatoms. The upper part of this zone is marked by the greatest occurrence of *Fenestrella antiqua* and the extinction of *Coscinodiscus morsianus* var. *moelleri*. This assemblage corresponds with the upper part of the Sparnacian facies. The last assemblage (D3), of Early Ypresian age, is characterized by the presence of *Aulacodiscus, Trinacria, Craspedodiscus* and the great diversity of triangular, oval and bipolar species; these are held to indicate a marked increase in marine influence. These diatom assemblages from the Dieppe–Hampshire Basin show similarities to those from the North Sea Basin. Correlations between these two basins are possible by the use of pyritized diatoms. Thanks to these correlations, it is now possible to locate the Carbon Isotope Excursion in the North Sea Basin.

This paper reports the first results and interpretations of an investigation of the diatoms from Palaeogene formations near the Palaeocene–Eocene boundary in the Dieppe–Hampshire Basin. Using dinoflagellates and calcareous nannoplankton for biostratigraphic analysis, a fairly good correlation of the Sele and Balder Formations with the onshore sections of the Dieppe–Hampshire and Paris Basin has been extensively discussed recently and is now well established (Knox *et al.* 1996; Steurbaut 1998). Thanetian and Ypresian sediments from the Saint-Josse borehole and Ailly sections of the Dieppe–Hampshire Basin are poor in the microfossils usually used for biostratigraphic analysis (e.g. dinoflagellates, foraminifera and calcareous nannoplankton) in contrast to pyritized diatoms. Correlations across this basin are

not obvious. Some previous works have revealed the presence of siliceous diatoms (Cayeux 1891) in Thanetian 'tuffeaux' and particularly of pyritized diatoms in Ypresian sediments from the Paris Basin (Bolin *et al.* 1982; Bignot 1983). Recognizing that pyritized diatoms have a proven utility for biostratigraphic studies (e.g. King 1983; Malm *et al.* 1984; Mudge & Copestake 1992; Mitlehner 1996) in the North Sea Basin, this paper seeks to examine the biostratigraphic potential of pyritized diatoms in the Dieppe–Hampshire Basin and their correlations with the Paris and North Sea basins.

Several explanations have been advanced for the presence and abundance of diatoms in the North Sea Basin. Some workers (Jacqué & Thouvenin 1975; Knox 1984) have linked the

From: BEAUDOIN, A.B. & HEAD, M.J. (eds) 2004. *The Palynology and Micropalaeontology of Boundaries.* Geological Society, London, Special Publications, **230**, 275–291. 0305-8719/04/$15 © The Geological Society of London 2004.

abundance of the diatoms to the volcanic ashes present in the North Sea Tertiary Basin. They suggested that contemporaneous volcanic activity may have led to silica enrichment of seawaters which, in turn, encouraged blooming. Bidgood (1995) and Mitlehner (1994) have shown that species of pyritized diatoms occurred throughout the Cenozoic in offshore North Sea sediments not associated with tuff deposition. The second explanation for diatom blooming in Palaeogene sediments is the presence of upwelling currents in the North Sea Basin (Malm *et al.* 1984; Mitlehner 1994, 1996; Bidgood 1995).

Previous studies on pyritized diatoms in the Palaeocene–Eocene deposits of the North Sea Basin

Pyritized diatoms and pyritization

Pyritized diatoms in the North Sea Basin and adjacent onshore deposits have been documented and illustrated by many studies, including: Bettenstaedt *et al.* (1962), Benda (1965, 1972), Bidgood *et al.* (1999), Jacqué & Thouvenin (1975), Hughes (1981), King (1983, 1990), Malm *et al.* (1984), Mudge & Copestake (1992), Neal *et al.* (1994), and especially by Mitlehner (1994). He described and identified about 40 diatom taxa, comprising siliceous and pyritized specimens of Tertiary age.

The pyritization process affects diatoms in two ways:

- by epigenesis: the siliceous frustule of the diatom is completely altered to pyrite, and all the details of the diatoms are preserved, including areolae, velum and labiate processes
- by early diagenetic infilling of the frustule by pyrite crystals, producing an internal mould, in many instances rendering a near-perfect impression of the interior morphology of the original diatom frustule.

Pyritization has some advantages for the preservation of the diatoms. Pyritized morphotypes usually preserve the original frustule shape with girdle bands intact – a feature not often observed in non-pyritized specimens, which are usually preserved as isolated valves (Bidgood *et al.* 1999).

Diatom biostratigraphy

The biostratigraphic importance of Palaeogene diatom taxa in offshore exploration was demonstrated by King (1983, 1990), Mudge & Copestake (1992) and Mitlehner (1994, 1996). King (1983) established a micropalaeontological zonation for the marine Cenozoic (Early Palaeocene to Early Pleistocene) of the North Sea. He proposed two parallel zonal schemes: one based on benthic foraminifera, and the other based on planktonic microfossils – including pyritized diatoms. This planktonic zonation was called NSP (North Sea Plankton). The NSP4 zone defined by King is important for biostratigraphy near the Palaeocene–Eocene boundary (Fig. 1). The top of this zone is characterized by the highest occurrence of *Fenestrella antiqua* (*Coscinodiscus* sp. 1 *sensu* King). The NSP4 zone was recognized around the Palaeocene–Eocene boundary, and the basal Eocene was placed within the upper part of zone NSP4.

Mudge & Copestake (1992) described two major diatom bio-events during the Palaeogene (Fig. 1). The first, M6, bio-event is defined by the downhole acme of a distinctive diatom assemblage containing common to abundant *Coscinodiscus* sp. 4 (=*Coscinodiscus morsianus* var. *morsianus*), *Coscinodiscus* sp. 2 (=*Coscinodiscus morsianus* var. *moelleri*) and *Coscinodiscus* sp. 7 (a resting spore of *Fenestrella antiqua*). The second, M7, bio-event is defined by a distinctive downhole diatom influx including *Coscinodiscus* sp. 1 (=*Fenestrella antiqua*) and *Coscinodiscus* sp. 2 (=*Coscinodiscus morsianus* var. *moelleri*). This influx occurs within a rich and diverse diatom association, including species of *Triceratium*, *Isthmia*, *Hemiaulus* and *Trinacria*.

Mitlehner's (1996) biozonation based on foraminifera and diatom marker species (Fig. 1) shows that the lowest occurrence of the widely occurring diatom *Fenestrella antiqua* is an efficient basin-wide marker for the base of the Eocene (Fig. 1).

Therefore, the stratigraphically important taxa for Palaeogene near the Palaeocene–Eocene boundary are *Coscinodiscus morsianus* var. *moelleri* and *Fenestrella antiqua*. A taxonomic revision of these two species was made by Mitlehner (1994).

Aims of the study

The principal purpose of this study is to provide a preliminary biozonation of the stratigraphy of Upper Palaeocene and Lower Eocene sediments exposed in northern France on the basis of the diatom stratigraphic record. Using two sections to erect a regional zonation is premature; therefore, this work is an exploratory study and not a detailed regional synthesis. The second purpose

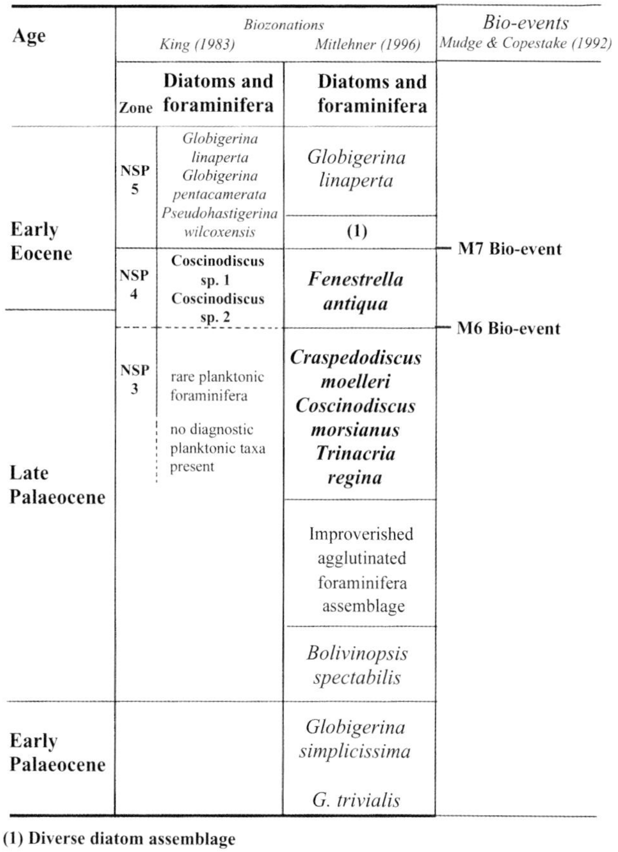

Age	Biozonations King (1983)		Mitlehner (1996)	Bio-events Mudge & Copestake (1992)
	Zone	Diatoms and foraminifera	Diatoms and foraminifera	
Early Eocene	NSP 5	*Globigerina linaperta* *Globigerina pentacamerata* *Pseudohastigerina wilcoxensis*	*Globigerina linaperta* (1)	M7 Bio-event
	NSP 4	*Coscinodiscus* sp. 1 *Coscinodiscus* sp. 2	*Fenestrella antiqua*	M6 Bio-event
Late Palaeocene	NSP 3	rare planktonic foraminifera no diagnostic planktonic taxa present	**Craspedodiscus moelleri** **Coscinodiscus morsianus** **Trinacria regina**	
			Improverished agglutinated foraminifera assemblage	
			Bolivinopsis spectabilis	
Early Palaeocene			*Globigerina simplicissima*	
			G. trivialis	

(1) Diverse diatom assemblage

Fig. 1. Lower Palaeogene (near the Palaeocene–Eocene boundary) biozonations of the central North Sea with main diatom marker species (in bold). (Compiled from King 1983, Mudge & Copestake 1992 and Mitlehner 1996.)

is to correlate our results with the biostratigraphic zonations based on diatom records in the North Sea Basin. In addition, diatom assemblages can give new data on correlation between the lithostratigraphic units of the Saint-Josse borehole and Ailly sections where the Carbon Isotope Excursion is observed.

Geological settings of Saint-Josse and Ailly

This work is based on the study of the borehole CC82 at Saint-Josse (50.4686° N, 1.6656° E) (Fig. 3a) and of the Cap d'Ailly (49.9167° N, 0.9514° E) sections (Fig. 3b) which are located in the northern part of France (Fig. 2).

The Palaeocene–Eocene boundary occurs in Cap d'Ailly sections approximately at the end of SP2 (Magioncalda *et al.* 2001) and in the 'Le Goulet' Unit of Saint-Josse (Magioncalda & Dupuis, in prep.). This is shown by carbon isotope analysis, which shows a very negative excursion value of $\delta^{13}C$. This negative Carbon Isotope Excursion (CIE) is the official reference for the base of the Eocene (Luterbacher *et al.* 2000).

Both sites are located in the Dieppe–Hampshire Basin which, together with the Paris, London and Belgian basins, forms the southern bight of the North Sea Basin (Fig. 2). The Dieppe–Hampshire Basin was intermittently separated from the North Sea Basin by the uplift of the Artois sill at various times during the Palaeogene. Three main groups or facies characterize the geology of the Palaeocene–Eocene interval. The Thanetian facies is formed essentially by continental or presumably related continental deposits (Fig. 2). The Sparnacian facies corresponds with the period when the Dieppe–Hampshire Basin formed a shallow embayment in which true marine deposits are uncommon, and brackish palaeoenvironments (Fig. 2) are frequent (Dupuis *et al.* 1998; Dupuis

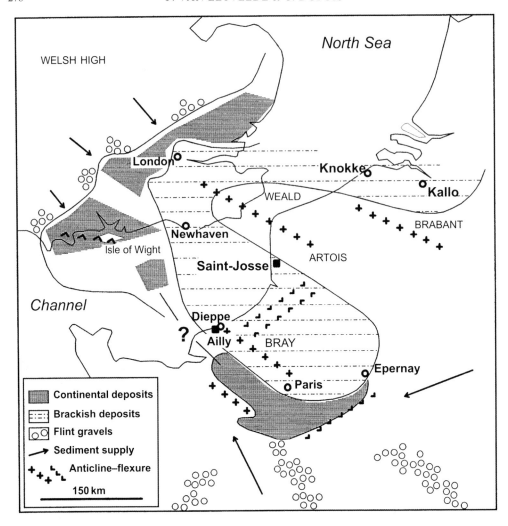

Fig. 2. Geographical location of Saint-Josse and Ailly, and distribution of Palaeogene facies in the Dieppe–Hampshire Basin.

& Thiry 1998). The Ypresian is marked by an important transgression and by fully marine conditions.

Lithostratigraphic correlations

Correlations between the lithostratigraphic units of the Saint-Josse borehole and the Cap d'Ailly sections (Fig. 3) are based on lithological and sedimentological data.

The Bois Gorguette Sands at Saint-Josse correspond with the sands, gravels, limestones, marls and lignites of the 'Sables et Grès du Pays de Caux' and 'Calcaires, marnes et lignites du

Cap d'Ailly' units of the Cap d'Ailly sections. The 'Le Goulet' Unit may be correlated with the uppermost lignite horizon (L1) of the 'Calcaires, marnes et lignites du Cap d'Ailly' Unit. This correlation is confirmed by the presence of the carbon isotope excursion in both units (Magioncalda & Dupuis, in prep.). Note the presence of a hiatus between the 'Le Goulet' and 'Saint-Aubin' units at Saint-Josse. A further correlation is for the shell-beds of the Saint-Aubin Unit which correspond with those of the lower and upper 'Sables et Argiles à Ostracodes et à Mollusques' (SAOM) units (SP3 and SP4).

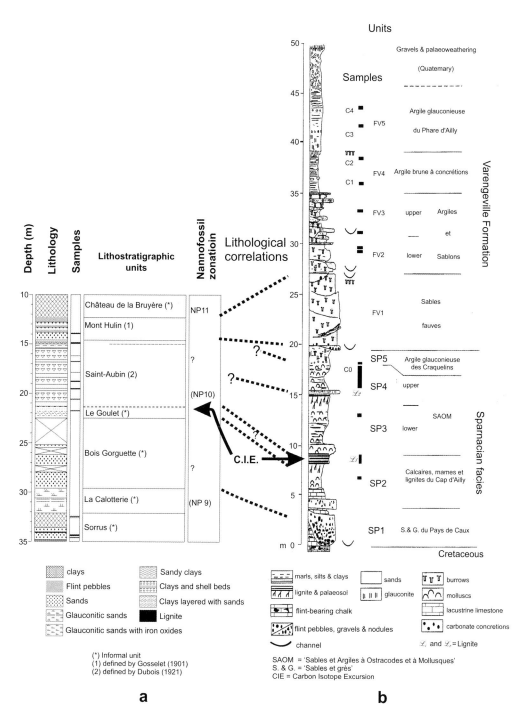

Fig. 3. Lithology and lithostratigraphy of Palaeogene deposits, and position of samples at Saint-Josse (**a**) and at Cap d'Ailly (**b**). (Modified after Dupuis *et al.* 1998.)

Sampling procedure

The stratigraphic position of the samples is shown in the stratigraphic summary logs (Fig. 3). Thirteen samples from Saint-Josse were processed for microfauna: four from the Sorrus Unit, seven from the Saint-Aubin Unit, and one further sample from the Mont-Hulin Unit. At Ailly, four samples were obtained from the SP2 Unit ('Calcaires, marnes et lignites du Cap d'Ailly' Unit). One sample was also obtained from the SP3 Unit. A further five samples were also obtained from the SP4 Unit (upper part of the SAOM Unit). Four samples from the FV2 and FV3 units (lower and upper part of the 'Argiles et sablons') were also processed. Finally, the unit FV4 ('Argile brune à concretions' Unit) (two samples) and the unit FV5 ('Argile glauconieuse du Phare d'Ailly' Unit) (two samples) were sampled.

Pyritized microfossils were extracted by chemical treatments which do not use any oxidant product, with the aim of preserving pyrite (Van Eetvelde & Cornet 2002). Samples, once crushed, were attacked first by HCl (20%) to eliminate carbonates and second by tetrasodium diphosphate ($Na_4P_2O_7$ 0.15 M) to suspend and disperse argillaceous matter which was eliminated by siphoning. Residues, after granulometric sorting by sieving, were placed into bromoform (specific gravity of 2.87–2.89) which permits a density separation; the pyritized fraction, including the diatoms, settles down and can be collected.

Pyritized diatoms were then mounted on slides and counted under a light microscope in transmitted and reflected lights. Diatoms were also examined with a scanning electron microscope (Philips XL-20) to confirm their identification. The slides were studied both qualitatively and quantitatively. The quantitative analysis comprised a minimum count of 200 diatoms where possible (Tables 1 & 2).

Diatom identifications were carried out with reference to Cleve-Euler (1951), Ross & Sims (1970), Van der Werff & Huls (1976), Sims (1989, 1990), Round *et al.* (1990), Homann (1991), Mitlehner (1994), Scherer & Koç (1996) and Hasle & Syversten (1997). The identification of some taxa is sometimes not easy, owing to the poor quality of the preservation of pyritized diatoms in some samples. In these instances, the identification of the genus is certain, but the specific epithet is left in open nomenclature. All material is stored in the collection of the Geology Department, University of Namur, Belgium.

Results

Pyritized residues collected from the different samples contain pyritized dinoflagellates and pyritized diatoms. Pyritized diatoms are more abundant than dinoflagellates in all cases. Contrary to previous studies (King 1990; Mitlehner 1994) which reported three to four taxa and only some tens of pyritized diatoms per sample, we often obtained more than 200 specimens counted, and ten to 16 different taxa (Table 3). This is attributable mainly to our improved recovery techniques.

Diatom assemblage zones of the studied borehole and sections

Although the samples from the Mont-Hulin Unit, and units SP2, SP5, FV2 and FV3, are barren of diatoms, most other samples contain reasonably well-preserved pyritized diatoms suitable for biostratigraphic analysis. Diatoms are poorly recorded in the Sorrus Unit. One sample (32.50–32.55) is barren of diatoms. The three other samples contain few diatoms: three to a maximum of 25 specimens. Pyritized diatoms are common to abundant in the Saint-Aubin, upper SAOM, 'Argile brune à concretions' and 'Argile glauconieuse du Phare d'Ailly' units.

Diatom preservation varies widely between different sediments. They are often well preserved by epigenesis in the Saint-Josse borehole (Figs 4–8), and most often as internal moulds in the Ailly sections (Figs 12–15). Pyrite crystals constituting the moulds are cubes, octahedrons (Figs 10 & 11), pyritohedrons and framboids (Figs 4 & 6–8).

Changes in the diatom assemblages permit establishment of a preliminary biozonation for the Dieppe–Hampshire Basin (Fig. 16). Diatom assemblages are complex and are defined on the basis of first and last appearance, lowest or highest occurrence, maximum and diversity of the species. These diatom assemblages confirm the lithological correlation between the Saint-Aubin Unit of Ailly and the lower and upper SAOM units of Ailly. This illustrates the biostratigraphic potential value of pyritized diatoms in the Dieppe–Hampshire Basin.

Saint-Josse diatom assemblage zones

Diatom assemblage D1

The diatom assemblage D1 is defined by the abundance of circular diatoms and the peak

Table 1. Fossilized diatom distribution (counts) at Saint-Josse, in alphabetical order: species diversity and diatom assemblages

Depth of samples (m)	Units	Actinoptychus senarius f. octoplicata	Actinoptychus senarius f. sexappendiculata	Biddulphia biddulphiana	Biddulphia sp. 1	Coscinodiscus communtatus	Coscinodiscus granii	Coscinodiscus morsianus var. moelleri	Coscinodiscus morsianus var. morsianus	Coscinodiscus perforatus	Coscinodiscus sp.	Fenestrella antiqua	Hemiaulus sp. 2	Hemiaulus sp. 3	Odontella heibergii	Odontella sp. 1	Melosira clavigera	Paralia ornata	Paralia siberica var. laevis	Pterotheca sp.	Rhizosolenia sp. 1	Stellarima microtrias	Stephanogonia danica	Stephanopyxis turris	Triceratium sp.	Trinacria regina	Circular diatoms indeterminate	Genus and species indeterminate	TOTAL NUMBER OF DIATOMS COUNTED	TAXA DIVERSITY	DIATOM ASSEMBLAGES
13.90–14.00	MH	—	—	—	—	—	—	—	—	—	—	—	—	—	—	—	—	—	—	—	—	—	—	—	—	—	—	—	0	—	
14.85–15.00		—	—	—	—	—	—	—	—	—	—	—	—	—	—	—	—	—	—	—	—	—	—	—	—	—	1	1	2	—	
16.20–16.20	SA	69	11	—	25	—	9	134	—	—	—	133	—	—	—	—	12	—	—	—	2	5	3	2	8	—	8	4	298	12	D2
16.75–16.85		57	3	—	1	—	1	5	13	—	7	142	—	—	—	—	7	—	—	1	—	1	—	5	—	—	19	2	381	10	
17.87–17.87		21	5	5	—	—	—	83	2	—	—	166	—	—	—	1	—	—	—	—	—	1	—	—	—	—	8	6	225	9	
18.75–18.85		10	3	—	38	2	—	113	7	—	—	107	—	—	—	—	—	—	—	—	1	—	2	3	9	—	7	2	270	10	D1
19.50–19.60		71	7	—	7	—	—	69	34	2	8	23	—	1	—	1	—	—	—	—	10	—	9	3	5	1	45	—	342	16	
20.55–20.65		—	3	—	—	—	—	—	9	—	—	23	1	—	14	117	—	—	—	—	1	5	5	—	—	—	3	3	248	9	D1
21.75–21.83	LG	—	2	—	30	12	—	61	31	—	19	19	—	—	—	—	—	1	—	—	2	1	—	—	4	2	38	—	222	12	
Not sampled	BG	—	—	—	—	—	—	—	—	—	—	—	—	—	—	—	—	—	—	—	—	—	—	—	—	—	—	—	0	—	
Not sampled	LC	—	—	—	—	—	—	—	—	—	—	—	—	—	—	—	—	—	3	—	—	—	—	—	—	—	—	—	0	—	
32.50–32.55	SO	—	—	—	—	—	—	—	—	—	—	—	—	—	—	—	—	—	—	—	—	—	—	—	—	—	—	—	0	—	
32.55–32.60		—	—	—	—	—	—	—	—	—	—	—	—	—	—	—	—	—	—	—	—	—	—	—	—	—	3	—	3	1	
34.31–34.45		2	1	—	—	2	—	5	—	—	—	1	—	—	—	—	—	—	—	—	1	—	—	—	1	—	11	2	25	6	D1
34.57–34.60		—	—	—	—	2	—	2	—	—	—	2	—	—	—	—	—	—	—	—	—	—	—	—	—	—	3	—	14	7	

MH, Mont Hulin; SA, Saint-Aubin; LG, Le Goulet; BG, Bois-Gorguette; LC, La Caloterie; SO, Sorrus

Table 2. Pyritized diatom distribution at Cap d'Ailly; total number of diatoms in comparison with pyritized dinoflagellates and diatom assemblages

Units	Position (m)	Paralia ornata	Coscinodiscus morsianus var. moelleri	Coscinodiscus morsianus var. morsianus	Actinoptychus senarius	Stephanopyxis turris	Stephanogonia danica	Fenestrella antiqua	Stellarima microtrias	Odontella sp. 1	Triceratium sp.	Rhizosolenia sp.	Trinacria excavata	Triceratium sp. 3	Hemiaulus sp. 2	Hemiaulus sp. 3	Hemiaulus sp. 4	Diatom ovalis sp. 1	Diatom ovalis sp. 2	Craspedodiscus oblongus	Aulacodiscus sp. 1	Trinacria regina	Actinoptychus sp. 1	Aulacodiscus sp. 2	Trigonium sp. 1	Aulacodiscus sp. 3	Hemiaulus sp. 5	Triceratium nobile	Eunotogramma weissei	Aulacodiscus hirtus	Aulacodiscus subexcavatus	Genus and species indeterminate	NUMBER OF DIATOMS	DINOFLAGELLATES	DIATOM ASSEMBLAGES
FV5	43.5	—	—	—	—	—	—	15	15	2	16	—	17	39	—	10	5	8	15	3	4	—	7	12	79	2	25	6	4	2	1	11	283	4	D3b
FV5	41	—	—	—	—	—	—	33	3	5	13	—	14	16	—	13	4	34	43	4	11	1	12	8	40	4	7	3	—	—	—	16	271	4	
FV4	38.8	—	—	—	—	—	—	21	13	16	18	—	11	11	—	13	11	24	16	4	4	13	4	4	61	—	—	—	—	—	—	8	252	34	D3a
FV4	36.2	—	—	—	—	—	—	23	15	12	3	1	6	5	2	13	7	36	24	12	7	7	—	—	—	—	—	—	—	—	—	9	182	19	
FV3	33.75	—	—	—	—	—	—	—	—	—	—	—	—	—	—	—	—	—	—	—	—	—	—	—	—	—	—	—	—	—	—	—	—	—	?
FV3	31.95	—	—	—	—	—	—	—	—	—	—	—	—	—	—	—	—	—	—	—	—	—	—	—	—	—	—	—	—	—	—	—	—	—	
FV2	29.8	—	—	—	—	—	—	—	—	—	—	—	—	—	—	—	—	—	—	—	—	—	—	—	—	—	—	—	—	—	—	—	—	—	?
FV2	29.3	—	—	—	—	—	—	—	—	—	—	—	—	—	—	—	—	—	—	—	—	—	—	—	—	—	—	—	—	—	—	—	—	—	
SP5	18.15	—	—	—	—	—	1	—	—	—	1	12	1	—	—	—	—	—	—	—	—	—	—	—	—	—	—	—	—	—	—	—	1	1	
SP4	18.35	8	—	1	—	1	1	2	—	—	—	—	—	—	—	—	—	—	—	—	—	—	—	—	—	—	—	—	—	—	—	4	9	1	
SP4	17.45	—	7	3	10	5	4	37	—	—	—	—	1	—	—	—	—	—	—	—	—	—	—	—	—	—	—	—	—	—	—	7	82	70	
SP4	17.10	—	—	—	6	2	—	1	—	—	—	—	—	—	—	—	—	—	—	—	—	—	—	—	—	—	—	—	—	—	—	3	12	7	
SP4	16.90	—	3	7	154	16	4	14	3	15	—	—	—	—	—	—	—	—	—	—	—	—	—	—	—	—	—	—	—	—	—	35	248	26	D2
SP4	16.55	—	107	9	10	5	—	71	6	29	—	—	—	—	—	—	—	—	—	—	—	—	—	—	—	—	—	—	—	—	—	20	275	4	
SP4	16.20	—	—	—	—	—	—	—	—	—	—	—	—	—	—	—	—	—	—	—	—	—	—	—	—	—	—	—	—	—	—	—	—	1	
SP4	15.75	—	6	1	3	—	—	7	1	—	—	—	—	—	—	—	—	—	—	—	—	—	—	—	—	—	—	—	—	—	—	4	22	14	
SP3	13.42	—	2	—	—	—	—	1	—	—	—	—	—	—	—	—	—	—	—	—	—	—	—	—	—	—	—	—	—	—	—	—	3	—	
SP2	9–9.5	—	—	—	—	—	—	—	—	—	—	—	—	—	—	—	—	—	—	—	—	—	—	—	—	—	—	—	—	—	—	—	—	—	
SP2	8.5–9	—	—	—	—	—	—	—	—	—	—	—	—	—	—	—	—	—	—	—	—	—	—	—	—	—	—	—	—	—	—	—	—	—	?
SP2	7	—	—	—	—	—	—	—	—	—	—	—	—	—	—	—	—	—	—	—	—	—	—	—	—	—	—	—	—	—	—	—	—	—	
SP2	6.9	—	—	—	—	—	—	—	—	—	—	—	—	—	—	—	—	—	—	—	—	—	—	—	—	—	—	—	—	—	—	—	—	—	

Table 3. *Author citations for diatom taxa encountered during this study*

Diatoms – author citations
Actinoptychus senarius Ehrenberg
Actinoptychus sp. *sensu* Round, Crawford & Mann
Aulacodiscus hirtus Barker & Meakin
Aulacodiscus subexcavatus Hustedt
Aulacodiscus sp. *sensu* Round, Crawford & Mann
Biddulphia biddulphiana (Smith) Boyer
Biddulphia sp. *sensu* Round, Crawford & Mann
Coscinodiscus commutatus Grunow
Coscinodiscus granii Gough
Coscinodiscus morsianus var. *moelleri* Mitlehner
Coscinodiscus morsianus var. *morsianus* (Sims) Mitlehner
Coscinodiscus perforatus Ehrenberg
Craspedodiscus oblongus (Greville) Schmidt
Eunotogramma weissei Ehrenberg
Fenestrella antiqua (Grunow) Swatmann
Hemiaulus sp. *sensu* Round, Crawford & Mann
Melosira clavigera Grunow
Odontella heibergii Grunow
Odontella sp. *sensu* Round, Crawford & Mann
Paralia ornata Grunow
Paralia siberica var. *laevis* Crawford
Stellarima microtrias (Ehrenberg) Hasle & Sims
Stephanogonia danica Grunow
Stephanopyxis turris (Greville & Arnott) Ralfs
Triceratium nobile Witt
Trinacria excavata Heiberg
Trinacria regina (Heiberg) Homann

abundance of *Coscinodiscus morsianus* var. *moelleri* (Figs 10 & 11) and *Coscinodiscus morsianus* var. *morsianus*. Triangular diatoms are very rare. In this biozone, *Paralia siberica* (Fig. 5) (not a marker species) can be found in the most 'continental' deposits (sample 32.55–32.60).

Diatom assemblage D2

The diatom assemblage D2 is defined by the abundance and the great diversity of circular diatom taxa. The most abundant diatoms are *Actinoptychus senarius* (Figs 6–9) and *Fenestrella antiqua*. The top of this zone is defined by the greatest abundance of *Fenestrella antiqua*. *Coscinodiscus morsianus* var. *moelleri* disappears near the top of this zone. *Actinoptychus senarius* and *Biddulphia* sp. 1 do not occur in higher beds, and are also marker species for this diatom assemblage.

Ailly biostratigraphy

Diatom assemblage D2

This has the same main characteristics as the D2 diatom assemblage of Saint-Josse.

Diatom assemblage D3

The diatom assemblage D3 is defined by the abundance of circular species (*Aulacodiscus* spp. (Figs 14 & 15) and *Actinoptychus* sp.), triangular species (*Trinacria* (Fig. 13), *Triceratium* and *Trigonium* species), oval species (*Craspedodiscus* sp. and diatom ovalis *sensu* Bidgood *et al.* (1999)) and bipolar diatoms (*Hemiaulus* and *Odontella* species). The D3 diatom assemblage is also characterized by the great diversity of triangular species. The most abundant diatoms are *Trinacria* species and *Aulacodiscus* species.

A distinction can be made between the lower (D3a) and upper part (D3b) of this assemblage. The D3b assemblage is characterized by the presence of three diagnostic taxa: *Aulacodiscus* sp. 3, *Hemiaulus* sp. 5 and *Triceratium nobile*, that are not recorded in the D3a assemblage. This D3 assemblage contains the most diverse diatom assemblage found in this study.

Comments on the diatom assemblages for the Dieppe–Hampshire Basin

No samples were taken in the 'La Calotterie' and Bois Gorguette units at Saint-Josse and in the 'Sables fauves' Unit (FV1) at Ailly, because

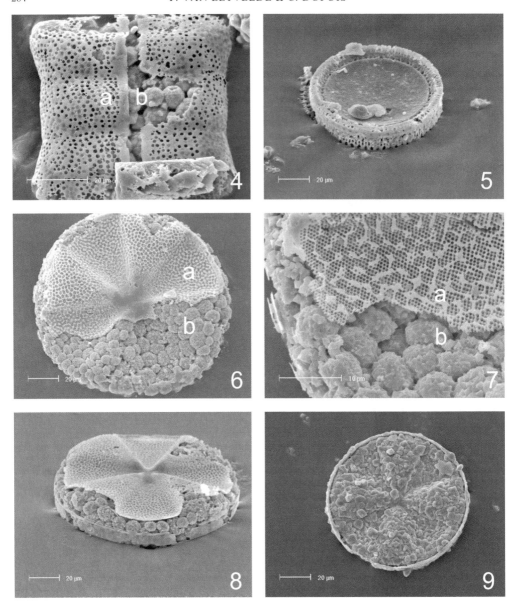

Fig. 4. *Biddulphia biddulphiana*, Saint-Josse, sample 17.87, SEM. Valve view. Frustule well preserved in pyrite (**a**); internal mould in framboids of pyrite (**b**). **Fig. 5.** *Paralia siberica*, Saint-Josse, sample 32.55–32.60, SEM. External view, specimen very well preserved. **Figs 6 & 7.** *Actinoptychus senarius*, sample 16.20, SEM. Valve view, details of areolae well preserved in pyrite (**a**) covering a mould constituted by framboids of pyrite (**b**). **Fig. 8.** *Actinoptychus senarius*, sample 19.50–19.60, SEM. External view. **Fig. 9.** *Actinoptychus senarius*, sample 19.50–19.60, SEM. Internal mould rendering a near-perfect impression of the interior morphology of the original diatom frustule.

these sediments are unsuited to diatom analysis, owing to oxidization and large grain size. In fact, the 'La Calotterie' Unit and the FV1 Unit comprise glauconitic and oxidized sands in which the opal-A of the diatom frustule is often dissolved. If the siliceous diatoms are preserved in pyrite, then oxidation corrodes and destroys the diatoms. The sediments of the FV2 and FV3 units are also very oxidized, making these units unsuitable for pyritized diatom analysis. To

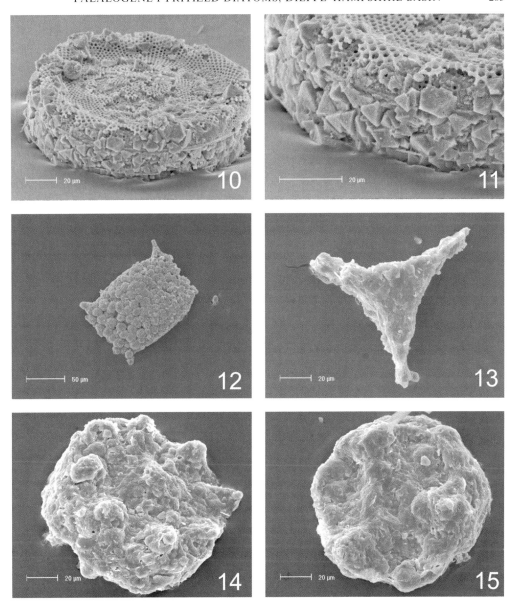

Figs 10–11. *Coscinodiscus morsianus* var. *moelleri*, Ailly, sample 16.55, SEM. External view, areolae well preserved on the valve surface. **Fig. 12.** *Odontella* sp. 1, Ailly, sample 16.55, SEM. Internal mould. **Fig. 13.** *Trinacria excavata*, Ailly, sample 43.5, SEM. Internal mould. **Fig. 14.** *Aulacodiscus* sp. 2, Ailly, sample 41, SEM. Internal mould. **Fig. 15.** *Aulacodiscus subexcavatus*, Ailly, sample 43.5, SEM. Internal mould.

confirm this assertion, four samples were processed and no pyritized diatoms were found in these units – only pyrite crystals strongly oxidized. Moreover, the Bois Gorguette Unit comprises fluviatile sands, and no diatoms are known to be present in this palaeoenvironment during the Palaeocene. Further studies are needed to confirm this assertion.

At Ailly, the 'Calcaires, marnes et lignites du Cap d'Ailly' Unit proved to be barren of diatoms. Four samples examined showed the presence of pyrite but no diatoms. One possible reason for the lack of diatoms in this unit is its continental palaeoenvironment, which is indicated by the presence of lignite horizons. This palaeoenvironment was not suitable for diatoms

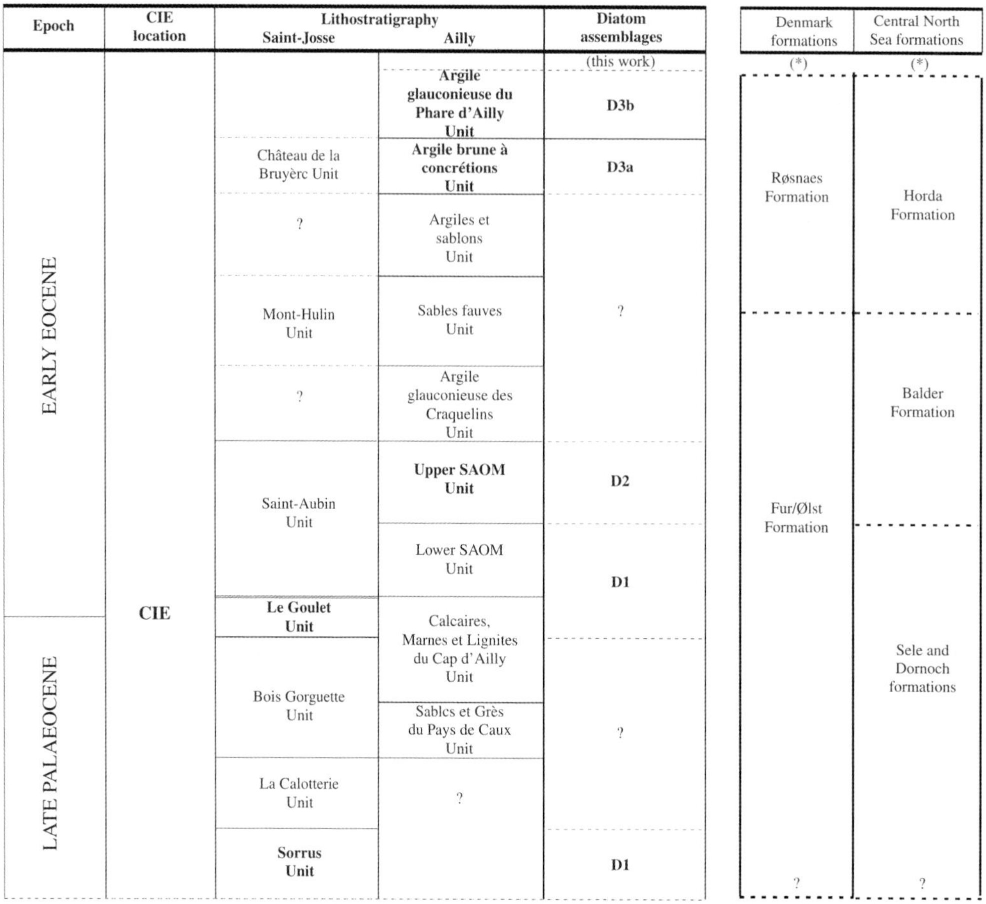

| Epoch | CIE location | Lithostratigraphy | | Diatom assemblages | Denmark formations | Central North Sea formations |
		Saint-Josse	Ailly			
				(this work)	(*)	(*)
EARLY EOCENE			Argile glauconieuse du Phare d'Ailly Unit	D3b	Røsnaes Formation	Horda Formation
		Château de la Bruyère Unit	Argile brune à concrétions Unit	D3a		
		?	Argiles et sablons Unit			
		Mont-Hulin Unit	Sables fauves Unit	?		Balder Formation
		?	Argile glauconieuse des Craquelins Unit			
		Saint-Aubin Unit	Upper SAOM Unit	D2	Fur/Ølst Formation	
			Lower SAOM Unit	D1		
LATE PALAEOCENE	CIE	Le Goulet Unit	Calcaires, Marnes et Lignites du Cap d'Ailly Unit			Sele and Dornoch formations
		Bois Gorguette Unit	Sables et Grès du Pays de Caux Unit	?		
		La Calotterie Unit	?			
		Sorrus Unit		D1	?	?

(*) compiled from Mitlehner (1996) and Mudge & Copestake (1992)
CIE = Carbon Isotope Excursion

Fig. 16. Lower Palaeogene lithostratigraphy and diatom assemblages of the Dieppe–Hampshire Basin (diatomaceous units shown in bold) – correlations with formations of Denmark and Central North Sea.

during the Palaeogene. No fluviatile freshwater diatoms are known prior to the Late Eocene (Strel'nikova & Lastivka 1999).

Comparison with previous work in the Dieppe–Hampshire and Paris basins

Bignot (1983) suggested that freshwater diatoms evolved during the Palaeogene in the lagoonal palaeoenvironment of the 'Sparnacian' facies. However, during this study, no freshwater diatoms were found, but some near-shore species (*Paralia siberica* and *Actinoptychus* spp.) were observed in continental deposits from the Sorrus Unit. The near-shore ecology of these species was demonstrated by Van der Werff & Huls (1976), Zong (1997) and Oresh-

kina (2000). The predominance of these near-shore diatoms in some strata is the only indication of a strong coastal influence. In contrast, less-abundant near-shore diatoms suggest a more pronounced transgressive palaeoenvironment. In summary, true freshwater diatoms have not been identified in strata older than Late Eocene (Lohmann & Andrews 1968). Bignot (1983) also stated that there is a low diversity of diatoms recorded in 'Sparnacian' deposits – contrasting with the rich assemblages observed in the Fur Formation. Our work has shown the contrary, with diatoms recovered in abundance in the 'Sparnacian' deposits (more than 16 different species were found in one sample analysed).

Bolin *et al.* (1982) made the first description of pyritized diatoms in 'Cuisian' (Ypresian) sediments from the Paris Basin. In our study, their species (*Actinoptychus* spp. and *Aulacodiscus* spp.) were also found in the Varengeville Formation, which seems to correspond with the 'Cuisian' of Bolin *et al.* (1982). The different *Aulacodiscus* species permit the attribution of the 'Cuisian' to our D3 assemblage.

Comparison and correlation with diatom biostratigraphy of the North Sea Basin: Palaeocene–Eocene boundary evidence

The changes in Palaeogene diatom zonal assemblages, taxonomic composition, and ecological structure dynamics in the Dieppe–Hampshire Basin are similar to the diatomaceous deposits of the North Sea Basin (King 1983, 1990; Mudge & Copestake 1992; Mitlehner 1994, 1996; see Fig. 17).

The M6 bio-event of Mudge & Copestake (1992) is found in the Dieppe–Hampshire Basin, and corresponds with the boundary between the assemblages D1 and D2. This implies that the Sele Formation (dated as Thanetian to Ypresian) can be correlated with the lower 'Sparnacian' Formations, and the Balder Formation with the upper part of the 'SAOM' Unit, and may be the 'Argile glauconieuse des Craquelins' Unit (Lower Ypresian) (Fig. 16).

The NSP4 biozone of King (1983) could be identified in the Dieppe–Hampshire Basin. The D2 diatom assemblage has approximately the same boundaries as the NSP4 biozone, but the D2 diatom assemblage shows a higher diversity of species and a different composition from the assemblage of NSP4. For example, *Actinoptychus senarius* and *Biddulphia* sp. are recorded in the D2 diatom assemblage but not in the NSP4 biozone. The M7 bio-event of Mudge & Copestake (1992), which corresponds with the upper boundary of the NSP4 biozone, is not recorded in the Dieppe–Hampshire Basin.

If the first peak abundance of *Fenestrella antiqua* is used to determine the base of the Eocene, as suggested by Mitlehner (1996), then this base can be placed in the vicinity of the 'Le Goulet' Formation at Saint-Josse, and by correlation, the end of the 'Calcaires, marnes et lignites du Cap d'Ailly' Unit (SP2) at Ailly. It confirms the results of the carbon isotope analysis, which shows the presence of the Carbon Isotope Excursion (reference of the base of the Eocene) in the Lignite horizon L1 at the top of the SP2 Unit at Ailly (Magioncalda *et al.* 2001) and in the 'Le Goulet' Unit at Ailly (Magioncalda & Dupuis, in prep.).

Diatom assemblages from the Dieppe–Hampshire Basin are similar to those encountered in deposits from the Fur Formation of Denmark (Homann 1991; Mitlehner 1994), the Balder Formation (central North Sea Basin) (Malm *et al.* 1984) and Eocene deposits of the southern North Sea (Hughes 1981) (Fig. 16). Pyritized diatom assemblages from the Ypresian sediments of Ailly are similar to the siliceous and pyritized diatom assemblages found in Ypresian deposits from North Germany (Benda 1965) and Denmark in the Moler Formation (Benda 1972). The same species are found, including *Eunotogramma weissei*, *Aulacodiscus hirtus*, *Aulacodiscus subexcavatus*, *Triceratium nobile*, and *Stephanopyxis turris*. The greatest difference is the absence, during the Ypresian, of *Coscinodiscus morsianus* var. *moelleri*, which corresponds with the *Craspedodiscus moelleri* described by Benda. Some cosmopolitan species, such as *Craspedodiscus oblongus* recorded in Early Eocene deposits from the Atlantic area (Gombos 1982), are also present in the Dieppe–Hampshire Basin.

It seems that some taxa, such as *Actinoptychus senarius*, are restricted in their paleogeographical occurrence, depending on the palaeoenvironment. *Actinoptychus senarius* occurs in brackish palaeoenvironments in the Dieppe–Hampshire Basin and is rare in the North Sea Basin. However, *Actinoptychus senarius* does occur in abundance in the lower part of the Fur Formation ('Negative Serie') in association with abundant pennate diatoms (Mitlehner 1996), suggesting the presence of shallower waters. Further environmental information suggesting a slightly brackish palaeoenvironment for the lower part of the Fur Formation is shown by palynological studies (e.g. Heilmann-Clausen 1985; Schröder 1992). Furthermore, a new diatom genus, *Cylindrospira*, described by Mitlehner (1995) was also recovered from this interval; its morphology bears striking similarities to several tubular freshwater taxa, such as *Aulacoseira*, found in lacustrine environments from the Late Eocene onwards – further suggesting lowered salinities.

The diatom assemblages found in the Saint-Aubin Unit at Saint-Josse comprise brackish and marine diatoms. The upper part of the Formation of Varengeville at Ailly shows a major change in diatom assemblages: there is a proliferation of bipolar, triangular and oval diatom species. This indicates a marked increase in marine influence in the Dieppe–Hampshire Basin during the Ypresian, as already shown for the North Sea Basin (Mitlehner 1996).

Epoch	Biozonation			
	North Sea Basin (*)	Paris Basin (this work)		
		Name	Main characteristics	
EARLY EOCENE	Diverse diatom assemblage, including: *Aulacodiscus hirtus* *Triceratium* spp. *Isthmia* spp. *Hemiaulus* spp. *Trinacria* spp. *Fenestrella antiqua* (resting spores)	D3	Great diversity of bipolar, oval and triangular species *Aulacodiscus* spp. *Craspedodiscus* spp. *Triceratium* spp. *Trigonium* sp. *Hemiaulus* spp. *Trinacria* spp.	
EARLY EOCENE	Most abundant: *Fenestrella antiqua*	D2	Great diversity of circular species Most abundant species: *Fenestrella antiqua* *Actinoptychus senarius*	
LATE PALAEOCENE	Most abundant species: *Coscinodiscus morsianus* var. *moelleri* *Coscinodiscus morsianus* var. *morsianus* *Trinacria regina*	D1	Most abundant species: *Coscinodiscus morsianus* var. *moelleri* *Actinoptychus senarius*	

CIE

(*) Compiled from Mitlehner (1996) and Mudge & Copestake (1992)
CIE = Carbon Isotope Excursion

Fig. 17. Comparison of latest Palaeocene and earliest Eocene North Sea diatom biozonations and the Dieppe–Hampshire Basin diatom assemblages proposed in this work, including the main diatom marker species.

Conclusions

This study has shown that pyritized diatoms are a good fossil marker in Palaeocene–Eocene sediments of the Dieppe–Hampshire Basin and have a great potential biostratigraphic value. Despite wide variations in preservation of the pyritized diatoms, they can often be identified and used for correlation, age dating and palaeonvironmental studies. This work has led to the recognition of three major diatom assemblages and some diatom events. The lowermost, D1, occurring in Sorrus and Saint-Aubin (lower part) units, contains essentially circular diatoms. This assemblage is characterized by the abundance peak of *Coscinodiscus morsianus* var. *moelleri*. The second, most diverse assemblage (called D2) includes circular and triangular species with a great diversity of circular diatoms, the most abundant of these being *Fenestrella antiqua*. This assemblage occurs in the Saint-Aubin (upper part) and upper 'Sables et Argiles à Ostracodes et Mollusques' units from the Sparnacian facies. The last and most diverse assemblage (D3), including more cosmopolitan species (*Craspedodiscus oblongus, Aulacodiscus* spp.), is found in the Varengeville Formation (Lower Eocene, Ypresian). This assemblage is marked by the great diversity of triangular species and the high occurrence of *Aulacodiscus* spp., *Trigonium* spp. and *Trinacria* spp. Diatoms confirm that the Saint-Aubin Unit in the Saint-Josse borehole corresponds with the lower and upper 'Sables et Argiles à Ostracodes et Mollusques' units at Ailly.

Our study documents the diatom assemblages in the vicinity of the Palaeocene–Eocene boundary in the Dieppe–Hampshire Basin, and permits correlation between boreholes and sections. The use of pyritized diatoms also allows correlation of the approximate position of the Carbon Isotope Excursion (the official reference for the base of the Eocene) in the Dieppe–Hampshire and North Sea basins.

Recommendations

The present study has revealed that the pyritized diatoms are suitable for correlations and biostratigraphic analysis in the Dieppe–Hampshire Basin, as already proven for the North Sea Basin. This work has also shown that correlations between the Dieppe–Hampshire and North Sea basins are possible owing to the diatoms. In order to erect biozones, clarify the influence of ecological controls and test the validity of the diatom biozonation, it will be necessary to examine other sections from the Dieppe–Hampshire and Paris basins and boreholes from the Belgian Basin, including a thorough investigation of the Kallo borehole and a re-examination of the Knokke borehole.

This work was carried out as part of a Ph.D. research project in the Geology Department of the Facultés Universitaires Notre-Dame de la Paix of Namur. The first author thanks C. Cornet for her valuable advice and comments in discussions during the different steps of this work. V. Hallet is acknowledged for financial assistance. We also thank J. P. Debar of the Centre d'Etudes Techniques de l'Equipement Nord-Picardie, who gave permission to use the samples of the Saint-Josse borehole CC82. We also wish to acknowledge J. Dagnelie and Y. Houbion for technical assistance with the treatment of the samples.

References

BENDA, L. 1965. Diatomeen aus dem Eozän Nord-deutschlands. *Paläontologisches Zeitschrift*, **39 (3/4)**, 165–187.

BENDA, L. 1972. The diatoms of the Moler Formation of Denmark (Lower Eocene). A preliminary report. *Nova Hedwigia*, **39**, 251–266.

BETTENSTAEDT, F., FAHRION, H., HILTERMANN, H. & WICK, W. 1962. Tertiär Norddeutschlands. *In*: SIMON, W. & BARTENSTEIN, H. (eds) *Arbeitskreis deutscher Mikropaläontologen: Leitfossilien der Mikropalaontologie*. Gebruder Borntraeger, Berlin, 2 vols.

BIDGOOD, M. D. 1995. *The Microbiostratigraphy of the Palaeocene of the Northwest European Continental Shelf*. PhD thesis, University of Plymouth.

BIDGOOD, M. D., MITLEHNER, A. G., JONES, G. D. & JUTSON, D. J. 1999. Towards a stable and agreed nomenclature for North Sea Tertiary diatom floras – the 'Coscinodiscus' problem. *In*: JONES, R. W. & SIMMONS, M. D. (eds) *Biostratigraphy in Production and Development Geology*. Geological Society, London, Special Publications, **152**, 139–153.

BIGNOT, G. 1983. Les Lagunes Sparnaciennes: Une étape dans la conquête des eaux douces par les diatomées. *Revue de Micropaléontologie*, **26(1)**, 15–21.

BOLIN, C., TOURENQ, J. & AMBROISE, D. 1982. Sédimentologie et microfossiles pyritisés du sondage de Cuise-la-motte (Bassin de Paris). *Bulletin d'Information des Géologues du Bassin de Paris*, **19(4)**, 55–65.

CAYEUX, L. 1891. Etude micrographique du Tuffeau à *Cyprina planata* du Nord de la France et de la Belgique. Du rôle des Diatomées dans la formation de ce tuffeau. *Annales de la Société géologique du Nord*, **XXIX**, 90–95.

CLEVE-EULER, A. 1951. *Die diatomeen von Schweden und Finnland*. Stockholm Almqvist & Wiksells Boktryckeri. Svenska Vetenskapsakademiens Handlingar, Band 2, **1**, 159 pp.

DUBOIS, G. 1921. Etude des faciès thanétien et sparnacien du Landénien à Saint-Josse-sur-Mer et Saint-Aubin. *Annales de la Société géologique du Nord*, **XLVI**, 79–133.

DUPUIS, C., STEURBAUT, E., DE CONINCK, J. & RIVELINE, J. 1998. The western Argiles à lignites facies–Cap d'Ailly sections. *In*: THIRY, M. & DUPUIS, C. (eds) *The Palaeocene–Eocene Boundary in the Paris Basin: the Sparnacian Deposits*. Field Trip Guide, Mémoires des Sciences de la Terre, Ecole des Mines de Paris, **34**, 60–71.

DUPUIS, C. & THIRY, M. 1998. Geological frame of the 'Sparnacian'. *In*: THIRY, M. & DUPUIS, C. (eds) *The Palaeocene–Eocene Boundary in the Paris Basin: the Sparnacian Deposits*. Field Trip guide, Mémoires des Sciences de la Terre, Ecole des Mines de Paris, **34**, 3–12.

GOMBOS, A. M. 1982. Early and Middle Eocene diatom evolutionary events. *Bacillaria*, **5**, 225–242.

GOSSELET, J. 1901. Sables à galets du Mont Hulin, près de Saint-Josse (Pas-de-Calais). *Annales de la Société Géologique du Nord*, **30**, 205–207.

HASLE, G. R. & SYVERTSEN, E. E. 1997. Marine diatoms. *In*: TOMAS, C. R. (ed.) *Identifying Marine Phytoplankton*. Academic Press, London, pp. 5–385.

HEILMANN-CLAUSEN, C. 1985. Lithostratigraphy and depositional environments in the upper Palaeocene and Eocene of Denmark. *Bulletin of the Geological Survey of Denmark*, **33**, 287–323.

HOMANN, M. 1991. Die Diatomeen der Fur-Formation (Alt-Tertiär) aus dem Limfjord-Gebeit, Nordjutland–Dänemark. *Geologisches Jahrbuch, Reihe A*, **123**, 285pp.

HUGHES, M. J. 1981. Contribution on Oligocene and Eocene microfossils from the southern North Sea. *In*: NEALE, J. W. & BRASIER, M. D. (eds) *Microfossils from Fossil and Recent Shelf Seas*. Ellis Horwood, Chichester, pp. 186–294.

JACQUÉ, M. & THOUVENIN, J. 1975. Lower Tertiary tuffs and volcanic activity in the North Sea. *In*: WOODLAND, A. W. (ed.) *Petroleum and the Continental Shelf of Northwest Europe, Vol. 1: Geology*. Applied Science Publishers, Barking, Essex, pp. 455–465.

KING, C. 1983. *Cainozoic Micropalaeontological Biostratigraphy of the North Sea*. Institute of Geological Sciences Report, **82/7**, HMSO, London.

KING, C. 1990. Eocene stratigraphy of the Knokke borehole (Belgium). *In*: LAGA, P. & VANDENBERGHE, N. (eds) *The Knokke Well (11E/138) with a Description of the Den Haan (22W/276) and Oostduinkerke (35E/142) Wells*. Mémoires Exploration Cartes Géologiques et Minières de la Belgique, **29**, 67–102.

KNOX, R. W. O'B. 1984. Nannoplankton zonation and the Palaeocene–Eocene boundary beds of northwest Europe: an indirect correlation by means of volcanic ash layers. *Journal of the Geological Society of London*, **141**, 993–999.

KNOX, R. W. O'B., CORFIELD, R. M. & DUNAY, R. E. 1996. *Correlation of the Early Palaeogene in Northwest Europe*. Geological Society, London, Special Publications, **101**, 480 pp.

LOHMANN, K. & ANDREWS, G. 1968. Late Eocene non-marine diatoms from the Beaver Divide area, Fremont County, Wyoming. *United States Geological Survey Professional Paper*, **593-e**, 1–31.

LUTERBACHER, H. P., HARDENBOL, J. & SCHMITZ, B. 2000. Decision of the voting members of the International Subcommission on Palaeogene Stratigraphy on the criterion for the recognition of the Palaeocene–Eocene boundary. *Newsletter, International Subcommission on Palaeogene Stratigraphy*, **9**, p. 13.

MAGIONCALDA, R., DUPUIS, C. *ET AL.* 2001. L'excursion isotopique du carbone organique ($\delta^{13}C_{org}$) dans les paléoenvironnements continentaux de l'intervalle Paléocène–Eocène de Varangeville (Haute-Normandie). *Société Géologique de France*, **172(3)**, 349–358.

MALM, O. A., CHRISTENSEN, O. B., FURNES, H., LOVLIE, R., RUSELÅTTEN, H. & OSTBY, K. L. 1984. The Lower Tertiary Balder Formation: an organogenic and tuffaceous deposit in the North Sea region. *In*: SPENCER, A. M. (ed.) *Petroleum Geology of the North European Margin*. Graham & Trotman, London, pp. 149–170.

MITLEHNER, A. G. 1994. *The Occurrence and Preservation of Diatoms in the Palaeogene of the North Sea Basin*. Ph.D. Thesis, University College, London.

MITLEHNER, A. G. 1995. *Cylindrospira*, a new diatom genus from the Palaeogene of Denmark with palaeoenvironmental significance. *Diatom Research*, **10(2)**, 321–331.

MITLEHNER, A. G. 1996. Palaeoenvironments in the North Sea Basin around the Palaeocene–Eocene boundary: evidence from diatoms and other siliceous microfossils. In: KNOX, R. W. O'B., CORFIELD, R. M. & DUNAY, R. E. (eds) *Correlation of the Early Palaeogene in Northwest Europe*. Geological Society, London, Special Publications, **101**, 255–273.

MUDGE, D. C. & COPESTAKE, P. 1992. Lower Palaeogene stratigraphy of the northern North Sea. *Marine and Petroleum Geology*, **9**, 287–301.

NEAL, J. E., STEIN, J. A. & GAMBER, J. H. 1994. Graphic correlation and sequence stratigraphy in the Palaeogene of NW Europe. *Journal of Micropalaeontology*, **13**, 55–80.

ORESHKINA, T. V. 2000. New data on early Eocene diatom successions of the West Polar Urals margin: biostratigraphic and paleogeographic implications. *GFF*, **122**, 124–126.

ROUND, F. E. CRAWFORD, R. M. & MANN, D. G. 1990. *The Diatoms. Biology and Morphology of the Genera*. Cambridge University Press, Cambridge, 747 pp.

ROSS, R. & SIMS, P. A. 1970. Studies of *Aulacodiscus* with the scanning electron microscope. *Nova Hedwigia*, **31**, 49–88.

SCHERER, R. P. & KOÇ, N. 1996. Late Palaeogene diatom biostratigraphy and palaeoenvironments of the Northern Norwegian–Greenland sea. *In*: THIEDE, J., MYHRE, A. M., FIRTH, J. V., JOHNSON, G. L. & RUDDIMAN, W. F. (eds), *Proceedings of the Ocean Drilling Program, Scientific Results*, **151**, 75–99.

SCHRÖDER, T. 1992. A palynological zonation for the Palaeocene of the North Sea Basin. *Journal of Micropalaeontology*, **11**, 113–126.

SIMS, P. A. 1989. Some Cretaceous and Palaeogene species of *Coscinodiscus*: a micromorphological and systematic study. *Diatom Research*, **4(2)**, 351–371.

SIMS, P. A. 1990. The fossil diatom genus *Fenestrella*, its morphology, systematics and paleogeography. *Nova Hedwigia*, **100**, 277–288.

STEURBAUT, E. 1998. High-resolution holostratigraphy of Middle Palaeocene to Early Eocene strata in Belgium and adjacent areas. *Palaeontographica Abteilung A*, **247**, 91–156.

STREL'NIKOVA, N. I. & LASTIVKA, T. V. 1999. The problem of the origin of marine and freshwater diatoms. *In:* MAYAMA, I. & KOTZUMI (eds) *Proceedings, 14th Diatom Symposium 1996.* Koeltz, Koenigstein, 113–123.

VAN DER WERFF, A. & HULS, H. 1976. *Diatomeeën-flora van Nederland (Diatom Flora of the Netherlands).* Otto Koeltz Science Publishers, Koenigstein, West Germany, 593 pp.

VAN EETVELDE, Y. & CORNET C. 2002. Some Eocene species of marine pyritized diatoms in the core of Saint-Josse (France). *Diatom Research*, **17**, 423–435.

ZONG, Y. 1997. Implications of *Paralia sulcata* abundance in Scottish isolation basins. *Diatom Research*, **12**, 125–150.

Palaeobiotope analysis and palaeoenvironmental reconstruction of the Palaeocene–Early Eocene ostracodes from east-central Sinai, Egypt

ASHRAF M. T. ELEWA[1] & ABDEL-MOHSEN M. MORSI[2]

[1]Geology Department, Faculty of Science, Minia University, Minia, Egypt
(e-mail: aelewa@Link.net)
[2]Geology Department, Faculty of Science, Ain Shams University, Cairo, Egypt

Abstract: Quantitative study of the ostracode assemblages from the Palaeocene to Early Eocene succession exposed along the area of east-central Sinai extending from the Egma Plateau in the south to Areif El Naqa in the north, using cluster analysis based on the customary presence/absence data matrix of frequencies (the Jaccard coefficient of similarity), has resulted in the distinction of five ecozones in the Early Palaeocene to Early Eocene intervals. Correspondence analysis applied to the same data matrix has led to the identification of five environmental factors affecting the distribution of the whole ostracode assemblage of the study area. These are the time factor or vertical distribution (second latent vector), water depth (third latent vector), degree of energy (fourth latent vector), water temperature as a function of depth (fifth latent vector), and oxygen concentration (sixth latent vector). From this, the prevailing palaeoenvironments in the study area during the Early Palaeocene to Early Eocene times have been reconstructed. A distinct faunal change has been detected at the Palaeocene–Eocene thermal maximum (PETM) as indicated by the second latent vector.

Study area and previous work

Our knowledge of the Palaeocene to Early Eocene ostracodes from the southern realm of the Tethys has been increased substantially through the works of Bassiouni et al. (1977), Boukhary et al. (1982), Khalifa et al. (1984), Bassiouni & Luger (1990), Ismail (1992, 1996), Aref (1995), Elewa et al. (1999) and Morsi (1999) in Egypt; Honigstein et al. (1991), Honigstein & Rosenfeld (1995) and Honigstein et al. (2002) in Israel; Bassiouni (1969, 1970) in Jordan; Barsotti (1963) and Whatley & Arias (1993) in Libya; Esker (1968), Donze et al. (1982) and Peypouquet et al. (1986) in Tunisia; and Grekoff (1969) and Damotte & Fleury (1987) in Algeria. Other relevant studies from areas such as West Africa, include Apostolescu (1961), Reyment (1963, 1966, 1981), Reyment & Reyment (1980), and Carbonnel et al. (1990). However, little attention has been paid to the Palaeocene to Early Eocene ostracodes of Sinai. Despite the abundance of ostracodes in strata of this age in Sinai, the only studies are by Ismail (1996) and Morsi (1999).

The present study represents one among a series of papers concerned with the stratigraphy, palaeontology and geodynamics of the Upper Cretaceous–Lower Tertiary succession in northeastern Egypt as part of a scientific co-operation project between Ain Shams University, Egypt and the University of Bremen, Germany. It deals with the Palaeocene–Lower Eocene ostracode fauna extracted from five stratigraphic sections measured in the area of east-central Sinai, Egypt (Fig. 1). The Sinai Peninsula covers an area of approximately 61,000 km[2] and is separated geographically from Egypt by the Suez Canal and the Gulf of Suez (Jenkins in Said 1990).

The detailed lithostratigraphic description as well as biostratigraphy of the studied sections have been discussed in other publications (Lüning et al. 1998a, b; Marzouk & Lüning 1998; Morsi 1999). The ostracode systematic palaeontology, biostratigraphy, palaeoecology and palaeobiogeography have been the subject of a separate publication (Morsi 1999). Age assignments are mainly based on planktonic foraminifera and calcareous nannofossils described by Lüning et al. (1998a, b) and Marzouk & Lüning (1998).

The aim of the present study is to establish an appropriate palaeoecological zonation for the Palaeocene to Early Eocene ostracodes of the study area, using cluster analysis. Reconstruction of the palaeoenvironment, with the help of correspondence analysis of the available ostracode data, is also attempted.

From: BEAUDOIN, A.B. & HEAD, M.J. (eds) 2004. The Palynology and Micropalaeontology of Boundaries. Geological Society, London, Special Publications, **230**, 293–308. 0305-8719/04/$15 © The Geological Society of London 2004.

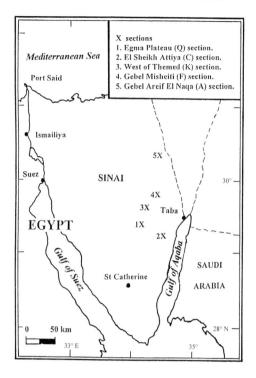

Fig. 1. Location map of the studied sections (after Morsi 1999).

Five sections, between latitudes 29°–30° 30′ N and longitudes 34°–34° 30′ E, were measured and studied (Fig. 1). These sections are:

(1) Egma Plateau (Q), between latitude 29° 25′ N and longitude 34° 10′ E;
(2) El Sheikh Attiya (C), between latitude 29° 15′ N and longitude 34° 30′ E;
(3) 10 km west of Gebel Themed (K), between latitude 29° 35′ N and longitude 34° 15′ E;
(4) Gebel Misheiti (F), between latitude 29° 50′ N and longitude 34° 20′ E;
(5) Gebel Areif El Naqa (A), between latitude 30° 25′ N and longitude 34° 20′ E.

Stratigraphy

The study area exposes a thick succession that ranges in age from Triassic to Mid-Eocene, of which only the Palaeocene–Lower Eocene sections are being studied herein. The Palaeocene–Lower Eocene part of the succession is predominantly composed of greenish hemipelagic marls and argillaceous limestones (the Esna Shale of Beadnell 1905). It is overlain by a succession of limestones, chalks and dolomites with flint intercalations representing the Lower–(?) Middle Eocene 'Thebes Formation' (Said

1962). The Esna Shale contains abundant planktonic foraminifera and calcareous nanno-fossils which permit a detailed biostratigraphic zonation (Marzouk & Lüning 1998). It unconformably overlies chalks and limestones of the Campanian–Maastrichtian Sudr Chalk (Allam & Khalil 1988; Ziko *et al.* 1993; Marzouk & Lüning, 1998; Lüning *et al.* 1998*a*). As described by Marzouk and Lüning (1998), this unconformity is of regional nature with varying vertical extension around the K–T boundary and is documented by missing biozones and/or reworked Late Maastrichtian microfauna. The hiatus is minimal at the El Sheikh Attiya (C) section, where the Late Maastrichtian plank-tonic foraminiferal *Abathomphalus mayaroensis* and calcareous nannofossil *Micula prinsii* Zones are followed on top by the *Parvularuglobigerina eugubina* and NP1 Zones respectively. It is larger in the section at Areif El-Naqa (A), where the *Parvularuglobigerina eugubina* and the calcareous nannofossil NP1 Zones are missing and the Palaeocene begins with the *Parasubbotina pseudobulloides* and NP2 Zones. In the Gebel Misheiti (F) section, these latest Maastrichtian zones are succeeded by the Palaeocene succession, which starts with the *Parasubbotina pseudobulloides* and NP2 Zones. In the Egma Plateau

(Q) and west of Themed (K) sections, the K–T boundary is not exposed and the section begins in the Palaeocene (*Praemurica trinidadensis* – NP3 Zones at the Egma Plateau and *Praemurica uncinata* – NP3 Zones west of Themed).

The Palaeocene–Eocene boundary lies within the upper part of the Esna Shale. It is placed at the planktonic foraminiferal *Morozovella velascoensis–Morozovella edgari* and the nannofossil NP9–NP10 zonal boundaries (Marzouk & Lüning 1998). The highest part of the fauna-yielding part of the Esna Shale is not synchronous in the studied sections. The *M. edgari* Zone (NP10) represents the uppermost zone in the sections of El Sheikh Attiya (C), west of Themed (K) and Gebel Misheiti (F); the *M. subbotinae* (NP11) is the uppermost zone at the Egma Plateau (Q). In the Areif El Naqa (A) section, *M. uncinata* (NP3) Zone is the highest recorded zone being unconformably succeeded by (?) Middle Eocene flinty dolomitic limestone of the 'Thebes Formation'.

The Palaeocene–Early Eocene lithological sequence in the study area (Fig. 2) can be divided into the following rock units in upward sequence based on lithological features.

Esna Formation

Beadnell (1905) introduced the term 'Esna Shale' to describe the thick shales of Gebel Aweina near Esna. In 1960 and later in 1971, Said named the shale outcropping in the succession of northern Wadi Qena as the Esna Formation, which we follow herein.

In the study area, this formation is composed of green–grey marl and argillaceous limestone with a white chalky interval near the top. The Esna Formation unconformably overlies the Maastrichtian Sudr Chalk (Allam & Khalil 1988; Ziko *et al.* 1993; Marzouk & Lüning 1998), and equates to the Dakhla Shale succession, the Tarawan Chalk and the Esna Shale in the Western Desert and Nile Valley. Allam & Khalil (1988) have introduced the term 'Beida Formation' for the succession outcropping at the area of Areif El Naqa. Based on planktonic foraminifera, the age of the Esna Formation is Palaeocene (Said 1960; Khalifa & El Sayed 1984; Nishi *et al.* 1994). However, by means of planktonic foraminifera and calcareous nannoplankton, as well as ostracodes, Marzouk & Lüning (1998) and Morsi (1999) assigned this formation to the Early Palaeocene (Danian) at the base to Early Eocene (Yprésian) at the top.

Thebes Formation

The Thebes Formation was originally described by Said (1960) in the Gebel Gurnah area (opposite Luxor). He later assigned the same term to the limestone facies overlying the Esna Formation in northern Wadi Qena (Said 1971).

In the study area, the Thebes Formation consists of chalky, argillaceous, occasionally dolomitic, bedded limestone with intercalations of yellowish, brownish flint. In the Areif El Naqa section, it consists of thick-bedded chalk with marly interlayers, thereby differing from the typical Thebes Formation of Said (1960).

Marzouk & Lüning (1998) and Morsi (1999) assigned the Thebes Formation to the Early Eocene (Ypresian). However, Nishi *et al.* (1994) attributed it to the Late Palaeocene to latest Early Eocene, using planktonic foraminifera.

Material and methods

Out of 116 marl and limestone samples collected from the five studied sections, 73 relatively soft marl and argillaceous limestone samples yielded well-preserved ostracodes. These ostracodes are deposited under the name of A. M. Morsi in the Geology Department, Faculty of Science, Ain Shams University, Cairo, Egypt. Serial reference numbers (S-42 to S-54) are given only to the specimens photographed by A. M. Morsi with the Cam Scan SEM of the FB5-Geowissenschaften, University of Bremen, Germany. Excluding samples containing rare species (R), and having less than five frequent occurrences in each of these samples, we have selected 38 ostracode-bearing samples suitable for faunal analysis. Cluster analysis based on the Jaccard coefficient of similarity (the group average linkage method) was made on 38 samples having 23 ostracode species, based on the presence/absence data matrix, for discriminating sample groups. For the next step, we applied the correspondence analysis to the same data matrix, expressed as a contingency table of frequencies with a constant sum, to elucidate the most important environmental factors affecting the distribution of the ostracode assemblages in the study area. Interpretations of the dendrogram resulted from cluster analysis as well as the latent vectors of the correspondence analysis were made by one of us (A. Elewa).

The cluster analysis program, used for this study, is contained in the BioDiversity Pro. software (version 2), 1997. The correspondence analysis program is included with the textbook by Reyment & Savazzi (1999).

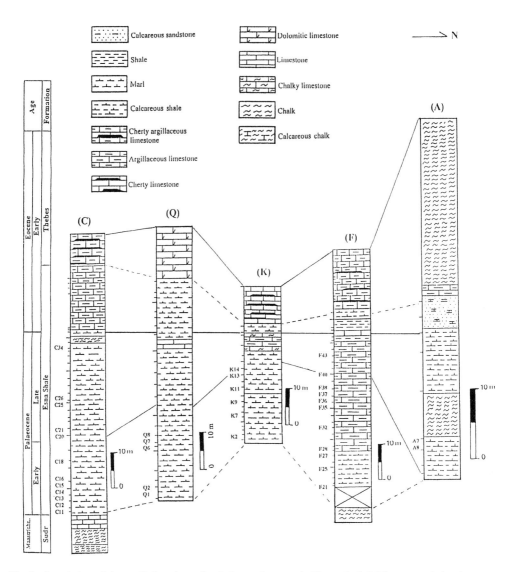

Fig. 2. Correlation of the studied sections. Symbols are the same in Figure 1. Solid lines: correlation by age; dashed lines: lithostratigraphic correlation. The 'X' symbol on section F indicates undefined portion of the section. Different vertical scales for the different sections are used so that they all span the correct relative time frame as given by the age column on the left.

The multivariate results separated here are in the fixed mode not the random mode (Reyment & Jöreskog 1993): hence our conclusions arrived at in this study cannot be extrapolated. We analysed one particular collection of data (sample) without regarding it as a sample from some statistical population of objects. The results can only be interpreted with respect to the objects in the sample, and no inference is made about a population larger than the actual sample. Additionally, the components of latent vectors are very susceptible to instability. For this reason, we have contented ourselves with a high level of 'significance' for the components accepted as being verifiable.

Brief notes on the techniques used in the present study

Cluster analysis

Cluster analysis is the name of a group of multivariate techniques whose primary purpose is to identify similar entities from the characteristics they possess. This technique has been variously referred to as Q analysis, typology, classification analysis and numerical taxonomy. The most commonly used clustering algorithms can be classified in two general categories: non-hierarchial and hierarchial. In the non-hierarchial or the K-means method, the first step is to select a cluster centre or seed, and all objects (individuals) within a prespecified threshold distance are included in the resulting cluster. On the other hand, the hierarchial procedures involve the construction of a hierarchy or treelike structure. There are basically two types of hierarchial clustering procedures: agglomerative and divisive. In the agglomerative methods, each observation starts out as its own cluster, then the two closest clusters (or individuals) are combined into a new aggregate cluster, and so on until all individuals are grouped into one large cluster. This process is shown in a dendrogram or tree graph. In general, five popular agglomerative procedures are used to develop clusters: single linkage, complete linkage, average linkage (used in the present study), Ward's method and centroid. On the other hand, the divisive method proceeds in the opposite direction to agglomerative methods. In divisive methods, the procedure begins with one large cluster containing all observations, and then the observations that are most dissimilar are split off and turned into smaller clusters, and so on until each observation becomes a cluster in itself. For more information about cluster analysis, see Everitt (1980) and Hair *et al.* (1992).

Correspondence analysis

Bénzecri (1973) has introduced correspondence analysis as a graphical technique, although the main features of the method have been known for many years. Bénzecri's unique contribution consists of a means of scaling the axes so that the variables (i.e. parts) can be graphically indicated in relation to the individuals of the sample. Reyment & Savazzi (1999) prefer to call it an 'analysis of associations' for the reason that the French word 'correspondance' is not an exact equivalent of the inexact English derivation – the word 'association' being closer to the idea involved in French. Correspondence analysis has the advantage over other interdependent techniques in its ability to accommodate both non-metric and non-linear relationships. Briefly, the aim of correspondence analysis is to obtain simultaneously, and on equivalent scales (i.e. dividing the data entries by the square roots of their respective row and column totals), what we have termed R-mode factor loadings and Q-mode factor loadings that represent the same principal components of the data matrix (Reyment & Jöreskog 1993). The method starts with presentation of a cross-tabulation table to yield a conditional expectation very similar to an expected chi-square value. Then these values are normalized, and a process much like factor analysis defines lower-dimensional solutions. The fundamental mathematical principle is known as the singular value decomposition, the properties of which were established by J. J. Sylvester more than 120 years ago. These factors simultaneously relate the rows and columns of the data matrix in a single joint plot. For detailed explanation of the technique, see Bénzecri (1973), Reyment (1991), Hair *et al.* (1992), Reyment & Jöreskog (1993) and Reyment & Savazzi (1999).

Ostracode regional distribution

The studied ostracode fauna are mainly represented by an outer neritic to upper bathyal assemblage (Morsi 1999). They belong to the type recognized by Bassiouni & Luger (1990) and Damotte (1995) as the 'South Tethyan Type'. Many of the recorded species have a wide distribution in the Palaeocene–Lower Eocene strata along the southern realm of the Tethys ocean. Among 27 species found in the present sections, 23 were previously recorded in different areas of North Africa and the Middle East. Almost identical fauna are also present in the same stratigraphic level in Algeria (Damotte & Fleury 1987), Tunisia (Esker 1968; Donze *et al.* 1982), Israel (Honigstein & Rosenfeld 1995) and Jordan (Bassiouni, 1969, 1970). Only two species, namely *Parakrithe crolifa* and *Reticulina sangalkamensis*, are also known from West Africa (Apostolescu 1961; Reyment 1981). These two species were able to inhabit inner to outer neritic depth ranges (Bassiouni & Luger 1990), thus being capable of migrating between the Southern Tethyan realm and the West African basins through the Trans-Saharan Sea-way (for detailed discussion see Morsi 1999).

The stratigraphic ranges of the recorded ostracode species are given in Table 1. This

Table 1. *Stratigraphic range of the recorded ostracode species (after Morsi 1999). Solid lines: occurrences in the area of the present study; dashed lines: other occurrences based on literature.*

Campanian–Maastricht.	Palaeocene		Eocene	Age
	Early	Late	Early	
- - - - - -	———			*Cytherelloidea attiyaensis*
- - - - - -	———			*Pontocyprella recurva*
- - - - - -	———			*Acanthocythereis meslei meslei*
- - - - - -	———			*Cythereis mesa mesa*
- - - - - -	———			*Cythereis mesa ventroreticulata*
- - - - - -	———			*Paracosta pervinquieri*
- - - - - -	———			*Bairdia* aff. *septentrionalis*
- - - - - -	———			*Krithe echolsae*
- - - - - -	———			*Martinicythere bassiounii*
- - - - - -	———			*Ordoniya ordoniya*
- - - - - -	———			*Phacorhabdotus inaequicostatus*
- - - - - -	———		- - - - - -	*Mauritsina coronata*
- - - - - -	———		- - - - - -	*Mauritsina jord. nodoreticulata*
- - - - - -	———		- - - - - -	*Megommatocythere denticulata*
	———			*Bythocypris* cf. *olaredodui*
	———			*Cytherella sinaensis*
	———			*Cristaeleberis reticulata*
	———			*Oertliella posterotriangulata*
	———			*Ordoniya bulaqensis*
	———		- - - - - -	*Cytherella* cf. *lagenalis*
	———		- - - - - -	*Parakrithe crolifa*
	———	- - - - - -	- - - - - -	*Paracosta parakefensis*
- - - - -	———	————	————	*Reticulina sangalkamensis*
		————	————	*Mauritsina martinii*
		————	————	*Ordoniya burmaensis*
		————	————	*Ordoniya hasaensis*
		————	————	*Reticulina proteros*

table establishes the distinction between three kinds of ostracode species:

(1) Species crossing the K–T boundary;
(2) Early Palaeocene species;
(3) Late Palaeocene species. These later species are found to extend higher in the Early Eocene.

Zonation based on palaeobiotopes

The five palaeobiotopes that were identified by cluster analysis (Fig. 3), were first plotted on the studied columnar sections and then extended farther vertically and horizontally (by adding those samples having smaller number of specimens but including the same species of the five palaeobiotopes), to define the exact ostracode zonation existing within these sections (Fig. 4).

Palaeobiotopes 1 and 2 are restricted to the south, whereas the other three palaeobiotopes are widely distributed through the area under investigation.

Each of these palaeobiotopes has its characteristic ostracode species that represent a particular environment, therefore these palaeobiotopes could be equated to the following ostracode ecozones.

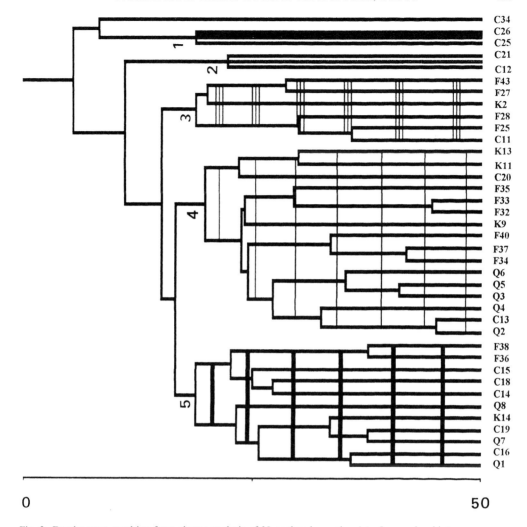

Fig. 3. Dendrogram resulting from cluster analysis of 38 analysed samples. 1 to 5 are palaeobiotopes.

Cytherelloidea attiyaensis Assemblage Zone (Fig. 5a, f & g)

Author: Defined here.
Definition: This zone is based on palaeobiotope 5 (Fig. 3). In addition to the nominate species, *Cytherella sinaensis* Morsi, *Martinicythere bassiounii* Honigstein & Rosenfeld and *Ordoniya ordoniya* (Bassiouni) are also common.
Type section: Bed no. 4 (marl), samples C14 to C16 and C18 to C19 from the El Sheikh Attiya section (C).
Occurrence: The Esna Formation; the base of the section exposed at the Egma Plateau (Q), samples Q1, Q7 and Q8; samples C14 to C16 and C18 to C19 from the El Sheikh Attiya section (C); sample K14 from the section at

10 km west of Gebel Themed (K); samples F36 and F38 from the Gebel Misheiti section (F).
Age: Early Palaeocene.

Cythereis mesa mesa Assemblage Zone (Fig. 5b, c, d, f, g, j & k)

Author: Defined here.
Definition: This zone is based on palaeobiotope 4 (Fig. 3). This zone is characterized by the consistent occurrences of *Cythereis mesa mesa* Honigstein, *Cytherella sinaensis* Morsi, *Bairdia* aff. *septentrionalis* Bonnema and *Martinicythere bassiounii* Honigstein & Rosenfeld. *Krithe echolsae* Esker also occurs in low abundance.
Type section: Samples Q2 to Q6 of bed no. 1 (marl) at the Egma Plateau section (Q).

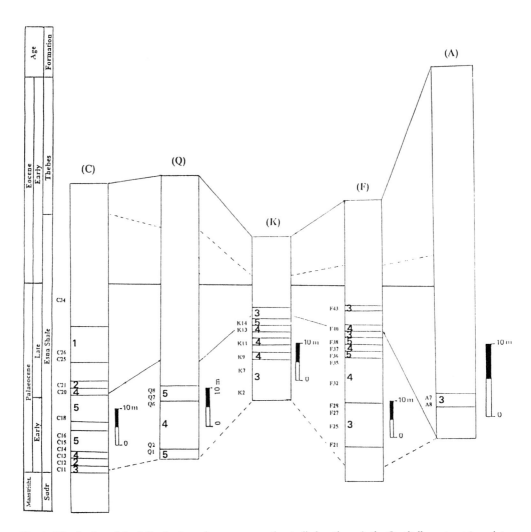

Fig. 4. Distribution of the defined ostracode ecozones on the studied sections. 1, the *Oertliella posterotriangulata–Megommatocythere denticulata* Assemblage Zone; 2, the *Parakrithe crolifa–Cristaeleberis reticulata* Assemblage Zone; 3, the *Krithe echolsae* Assemblage Zone; 4, the *Cythereis mesa mesa* Assemblage Zone; 5, the *Cytherelloidea attiyaensis* Assemblage Zone.

Occurrence: The Esna Formation; samples Q2 to Q6 from the Egma Plateau section (Q); sample C13 and C20 at El Sheikh Attiya section (C); samples K9, K11 and K13 at 10 km west of the Gebel Themed (K); samples F29 to F35, F37 and F40 from the Gebel Misheiti section (F).

Age: Early Palaeocene.

Krithe echolsae Assemblage Zone (Fig. 5b, c, d, e, f & g)

Author: Defined here.

Definition: This zone is based on palaeobiotope 3 (Fig. 3). It is characterized by the frequent occurrence of the nominate species. *Martinicythere bassiounii* Honigstein & Rosenfeld, *Bairdia* aff. *septentrionalis* Bonnema, *Phacorhabdotus inaequicostatus* Colin & Donze, *Ordoniya ordoniya* (Bassiouni) and *Pontocyprella recurva* Esker consistently occur in this zone.

Type section: Bed no. 3 (calcareous shale), samples F21 to F27 and the base of bed no. 4 (argillaceous limestone), sample F28 of the section at Gebel Misheiti (F).

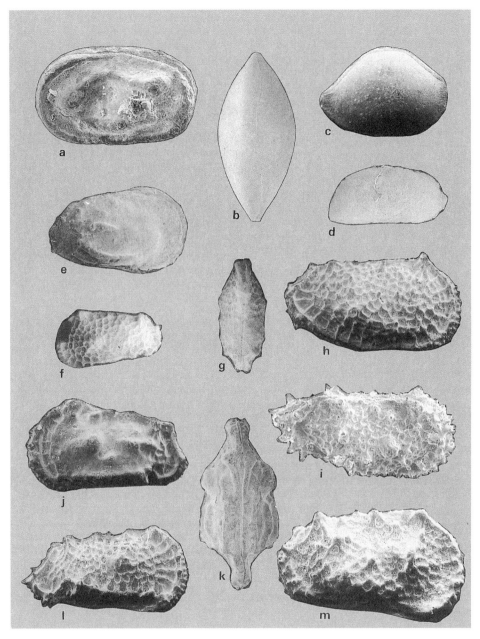

Fig. 5. RV, right view; LV, left view; DV, dorsal view.
(**a**) *Cytherelloidea attiyaensis* Morsi; El Sheikh Attiya section, sample C12; S-42, length 0.90 mm, LV.
(**b–c**) *Bairdia* aff. *septentrionalis* Bonnema; El Sheikh Attiya section, sample C24; S-43, length 1.62 mm, width 0.85 mm. (**b**) DV; (**c**) RV. (**d**) *Krithe echolsae* Esker; El Sheikh Attiya section, sample C11; S-45, length 0.74 mm, RV. (**e**) *Phacorhabdotus inaequicostatus* Colin & Donze; Gebel Misheiti section, sample F25; S-54, length 0.61 mm, RV. (**f–g**) *Martinicythere bassiounii* Honigstein & Rosenfeld; Egma Plateau section, sample Q2; S-46, width 0.33 mm, length 0.62 mm. (**f**) LV; (**g**) DV. (**h**) *Megommatocythere denticulata* (Esker); El Sheikh Attiya section, sample C13; S-51, length 1.02 mm, RV. (**i**) *Oertliella posterotriangulata* Morsi; West Themed section, sample K3; S-52, length 0.68 mm, RV. (**j & k**) *Cythereis mesa mesa* Honigstein; Egma Plateau section, sample Q7; S-49, width 0.40 mm, length 0.90 mm; (**j**) LV; (**k**) DV. (**l**) *Mauritsina martinii* Bassiouni; El Sheikh Attiya section, sample C33; S-48, length 0.90 mm, RV. (**m**) *Cristaeleberis reticulata* Bassiouni; El Sheikh Attiya section, sample C16; S-50, length 0.91 mm, RV.

Occurrence: The Esna Formation; the base of sections at the El Sheikh Attiya (C), sample C11 and at 10 km west of the Gebel Themed (K), samples K1 to K8 and K15 to K16; samples F21 to F28, F39 and F43 from the section at Gebel Misheiti (F); samples A7 and A8 from the section at Gebel Areif El Naqa (A).
Age: Early to Late Palaeocene.

Parakrithe crolifa–Cristaeleberis reticulata Assemblage Zone (Fig. 5a, f, g & h)

Author: Defined here.
Definition: This zone is based on palaeobiotope 2 (Fig. 3). This zone is characterized by the dominance of *Parakrithe crolifa* Bassiouni & Luger and *Cristaeleberis reticulata* Bassiouni. *Martinicythere bassiounii* Honigstein & Rosenfeld also occurs in this zone.
Type section: Samples C12 and C21 of bed no. 4 (marl) at El Sheikh Attiya section (C).
Occurrence: The Esna Formation; samples C12 and C21 of bed no. 4 (marl) from the El Sheikh Attiya section (C).
Age: Early to Late Palaeocene.

Oertliella posterotriangulata– Megommatocythere denticulata Assemblage Zone (Fig. 5a, b, c, e, h, i & l)

Author: Defined here.
Definition: This zone is based on palaeobiotope 1 (Fig. 3). This zone is characterized by the frequent occurrences of the nominate species as well as *Mauritsina coronata* Esker, *Bairdia* aff. *septentrionalis* Bonnema, *Ordoniya burmaensis* (Bassiouni), *Phacorhabdotus inaequicostatus* Colin & Donze, *Cytherella sinaensis* Morsi. *Mauritsina martinii* Bassiouni rarely occurs in this zone.
Type section: Samples C25 to C30 of bed no. 4 (marl) at El Sheikh Attiya section (C).
Occurrence: The Esna Formation; samples C25 to C30 of bed no. 4 (marl) from the El Sheikh Attiya section (C).
Age: Late Palaeocene to Early Eocene.

Analysis of correspondences for defining palaeoenvironments

Reyment (1991) stated that correspondence analysis is appropriate for the analysis of presence/absence data and counts in a contingency table (i.e. a table of frequencies with constant row-sums). It means that the sums of the rows are all about 100, because the method was specifically devised for the analysis of contingency tables, the entries in which may be interpreted as probabilities, and hence have a constant sum. Correspondence analysis is entirely graphical, in that the reason for doing the analysis is to look for clustering in the data and to look for a relationship between the variables (parts) and the data-points (see Reyment & Savazzi 1999).

In the present study, 38 ostracode-bearing samples, were selected and treated by correspondence analysis for 23 ostracode species to extract the effective latent roots of the data matrix. The results are summarized in Table 2. This table shows that the first five latent roots account for about 59% of the variance. This contains adequate information for modelling the palaeoenvironmental patterns of the ostracode faunas in the study area. Notice that the first latent root is lost because of the effects of the contingency table and the effect of scaling (see Reyment & Savazzi 1999), thus, the second latent root becomes the first real and interpretable latent root.

The five latent roots were examined by comparing their associated vectors (Figs 6a–d). From these figures it was possible to reach an appropriate results about the most important factors affecting the distribution of the ostracode assemblages of the study area. The second latent vector (Fig. 6a) is successful in identifying species that range from Late Palaeocene into the Early Eocene (with high positive second latent vector), such as *Reticulina proteros* Bassiouni (no. 60) and *R. sangalkamensis* (Apostolescu) (no. 61), from the remaining species restricted to Palaeocene (with low positive second latent vector). In other words, this latent vector represents the time factor. It is remarkable that *Reticulina proteros* Bassiouni and *R. sangalkamensis* (Apostolescu) are close to sample C34 (no. 21). This is the most recent sample of the 38 analysed and is located at the top of bed no. 4 (Marl), near the contact between the Late Palaeocene and the Early Eocene of the section at El Sheikh Attiya (see Fig. 2). This sample

Table 2. *Summary of correspondence analysis. Latent roots 7 to 20 are not included because they do not add significantly to the explained variance.*

No.	Latent root	Variance per cent	Cumulative per cent
2	0.48981	21.727	21.727
3	0.27059	12.003	33.730
4	0.20598	9.137	42.867
5	0.19687	8.733	51.600
6	0.16663	7.391	58.991

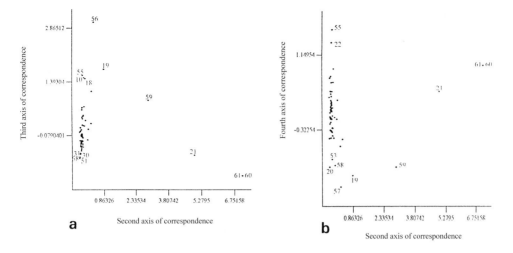

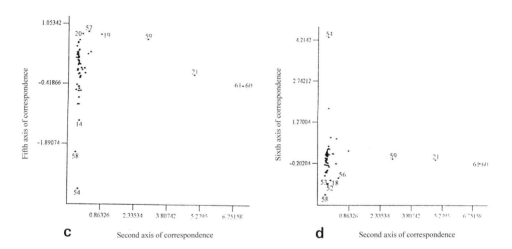

Fig. 6a–d. Plot of second *v.* third, fourth, fifth, and sixth axes of correspondence, respectively. (**a**) time factor for the second axis and water depth for the third axis, (**b**) degree of energy for the fourth axis; (**c**) water temperature as a function of depth for the fifth axis; (**d**) oxygenation for the sixth axis. Points 1–38 represent samples and points 39–61 represent species.

shows changes in the ostracode fauna at the Palaeocene–Eocene thermal maximum (PETM) in the study area as indicated by the second latent vector.

The same graph (Fig. 6a), shows that the third latent vector groups the species according to their water depth. It could separate middle to outer shelf species (with high positive third latent vector) from outer shelf to upper bathyal ones (with high negative third latent vector). The middle to outer shelf species are *Cristaeleberis*

reticulata Bassiouni (no. 56); *Cythereis mesa ventroreticulata* Honigstein (no. 55), according to Bassiouni & Luger (1990) who assigned a species belonging to the genus *Cristaeleberis* to the middle to outer shelf and Keen *et al.* (1994) who pointed out that species with a localized distribution (like *Cythereis mesa ventroreticulata*) probably indicate infraneritic depths. Those with outer shelf to upper bathyal depths include: *Reticulina proteros* Bassiouni (no. 60); *R. sangalkamensis* (Apostolescu) (no. 61); *Maur-*

itsina jordanica nodoreticulata Bassiouni (no. 51) and *Paracosta parakefensis* Bassiouni & Luger (no. 58), according to Bassiouni & Luger (1990) and Donze *et al.* (1982). The shallower species are close to samples C12, C21 and C25 (nos 10, 18 and 19 in the graph Fig. 5a) of the section at El Sheikh Attiya (C) (Fig. 2). Those species indicating deeper zones are close to samples F32 and F33 (nos 30 and 31) of the section at Gebel Misheiti (F) (Fig. 2).

The fourth latent vector (Fig. 6b) separates between species indicating turbulent, rather shallow-water conditions (with high positive fourth latent vector) and those confined to tranquil, deep-water conditions (with high negative fourth latent vector). The first group is represented in the graph by species inhabiting infraneritic depths, such as *Cythereis mesa ventroreticulata* (no. 55) (Keen *et al.* 1994). The second group represents species living in outer shelf to upper bathyal depths, according to Bassiouni & Luger (1990), Keen *et al.* (1994) and Morsi (1999). These include *Mauritsina coronata* (no. 57), *Ordoniya burmaensis* (Bassiouni) (no. 59), *Paracosta parakefensis* (no. 58), *Cytherelloidea attiyaensis* Morsi (no. 53) and *Krithe echolsae*. Notice from the graph that *Cythereis mesa ventroreticulata* is very close to sample K2 (no. 22) of the section located at 10 km west of Themed (K), while the species belonging to the deeper zones are close to samples C25 and C26 (nos 19 and 20 in the graph, respectively) of the section at El Sheikh Attiya (C).

The fifth latent vector (Fig. 6c) is clearly successful in distinguishing between species (with high positive fifth latent vector) occupying the outer circum-littoral (125–200 m; Keen *et al.* 1994) to outer shelf (deep infraneritic; Bassiouni & Luger 1990) such as *Mauritsina coronata* (no. 57) and those (with high negative fifth latent vector) occupying the upper bathyal zones such as *Acanthocythereis meslei meslei* Donze & Oertli (no. 54), which is characterized by its high spinosity and *Paracosta parakefensis* (no. 58), see Benson (1975), Donze *et al.* (1982) and Bassiouni & Luger (1990). On the other hand, Athersuch *et al.* (1989) recognized a species belonging to the genus *Acanthocythereis* within a group of species that prefer to live in colder water in the southern limits of the British Isles. Many species of this group also live in Arctic waters. From these notes, it seems that the fifth latent vector could differentiate between species inhabiting the outer circum-littoral zones with warm-water conditions (samples C25 and C26; nos 19 and 20 in the graph, respectively) of the section at El Sheikh Attiya (C) and those preferring to live in upper bathyal zones with

colder waters (sample C16; no. 14). In conclusion, this latent vector represents the water temperature as a function of depth.

The sixth latent vector (Fig. 6d) prominently discriminates between *Acanthocythereis meslei meslei* Donze & Oertli (no. 54) (with high positive sixth latent vector) that prefer well-oxygenated water conditions from those (with high negative latent vector) in poorly oxygenated conditions, including *Paracosta parakefensis* (no. 58), *Parakrithe crolifa* Bassiouni & Luger (no. 52), *Cytherelloidea attiyaensis* Morsi (no. 53) and *Cristaeleberis reticulata* Bassiouni (no. 56), according to Peypouquet (*in* Donze *et al.* 1982), Peypouquet *et al.* (1986) and Whatley (1991). It is clear that those species associated with poorly oxygenated conditions are close to sample C21 (no. 18 in the graph). It seems that this latent vector represents the oxygenation of water.

History of environmental conditions of the study area

The studied succession ranges in age from Palaeocene to Early Eocene. The Palaeocene is restricted to the Esna Formation, while the Early Eocene is included within both the Esna and Thebes formations (Fig. 2).

Using correspondence analysis and the distribution of the identified ostracode assemblages (Fig. 7), the palaeoenvironmental history of the study area was reconstructed as follows:

Sample C16, of the *Cytherelloidea attiyaensis* Assemblage Zone and containing *Acanthocythereis meslei meslei*, has a negative fifth latent vector indicating a distinct fluctuation of the water temperature in outer shelf to upper bathyal depths.

Samples F32 and F33, of the *Cythereis mesa mesa* Assemblage Zone, were deposited under outer shelf to upper bathyal depths (negative third latent vector).

Sample K2, of the *Krithe echolsae* Assemblage Zone, shows turbulent water conditions (positive fourth latent vector).

Samples C12 and C21, of the *Parakrithe crolifa–Cristaeleberis reticulata* Assemblage Zone, were deposited under middle to outer shelf environments (positive third latent vector) and reduced oxygen content of water (negative sixth latent vector).

Samples C25 and C26, of the *Oertliella posterotriangulata–Megommatocythere denticulata* Assemblage Zone, were deposited under outer shelf to upper bathyal depths (negative

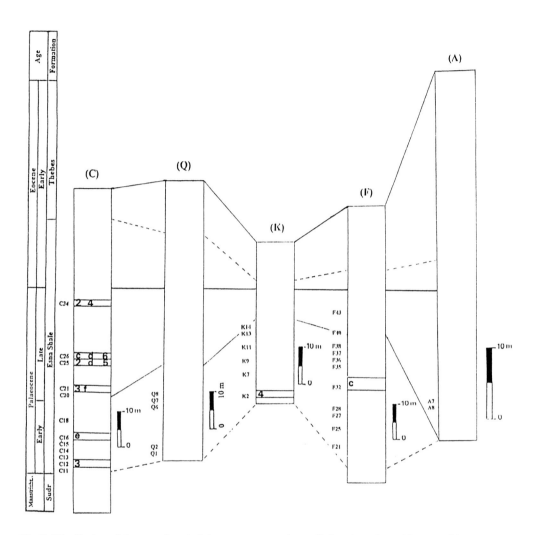

Fig. 7. Distribution of the second to sixth latent vectors on the studied sections. 2, positive second latent vector; 3, positive third latent vector; (**c**) negative third latent vector; 4, positive fourth latent vector; (**d**) negative fourth latent vector; 5, positive fifth latent vector; (**e**) negative fifth latent vector; 6, positive sixth latent vector; (**f**) negative sixth latent vector.

third latent vector) associated with calm water conditions (negative fourth latent vector), warm water (positive fifth latent vector) and good oxygenation (positive sixth latent vector).

The analysis (Table 3) suggests that during the Early Palaeocene (the interval of the *Acanthocythereis meslei meslei* Donze & Oertli), the whole succession was affected by a distinct fluctuation of water temperature in the outer shelf to upper bathyal environments. This interval is dominated by the *Cytherelloidea*

attiyaensis Assemblage Zone and the *Cythereis mesa mesa* Assemblage Zone. Although *Cytherelloidea* is generally known from shallow, warm waters, species belonging to this genus have been recognized by Bassiouni & Luger (1990) from the outer infraneritic depths, as indicated by their accompanying foraminifera (see Morsi 1999). In the interval from Early to Late Palaeocene, the succession shows almost calm, warm, well-oxygenated water conditions in the outer shelf to upper bathyal environments,

Table 3. *Summary of the proposed palaeoenvironmental conditions of the study area.*

Sample no.	Age	Biotope no.	Ecozone	Latent vector	Environment
C25 and C26	Late Palaeocene to Early Eocene	1	*Oertliella posterotriangulata– Megommatocythere denticulata*	Negative third, negative fourth, positive fifth and positive sixth	Calm, well-oxygenated conditions as outer shelf to upper bathyal depths
C12 and C21	Early to Late Palaeocene	2	*Parakrithe crolifa– Cristaeleberis reticulata*	Positive third and negative sixth	Reduced oxygen content of water in middle to outer shelf environments
K2	Early to Late Palaeocene	3	*Krithe echolsae*	Positive fourth	Turbulent water conditions
F32 and F33	Early Palaeocene	4	*Cythereis mesa mesa*	Negative third	Outer shelf to upper bathyal depths
C16	Early Palaeocene	5	*Cytherelloidea attiyaensis*	Negative fifth	Fairly cold water conditions at outer shelf to upper bathyal depths

except for the intervals dominated by the *Parakrithe crolifa–Cristaeleberis reticulata* Assemblage Zone, in the south (section C), which is characterized by reduced oxygen content of water in middle to outer shelf environments. Normal marine conditions in outer shelf to upper bathyal depths prevailed during the Late Palaeocene. Species extending to the Early Eocene, such as *Megommatocythere denticulata, Mauritsina martini* and *Ordoniya burmaensis*, are included within the *Oertliella posterotriangulata–Megommatocythere denticulata* Assemblage Zone (samples C25 to C30), representing normal marine conditions. However, the most recent sample in the 38 analysed samples (C34), which has a positive fourth latent vector (indicating turbulent conditions), contains species that survived to Early Eocene times (e.g. *Reticulina sangalkamensis* and *R. proteros*). Generally, the latter species were recognized within more recent samples (of Early Eocene age). Thus, during Early Eocene times, there was a gradual change from tranquil to turbulent marine conditions.

In general, a distinct change in the fauna has been detected at the Palaeocene–Eocene thermal maximum (PETM) as indicated by the second latent vector which separates species restricted to Late Palaeocene times from those that survived to Early Eocene times.

Conclusions

The present study of ostracode faunas from the Palaeocene to Early Eocene sediments of east-central Sinai has enabled the distinction of five ecozones: *Cytherelloidea attiyaensis* Assemblage Zone (Early Palaeocene), *Cythereis mesa mesa*

Assemblage Zone (Early Palaeocene), *Krithe echolsae* Assemblage Zone (Early to Late Palaeocene), *Parakrithe crolifa–Cristaeleberis reticulata* Assemblage Zone (Early to Late Palaeocene) and *Oertliella posterotriangulata–Megommatocythere denticulata* Assemblage Zone (Late Palaeocene to Early Eocene). Water depth, turbulence, water temperature, and the dissolved oxygen content of water were probably the most important environmental factors affecting the distribution of ostracode assemblages in the study area.

The results indicate that faunal change in these ostracode assemblages is due to the change in their distribution, as a result of changes in the environmental conditions, rather than origination or extinction. This result seems reasonable, because many species that disappeared below or at the Late Palaeocene–Early Eocene boundary in the study area were recognized at that boundary or even higher in other provinces from North and West Africa and the Middle East (see Morsi 1999; Elewa 2002).

The authors would like to express their deep appreciations to R. A. Reyment of the Swedish Natural History Museum, Sweden, and M. A. Bassiouni of the Geology Department, Faculty of Science, Ain Shams University, Egypt, for their kind help throughout the course of the present study, and their valuable comments as well as critical reading of the manuscript. We are much indebted to H. J. Kuss of the University of Bremen, Germany and S. Lüning of the University of Aberystwyth, Wales, for the various necessary types of assistance, and M. Brinkmann of the University of Bremen, Germany, for technical assistance. A special word of thanks is due to A. Beaudoin of the Provincial Museum of Alberta, Canada and M. Head of Cambridge University, UK, for their great efforts in editing this volume. The reviewers, A. Rosenfeld of the Geological Survey of Israel, A. Honigstein of the Ministry of National Infrastructures, Oil and Gas Section, Israel, and E. Brouwers of the US Geological Survey, are acknowledged for their valuable comments and suggestions.

References

ALLAM, A. & KHALIL, H. 1988. Geology and stratigraphy of the Areif El Naqa area, Sinai, Egypt. *Egyptian Journal of Geology*, **32(1–2)**, 199–218.

APOSTOLESCU, V. 1961. Contribution à l'étude paléontologique (Ostracodees) et stratigraphique des bassins cretacés et tertiaires de l'Afrique Occidentale. *Revue de l'Institut Français du Pétrole*, **16(7/8)**, 779–867.

AREF, M. 1995. Early Eocene Ostracoda from the Thebes Formation along the Red Sea coastal area, Egypt. *Egyptian Journal of Geology*, **39(1)**, 202–217.

ATHERSUCH, J., HORNE, D. & WHITTAKER, J., 1989. Marine and brackish water ostracodes (superfamilies Cypridacea and Cytheracea). *In: Synopses of the British Fauna*, KERMACK & R. S. K. BARNES, **43**, Bath Press, Avon, UK.

BASSIOUNI, M. A. 1969. Einige *Costa* – und *Carinocythereis* (*Reticulina*) arten aus dem Paleozän und Eozän von Jordanien (Ostracoda). *Neues Jahrbuch für Geologie und Paläontologie Abhandlungen*, **134(1)**, 1–16.

BASSIOUNI, M. A. 1970. Ostracodeen (Mauritsininae und Trachyleberidinae) und ihre Bedeutung für die Biostratigraphie des Maastrichts und Alttertiärs von Jordanien. *Beihegte Geologische Jahrbuch*, **106**, 5–52.

BASSIOUNI, M. A. & LUGER, P. 1990. Maastrichtian to early Eocene Ostracoda from Southern Egypt (palaeontology, palaeoecology, palaeobiogeography and biostratigraphy). *Berliner Geowissenschaft Abhandlungen (A)*, **120(2)**, 755–928.

BASSIOUNI, M. A., BOUKHARY, M. A. & ANAN, H. S. 1977. Ostracodees from Gebel Gurnah, Nile Valley, Egypt. *Proceedings of the Egyptian Academy of Science*, **30**, 1–9.

BARSOTTI, G. 1963. Palaeoceanic ostracodes of Libya (Sirte Basin) and their wide African distribution. *Revue de l'Institut Français du Pétrole*, **18(10/11)**, 779–867.

BEADNELL, H. J. 1905. The relations of the Eocene and Cretaceous systems in the Esna–Aswan reach of the Nile Valley. *Quarterly Journal of the Geological Society of London*, **61**, 667–678.

BENSON, R. H. 1975. Morphologic stability in Ostracoda. *In: F. M. SWAIN* (ed.) *Biology and Paleobiology of Ostracoda*. Bulletins of American Paleontology, **65**, 11–46.

BÉNZECRI, J.-P. 1973. *L'Analyse des Données. 2. L'analyses des Correspondances*. Dunod, Paris.

BOUKHARY, M. A., GUERNET, C. & MANSOUR, H. 1982. Ostracodes du Tertiaire inférieur de l'Égypte. *Cahiers de Micropaléontologie*, **1982(1)**, 13–20.

CARBONNEL, G., ALZOUMA, K. & DIKOUMA, M. 1990. Les ostracodees Paléocènes du Niger: taxonomie – Un témoignage de l'existence éventuelle de la mer transsaharienne? *Geobios*, **23(6)**, 671–697.

DAMOTTE, R. 1995. The biostratigraphy and palaeobiogeography of the Upper Cretaceous–basal Tertiary ostracodes from North Africa, Mali and Congo. *Cretaceous Research*, **16**, 35–366.

DAMOTTE, R. & FLEURY, J.-J. 1987. Ostracodees Maastrichtiens et Paléocènes du Djebel Dyr, près de Tebessa (Algérie orientale). *Géologie Mediterranéenne*, **14(2)**, 87–107.

DONZE, P., COLIN, J. P., DAMOTTE, R., OERTLI, H., PEYPOUQUET, J. P. & SAID, R. 1982. Les ostracodees du Campanien Terminal a l'Éocène inférieur de la coupe de Kef, Tunisie Nord-Occidental. *Bulletin des Céntres de Recherches Elf-Aquitaine, France*, **6**, 273–355.

ELEWA, A. M. T. 2002. Paleobiogeography of Maastrichtian to early Eocene Ostracoda of North and West Africa and the Middle East. *Micropaleontology*, **48(4)**, 391–398.

ELEWA, A. M. T., BASSIOUNI, M. A. & LUGER, P. 1999. Multivariate data analysis as a tool for reconstructing palaeoenvironments: the Maastrichtian to early Eocene Ostracoda of southern Egypt. *Bulletin of Faculty of Science, Minia University*, **12(2)**, 1–20.

ESKER, G. L. 1968. Danian ostracodes from Tunisia. *Micropaleontology*, **14(3)**, 319–333.

EVERITT, B. 1980. *Cluster Analysis*. 2nd edn, Halsted Press, New York.

GREKOFF, N. 1969. Sur la valeur stratigraphique et les relations paléogéographique des quelques ostracodees du Crétacé, du Paléocène et de l'Éocène inférieur d'Algérie orientale. *Proceedings of the 3rd African Micropaleontological Colloque, Cairo*, pp. 227–248.

HAIR, J. ANDERSON, R., TATHAM, R. & BLACK, W. 1992. Multivariate data analysis with readings. 3rd edn, Macmillan, New York, 544 pp.

HONIGSTEIN, A. & ROSENFELD, A. 1995. Paleocene ostracodes from southern Israel. *Revue de Micropaléontologie, Paris*, **38(1)**, 49–62.

HONIGSTEIN, A., ROSENFELD, A. & BENJAMINI, C. 1991. Ostracodes and Foraminifera from the early–middle Eocene of Qeren Sartaba, Jordan Valley, Israel. *Journal of Micropalaeontology*, **10(1)**, 95–107.

HONIGSTEIN, A., ROSENFELD, A. & BENJAMINI, C. 2002. Eocene ostracode faunas from the Nejev, southern Israel. *Micropaleontology*, **48(4)**, 365–389.

ISMAIL, A. 1992. Late Campanian to early Eocene Ostracoda from Esh El Mellaha area, Eastern Desert, Egypt. *Revue de Micropaléontologie*, **35(1)**, 39–52.

ISMAIL, A. 1996. Biostratigraphy and palaeoecology of Maastrichtian–early Eocene ostracodes of west-central Sinai, Egypt. *Revue de Paléobiologie*, **15(1)**, 37–54.

KEEN, M., AL SHEIKHLY, S., ELSOGHER, A. & GAMMUDI, A. 1994. Tertiary ostracodes of North Africa and the Middle East. *In*: M. D. SIMMONS (ed.) *Micropalaeontology and Hydrocarbon Exploration in the Middle East*. Chapman and Hall London, pp. 371–400.

KHALIFA, H. & EL SAYED, G. 1984. Biostratigraphic zonation of the Late Cretaceous–Early Palaeogene succession along El Sheikh Fadl–Ras Gharib road, Eastern Desert, Egypt. *Bulletin of Faculty of Science, Assiut University*, **13**, 175–190.

KHALIFA, H., EL YOUNSY, A. & BOUKHARY, M. 1984. The Cretaceous–Palaeocene boundary as defined by ostracodes at the north western approach of Kharga Oasis, Western Desert, Egypt. *Bulletin of Faculty of Science, Assiut University*, **B(1)**, 159–173.

LÜNING, S., KUSS, J., BACHMANN, M., MARZOUK, A. & MORSI, A. M. 1998*a*. Sedimentary response to basin inversion, Mid Cretaceous–Early Tertiary pre- to syndeformational deposition of the Areif El-Naqa Anticline (Sinai, Egypt). *Facies*, **38**, 103–136.

LÜNING, S., MARZOUK, A. & KUSS, J. 1998*b*. The Paleocene of Central East Sinai, Egypt: sequence stratigraphy in monotonous hemipelagites. *Journal of Foraminiferal Research*, **28(1)**, 19–39.

MARZOUK, A. and LÜNING, S. 1998. Comparative biostratigraphy of calcareous nannofossils and planktonic Foraminifera in the Paleocene of Eastern Sinai, Egypt. *Neues Jahrbuch für Geologie und Paläontologie Abhandlungen*, **207(1)**, 77–105.

MORSI, A. M. 1999. Paleocene to early Eocene ostracodes from the area of east-central Sinai, Egypt. *Revue de Paléobiologie*, **18(1)**, 31–55.

NISHI, H., ELEWA, A. M. T. & ISHIZAKI, K. 1994. Planktonic foraminiferal biostratigraphy of upper Paleocene to middle Eocene sequences in the Eastern Desert area, Egypt. *Transactions of the Proceedings of the Palaeontological Society of Japan*, **175**, 521–552.

PEYPOUQUET, J. P., GROUSSET, F. & MOURGUIART, P. 1986. Palaeoceanography of the Mesogean Sea based on ostracodes of the Northern Tunisian Continental Shelf between the Late Cretaceous and Early Palaeogene. *Geologische Rundschau*, **75**, 159–174.

REYMENT, R. A. 1963. Studies on Nigerian Upper Cretaceous and Lower Tertiary Ostracoda. Part 2, Danian, Paleocene and Eocene Ostracoda. *Stockholm Contributions in Geology*, **10**, 286 pp.

REYMENT, R. A. 1966. Studies on Nigerian Upper Cretaceous and Lower Tertiary Ostracoda. Part 3, Stratigraphical, palaeoecological and biometrical conclusions. *Stockholm Contributions in Geology*, **14**, 151 pp.

REYMENT, R. A. 1981. The Ostracoda of the Kalambaina Formation (Paleocene), north-western Nigeria. *Bulletin of the Geological Institutions of the University of Uppsala*, **9**, 51–65.

REYMENT, R. A. 1991. *Multidimensional Palaeobiology*. Pergamon Press, Oxford, 416 pp.

REYMENT, R. A. & JÖRESKOG, K. G. 1993. *Applied Factor Analysis in the Natural Sciences*. Cambridge University Press, New York, USA, 2nd edn (1996).

REYMENT, R. A. & REYMENT, E. R. 1980. The Paleocene Trans-Saharan transgression and its ostracode fauna. *In*: SALEM, M. J. and BUSREVIL, M. I. (eds) *The Geology of Libya. Vol. 1*, Academic Press, London, pp. 245–254.

REYMENT, R. A. and SAVAZZI, E. 1999. *Aspects of Multivariate Statistical Analysis in Geology*. Elsevier, Amsterdam, The Netherlands, 285 pp.

SAID, R. 1960. Planktonic Foraminifera from the Thebes Formation, Luxor, Egypt. *Micropaleontology*, **6**, 277–286.

SAID, R. 1962. *The Geology of Egypt*. Elsevier, Amsterdam, 377 pp.

SAID, R. 1971. Explanatory notes to accompany the geological map of Egypt. *Annals of the Geological Survey of Egypt*, **56**, 123 pp.

SAID, R. 1990. *The Geology of Egypt*, Balkema, Rotterdam, 734 pp.

WHATLEY, R. 1991. The platycopid signal, a means of detecting kenoxic events using Ostracoda. *Journal of Micropalaeontology*, **10(2)**, 181–185.

WHATLEY, R. and ARIAS, C. 1993. Palaeogene Ostracoda from the Tripoli Basin, Libya. *Revista Española de Micropaleontologia*, **15(2)**, 125–154.

ZIKO, A., DARWISH, M. and EWEDA, S. 1993. Late Cretaceous–Early Tertiary stratigraphy of the Themed area, east-central Sinai, Egypt. *Neues Jahrbuch für Geologie und Paläontologie Monatshefte*, **3**, 135–149.

Dinoflagellate cyst record of the Eocene–Oligocene boundary succession in flysch deposits at Leluchów, Carpathian Mountains, Poland

PRZEMYSŁAW GEDL

Institute of Geological Sciences, Polish Academy of Sciences, Senacka 1, 31–002 Kraków, Poland (e-mail: ndgedl@cyf-kr.edu.pl)

Abstract: Organic-walled dinoflagellate cysts from Eocene–Oligocene transitional deposits have been studied in a section at Leluchów, Flysch Carpathians, Poland. The Eocene–Oligocene boundary, as based on dinoflagellate cyst distribution, is placed in the upper part of the Leluchów Marl Member. The main biostratigraphic events associated with this boundary interval are the highest occurrence of *Areosphaeridium michoudii* and *Areosphaeridium diktyoplokum*, and the lowest occurrence of *Wetzeliella gochtii*. Distinct changes in dinoflagellate cyst assemblages and palynofacies across the Eocene–Oligocene boundary at Leluchów imply a drop in relative sea-level within the Carpathian flysch basin that might correlate with a major eustatic fall during the earliest Oligocene. A drop in sea surface temperature is recognized prior to the Eocene–Oligocene boundary, and evidence is presented for an increase in nutrient level and decrease in salinity within the photic zone during the earliest Oligocene.

The Eocene–Oligocene transition in the Flysch Carpathians is marked by a distinct facies change. The Upper Eocene is developed as turbiditic and/or hemipelagic, mainly light-coloured sediments, which were deposited in relatively well-oxidized settings at depths below the carbonate compensation depth (CCD). In contrast, dark-coloured bituminous deposits (the Menilite Beds *sensu lato*) represent the Lower Oligocene. Pale-coloured marly deposits – the Sub-Menilitic Globigerina Marl – usually separate these two lithofacies (Leszczyński 1997, fig. 2). Such a significant transformation of facies must have been related to prominent palaeoenvironmental changes in the Carpathian flysch sea. An attempt to reconstruct these changes as recorded in the Leluchów section was the objective of this study. For this purpose, the analysis of palynofacies and organic-walled dinoflagellate cyst (hereafter 'dinocyst') distribution was applied, and the results have been compared to those from other Eocene–Oligocene transitional successions in more external tectonic units of the Flysch Carpathians.

Geological setting

The uppermost Eocene–lowermost Oligocene interval of the Sub-Menilite Globigerina Marl (Olszewska 1985; Leszczyński 1997) reaches up to 25 metres in thickness, and is widely distributed throughout the Flysch Carpathians (Blaicher *et al.* 1963; Rögl & Steininger 1983). It is known from the Polish Flysch Carpathians in tectonic units that occur north of the Magura Nappe (so-called 'external units'; Fig. 1). However, it has not yet been recognized in the Magura Nappe itself, the southernmost and largest tectonic unit, where these marly deposits have possibly been replaced by thick-bedded turbiditic sedimentation that dominated Late Eocene deposition in the Magura Basin (N. Oszczypko 1992). The equivalent of these marls, the Leluchów Marl Member, has been found only at one place in the Polish part of the Magura Nappe, at Leluchów (Fig. 2). Similar deposits were reported from neighbouring Slovakia (Świdziński 1934; Oszczypko-Clowes 1998). The Leluchów Marl Member passes upwards into the Smereczek Shale Member, which is an equivalent of the Menilite Beds in external units (Birkenmajer & Oszczypko 1989).

Świdziński (1939, 1961*a*) included these marly deposits in the Richvald Series, where, according to him, they crop out in tectonic windows. Książkiewicz & Leško (1959) regarded these deposits as the youngest strata of the Magura Nappe in this area. They noted the presence of possible tectonic discontinuities between deposits representing the Richvald Series and the Magura Nappe, but they hesitated to define the exact relationship between these units

From: BEAUDOIN, A.B. & HEAD, M.J. (eds) 2004. *The Palynology and Micropalaeontology of Boundaries.* Geological Society, London, Special Publications, **230**, 309–324. 0305-8719/04/$15 © The Geological Society of London 2004.

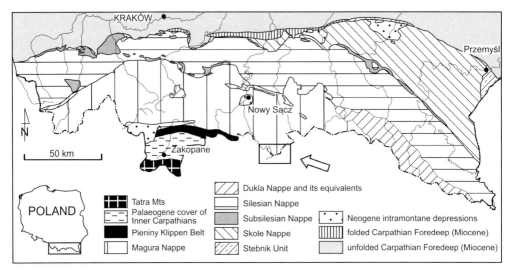

Fig. 1. Tectonic sketch-map of the Polish Carpathians (after Książkiewicz 1977) with location of the study area (arrowed).

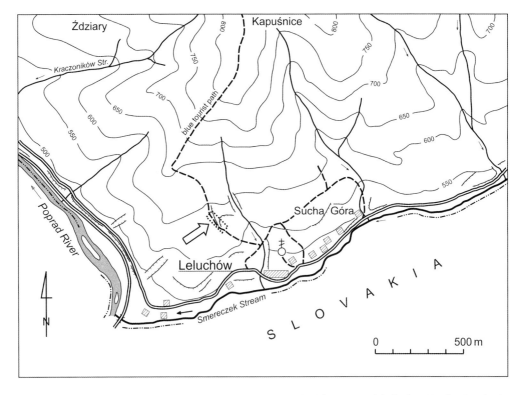

Fig. 2. Location of the Eocene–Oligocene boundary section at Leluchów (arrowed; latitude: 49° 20′ N, longitude: 20° 56′ E).

(Książkiewicz & Leško 1959, p. 776). Birkenmajer & Oszczypko (1989) included the studied deposits within the basal part of the Malcov Formation.

The age of the Leluchów Marl Member and the Smereczek Shale Member at Leluchów was studied by means of planktonic foraminifera (Malata *in* Oszczypko *et al.* 1990) and calcareous nannoplankton (M. Oszczypko 1996; Oszczypko-Clowes 1998, 1999). The results, although inconsistent for the calcareous nannoplankton, suggest a Late Eocene age for at least the lower part of the Leluchów Marl Member, and an Early Oligocene age for the Smereczek Shale Member.

Material

The studied deposits (49° 20′ N, 20° 56′ E) are exposed along the left slope of the Poprad River Valley at Leluchów. They crop out in a country road-cutting above an old orthodox church at Leluchów (Fig. 2; Oszczypko-Clowes 2001, fig. 31). The outcrop is tectonically disturbed and the boundary between the studied deposits and the subjacent Magura Formation is not exposed. The Leluchów Marl Member is developed as reddish and olive-greenish marls with green shales at the bottom. Greenish, brownish-spotted marls occur in the uppermost part of this member. The Smereczek Shale Member is composed of poorly calcareous dark-brownish, siliceous shales with non-calcareous hornstones (Fig. 3). Seventeen samples were taken from studied deposits: their position is indicated in Figure 3.

Methods

The samples were processed following standard palynological procedure, including 38% hydrochloric acid (HCl) treatment, 40% hydrofluoric acid (HF) treatment, heavy liquid ($ZnCl_2 + HCl$; density $2.0\,g\,cm^3$) separation, ultrasound for 10–15 s and sieving at 15 μm on a nylon mesh. A 10-minute 100% fuming nitric acid (HNO_3) treatment was applied to samples Lch15, Lch17 and Lch18. Two microscope slides were made from each sample (four slides for samples Lch16, Lch17 and Lch18) using glycerine jelly as a mounting medium. The quantity of rock processed depended on the amount of organic matter suspected: 80–100 g for reddish marl, 20–30 g for olive-greenish marl and shale and 10 g for bituminous brownish shale. The rock samples, palynological residues and slides are stored in the collection of the Institute of Geological Sciences, Polish Academy of Sciences, Kraków.

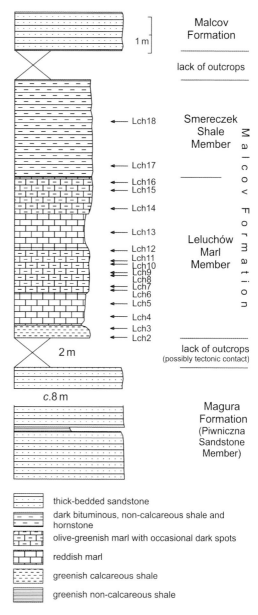

Fig. 3. Simplified lithology and lithostratigraphy of the section at Leluchów (lithostratigraphy after Birkenmajer & Oszczypko 1989), including the position of investigated samples.

Palynomorphs and phytoclasts were counted up to a total of 500. Additionally, all dinocysts were counted from one slide. The second slide was scanned for additional dinocyst taxa. In the case of samples Lch16, Lch17 and Lch18, four slides were counted for dinocysts, due to the dilution of dinocysts by plant remains.

Results

Ten of the 17 samples analysed were found to contain dinocysts. The dinocyst distribution and palynofacies changes through the studied succession are shown in Figures 4 & 5 respectively. An alphabetical species list of dinocyst taxa found in the Leluchów section is provided in Appendix I. Selected dinocyst taxa are illustrated in Figures 6–8.

Leluchów Marl Member

The two lowermost samples, Lch2 and Lch3 (greenish marly shales), contain frequent dinocysts. They represent 20–15% of the palynofacies, with opaque phytoclasts up to 80%. Sporomorphs and translucent structured phytoclasts occur in trace amounts only (Fig. 5). The most frequent dinocysts in this interval are *Corrudinium incompositum* and *Impagidinium* spp. (10–20%), *Deflandrea* spp. (10–15%), *Heterosphaeridium* sp. A (45% in sample Lch2), *Spiniferites* spp. in sample Lch2, and *Achomosphaera alcicornu* in sample Lch3.

The reddish marls are barren (samples Lch 4 and Lch5), whereas the palynofacies of the greenish-olive marls just above the reddish marls is composed entirely of opaque phytoclasts (Lch6 and Lch7). Higher within the greenish-olive marls, samples Lch8–11 are characterized by frequent dinocysts, which represent 30–50% of the palynofacies. The dinocyst assemblages from this part of the section show the highest species richness. The most frequent dinocysts in this interval are *Impagidinium* spp. (more than 30% in the lower part) and *Deflandrea* spp. (above 30% in the upper part). *Stoveracysta?* sp. *sensu* Brinkhuis (1992) occurs as the most frequent taxon in sample Lch9 – 28%. *Impagidinium* becomes relatively more frequent in the higher part of the greenish-olive marl interval (sample Lch11), and is the only dinocyst found in the highest part (sample Lch12). Sporomorphs and translucent-structured phytoclasts occur subordinately, although they are more frequent than in the lowermost samples (Fig. 5). They are absent from the highest sample Lch12.

The reddish marls from the upper interval (sample Lch13) contain opaque phytoclasts only. A similar palynofacies occurs in the lowermost part of the second greenish-olive marl interval (sample Lch14; Fig. 5). Two palynofacies types occur higher within this greenish-olive marl interval (samples Lch15 and Lch16). The palynofacies of the lower sample, Lch15, is dominated by dinocysts (almost 70%), and is composed of an almost

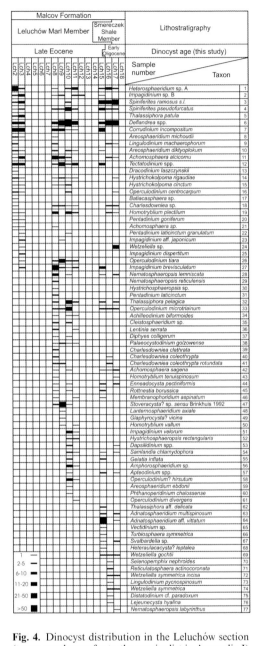

Fig. 4. Dinocyst distribution in the Leluchów section (taxon numbers refer to the species list in Appendix I). The inferred age is based on dinocysts (this study, Fig. 9). Line widths reflect the number of specimens counted.

monospecific assemblage of *Adnatosphaeridium* (Fig. 5). *Impagidinium*, *Spiniferites* and *Deflandrea* occur subordinately, representing only a few per cent of the dinocyst assemblage. Sporomorphs and translucent-structured phyto-

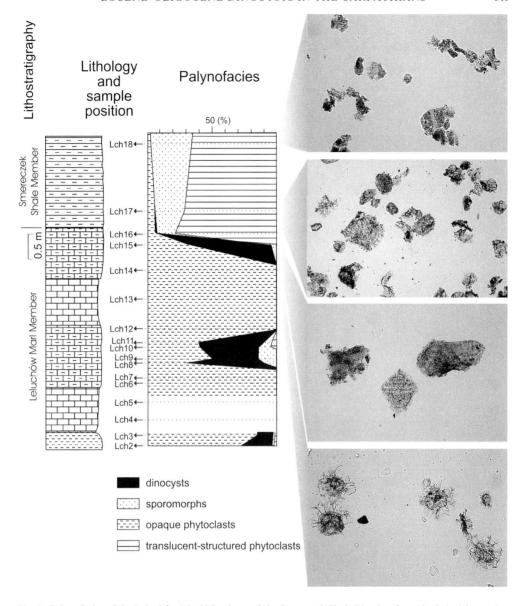

Fig. 5. Palynofacies of the Leluchów Marl Member and the Smereczek Shale Member from the Leluchów section (photographs of palynofacies from samples near the Eocene–Oligocene boundary are shown).

clasts represent only a few per cent of the palynofacies. The highest part of the Leluchów Marl Member (sample Lch16) is characterized by a palynofacies comprising 90% translucent-structured phytoclasts and sporomorphs (mainly bisaccate pollen grains). Among the infrequent dinocysts present (1–2% of the palynofacies), members of the Wetzeliellaceae, together with *Deflandrea* and *Spiniferites* are the most common (Fig. 5).

Smereczek Shale Member

The palynofacies of these bituminous shales is similar to that of the highest sample in the Leluchów Marl Member (Lch16). Terrestrial elements (plant remains and sporomorphs; Fig. 5) predominate. The dinocysts found in the lower sample (Lch17) are, as with sample Lch16, dominated by *Wetzeliella*, *Deflandrea* and *Spiniferites*. The prasinophycean alga

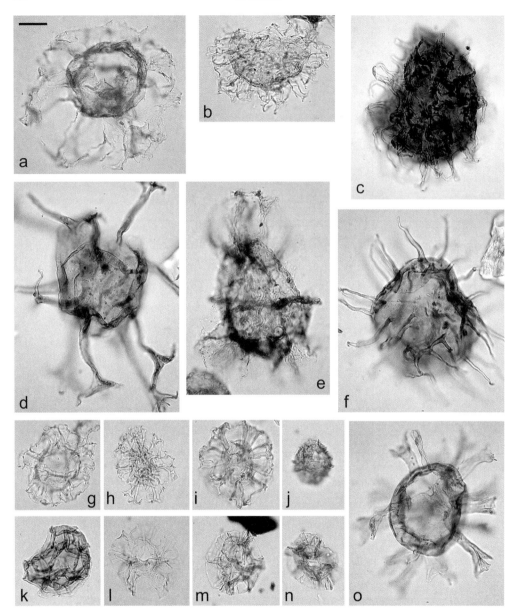

Fig. 6. Selected dinocysts from the Leluchów section. Scale bar in (**a**) represents 15 μm and refers to all other photomicrographs. Slide code and England Finder references are given. (**a**) *Adnatosphaeridium* aff. *vittatum*, Lch16a, E39/3; (**b**) *Adnatosphaeridium multispinosum*, Lch16a, C37/1; (**c**) *Operculodinium divergens*, Lch11b, C42/3; (**d**) *Areosphaeridium michoudii*, Lch3a, P29/4; (**e**) *Turbiosphaera symmetrica*, Lch16a, Q43/3; (**f**) *Operculodinium microtriainum*, Lch8b, O33/4; (**g**) *Nematosphaeropsis labyrinthus*, Lch17c, D47/4; (**h**) *Nematosphaeropsis lemniscata*, Lch8a, D30/1–2; (**i**) *Nematosphaeropsis reticulensis*, Lch8b, E35; (**j**) *Corrudinium incompositum*, Lch2a, C33/C34; (**k**) *Impagidinium dispertitum*, Lch3, B41/1; (**l**) *Impagidinium velorum*, Lch10a, H30/3; (**m**) *Impagidinium* aff. *japonicum*, Lch9a, F43/2; (**n**) *Impagidinium* sp. B, Lch2a, O32/2; (**o**) *Achomosphaera alcicornu*, Lch8a, F34/4.

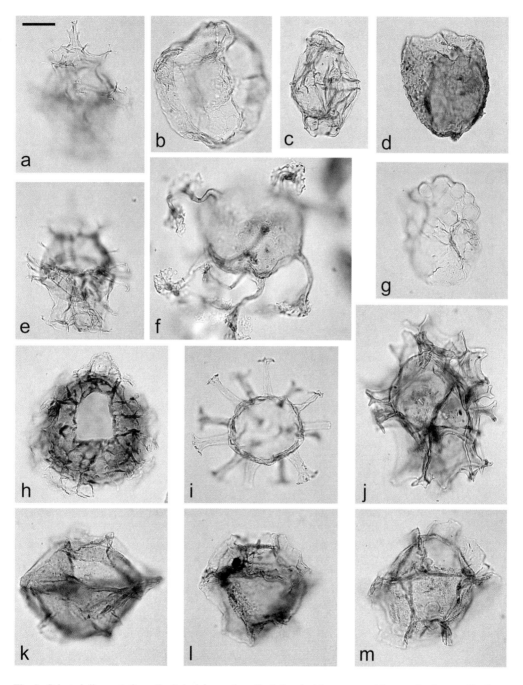

Fig. 7. Selected dinocysts from the Leluchów section. Scale bar in (a) represents 15 μm and refers to all other photomicrographs. Slide code and England Finder references are given. (**a** & **e**) *Rottnestia borussica*, Lch16a, U37/2, **a** – focus on epicyst, **e** – focus on hypocyst; (**b**) *Thalassiphora* aff. *delicata*, Lch16b, J45/3; (**c**) *Hystrichosphaeropsis* sp., Lch8a, B50/3; (**d**) *Stoveracysta*? sp. *sensu* Brinkhuis 1992, Lch9a, T46/4; (**f**) *Areosphaeridium diktyoplokum*, Lch8b, N36/3; (**g**) *Gelatia inflata*, Lch10a, S36; (**h**) *Samlandia chlamydophora*, Lch10a, T46/1–3; (**i**) *Homotryblium plectilum*, Lch8b, V40/3; (**j**) *Hystrichosphaeropsis rectangularis*, Lch10a, O29/2; (**k**) *Pentadinium goniferum*, Lch2b, Q31/4; (**l**) *Pentadinium laticinctum* subsp. *granulatum*, Lch10a, C31/4; (**m**) *Pentadinium laticinctum*, Lch8a, S50.

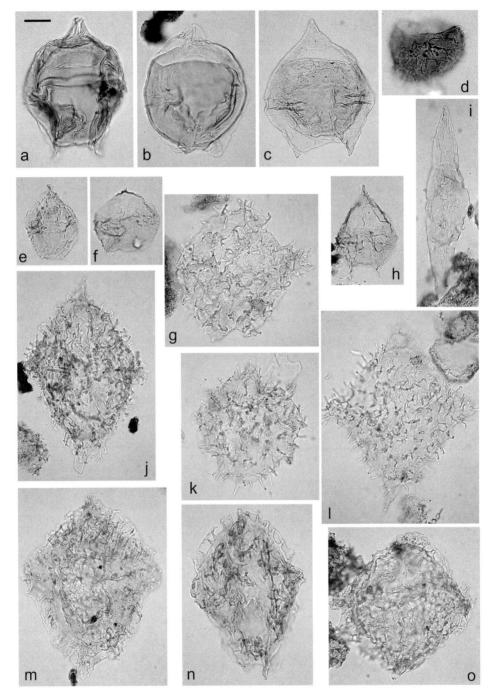

Fig. 8. Selected dinocysts from the Leluchów section. Scale bar in (a) represents 15 μm and refers to all other photomicrographs. Slide code and England Finder references are given. (**a, b & c**) *Deflandrea* sp., Lch8a, U38; Lch10a, E42; Lch16a, C46; (**d**) *Heterosphaeridium* sp. A, Lch2a, D44/1–2; (**e**) *Phthanoperidinium chalossense*, Lch10a, Q31/4; (**f**) *Vectidinium* sp., Lch16a, O36/4; (**g & k**) *Wetzeliella gochtii*, Lch15a, X32/3–4; Lch17b, P30/1; (**h**) *Lentinia serrata*, Lch11b, T36/4; (**i**) *Svalbardella* sp., Lch17a, V30/3–4; (**j & l**) *Wetzeliella symmetrica*, Lch15b, D39/1–3; Lch17c, Q35/2; (**m**) *Charlesdowniea coleothrypta*, Lch15a, C30/1–2; (**n**) *Charlesdowniea clathrata*, Lch8a, X42/2; (**o**) *Charlesdowniea coleothrypta* subsp. *rotundata*, Lch15a, W35.

Pterospermella occurs in sample Lch17. No aquatic palynomorphs were found in the highest sample, Lch18.

Age interpretation and the position of the Eocene–Oligocene boundary

The presence of *Areosphaeridium michoudii* and *Areosphaeridium diktyoplokum*, and the lack of Oligocene taxa in the studied section, up to the sample Lch11 inclusive, together indicate a Late Eocene age. The highest occurrence of *Areosphaeridium michoudii* in the North Sea is tentatively correlated with the top of calcareous nannoplankton Zone NP18 (Bujak 1994; Bujak & Mudge 1994). This species occurs in that part of the Leluchów section assigned to the NP19/20 Zone (continuous presence of *Isthmolithus recurvus* in the Leluchów Marl Member; M. Oszczypko 1996). Thus, *Areosphaeridium michoudii* has a possibly diachronous last appearance, becoming extinct later in lower latitudes.

Lack of dinocysts in samples Lch12–14 does not allow the age of this narrow interval to be estimated. An Early Oligocene age can tentatively be suggested for the remaining part of the succession above sample Lch15, where *Wetzeliella gochtii* has its lowest occurrence. Costa & Downie (1976) suggested that the lowest occurrence of *Wetzeliella gochtii* is in the upper part of Zone NP22 or possibly in NP21 according to Costa (*in* Van Couvering *et al.* 1981, p. 338). Powell (1992) stated that this event occurs at the base of NP22. These datings were based on evidence from Northwestern Europe and the North Atlantic, where the Eocene–Oligocene transitional interval is often devoid of dinocysts (e.g. Châteauneuf & Gruas-Cavagnetto 1978; Costa & Downie 1979; Manum *et al.* 1989). Brinkhuis (1992) found the lowest occurrence of *Wetzeliella gochtii* in the Mediterranean within his *Reticulatosphaera actinocoronata* Interval Zone calibrated with the middle part of NP21 Zone (=CP16B Subzone of Okada & Bukry 1980). In the same sample, Lch15, *Areosphaeridium diktyoplokum* has its highest occurrence in the studied succession. This event is widely associated with the Eocene–Oligocene boundary (e.g. Biffi & Manum 1988; Williams *et al.* 1993; Stover *et al.* 1996). In the Mediterranean area, as well in NW Europe, these two events are not coincident: *Areosphaeridium diktyoplokum* has its highest occurrence below the lowest occurrence of *Wetzeliella gochtii*, and the latter event is reported from the Lower Oligocene (Powell

1992; Brinkhuis 1994; Wilpshaar *et al.* 1996). The co-occurrence of *Areosphaeridium diktyoplokum* and *Wetzeliella gochtii* in the same sample may be interpreted as reworking of the former species. However, *Wetzeliella gochtii* was found in the Polish Flysch Carpathians in the upper part of the Sub-Menilitic Globigerina Marl in Znamirowice (sample no. 6 of Bujak *in* Van Couvering *et al.* 1981). This sample was dated by Aubry (*in* Van Couvering *et al.* 1981) as the uppermost part of NP19/20 Zone, i.e. as Upper Eocene. Hence, it is likely that *Wetzeliella gochtii* had already appeared in the Carpathian Basin by the latest Eocene.

The internationally ratified Eocene–Oligocene boundary is placed in the Massignano section (Apennines), where *Hantkenina* spp. have their highest occurrence (for discussion and earlier citations, see Berggren *et al.* 1995). This event was correlated by Brinkhuis & Biffi (1993) using dinocysts with the middle part of the Priabonian in the boundary stratotype at Priabona (Barbin & Bignot 1986). The dinocyst event coinciding with the top of the Priabonian is the highest occurrence of *Areosphaeridium diktyoplokum*, designated as the Eocene–Oligocene boundary event by Brinkhuis & Visscher (1995). This criterion is applied in the present paper. Therefore, the Eocene–Oligocene boundary is tentatively placed at, or close to, sample Lch15. This interpretation agrees with data obtained by Malata (*in* Oszczypko *et al.* 1990) based on the foraminifera. The undivided Eocene–Oligocene interval of Malata's study correlates with the inferred Eocene–Oligocene boundary interval based on dinocysts (Fig. 9). The age interpretation based on calcareous nannoplankton varies depending on the particular paper consulted (Fig. 9). The dinocyst-based age interpretation is comparable to the calcareous nannoplankton-based age interpretation of M. Oszczypko (1996). Her interpretations in later papers (Oszczypko-Clowes 1998, 1999) seem unjustified. An Upper Eocene Zone NP19/20 was originally recognized, based on the presence of species such as *Discoaster barbadiensis* and *Discoaster saipanensis* (M. Oszczypko 1996). In later papers (Oszczypko-Clowes 1998, 1999), these records were arbitrarily treated as recycled, although no evidence of their being reworked was mentioned earlier (M. Oszczypko 1996, p. 12), and the Leluchów Marl Member was interpreted to comprise NP19–20 (pars?) to NP22. Most of the equivalents of the Sub-Menilite Globigerina Marl in the Carpatho-Alpine belt are no younger than NP21 (Leszczyński 1997, tables 2 and 5).

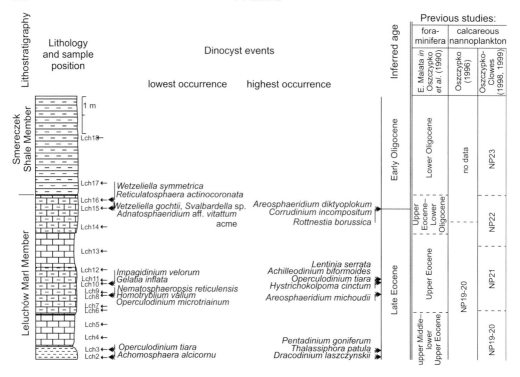

Fig. 9. Inferred age of the Leluchów section based on dinocyst events. Comparison with interpretations of previous micropalaeontological studies is given.

Palaeoenvironmental changes across the Eocene–Oligocene boundary succession at Leluchów

Sedimentary setting and changes in nutrient levels

The frequent occurrence of *Impagidinium* and *Nematosphaeropsis*, of which modern and fossil representatives are known from oceanic settings (Wall *et al.* 1977; Harland 1983; Dale 1996; Rochon *et al.* 1999; Vink *et al.* 2000), in the Leluchów Marl Member indicates that this unit was deposited in an open-water environment (Fig. 10). The fossil species *Corrudinium incompositum*, morphologically similar to *Impagidinium*, is included in this group. The presence of oceanic species and marine palynofacies suggest pelagic sedimentation. Fluctuations of palynofacies and dinocyst assemblages in relation to lithology (red–green alternation of marls; Fig. 5) reflect changing bottom-water conditions. Reddish marls devoid of dinocysts represent pelagic sedimentation with highly aerobic bottom conditions in which dinocysts became oxidized. Greenish marls, which presumably represent diluted distal turbidite (hemipelagic) deposits

(Leszczyński 1997, fig. 3), were favourable for dinocyst preservation. Influxes of organic matter changed the aerobic conditions on the sea-floor or accelerated burial rates.

Dinocyst assemblages from the investigated site show a progressive vertical change in their composition. *Impagidinium* species and *Corrudinium incompositum*, the only oceanic dinocysts in the lower part of the section, are steadily replaced by *Nematosphaeropsis* until the latter form dominates in the uppermost part of the Leluchów Marl Member and in the overlying Smereczek Shale Member (Fig. 11a). This seems to reflect a decreasing oceanic influence with time, because *Nematosphaeropsis* is tolerant of mesotrophic environments, whereas *Impagidinium* is limited to oligotrophic waters (Dale 1996; Vink *et al.* 2000).

An increase in nutrient levels in the highest part of the Leluchów Marl Member and in the overlying Smereczek Shale Member is also marked by the appearance of frequent Peridinialeans (Fig. 11b). Representatives of the genera *Deflandrea* and *Wetzeliella* together dominate this interval (Fig. 10), and have been associated with eutrophic environments (Köthe 1990; Brinkhuis 1994). Eutrophication of the

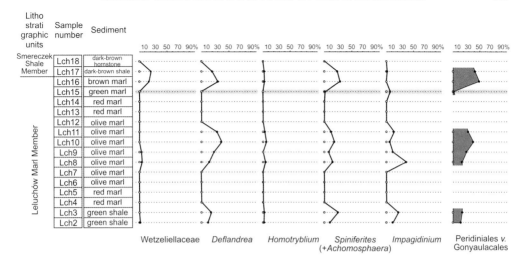

Fig. 10. Quantitative distribution of selected dinocyst morphogroups in relation to sediment type (dark line placed in sample Lch15 indicates the inferred Eocene–Oligocene boundary).

photic zone close to the Eocene–Oligocene boundary seems to be related to freshwater influx. This is interpreted from the analysis of the palynofacies assemblages, which are entirely composed of terrestrial elements, in contrast to the lower part of the section (Figs 5 & 11d). Brackish surface waters are therefore envisioned. Further progressive decrease in salinity of the surface waters would have resulted in unfavourable conditions for dinoflagellates – the highest sample Lch18 taken from the Smereczek Shale Member is devoid of dinocysts (Figs 11a & c).

This rapid change in palynofacies, starting in sample Lch16, seems to represent river input and implies a fall in relative sea-level. The change occurs just above the Eocene–Oligocene boundary, as interpreted by the highest occurrence of *Areosphaeridium diktyoplokum* in sample Lch15 immediately below. This event may be correlated with a major eustatic drop that took place in the earliest Oligocene (base of the TA4.4 cycle; Haq *et al.* 1988). This fall in sea-level has been identified in northern Italy where it occurs at the same biostratigraphic horizon as in Leluchów, namely just above the highest occurrence of *Areosphaeridium diktyoplokum* (Brinkhuis 1994).

Changes in sea surface temperature

Climatic fluctuations may also have influenced changes in the dinocyst assemblages across the Eocene–Oligocene boundary transition at Leluchów. The occurrence of *Impagidinium velorum* and *Gelatia inflata*, both characteristic of higher

latitudes, in the interval between samples Lch10 and Lch15 suggests a possible temperature drop in the surface water layer (Fig. 11e). This evidence seems to be reliable because oceanic dinocysts appear to be more sensitive indicators of water temperature than neritic ones (Zevenboom 1995). The lowest occurrence of these high-latitude dinocysts in the sample Lch10 indicates that the suggested drop in temperature of surface waters in the Magura Basin began during the Late Eocene. This event continued into the Early Oligocene, since another high-latitude species, *Svalbardella* sp., occurs in the Lower Oligocene Smereczek Shale Member (Fig. 4). More precise dating of this event is not possible because the interval between samples Lch12 and 14 is almost devoid of dinocysts. Brinkhuis (1994) used the occurrence of high-latitude dinocysts (e.g. *Corrudinium incompositum*, *Achomosphaera alcicornu*, *Gelatia inflata*, *Impagidinium pallidum* and *Rottnestia borussica*) to provide evidence of cooling events, C1 during the latest Eocene, and C2 at the Eocene–Oligocene boundary (*sensu* Brinkhuis & Visscher 1995). The latter cooling event C2 might be correlated with the event recognized in the Leluchów section, since it embraces the highest occurrence of *Areosphaeridium diktyoplokum*.

The Eocene–Oligocene boundary in the Flysch Carpathians – a comparison

The dinocyst succession from the Eocene–Oligocene boundary interval at Leluchów is

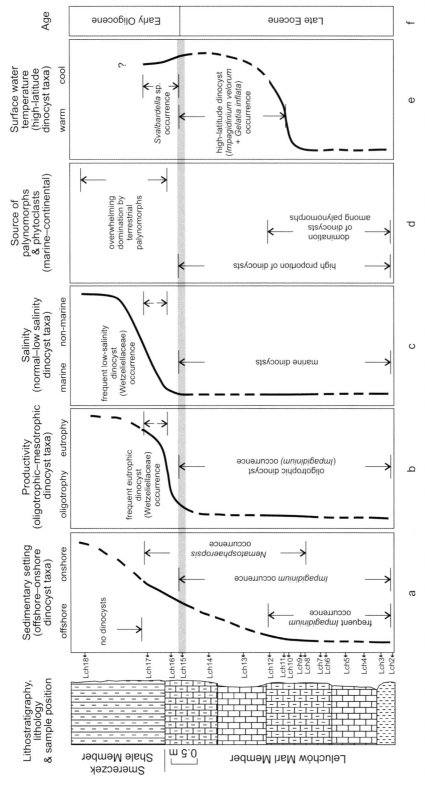

Fig. 11. Palaeoenvironmental interpretation of dinocyst and palynofacies events reflecting changes during the deposition of the Leluchów section. The curves are conceptual only, and are not plotted to specific data. The curve in diagram (**a**) is based on the presence of offshore *Impagidinium* (*I. brevisculatum*, *I. dispertitum*, *I.* aff. *japonicum*, *I. velorum*, *I.* sp. **B**) and *Nematosphaeropsis* (*N. labyrinthus*, *N. lemniscata*, *N. reticulensis*). The curve in diagram (**b**) reflects the decline of oligotrophic *Impagidinium*, followed by frequent occurrence of mesotrophic Wetzeliellaceae (*Wetzeliella gochtii*, *W. symmetrica incisa*, *Wetzeliella* sp.). Frequent occurrence of Wetzeliellaceae determines also the changes in shape of the curve in diagram (**c**), whereas the shape of the curve in diagram (**e**) reflects the occurrence of high-latitude *Impagidinium velorum*, *Gelatia inflata* and *Svalbardella* sp. Inferred age (diagram **f**) is based on the highest occurrence of *Areosphaeridium diktyoplokum* (dark line placed in sample Lch15 indicates the inferred Eocene–Oligocene boundary *sensu* Brinkhuis & Visscher 1995).

similar to those known from other tectonic units of the Flysch Carpathians. A major change in the palynomorph distribution pattern across this boundary in the Leluchów section, notably the rich and taxonomically diverse dinocyst assemblages of the Late Eocene and their replacement by terrigenous palynofacies during the Early Oligocene, is comparable to the palynofacies variations in the Eocene–Oligocene transitional sections from the Silesian, Dukla and Skole units (Bujak *in* Van Couvering *et al.* 1980; Gedl 1999). This indicates the regional significance of the Eocene–Oligocene boundary changes that occurred in the Flysch Carpathian Basin.

Upper Eocene pelagic and hemipelagic sediments of the external Flysch Carpathian units are characterized by diverse dinocyst assemblages with relatively frequent examples of the oceanic genus *Impagidinium*. These are comparable with dinocyst assemblages from the greenish shales and marls of the Leluchów Marl Member. Turbiditic sediments of the external Flysch Carpathian units, usually dark-coloured deposits, contain common inshore taxa such as the Areoligeraceae (*Membranophoridium, Glaphyrocysta, Areoligera*) and *Homotryblium*. Almost monospecific *Homotryblium* assemblages often characterize the uppermost Eocene parts of the Sub-Menilite Globigerina Marl. No similar *Homotryblium*-dominated assemblage has been found in the Leluchów section (Fig. 10). These monospecific assemblages reflect stressed environmental conditions, possibly related to sea-level fall in the latest Eocene. The acme of *Adnatosphaeridium* aff. *vittatum* (sample Lch15) possibly reflects a restricted environmental setting, although different from those of coeval deposits of the external units. These differences presumably reflect a more offshore setting for the Leluchów Upper Eocene deposits.

The initiation of the Early Oligocene organic-rich deposition in external units, i.e. the Menilite Beds *sensu lato*, is associated with an increased frequency of peridinialeans (Gedl 1999). This trend, as at Leluchów, reflects brackish waters, as concluded from palynofacies. A Late Eocene drop in sea-surface temperature interpreted in the Leluchów Marl Member has also been identified in other Carpathian units. High-latitude dinocysts such as *Gelatia inflata, Impagidinium velorum* and *Impagidinium pallidum* occur in the Silesian and Skole units below the Eocene–Oligocene boundary (Gedl unpubl.).

Conclusions

These are as follows.

(1) The age of the Leluchów Marl Member is Late Eocene and Early Oligocene based on dinocysts. Three local dinocyst events were recognized in this part of the studied succession. These are: the highest occurrence of *Areosphaeridium michoudii*, the highest occurrence of *Areosphaeridium diktyoplokum* and the lowest occurrence of *Wetzeliella gochtii*. Comparison with calcareous nannoplankton data suggests that *Areosphaeridium michoudii* appeared for the last time in the Magura Basin during the Priabonian (Zone NP19/20), i.e. later than in the North Sea. The highest occurrence of *Areosphaeridium diktyoplokum* and the lowest occurrence of *Wetzeliella gochtii* in the same sample suggest a Late Eocene first appearance of the latter species in the Carpathian Basin, although the reworking of *Areosphaeridium diktyoplokum* cannot be excluded. It must be noted that the Eocene–Oligocene boundary succession in the Carpathians is continuous. The Smereczek Shale Member is Early Oligocene in age, but the scarcity of dinocysts in this member prohibits precise dating.

(2) The Eocene–Oligocene boundary (*sensu* Brinkhuis & Visscher 1995) is placed within the uppermost part of the Leluchów Marl Member at the highest occurrence of *Areosphaeridium diktyoplokum*, in sample Lch15.

(3) The palynological record of the Eocene–Oligocene transition at Leluchów is characterized by a major change in palynofacies and the composition of the dinocyst assemblages. Marine palynofacies are replaced in the uppermost part of the section by terrigenous palynofacies. Rich and diverse marine dinocyst assemblages undergo gradual impoverishment until they disappear in the uppermost part of the section. These reflect palaeoenvironmental changes that occurred during the latest Eocene and earliest Oligocene in the Magura Basin. The most pronounced changes were a reduction in salinity and increase in nutrient levels in the surface waters, which, along with evidence from the palynofacies, point to increasing proximity to shore and imply a fall in relative sea-level close to the boundary. A decline in sea-surface temperature is also registered during the latest Eocene and earliest Oligocene.

(4) Similar changes are recognized in the Eocene–Oligocene boundary succession of the external Flysch Carpathian units. A decline in the dinocyst record and changes in palynofacies reflect major palaeoenvironmental changes of regional significance that occurred during the latest Eocene and earliest Oligocene times in the Carpathian Basin. This contrasts with the palynological record of the Eocene–Oligocene boundary succession from NW Europe and the Mediterranean, where the changes in dinocyst assemblages are subtle.

I would like to thank S. Leszczyński, N. Oszczypko and M. Oszczypko-Clowes (Jagiellonian University, Kraków) for helpful discussions. K. Birkenmajer (Institute of Geological Sciences, Polish Academy of Sciences, Kraków) most kindly helped to improve the text. Critical remarks by G. L. Eaton, M. J. Head, A. B. Beaudoin and an anonymous reviewer significantly improved the manuscript. This research was conducted within the framework of a project financed by the Polish State Committee for Scientific Research, research grant no. 6 PO4D 042 15.

Appendix

An alphabetical listing of dinocyst taxa found in the Leluchów section is provided below. Full taxonomic citations are given in Williams *et al.* (1998). Numbers in parentheses refer to Figure 4, followed by reference to the appropriate photomicrographs in Figures 6 to 8.

Achilleodinium biformoides (34)
Achomosphaera alcicornu (11; Fig. 6o)
Achomosphaera sagena (42)
Achomosphaera sp. (21)
Adnatosphaeridium multispinosum (63; Fig. 6b)
Adnatosphaeridium aff. *vittatum* (64; Fig. 6a)
Amphorosphaeridium sp. (56)
Apteodinium spp. (57)
Areosphaeridium diktyoplokum (10; Fig. 7f)
Areosphaeridium ebdonii (59)
Areosphaeridium michoudii (8; Fig. 6d)
Batiacasphaera sp. (17)
Charlesdowniea clathrata (39; Fig. 8n)
Charlesdowniea coleothrypta (40; Fig. 8m)
Charlesdowniea coleothrypta subsp. *rotundata* (41; Fig. 8o)
Charlesdowniea sp. (18)
Cleistosphaeridium sp. (35)
Corrudinium incompositum (7; Fig. 6j)
Dapsilidinium spp. (53)
Deflandrea spp. (6; Fig. 8a, b, c)
Diphyes colligerum (37)
Distatodinium cf. *paradoxum* (75)
Dracodinium laszczynskii (13)
Enneadocysta pectiniformis (44)
Gelatia inflata (55; Fig. 7g)
Glaphyrocysta? *vicina* (49)

Heterelaucacysta? *leptalea* (68)
Heterosphaeridium sp. A (1; Fig. 8d)
Homotryblium plectilum (19; Fig. 7i)
Homotryblium tenuispinosum (43)
Homotryblium vallum (50)
Hystrichokolpoma cinctum (15)
Hystrichokolpoma rigaudiae (14)
Hystrichosphaeropsis rectangularis (52; Fig. 7j)
Hystrichosphaeropsis sp. (30; Fig. 7c)
Impagidinium brevisculatum (27)
Impagidinium dispertitum (25; Fig. 6k)
Impagidinium aff. *japonicum* (23; Fig. 6m)
Impagidinium velorum (51; Fig. 6l)
Impagidinium sp. B (2; Fig. 6n)
Lanternosphaeridium axiale (48)
Lejeunecysta hyalina (76)
Lentinia serrata (36; Fig. 8h)
Lingulodinium machaerophorum (9)
Lingulodinium pycnospinosum (73)
Membranophoridium aspinatum (46)
Nematosphaeropsis labyrinthus (77; Fig. 6g)
Nematosphaeropsis lemniscata (28; Fig. 6h)
Nematosphaeropsis reticulensis (29; Fig. 6i)
Operculodinium centrocarpum (16)
Operculodinium divergens (61; Fig. 6c)
Operculodinium? *hirsutum* (58)
Operculodinium microtriainum (33; Fig. 6f)
Operculodinium tiara (26)
Palaeocystodinium golzowense (38)
Pentadinium goniferum (20; Fig. 7k)
Pentadinium laticinctum (31; Fig. 7m)
Pentadinium laticinctum subsp. *granulatum* (22; Fig. 7l)
Phthanoperidinium chalossense (60; Fig. 8e)
Reticulatosphaera actinocoronata (71)
Rottnestia borussica (45; Fig. 7a, e)
Samlandia chlamydophora (54; Fig. 7h)
Selenopemphix nephroides (70)
Spiniferites pseudofurcatus (4)
Spiniferites ramosus s.l. (3)
Stoverocysta? sp. *sensu* Brinkhuis 1992 (47; Fig. 7d)
Svalbardella sp. (67; Fig. 8i)
Tectatodinium spp. (12)
Thalassiphora aff. *delicata* (62; Fig. 7b)
Thalassiphora patula (5)
Thalassiphora pelagica (32)
Turbiosphaera symmetrica (66; Fig. 6e)
Vectidinium sp. (65; Fig. 8f)
Wetzeliella gochtii (69; Fig. 8g, k)
Wetzeliella symmetrica (74; Fig. 8j, l)
Wetzeliella symmetrica subsp. *incisa* (72)
Wetzeliella sp. (24)

References

BARBIN, V. & BIGNOT, G. 1986. New proposal for an Eocene–Oligocene boundary according to microfacies from the Priabonian-type section. *In*: POMEROL, C. & PREMOLI SILVA, I. (eds) *Terminal Eocene Events*. Developments in Paleontology and Stratigraphy, **9**, 49–52.

BERGGREN, W. A., KENT, D. V., SWISHER, C. C. III & AUBRY, M.-P. 1995. A revised Cenozoic geochronology and chronostratigraphy. *In*: BERGGREN, W. A., KENT, D. V., AUBRY, M.-P.

& HARDENBOL, J. (eds) *Geochronology, Time Scales and Global Stratigraphic Correlation. Society of Economic Palaeontologists and Mineralogists, Special Publication,* **54**, 129–212.

BIFFI, U. & MANUM, S. B. 1988. Late Eocene–Early Miocene dinoflagellate cyst stratigraphy from the Marche Region (central Italy). *Bollettino della Società Paleontologica Italiana,* **27**, 163–212.

BIRKENMAJER, K. & OSZCZYPKO, N. 1989. Cretaceous and Palaeogene lithostratigraphic units of the Magura Nappe, Krynica Subunit, Carpathians. *Annales Societatis Geologorum Poloniae,* **59**, 145–181.

BLAICHER, J., JASIONOWICZ, J. & WDOWIARZ, S. 1963. Sur l'importance de marnes a Globigerines pour la stratigraphie du Flysch carpatique. *Résumé des communications, Association Géologique Karpatho-Balkanique V-ème Congrès, Bucarest,* 67–73.

BRINKHUIS, H. 1992. *Late Eocene to Early Oligocene dinoflagellate cysts from central and northeast Italy.* Ph.D. thesis, University of Utrecht, 169pp.

BRINKHUIS, H. 1994. Late Eocene to Early Oligocene dinoflagellate cysts from the Priabonian type-area (Northeast Italy): biostratigraphy and palaeoenvironmental interpretation. *Palaeogeography, Palaeoclimatology, Palaeoecology,* **107**, 121–163.

BRINKHUIS, H. & BIFFI, U. 1993. Dinoflagellate cyst stratigraphy of the Eocene/Oligocene transition in central Italy. *Marine Micropaleontology,* **22**, 131–183.

BRINKHUIS, H. & VISSCHER, H. 1995. The upper boundary of the Priabonian Stage; a reappraisal based on dinoflagellate cyst biostratigraphy. *In*: BERGGREN, W. A., KENT, D. V., AUBRY, M.-P. & HARDENBOL, J. (eds) *Geochronology, Time Scales and Global Stratigraphic Correlation.* Society of Economic Palaeontologists and Mineralogists, Special Publication, **54**, 295–304.

BUJAK, J. P. 1994. New dinocyst taxa from the Eocene of the North Sea. *Journal of Micropalaeontology,* **12**, 119–131.

BUJAK, J. P. & MUDGE, D. 1994. A high-resolution North Sea Eocene dinocyst zonation. *Journal of the Geological Society, London,* **151**, 449–462.

CHÂTEAUNEUF, J.-J. & GRUAS-CAVAGNETTO, C. 1978. Les zones de Wetzeliellaceae (Dinophyceae) du bassin de Paris. *Bulletin du Bureau de Recherches Géologiques et Minières (2-ème Série), Section IV,* **2–1978**, 55–93.

COSTA, L. I. & DOWNIE, C. 1976. The distribution of the dinoflagellate *Wetzeliella* in the Palaeogene of north-western Europe. *Palaeontology,* **19**, 591–614.

COSTA, L. I. & DOWNIE, C. 1979. Cenozoic dinocyst stratigraphy of Sites 403 to 406 (Rockall Plateau), IPOD, Leg 48. *In*: MONTADERT, L. & ROBERTS, D. G., *Deep Sea Drilling Project, Initial Reports,* **48**, 513–529.

DALE, B. 1996. Dinoflagellate cyst ecology: modelling and geological applications. *In*: JANSONIUS, J. & McGREGOR, D. C. (eds) *Palynology: Principles and Applications,* **3**. American Association of

Stratigraphic Palynologists Foundation, Dallas, Texas, pp. 1249–1275.

GEDL, P. 1999. Palynology of the Eocene–Oligocene boundary in the Polish Flysch Carpathians. *Przegląd Geologiczny,* **47**, 394–399 (in Polish with English summary).

HAQ, B. U., HARDENBOL, J. & VAIL, P. R. 1988. Mesozoic and Cenozoic chronostratigraphy and cycles of sea-level change. *In*: WILGUS, C. K., HASTINGS, B. S. *et al.* (eds) *Sea Level Changes; an Integrated Approach.* Society of Economic Palaeontologists and Mineralogists, Special Publication, **42**, 71–108.

HARLAND, R. 1983. Dinoflagellate cysts in bottom sediments from the North Atlantic Ocean and adjacent seas. *Palaeontology,* **26**, 321–387.

KÖTHE, A. 1990. Paleogene dinoflagellates from northwest Germany – biostratigraphy and paleoenvironment. *Geologisches Jahrbuch,* **A118**, 1–111.

KSIĄŻKIEWICZ, M. 1977. The tectonics of the Carpathians. *In*: KSIĄŻKIEWICZ, M. (ed.) *Geology of Poland, IV, Tectonics.* Wydawnictwa Geologiczne, Warszawa, pp. 476–618.

KSIĄŻKIEWICZ, M. & LEŠKO, B. 1959. On relation between the Krosno- and Magura-Flysch. *Bulletin de l'Académie Polonaise des Sciences, Série des Sciences Chimiques, Géologiques et Géographiques,* **7**, 773–780.

LESZCZYŃSKI, S. 1997. Origin of the Sub-Menilite Globigerina Marl (Eocene–Oligocene transition) in the Polish Outer Carpathians. *Annales Societatis Geologorum Poloniae,* **67**, 367–427.

MANUM, S. B., BOULTER, M. C., GUNNARSDOTTIR, H., RANGNES, K. & SCHOLZE, A. 1989. Eocene to Miocene palynology of the Norwegian Sea (ODP Leg 104). *In*: ELDHOLM, O., THIEDE, J. *et al. Proceedings of the Ocean Drilling Program, Scientific Results,* **104**, 611–662.

OKADA, H. & BUKRY, D. 1980. Supplementary modification and introduction of code numbers to the low latitude coccolith biostratigraphy zonation. *Marine Micropaleontology,* **5**, 321–324.

OLSZEWSKA, B. 1985. Remarks concerning the Eocene–Oligocene boundary in the Polish External Carpathians: results of foraminiferal investigations. *Proceedings Reports of the XIIIth Congress of KBGA, Poland – Cracow, September 5–10 1985,* **1**, 57–59.

OSZCZYPKO, N. 1992. Late Cretaceous through Paleogene evolution of Magura Basin. *Geologica Carpathica,* **43**, 333–338.

OSZCZYPKO, M. 1996. Calcareous nannoplankton of the Globigerina Marls (Leluchów Marls Member), Magura Nappe, West Carpathians. *Annales Societatis Geologorum Poloniae,* **66**, 1–15.

OSZCZYPKO, N., DUDZIAK, J. & MALATA, E. 1990. Stratigraphy of the Cretaceous through Palaeogene deposits of the Magura Nappe in the Beskid Sądecki Range, Polish Outer Carpathians. *Studia Geologica Polonica,* **97**, 109–181.

OSZCZYPKO-CLOWES, M. 1998. Late Eocene–Early Oligocene calcareous nannoplankton and stable isotopes (δ^{13}C, δ^{18}O) of the Globigerina Marls in the Magura Nappe. *Slovak Geological Magazine*, **4**, 107–120.

OSZCZYPKO-CLOWES, M. 1999. The Late Eocene to Early Miocene nannoplankton stratigraphy of the Magura Nappe (Western Carpathians, Poland). *Geologica Carpathica*, **50**, 59–62.

OSZCZYPKO-CLOWES, M. 2001. The nannofossil biostratigraphy of the youngest deposits of the Magura Nappe (East of the Skawa river, Polish Flysch Carpathians) and their palaeoenvironmental conditions. *Annales Societatis Geologorum Poloniae*, **71**, 139–188.

POWELL, A. J. 1992. Dinoflagellate cysts of the Tertiary System. *In*: POWELL, A. J. (ed.) *A Stratigraphic Index of Dinoflagellate Cysts. British Micropalaeontological Society Publication Series.* Chapman & Hall, London, pp. 155–249.

ROCHON, A., DE VERNAL, A., TURON, J.-L., MATTHIESSEN, J. & HEAD, M. J. 1999. Distribution of recent dinoflagellate cysts in surface sediments from the North Atlantic and adjacent seas in relation to sea-surface parameters. *American Association of Stratigraphic Palynologists, Contributions Series*, **35**, 1–146.

RÖGL, F. & STEININGER, F. 1983. Vom Zerfall der Tethys zu Mediterran und Paratethys. Die Neogene Paläogeographie und Palinspastik des Zirkum-mediterranen. *Annales des Naturhistorischen Museums Wien*, **85**, 135–163.

STOVER, L. E., BRINKHUIS, H. *ET AL.* 1996. Mesozoic–Tertiary dinoflagellates, acritarchs and prasinophytes. *In*: JANSONIUS, J. & MCGREGOR, D. C. (eds) *Palynology: Principles and Applications*, **2**. American Association of Stratigraphic Palynologists Foundation, Dallas, Texas, pp. 641–750.

ŚWIDZIŃSKI, H. 1934. Recherches géologiques au groupe de Magóra. *Posiedzenia Naukowe Państwowego Instytutu Geologicznego*, **39**, 18–20.

ŚWIDZIŃSKI, H. 1939. Zarys geologii okolic Krynicy i Muszyny. *Biuletyn Państwowego Instytutu Geologicznego*, **18**, 88–89.

ŚWIDZIŃSKI, H. 1961a. Observations géologiques faites dans les environs de Leluchów, de Plavec sur le Poprad et d'Ujak (Karpates polonoslovaques). *Bulletin de l'Académie Polonaise des Sciences, Série des Sciences Chimiques, Géologiques et Géographiques*, **9**, 99–107.

ŚWIDZIŃSKI, H. 1961b. Le Série de Richvald dans les Karpates Flyscheuses. *Bulletin de l'Académie Polonaise des Sciences, Série des Sciences Chimiques, Géologiques et Géographiques*, **9**, 109–119.

VAN COUVERING, J. A., AUBRY, M.-P., BERGGREN, W. A., BUJAK, J. P., NAESER, C. W. & WIESER T. 1981. The terminal Eocene event and the Polish connection. *Palaeogeography, Palaeoclimatology, Palaeoecology*, **36**, 321–362.

VINK, A., ZONNEVELD, K. A. F. & WILLEMS, H. 2000. Organic-walled dinoflagellate cysts in western equatorial Atlantic surface sediments: distribution and their relation to environment. *Review of Palaeobotany and Palynology*, **112**, 247–286.

WALL, D., DALE, B., LOHMANN, G. P. & SMITH, W. K. 1977. The environmental and climatic distribution of dinoflagellate cysts in modern marine sediments from regions in the North and South Atlantic oceans and adjacent seas. *Marine Micropaleontology*, **2**, 121–200.

WILLIAMS, G. L., LENTIN, J. K. & FENSOME, R. A. 1998. The Lentin and Williams index of fossil dinoflagellates, 1998 edition. *American Association of Stratigraphic Palynologists, Contributions Series*, **28**, 1–856.

WILLIAMS, G. L., STOVER, L. E. & KIDSON, E. J. 1993. Distribution of some biostratigraphically significant Cenozoic and Mesozoic dinoflagellates in the Northern Hemisphere. *Geological Survey of Canada, Paper*, **92–10**, 1–137.

WILPSHAAR, M., SANTARELLI, A., BRINKHUIS, H. & VISSCHER, H. 1996. Dinoflagellate cysts and mid-Oligocene chronostratigraphy in the central Mediterranean region. *Journal of the Geological Society, London*, **153**, 553–561.

ZEVENBOOM, D. 1995. *Dinoflagellate cysts from the Mediterranean Late Oligocene and Miocene.* Ph.D. thesis, University of Utrecht, 221pp.

Palynostratigraphy and palaeoenvironments across the Oligocene–Miocene boundary within the Centinela Formation, southwestern Argentina

G. R. GUERSTEIN[1], M. V. GULER[1] & S. CASADÍO[2]

[1]Departamento de Geología, Universidad Nacional del Sur – San Juan 670 (8000) Bahía Blanca – Consejo Nacional de Investigaciones Científicas y Técnicas, Argentina

[2]Facultad de Ciencias Exactas y Naturales, Universidad Nacional de La Pampa, Uruguay 151, Santa Rosa, 6300, Argentina

Abstract: Palynological analysis of the Centinela Formation, exposed in the foothills of the Patagonian Andes, has revealed the presence of pollen, dinoflagellate cysts, and chlorococcalean and prasinophycean algae. These groups are here reported from the Centinela Formation for the first time. Sporomorph and dinoflagellate cyst assemblages suggest a Late Oligocene and Early Miocene age. These results coincide with a $^{87}Sr/^{86}Sr$ age close to the age of the Oligocene–Miocene boundary obtained from the lower part of the section. Palynological information from the Centinela Formation permits correlation with Upper Oligocene and Lower Miocene units cropping out along the Atlantic Patagonian coast. Assemblages from the lower part of the section suggest that the beds were deposited under marine, near-shore palaeoenvironmental conditions with a strong continental influence. In the middle part of the section, high dinoflagellate cyst ratios coincide with a maximum flooding surface recorded in the Centinela Formation. Towards the top of the Centinela Formation, the sporomorph assemblages reflect the development of vegetation adapted to coastal environments, which agrees with the sparse occurrence of marine palynomorphs. A new dinoflagellate species, *Hystrichostrogylon sulcatum*, is proposed. This species appears to range across the Oligocene–Miocene boundary and is particularly abundant in the lowest Miocene.

During the Late Oligocene and Early Miocene, one of the most important marine transgressions during the Cenozoic occurred in the southernmost part of South America. The sediments deposited during this event, informally known as 'Patagoniano', are an important component of the sedimentary succession of the Colorado, San Jorge, and Austral basins (Fig. 1). These sediments also attracted the interest of d'Orbigny (1842) and Darwin (1846). Subsequent work has revealed the key role of these sediments in the unravelling of palaeobiogeographical problems in the Southern Hemisphere (Legarreta & Uliana 1994).

Upper Oligocene–Lower Miocene marine sediments in the Colorado Basin are represented by the lowermost beds of the Barranca Final Formation (Malumián *et al.* 1998; Guerstein & Guler 2000; Guerstein & Junciel 2001). Farther south, in the San Jorge Basin, the 'Patagonian transgression' is recorded in the Chenque Formation. This unit has been the focus of the great controversy concerning the age of this transgressive event, which ranges from Late Eocene to Early Miocene according to different authors (Camacho 1995; Barreda 1996). However, recent micropalaeontological evidence indicates its Late Oligocene? and Early to early Mid-Miocene age (Malumián 1999; Barreda 2002).

In the Austral Basin there are excellent exposures of the 'Patagoniano' along the foothills of the Andes between Lago Posadas and Río Turbio as well as along the Atlantic coast. In the western area, these deposits are known as the Centinela Formation (Furque 1973), whereas along the eastern coastal area they are grouped into the San Julián and Monte León formations, dated as Late Oligocene–Early Miocene. The latter formation records the highest relative sea-level and the first influx of Antarctic waters on to the Argentine continental shelf (Malumián 2002).

In this work we describe the palynological assemblages recovered from the Centinela Formation exposed south of El Calafate. The assemblages suggest a Late Oligocene to Early Miocene age for this unit, in agreement with $^{87}Sr/^{86}Sr$ ages (Casadío *et al.* 2000b, 2001). The fluctuating dinocyst frequencies reflect shallow-marine to coastal-marine conditions. The palynological assemblages from the overlapping

From: BEAUDOIN, A.B. & HEAD, M.J. (eds) 2004. *The Palynology and Micropalaeontology of Boundaries.* Geological Society, London, Special Publications, **230**, 325–343. 0305-8719/04/$15 © The Geological Society of London 2004.

Santa Cruz Formation indicate a continental environment toward the top of the section.

Stratigraphic setting

In the studied area, the Upper Oligocene–Lower Miocene sedimentary section overlies Eocene (Middle to Upper?) rocks and is separated from them by a regional unconformity. The unit overlying the unconformity is the continental Río Leona Formation (100–200 m) which displays a fining-upwards succession from conglomerates to coal-rich clays (Fig. 1). Transitionally overlying this unit are the marine sandstones, fossiliferous muddy-sandstones, shell-beds, and mudstones of the Centinela Formation (120–250 m). This formation is unconformably overlain by the Middle Miocene Santa Cruz Formation. The Río Leona Formation and Centinela Formation thus constitute a single depositional sequence between the two unconformities (S. Casadío & S. Marenssi, unpublished data).

The preserved succession in the study area shows a vertical arrangement of facies passing upwards from fluviatile high-energy to low-energy fluviatile–deltaic environments, which are covered by marine deposits. Thus, the coal-rich beds of the uppermost part of the Río Leona Formation preceded the marine transgression of the Centinela Formation. This part of the succession shows evidence of reworking, not only from the underlying Eocene rocks, but also from Upper Cretaceous rocks (Carrizo *et al.* 1990). Thus, sediments below the unconformity would have been exposed as early as the Oligocene (S. Casadío & S. Marenssi, unpublished data).

The section studied, 380 m thick, is exposed along the banks of the Arroyo de las Bandurrias (50° 30' S, 72° 15' W), south of the Puesto Estancia 25 de Mayo. The analysed stratigraphic interval is between the 110 and 490 m height in the integrated section illustrated in Figure 1. The lower Centinela Formation is composed of fine sandstones and siltstones bearing a diverse fauna of crustaceans, including nine families of Decapoda and one of Isopoda. These fossils show strong affinities with temperate and subtropical faunas of the Atlantic Ocean basins (Casadío *et al.* 2000a). These fossils document the southernmost extension of low-latitude oceanographic influence on this region during the Palaeogene–Neogene transition. A bed of white, massive tuff overlies these rocks, followed by siltstones, tuffs, and sandstones with decapods and specimens of the bivalve *Panopea* sp. in life position. These sediments were presumably formed in predomi-

nantly subtidal environments. A valve of the oyster *Crassostrea*? *hatcheri* (Ortmann) collected 25 m below the tuff bed yielded an $^{87}Sr/^{86}Sr$ age of 23.19 Ma (Casadío *et al.* 2000b).

The upper part of the Centinela Formation comprises fine- to medium-grained sandstones with intercalated siltstones exhibiting sigmoid and planar bidirectional cross-stratification and also beds containing valves of *Crassostrea*? *hatcheri*. Specimens of this oyster may be distinguished by the large size and great thickness of its shell. They may be found either in life position or as post-mortem accumulations. Samples of the shells collected 110 m above the base of the section (Fig. 1) were analysed for $\delta^{13}C$ and $\delta^{18}O$. The results suggest that the oysters grew under normal marine conditions and in water temperatures ranging between 15° C in winter and 21° C in summer (Casadío *et al.* 2000a). These results agree with information available from other fossil species belonging to this genus (Nelson 1978; Kirby 2000, 2001).

Sedimentary and palaeontological evidence suggest a shallow, subtidal depositional environment for the section between 150 and 270 m (Fig. 1). R. Melchor & S. Casadío (unpublished data) reached similar conclusions based on the presence of well-developed bio-erosion sculpture on specimens of *Crassostrea*? *hatcheri*.

Materials and methods

Forty-five samples were collected from the type section of the Centinela Formation, of which 17 were selected for palynological analysis. The stratigraphic position of the samples is shown in Figure 2. The samples were prepared at the Geological Survey of Canada (Atlantic). Preparation techniques included hydrofluoric and hydrochloric acid treatment, mild oxidation (10% nitric acid for one minute) and a 10% ammonia hydroxide wash for one minute. The organic fraction was concentrated by separation in zinc bromide (specific gravity 2.0). Differential centrifuging was used to remove fine particles, and the residues were sieved to concentrate the 10–180 μm fraction. The residues were stained using Bismarck C and mounted and dried on coverslips in hydroxyethyl cellulose with ethylene glycol monomethyl ether as a dispersal agent. The coverslips were then affixed to the slides with elvacite.

Specimens were illustrated with a Nikon Coolpix 950 camera attached to a Nikon Eclipse 600 microscope. Digital images are not reversed and all line drawings show external views. Co-ordinates quoted from the Vernier scale of Nikon microscope serial no. 772751 follow the

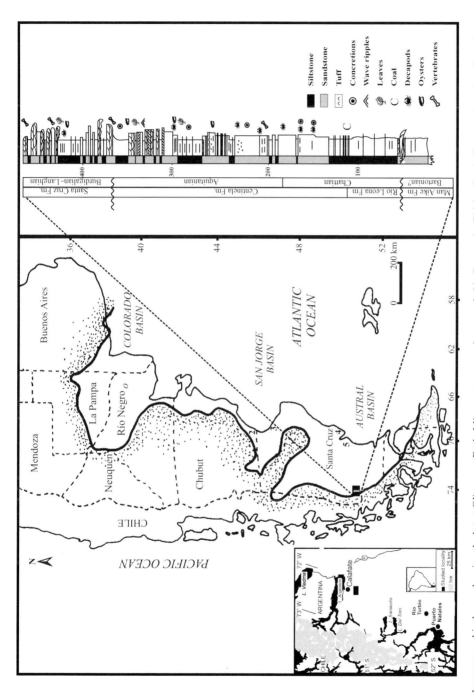

Fig. 1. Palaeogeographical map showing the latest Oligocene–Early Miocene transgression recorded in Patagonia. Thicker line indicates palaeo-shorelines (from Malumián 1999). Integrated section showing the lithological units exposed at the Bandurrias River area, SW Argentina. **1**, Centinela Formation at its type area (this study); **2**, Chenque Formation, San Jorge Basin (Barreda 1996; Palamarczuk & Barreda 1998); **3**, Mazarredo sub-basin (Barreda & Palamarczuk 2000a); **4**, San Julián Formation in Playa La Mina area (Barreda 1997); **5**, Monte León Formation at its type area (Barreda & Palamarczuk 2000b)

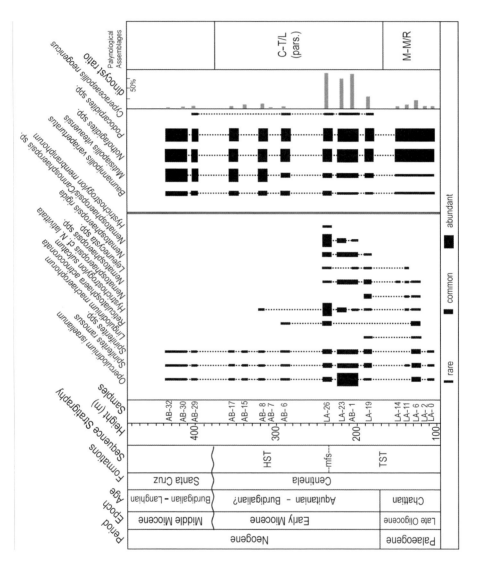

Fig. 2. Distribution and frequencies of selected dinocysts and sporomorphs from the Centinela Formation at its type section. Proposed age based on palynological analysis. Comparison with the two lowest palynological assemblages from Barreda & Palamarczuk (2000*c*). TST: transgressive system tract; MFS: maximum flooding surface; HST: highstand system tract.

sample and slide number for each specimen illustrated. England Finder (EF) references are provided in the corresponding figure explanations. The types and illustrated specimens are stored in the collection of the Laboratory of Palynology, Universidad Nacional del Sur, Bahía Blanca, Argentina (UNSLP). The dinoflagellate cyst nomenclature follows Williams *et al.* (1998) and the systematic section uses the classification of Fensome *et al.* (1993). The geological time-scale of Berggren *et al.* (1995) is used.

Palynological assemblages and palaeoenvironments

Palynological assemblages from the Centinela Formation are rich in palynomorphs, mainly pollen and spores with variable amounts of dinoflagellate cysts (dinocysts) and green algae remains. All the pollen types recognized in this study and their botanical affinities are included in Appendix Ia. The dinocyst species identified in the Centinela Formation are listed in Appendix Ib. Figure 2 shows the distribution and frequencies of selected palynomorphs recovered from the Centinela Formation along with dinocyst/total palynomorph ratios, expressed as percent.

Samples from LA-0 to LA-14 have dinocyst ratios under 10% of total palynomorphs. Dinocyst assemblages are poorly represented, and are mainly composed of *Operculodinium israelianum*, *Spiniferites ramosus*, *Lingulodinium machaerophorum* and *Reticulatosphaera actinocoronata*. The sporomorph assemblages are dominated by arboreal pollen of Podocarpaceae and Fagaceae throughout the section. Small amounts of Asteraceae, Malvaceae, Ephedraceae and Poaceae pollen are also present from the bottom of the Centinela Formation. These assemblages indicate marine near-shore conditions with a strong influence from the continental area.

Sample LA-19 shows the lowest stratigraphic occurrences of *Nematosphaeropsis rigida* and *Cyperaceaepollis neogenicus*. A notable increase in the dinocyst ratio is recorded in samples AB-1 and LA-23, reaching 83% and 73% of the total palynomorphs, respectively. These assemblages are dominated by *Operculodinium israelianum*, a species abundant in very shallow depths, particularly in estuaries (Edwards & Andrle 1992; Head 1998).

Sample LA-26 shows a relatively high abundance of species of *Nematosphaeropsis*, *Nematosphaeropsis/Cannosphaerospsis* sp. and *Hystrichostrogylon sulcatum*. Some of the dinocyst species from LA-19, AB-1, LA-23 and LA-26 show high variability in their morphologies, as described in the systematic palaeontology. A stressed environment subjected to salinity, temperature, and/ or water-depth changes may be responsible for these gradational morphotypes.

According to S. Casadío & S. Marenssi (unpublished data), the stratigraphic interval between 110 and 250 m corresponds with the transgressive system tract (TST in Fig. 2), and the contact between Río Leona and Centinela formations represents the transgressive surface (TS). In this context, the assemblage LA-26 coincides with the maximum flooding surface (MFS, Fig. 2) of the sequence described by S. Casadío & S. Marenssi, unpublished data.

Overlying deposits (AB-6 to AB-17) are characterized by high frequencies of sporomorphs, with the absence of most of the dinocyst taxa encountered in the lower assemblages. These deposits contain increasing amounts of Asteraceae, Malvaceae and scarce Poaceae, Chenopodiaceae and Sparganiaceae pollen as well as rare *Tasmanites* sp. and *Pediastrum* sp. These pollen associations reflect the development of coastal vegetation, and indicate that the coastline was moving closer to the study area. The weak marine signal and the progradational conditions described above correspond with the highstand system tract (HST, Fig. 2) of the sequence.

The palynological assemblages from samples AB-29 to AB-32 do not show compositional changes related to underlying samples (AB-15 and AB-17), and represent the lowest palynological record from the Santa Cruz Formation.

All samples contain small amounts of Late Cretaceous reworked dinocyst specimens, including *Isabelidinium pellucidum*, *Litosphaeridium* sp., *Manumiella? cretacea*, *M. seelandica*, *Nelsoniella aceras* and *Odontochitina* sp. cf. *O. costata*. Middle Eocene to Lower Oligocene reworked material is represented by a few specimens of *Phthanoperidinium comatum* in samples LA-6 and LA-19.

Age and correlation

The Asteraceae, recorded in pollen assemblages from the bottom of the section, indicate an age no older than Oligocene. According to Macphail & Hill (1994), *Mutisiapollis patersonii*, described from the Lower Oligocene deposits of Tasmania, represents one of the earliest records of Asteraceae.

Mutisiapollis viteauensis, the only Asteraceae recorded in the Centinela Formation, is generally associated with *Baumannipollis variaperturatus*. Both species were erected by Barreda (1993) from the Chenque Formation (Lower Miocene) in the San Jorge Basin, Argentina. *Mutisiapollis viteauensis* and *Baumannipollis variaperturatus* have not been recovered from deposits older than Late Oligocene, and have been widely recorded from Neogene deposits of Argentina (Barreda 1996; Barreda *et al.* 1998; Ottone *et al.* 1998; Barreda & Palamarczuk 2000*a*, 2000*b*; Guler *et al.* 2001). Thus, the sporomorph assemblages found in the Centinela Formation suggest an age no older than Late Oligocene.

Fifteen dinocyst taxa were recognized in the Centinela Formation. Most have long stratigraphic ranges. Some of these taxa have their first appearance datums (FADs) in the Palaeogene, including *Reticulatosphaera actinocoronata* (Late Priabonian), *Lingulodinium machaerophorum* (Late Palaeocene) and *Hystrichostrogylon membraniphorum* (Lutetian).

Nematosphaeropsis rigida is a common species in some Neogene assemblages, with confirmed records supporting an FAD at about the Middle Miocene (Wrenn 1988; Versteegh & Zonneveld 1994; de Verteuil 1996; de Verteuil & Norris 1996; Poulsen *et al.* 1996; Head & Westphal 1999). In Argentina, the presence of *Nematosphaeropsis rigida* has been documented in units dated as Early Miocene or younger (Palamarczuk & Barreda 1998; Barreda & Palamarczuk 2000*a*; Barreda 2002; Guler *et al.* 2002). This species is rare in sample LA-19 and becomes common in samples AB-1 and LA-26, and, in the absence of more reliable indices, suggests an age no older than Miocene for these levels

This is the first palynological analysis of Oligocene–Miocene beds from the western part of Santa Cruz Province. Previous palynological studies were carried out on units cropping out along the Atlantic Patagonian coast in the San Jorge and Austral basins. Barreda (1996) proposed four informal palynological zones based on the sporomorph assemblages from the Chenque Formation in SE Chubut Province. The age postulated for these palynozones ranges from Late Oligocene? to Early–Mid-? Miocene. Subsequently, Palamarczuk & Barreda (1998) analysed the dinocysts recovered from these deposits and restricted the age of the Chenque Formation to the Early Miocene. Barreda & Palamarczuk (2000*a*) studied the palynological assemblages from deposits cropping out in NE Santa Cruz Province in the Mazarredo sub-Basin (*sensu* Bellosi 1995). These authors recognized two palynological units, which they

assigned to the Late Oligocene and Early Miocene respectively.

To the south, in the Austral Basin, the sporomorph assemblages indicate an Oligocene (possibly Late Oligocene) age for the base of San Julián Formation (Barreda 1997). Barreda & Palamarczuk (2000*b*) studied both sporomorph and dinocyst assemblages from the Monte León Formation in its type area and assigned the formation to the Miocene.

Further palynostratigraphic discussion was presented by Barreda & Palamarczuk (2000*c*) based on the published information mentioned above. They proposed, from bottom to top, the following four informal palynological assemblages:

(1) the *Mutisiapollis viteauensis*, *Margocolporites tenuireticulatus* and *Reticulatosphaera? actinocoronata* assemblage (M–M/R, Late Oligocene; see Fig. 2). This assemblage was compared with the lower unit described by Barreda & Palamarczuk (2000*a*) in sections from NE Santa Cruz Province (Mazarredo Basin);

(2) the *Cyperaceaepollis neogenicus*, *Tricolpites trioblatus* and *Lingulodinium hemicystum* assemblage (C–T/L, Early Miocene). This assemblage was identified at the bottom of the Chenque Formation and the lower part of the Monte León Formation and was compared with the upper unit described by Barreda & Palamarczuk (2000*a*);

(3) the *Glencopollis ornatus* and *Cannosphaeropsis quattrocchiae* (as *C. utinensis*) assemblage (G/C, Early Miocene) was identified in the middle part of the Chenque Formation and the upper part of the Monte León Formation; and

(4) the *Tubulifloridites antipodica*, *Baumannipollis chubutensis* and *Hystrichosphaeropsis obscura* assemblage (T–B/H, Middle? Miocene) was only recognized in the uppermost part of the Chenque Formation.

Figure 3 shows the comparison between the units identified in western Santa Cruz and those cropping out in the Atlantic coastal area. The palynological assemblages from the lower part of the Centinela Formation are characterized by the presence of *Mutisiapollis viteauensis* and *Reticulatosphera actinocoronata*. These assemblages, even though not identical, may be equivalent to the Late Oligocene M–M/R palynological assemblage.

The samples from the middle and upper part of the Centinela Formation yield some of the diagnostic species that define the base of the

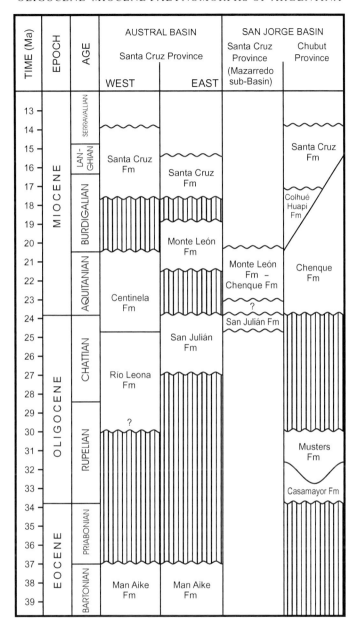

Fig. 3. Correlation of lithostratigraphic units cropping out in the western part of Santa Cruz Province with those exposed along the Atlantic coast in the San Jorge and Austral basins.

Early Miocene C–T/L assemblage. Furthermore, *Mutisiapollis viteauensis* and *Baumannipollis variaperturatus* are poorly represented in the palynological samples from the lower part of the Centinela Formation (LA-0 to LA-14), but become common to abundant toward the upper part of the section (LA-19 to AB-32). This increase in the frequencies of *Mutisiapollis viteauensis* and *Baumannipollis variaperturatus*, along with the lowest occurrence of *Nematosphaeropsis rigida*, has also been shown by Barreda & Palamarczuk (2000*a*; page 105, fig. 3) to be at the base of the Early Miocene C–T/L assemblage (Barreda & Palamarczuk 2000*c*).

The absence in our assemblages of species representing an evolved flora characteristic of Early to Mid-? Miocene palynological assemblages G/C and T–B/H is remarkable. We conclude that deposits of late Early Miocene or younger ages are not represented in the studied section.

Discussion and conclusions

The rocks exposed in western Santa Cruz, assigned to the Centinela Formation, were considered to be Oligocene–Miocene in age, based on molluscan assemblages (Furque & Camacho 1972; Riccardi & Rolleri 1980). Furque (1973) and Griffin (1990) suggested a Miocene age for this unit, whereas Piñero (1983), using foraminiferal data, considered an Oligocene–Miocene age for this formation.

Recent radiometric results reveal great discrepancies related to the age of the Centinela Formation. The ^{40}Ar/^{39}Ar analysis of a volcanic ash bed from the lower part of the formation yielded an age of approximately 46 Ma (Casadío *et al.* 2000*a*). Subsequently, Casadío *et al.* (2000*b*) obtained a younger age based on the ^{87}Sr/^{86}Sr ratio from a valve of *Crassostrea? hatcheri*, indicating an age of 23.19 Ma for the lowermost part of the Centinela Formation, which is in agreement with the palynological interpretation.

The palynological assemblages from the lower part of the studied section, in conjunction with sedimentological data, reflect a subtidal palaeoenvironment. The sedimentological information from the upper part of the Centinela Formation suggests a more shallow subtidal palaeoenvironment confirmed by a decreasing abundance and diversity of dinocysts. The pollen assemblages also reflect the development of vegetation adapted to a coastal environment.

The palynological assemblages suggest that the lower part of the Centinela Formation may be equivalent to the Upper Oligocene units from the southern area of the San Jorge Gulf. Likewise, the middle and upper part of the Centinela Formation suggests a correlation with the lowermost beds of the Chenque Formation, the uppermost levels cropping out in southern San Jorge Gulf, and possibly with the bottom of the Monte León Formation. Otherwise, there are insufficient elements in common to establish a close correlation with the Oligocene San Julián Formation.

Systematic palaeontology

Division **Dinoflagellata** (Bütschli 1885) Fensome *et al.* 1993
Class **Dinophyceae** Pascher 1914
Order **Gonyaulacales** Taylor 1980
Family **Gonyaulacaceae** Lindemann 1928
Genus *Hystrichostrogylon* (Agelopoulos) Stover & Evitt 1978
Type species: *Hystrichostrogylon membraniphorum* Agelopoulos 1964

Hystrichostrogylon sulcatum sp. nov.
Fig. 4a–f, Fig. 5a–l, Fig. 6a–c

Holotype: Laboratory of Palynology Universidad Nacional del Sur (UNSLP) slide no. LA-26 45 × 102. England Finder L31/3, Fig. 4 a & b, Fig. 5 a–c.
Type locality: Centinela Formation, Bandurrias River, southern Calafate, Santa Cruz, Argentina.
Stratigraphic horizon: Centinela Formation, at 140 m above the base of the section (Fig. 2).
Stratigraphic occurrence: Upper Oligocene to Lower Miocene.
Etymology: Adjective derived from the Latin *sulcus*: ventral furrow or groove in reference to the mid-ventral position of the cavation.
Diagnosis: A species of *Hystrichostrogylon* characterized by a narrow mid-ventral cavation and an antapical structure composed of two large gonal processes joined by a suturocavate membrane. All the processes are hollow, tapering, trifurcate with solid distal ends.
Description: Cysts camocavate with spherical to subspherical central body. Endophragm smooth, periphragm finely granulate, always appressed except on the sulcal area, where endophragm and periphragm are narrowly separated. The pericoel communicates with the exterior through a small hole or claustrum in the mid-ventral part of the periphragm. The processes are variable in size and shape. Most of the processes are gonal, triangular in cross-section, broad, tapering, hollow, joined proximally by very faint sutural ridges. Distally the processes are trifurcate with solid ends. The apex of the cyst is consistently indicated by a single, thin, distally bifid process. Processes on opposite margins of the cingulum may be connected in pairs by relatively high membranes. Two large antapical processes are joined at their bases by a common suturocavate membrane developing an antapical structure. The height of the processes

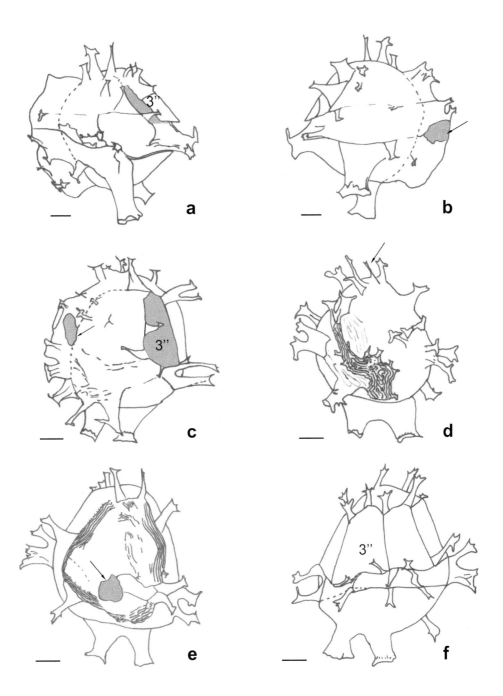

Fig. 4. *Hystrichostrogylon sulcatum* sp. nov., line sketches. Archeopyle and claustrum shown in grey. (**a & b**) Holotype. UNSLP slide no. LA26: 45 × 102 (EF L31/3). (**a**) left lateral surface. (**b**) right lateral surface, claustrum arrowed. (**c**) UNSLP slide no. LA26: 50.8 × 104.7 (EF O25/1). Claustrum arrowed. (**d**) UNSLP slide no. LA26: 34 × 100 (EF J42/4). Ventral surface showing pericoel folded, single, thin, process at the apex arrowed. (**e & f**) UNSLP slide no. LA26: 45.2 × 109 (EF S30/4). (**e**) ventral surface showing sulcal pericoel in ventral view; claustrum arrowed. (**f**) dorsal surface; processes at both sides connected by membranes in pairs.

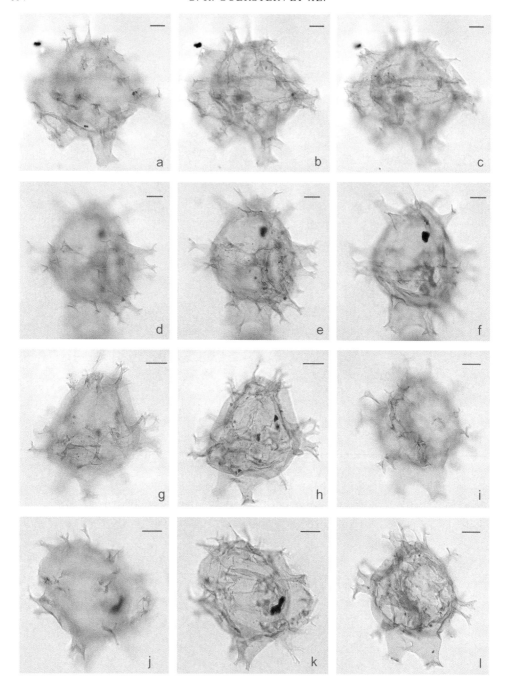

Fig. 5. All digital images were taken using an interference contrast optical system. **EF**: England Finder references. Scale bar: 10 μm. *Hystrichostrogylon sulcatum* sp. nov. (**a & c**) Holotype. UNSLP slide no. LA26: 45 × 102 (EF L31/3). Left lateral view; (**a**) high focus, left lateral surface; (**b**) intermediate focus; (**c**) low focus, right lateral surface. (**d & f**) UNSLP slide no. LA26: 33.7 × 101.7 (EF L43/3). Oblique dorsal view. (**d**) high focus; (**e**) intermediate focus showing sulcal pericoel folded to the right; (**f**) low focus. (**g & h**) UNSLP slide no. LA26: 45.2 × 109 (EF S30/4). Dorsal view. (**g**) high focus; (**h**) low focus. (**i & l**) UNSLP slide no. LA26: 34 × 100 (EF J42/4) Ventral view. (**i**) High focus showing sulcal pericoel folded on the ventral surface; (**l**) Intermediate focus. (**j & k**) UNSLP slide no. LA26: 50.4 × 101 (EF K25/3). Right lateral view. (**j**) high focus; (**k**) low focus.

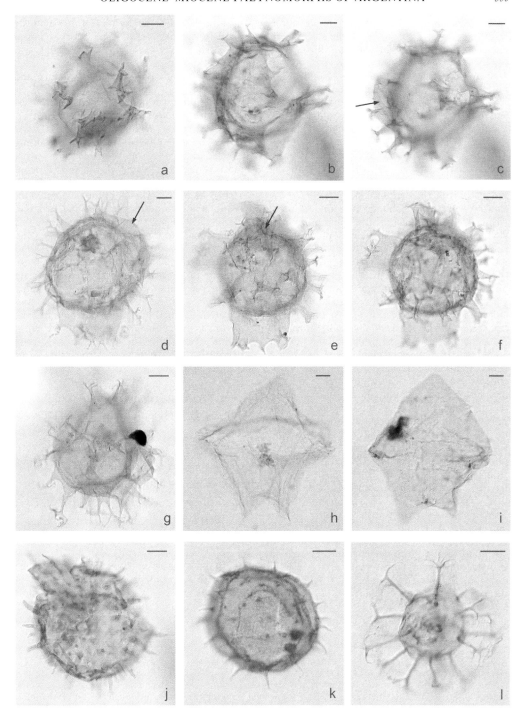

Fig. 6. All digital images were taken using an interference contrast optical system. **EF**: England Finder references. Scale bar: 10 μm. (**a & c**) *Hystrichostrogylon sulcatum* sp. nov. **a**, UNSLP slide no. LA26: 35.5 × 101 (EF K41/3) right lateral view, low focus. (**b & c**) UNSP slide no. LA26: 50.8 × 104.7 (EF O25/1). Left lateral view. (**b**) intermediate focus; (**c**) low focus, claustrum arrowed. (**d & f**) Specimens showing gradational features between *Hystrichostrogylon sulcatum* and *Spiniferites mirabilis* (Rossignol) Sarjeant. (**d**) UNSLP slide no. LA11:

varies depending on the degree of cavation, resulting in shorter processes at the sulcus than elsewhere. Archeopyle precingular, formed by the loss of plate 3″.

Dimensions: Central body length: 32 (49) 65 μm (40 specimens measured); central body width: 32 (45) 55 μm (20 specimens measured); processes length: 8–18 μm; antapical process structure: length 13 (15) 17 μm; width 19 (24) 34 μm (16 specimens measured).

Comparisons: This species of *Hystrichostrogylon* is characterized by a pericoel confined to the sulcal area with a small claustrum at the mid-ventral part of the periphragm. In both *Hystrichostrogylon borisii* Schiøler 1993 and *H. coninckii* Heilmann-Clausen *in* Thompsen and Heilmann-Clausen (1985) the endophragm and periphragm are appressed dorsally, but with relatively large ventral pericoels, and a large rounded mid-ventral claustrum, in the periphragm. In *H. membraniphorum* Agelopoulos 1964 the pericoel is only developed antapically, although according to Eaton (1976), this species (as *Achomosphaera membraniphora*) forms a distinctive pericoel in the antapical and ventral areas. In *H. holohymenium* Islam 1983 the pericoel almost completely surrounds the endocyst, whereas in *H. clausenii* Bujak 1994 the periphragm and endophragm are in contact in the mid-dorsal and mid-ventral regions with a pericoel surrounding the ambital periphery of the cyst; the claustrum is typically developed on the left cingular–postcingular side of the periphragm. The new species described here differs from all other species of *Hystrichostrogylon* in having a characteristic antapical process structure. The features of *H. sulcatum* strongly resemble those described for *Spiniferites falcipedius* Warny & Wrenn 1997. These two species also have in common a consistent, thin preapical process and with the cingular area defined by pairs of processes transversally joined by high membranes. In dorso-ventral view *H. sulcatum* is therefore remarkably similar to *Spiniferites falcipedius* (Fig. 6e & f). However, most of the specimens recovered from the Centinela Forma-

tion show the sulcal pericoel, a feature obviously absent in *S. falcipedius*. The morphological features shared by these two species suggest a close relationship.

Remarks: The antapical process structure and the distal process morphology show a gradational variation within the dinoflagellate cyst assemblages recovered from the Centinela Formation. Warny & Wrenn (1997) have already noted a gradation between specimens sharing characteristics of *Spiniferites mirabilis* (Rossignol) Sarjeant 1979 and *S. falcipedius*, from the upper Neogene succession of the Atlantic Coast of Morocco. These authors suggested an evolutionary relationship between the two species. Similarly, some Argentinian specimens of *H. sulcatum* and *Spiniferites falcipedius* (Fig. 6e–f) possess broad, gonal and distally solid processes with an antapical process structure giving rise to three short bifurcate and trifurcate processes, typical of *S. mirabilis* (Fig. 6e & f). Other specimens bear thin, trifurcate gonal and bifurcate intergonal processes with an antapical structure as in *S. mirabilis*, but possess the sulcal cavation (Fig. 6d). The last case was only observed in the assemblages from the lower part of the section.

Genus *Nematosphaeropsis* Deflandre & Cookson 1955 emend. Williams & Downie 1966

Type species: *Nematosphaeropsis balcombiana* Deflandre & Cookson 1955
Nematosphaeropsis rigida Wrenn 1988
Fig. 7g–n

Remarks: Very few specimens of *Nematosphaeropsis* found in the Centinela Formation can be assigned to *Nematosphaeropsis rigida*. Most of them possess processes with complex distal ends showing a highly variable trabecular network. The presence of small loops next to the gonal

---

37.7 × 101.7 (EF L38/2). Dorsal view, intermediate focus. Processes and antapical structure as in *Spiniferites mirabilis*. Pericoel arrowed. (**e & f**) UNSLP slide no. LA26: 39.9 × 108.9 (EF T36/6). Processes and pericoel typical of *H. sulcatum*; antapical structure as in *S. mirabilis*. Ventral view. (**e**) high focus, pericoel folded on the ventral surface arrowed; (**f**) low focus; (**g**) *Hystrichostrogylon membraniphorum* Agelopoulos. UNSLP slide no. LA26: 34.7 × 104.6 (EF O41/4). Dorsal view, intermediate focus. (**h**) *Lejeunecysta* cf. *fallax* (Morgenroth) Artzner & Dörhöfer emend. Biffi & Grignani. UNSLP slide no. AB1: 44.8 × 96.6 (EF F31/0). Dorsal view, intermediate focus. (**i**) *Lejeunecysta* sp. UNSLP slide no. LA26: 51 × 1001 (EF K24/4). Ventral view, intermediate focus. (**j**) *Lingulodinium machaerophorum* (Deflandre & Cookson) Wall. UNSLP slide no. LA6: 47.1 × 100.5 (EF K34/4). Ventral view. (**k**) *Operculodinium israelianum* (Rossignol) Wall. UNSLP slide no. AB1: 46 × 93.7 (EF C30/1). Dorsal view, high focus. (**l**) *Reticulatosphaera actinocoronata* (Benedek) Bujak & Matsuoka. UNSLP slide no. LA6: 39.2 × 109.7 (EF T37/3). Uncertain view.

and intergonal junctions is a remarkable trabecular feature (Fig. 7i & j, m & n). Although these loops were not described when the species was named, these features were noticed by J. Wrenn (pers. comm. 2002) in the type material and are clearly observable on his SEM photomicrographs (Wrenn 1988; plate 4, figs 1–5). Moreover, the distal ends of processes are commonly expanded into perforate platforms (Fig. 7h). These platforms are absent on the type material from the Gulf of Mexico and on other species of *Nematosphaeropsis*. However, Guler & Guerstein (2003) illustrate specimens of *N. rigida* from Miocene to Pliocene deposits of the Colorado Basin bearing perforate platforms. In addition, some specimens possess a few thick single trabeculae, just below the external pair of trabeculae, joining adjacent processes (Fig. 7k & l, n). The combination of these features gives rise to a complex trabecular network which characterizes specimens of *N. rigida* from the Centinela Formation.

Nematosphaeropsis/Cannosphaeropsis sp.
Fig. 7a–f

Remarks: Specimens are characterized by a subspherical to ellipsoidal central body with regular gonal processes supporting a complex trabecular network. Single ribbon-like trabeculae are connected to the central body by lateral, polar and dorsal processes, the latter being the shortest. Therefore, they form an asymmetrical network which is ventrally expanded, with the ventral area devoid of processes (Fig. 7a–c). The distal ends of the processes are expanded forming membranous platforms giving rise to pairs of thin, cylindrical trabeculae closely surrounding the underlying thicker trabeculae. Thus, these peculiar forms share features of both *Cannosphaeropsis* and *Nematospheropsis*, and represent a possible morphological link between these two genera. We suspect that the significant morphological variability exhibited by the specimens included in *Nematosphaeropsis/Cannosphaeropsis* sp. and *Nematosphaeropsis rigida* is a response to a stressed environment.

The authors thank the critical readers: V. D. Barreda (Museo Argentino de Ciencias Naturales B. Rivadavia, Buenos Aires), R. M. Feldmann, C. Schweitzer (Kent State University), and J. H. Wrenn (Louisiana State University), and the reviewers. A. J. Powell (Dinosytems, UK), L. E. Edwards (US Geological Survey), and M. J. Head (University of Cambridge), whose constructive comments considerably improved the manuscript. B. J. Crilley (Geological Survey of Canada, Atlantic) is kindly thanked for technical assistance. This study was partially supported by grants from the Universidad Nacional de La Pampa, Fundación Antorchas and Fondo Nacional para la Investigación Científica y Tecnológica (PICT no. 07–09659).

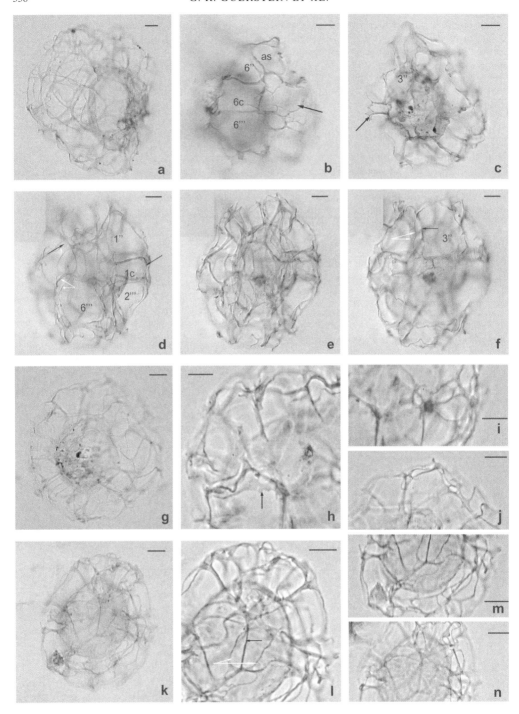

Fig. 7. All digital images were taken using an interference contrast optical system, except when indicated. **EF**: England Finder references. Scale bar: 10 μm. (**a & f**) *Nematosphaeropsis/Cannosphaeropsis* sp. a, UNSLP slide no. LA26: 37 × 101 (EF K39/0). General view. (**b & c**) UNSLP slide no. LA26: 37 × 93.5 (EF C39/0). Right lateral view. (**b**) high focus, sulcal area arrowed; (**c**) low focus, arrow showing the shortest cingular processes on the dorsal area. (**d & f**) UNSLP slide no. LA26: 30.5 × 109.9 (EF T46/3). Ventral view. (**d**) high focus, perforate

Appendix I List of species identified in the Centinela Formation

a   Pollen

Species	Botanical affinity
Baumannipollis variaperturatus Barreda 1993 (Fig. 8a)	Malvaceae
Chenopodipollis chenopodiaceoides (Martin) Truswell 1985 (Fig. 8m)	Chenopodiaceae
Cyperaceaepollis neogenicus Krutzsch 1970 (Fig. 8f)	Cyperaceae
Equisetosporites claricristatus (Shakmundes) Barreda 1997 (Fig. 8g)	Ephedraceae
Graminidites sp. (Fig. 8o)	Poaceae
Mutisiapollis viteauensis (Barreda) Barreda *in* Barreda *et al.* 1998 (Fig. 8b–d & h)	Asteraceae
Nothofagidites saraensis Menéndez & Caccavari 1975 (Fig. 8l)	Fagaceae
Nothofagidites dorotensis Romero 1973 (Fig. 8i & j)	Fagaceae
Nothofagidites rocaensis Romero 1973 (Fig. 8k)	Fagaceae
Podocarpidites marwckii Couper 1953 (Fig. 8r)	Podocarpaceae
Phyllocladidites mawsonii Cookson 1947 (Fig. 8s)	Podocarpaceae
Sparganiaceapollenites barungensis Harris 1972 (Fig. 8p)	Sparganiaceae
Tricolpites reticulatus Cookson 1947 (Fig. 8n)	Gunneraceae
Tricolpites trioblatus Mildenhall & Pocknall 1989 (Fig. 8e)	Scrophulariaceae

b   Dinoflagellate cysts

Hystrichostrogylon sulcatum sp. nov. (Fig. 5a–l, Fig. 6a–c)
Hystrichostrogylon membraniphorum Agelopoulos 1964 (Fig. 6g)
Lejeunecysta sp. cf. *L. fallax* (Morgenroth) Artzner & Dörhöfer 1978 emend. Biffi & Grignani 1983 (Fig. 6h)
Lejeunecysta sp. (Fig. 6i)
Lingulodinium machaerophorum (Deflandre & Cookson) Wall 1967 (Fig. 6j)
Nematosphaeropsis sp. cf. *N. lativittata* Wrenn 1988
Nematosphaeropsis rigida Wrenn 1988 (Fig. 7g–n)
Nematosphaeropsis/Cannosphaeropsis sp. (Fig. 7a–f)
Operculodinium israelianum (Rossignol) Wall 1967 (Fig. 6k)
Reticulatosphaera actinocoronata (Benedek) Bujak & Matsuoka 1986 (Fig. 6l)
Spiniferites ramosus (Ehrenberg) Mantell 1854

c   Algae

Pediastrum sp. (Fig. 8q & t)
Tasmanites sp.

d   Reworked dinoflagellate cysts

Isabelidinium pellucidum (Deflandre & Cookson) Lentin & Williams 1977
Litosphaeridium sp.
Manumiella? cretacea (Cookson) Bujak & Davies 1983
Manumiella seelandica (Lange) Bujak & Davies 1983
Nelsoniella aceras Cookson & Eisenack 1960
Odontochitina sp. cf. *O. costata* Alberti 1961 emend. Clarke & Verdier 1967
Phthanoperidinium comatum (Morgenroth) Eisenack & Kjellström

platform arrowed; (**e**) intermediate focus; (**f**) low focus, single trabecula arrowed in black; double trabecula arrowed in white. (**g & n**) *Nematosphaeropsis rigida* Wrenn. (**g & j**) UNSLP slide no. LA23: 39.3 × 94.6 (EF D37/ 0). (**g**) general view; (**j**) detail showing loops on trabeculae. Phase contrast. (**h & i**) UNSLP slide no. LA23: 39.3 × 99.5 (EF J37/1). (**h**) detail showing gonal platforms (arrowed); (**i**) detail showing loops on trabeculae. (**k & n**) UNSLP slide no. LA26: 44 × 95.7 (EF E32/3). (**k**) general view; (**l**) detail showing single trabecula arrowed in black and double trabecula arrowed in white. (**m & n**) details showing loops on the trabecular network.

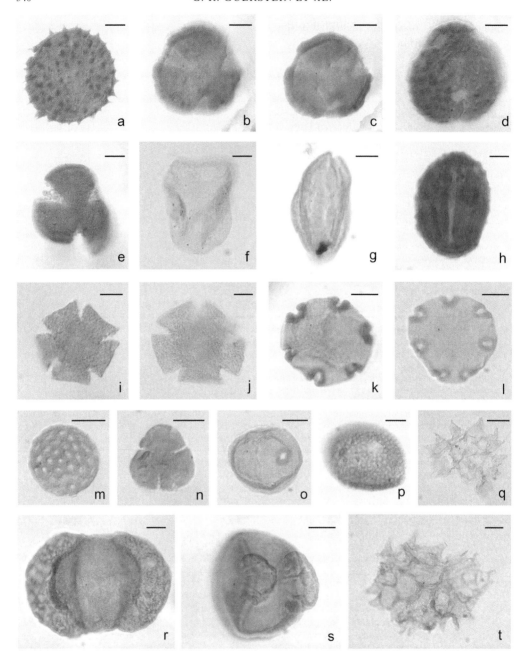

Fig. 8. All digital images were taken using an interference contrast optical system, except when indicated. **EF**: England Finder references. Scale bar: 10 μm. (**a**) *Baumannipollis variaperturatus* Barreda. UNSLP slide no. AB-29: 41.8 × 99 (EF H43). Polar view, cross-section. (**b & d, h**) *Mutisiapollis viteauensis* (Barreda) Barreda. (**b & c**) UNSLP slide no. LA19: 34 × 110.5 (EF U42). Polar view. (**b**) High focus; **c**, Cross-section. (**d**) UNSLP slide no. LA11: 15.5 × 100 (EF K61). Oblique polar view, high focus. (**h**) UNSLP slide no. LA 26: 43.7 × 108 (EF R32/3). Equatorial view, intermediate focus. (**e**) *Tricolpites trioblatus* Mildenhall & Pocknall. UNSLP slide no. AB30: 32.5 × 107.5 (EF R43/4). Polar view, intermediate focus. (**f**) *Cyperaceaepollis neogenicus* Krutzsch. UNSLP slide no. LA19: 38.5 × 106 (EF P38/3) (× 60). General view. (**g**) *Equisetosporites claricristatus* (Shakmundes) Barreda. UNSLP slide no. LA19: 43.5 × 98.8 (EF H32/4). General view. (**i & j**) *Nothofagidites dorotensis* Romero. (**i**) UNSLP slide no. AB8: 40.5 × 99 (EF H35/4). Polar view, intermediate focus. (**j**) UNSLP slide no. AB8:

Appendix II Other species cited in the text

a *Pollen*

Baumannipollis chubutensis Barreda 1993
Glencopollis ornatus Pocknall & Mildenhall 1984
Margocolporites tenuireticulatus Barreda 1997
Mutisiapollis patersonii Macphail & Hill 1994
Tubulifloridites antipodica Cookson 1947

---

b *Dinoflagellate cysts*

Cannosphaeropsis quattrocchiae Guerstein *et al.* 2001
Cannosphaeropsis utinensis Wetzel 1933
Hystrichosphaeropsis obscura Habib 1972
Hystrichostrogylon borisii Schiøler 1993
Hystrichostrogylon clausenii Bujak 1994
Hystrichostrogylon coninckii Heilmann-Clausen *in* Thomsen & Heilmann-Clausen 1985
Hystrichostrogylon holohymenium Islam 1983
Lingulodinium hemicystum McMinn 1991
Spiniferites falcipedius Warny & Wrenn 1997
Spiniferites mirabilis (Rossignol) Sarjeant 1970

References

BARREDA, V. D. 1993. Late Oligocene?–Miocene pollen of the families Compositae, Malvaceae and Polygonaceae from the Chenque Formation, Golfo San Jorge Basin, Southeastern Argentina. *Palynology*, **17**, 169–186.

BARREDA, V. D. 1996. Bioestratigrafía de polen y esporas de la Formación Chenque, Oligoceno tardío-Mioceno de las provincias de Chubut y Santa Cruz, Patagonia, Argentina. *Ameghiniana*, **33**, 35–56.

BARREDA, V. D. 1997. Palinoestratigrafía de la Formación San Julián en el área de la playa La Mina (provincia de Santa Cruz), Oligoceno de la cuenca Austral. *Ameghiniana*, **34**, 283–294.

BARREDA, V. D. 2002. Palinofloras cenozoicas. *In*: HALLER, M. J. (ed.). *Geología y Recursos Naturales de Santa Cruz*. Relatorio del XV Congreso Geológico Argentino, **11–12**, 545–567.

BARREDA, V. D. & PALAMARCZUK, S. 2000*a*. Palinoestratigrafía de depósitos del Oligoceno tardío-Mioceno en el área sur del Golfo San Jorge, provincia de Santa Cruz, Argentina. *Ameghiniana*, **37**, 103–117.

BARREDA, V. D. & PALAMARCZUK, S. 2000*b*. Palinomorfos continentales y marinos de la Formación Monte León en su área tipo, provincia de Santa Cruz, Argentina. *Ameghiniana*, **37**, 3–12.

BARREDA, V. D. & PALAMARCZUK, S. 2000*c*. Estudio palinoestratigráfico del Oligoceno tardío-Mioceno en secciones de la costa patagónica y plataforma continental argentina. *In*: ACEÑOLAZA, F. G. & HERBST, R. (eds) *El Neógeno de Argentina*, INSUGEO, Serie Correlación Geológica, **14**, 103–138.

BARREDA, V. D., GUTIERREZ, P. R. & LIMARINO, C. O. 1998. Edad y paleoambiente de la 'Serie del Yeso', Valle del Cura, provincia de San Juan: evidencias palinológicas. *Ameghiniana*, **35**, 321–335.

BELLOSI, E. 1995. Paleogeografía y cambios ambientales de la Patagonia Central durante el Terciario medio. *Boletín de Informaciones Petroleras*, **44**, 50–83.

43.4 × 102 (EF L33/3). (**k**) *Nothofagidites rocaensis* Romero. UNSLP slide no. AB8: 47 × 111.5 (EF V29/3). Polar view, intermediate focus. (**l**) *Nothofagidites saraensis* Menéndez & Caccavari. UNSLP slide no. LA19: 36 × 106.9 (EF Q40/3). Polar view, intermediate focus. (**m**) *Chenopodipollis chenopodiaceoides* (Martin) Truswell. UNSLP slide no. AB30: 49 × 101 (LF K27/3). General view. (**n**) *Tricolpites reticulatus* Cookson. UNSLP slide no. AB30: 43.2 × 103 (EF M33/0). General view. (**o**) *Graminidites* sp. UNSLP slide no. LA19: 35.8 × 106.5 (EF Q40/4). (**p**) *Sparganiaceaepollenites barungensis* Harris. UNSLP slide no. AB30: 29.5 × 103 (EF M47/3). General view. (**q & t**) *Pediastrum* spp. (**q**) UNSLP slide no. AB8: 35.4 × 110.5 (EF U40/1). General view. (**t**) UNSLP slide no. AB8: 31 × 105.5 (EF P46/3). (**r**) *Podocarpidites marwickii* Couper. UNSLP slide no. AB8: 34 × 104 (EF N42/4). Distal polar view. (**s**) *Phyllocladidites mawsonii* Cookson *ex* Couper. UNSLP slide no. AB8: 48 × 108.5 (EF S27/4). Distal polar view.

BERGGREN, W. A., KENT, D. V., SWISHER, III, C. C. & AUBRY, M. P. 1995. A revised Cenozoic geochronology and chronostratigraphy. *In*: BERGGREN, W. A., KENT, D. V., AUBRY, M. P. & HARDENBOL, J. (eds) *Geochronology, Time Scales and Global Stratigraphic Correlation.* Tulsa, SEPM Special Publication, **54**, 129–212.

CAMACHO, H. H. 1995. La Formación Patagónica (F. AMEGHINO, 1894): su actual significación estratigráfica y paleontológica. *Anales de la Academia Chilena de Ciencias*, **5**, 117–151.

CARRIZO, R., MALUMIÁN, N., NÁÑEZ, C., CARAMÉS, A. & CONCHEYRO, A. 1990. Micropalentología y correlación del Terciario del área carbonífera de Río Turbio, provincia de Santa Cruz, Argentina. *Segundo Simposio sobre el Terciario de Chile, Actas*, **1**, 29–50.

CASADÍO, S., FELDMANN, R. M. & FOLAND, K. A. 2000a. $^{40}Ar/^{39}Ar$ age and oxygen isotope temperature of the Centinela Formation, southwestern Argentina: an Eocene age for crustacean-rich 'Patagonian' beds. *Journal of South American Earth Sciences*, **13**, 123–132.

CASADÍO, S., GUERSTEIN, G. R., MARENSSI, S., SANTILLANA, S., FELDMANN, R., PARRAS, A. & MONTALVO, C. 2000b. Evidencias para una edad oligocena de la Formación Centinela, suroeste de Santa Cruz, Argentina. *Ameghiniana*, **37**, 71R.

CASADÍO, S., PARRAS, A., MARENSSI, S. A. & GRIFFIN, M. 2001. Edades $^{87}Sr/^{86}Sr$ de *Crassostrea? hatcheri* (Ortmann) – Bivalvia, Ostreoidea– en el 'Patagoniano' de Santa Cruz, Argentina. *Ameghiniana*, **38**, 30R.

DARWIN, C. 1846. *Geological Observation on South America. Being the Third Part of the Voyage of the Beagle, Under the Command of Capt. Fitzroy, R. N. During the Years 1832 to 1836.* Smith, Elder & Co London, p. 279.

DE VERTEUIL, L. 1996. Data report: Upper Cenozoic dinoflagellate cysts from the continental slope and rise off New York. *In*: Mountain, G. S, MILLER, K. G., BLUM, P., POAG, C. W. & TWICHELL, D. C. (eds). *Proceedings of the Ocean Drilling Program, Scientific Results*, **150**, 439–454.

DE VERTEUIL, L. & NORRIS, G. 1996. Miocene dinoflagellate stratigraphy and systematics of Maryland and Virginia. *Micropaleontology*, **42**, supplement, 1–172.

EATON, G. L. 1976. Dinoflagellate cysts from the Bracklesham Beds (Eocene) of the Isle of Wight, southern England. *British Museum (Natural History) Geology, Bulletin*, **26**, 227–332.

EDWARDS, L. E. & ANDRLE, V. A. S. 1992. Distribution of selected dinoflagellate cysts in modern marine sediments. *In*: HEAD, M. J. & WRENN, J. H. (eds) *Neogene and Quaternary Dinoflagellate Cysts and Acritarchs.* American Association of Stratigraphic Palynologists Foundation, Dallas, Texas, pp. 259–288.

FENSOME, R. A., TAYLOR, F. J. R., NORRIS, G., SARJEANT, W. A. S., WHARTON, D. I. & WILLIAMS, G. L. 1993. A classification of fossil and living dinoflagellates. *Micropaleontology*, Special Publication, **7**, 1–351.

FURQUE, G. 1973. Descripción geológica de la Hoja 58b, Lago Argentino, provincia de Santa Cruz. *Servicio Nacional Minero Geológico, Boletín*, **140**, 1–51.

FURQUE, G. & CAMACHO, H. H. 1972. El Cretácico Superior y Terciario de la región austral del Lago Argentino (provincia de Santa Cruz). *Cuartas Jornadas Geológicas Argentinas, Actas*, **3**, 61–75.

GRIFFIN, M. 1990. *Modiomytilus*, a new mytilid bivalve from the Tertiary of southern Patagonia. *Journal of Paleontology*, **64**, 377–382.

GUERSTEIN, G. R. & GULER, M. V. 2000. Bioestratigrafía basada en quistes de dinoflagelados del Eoceno–Mioceno del pozo (YPF) Ombucta x-1, cuenca del Colorado, Argentina. *Ameghiniana*, **37**, 81–90.

GUERSTEIN, G. R. & JUNCIEL, G. L. 2001. Quistes de dinoflagelados del Cenozoico de la cuenca del Colorado, Argentina. *Ameghiniana*, **38**, 299–316.

GULER, M. V. & GUERSTEIN, G. R. 2003. Quistes de dinoflagelados (Cladopyxiaceae, Gonyaulacaceae, Goniodomaceae e incierta) del Cenozoico de la cuenca del Colorado, Argentina. *Revista Española de Paleontología*, **18**, 23–27.

GULER, M. V., GUERSTEIN, G. R. & QUATTROCCHIO, M. E. 2001. Palinología del Neógeno de la perforación Cx-1, cuenca del Colorado, Argentina. *Revista Española de Micropaleontología*, **33**, 183–204.

GULER, M. V., GUERSTEIN, G. R. & MALUMIÁN, N. 2002. Bioestratigrafía de la Formación Barranca Final, Neógeno de la cuenca del Colorado. *Ameghiniana*, **39**, 103–110.

HEAD, M. J. 1998. Marine environmental change in the Pliocene and Early Pleistocene of eastern England: the dinoflagellate evidence reviewed. *Mededelinger Nederlands Instituut voor Toegepaste Geowetenshappen TNO*, **60**, 199–226.

HEAD, M. J. & WESTPHAL, H. 1999. Palynology and paleoenvironments of a Pliocene carbonate platform: the Clino core, Bahamas. *Journal of Paleontology*, **73**, 1–25.

KIRBY, M. X. 2000. Paleoecological differences between Tertiary and Quaternary *Crassostrea* oysters, as revealed by stable isotope sclerochronology. *Palaios*, **15**, 132–141.

KIRBY, M. X. 2001. Differences in growth rate and environment between Tertiary and Quaternary *Crassostrea* oysters. *Paleobiology*, **27**, 84–103.

LEGARRETA, L. & ULIANA, M. A. 1994. Asociaciones de fósiles y hiatos en el Supracretácico–Neógeno de Patagonia: una perspectiva estratigráfico-secuencial. *Ameghiniana*, **31**, 257–281.

MACPHAIL, M. K. & Hill, R. S 1994. K–Ar dated palynofloras in Tasmania. 1: Early Oligocene, *Proteacidites tuberculatus* Zone sediments. Wilmot Dam, northwestern Tasmania. *Papers and Proceedings of the Royal Society of Tasmania*, **128**, 1–15.

MALUMIÁN, N. 1999. La sedimentación y el volcanismo terciarios en la Patagonia Extraandina. *In*: CAMINOS, R. (ed.) *Geología Argentina*. Instituto de Geología y Recursos Minerales. Anales, **29**, 557–612.

MALUMIÁN, N. 2002. El Terciario marino. Sus relaciones con el eustatismo. *In*: HALLER, M. J. (ed.) *Geología y Recursos Naturales de Santa Cruz*. Relatorio XV Congreso Geológico Argentino, **I-15**, 237–244.

MALUMIÁN, N., SURIANO, J. M. & COBOS, J. C. 1998. La Formación Barranca Final en su localidad tipo. Mioceno, cuenca del Colorado. *X Congreso Latinoamericano de Geología y VI Congreso Nacional de Geología Económica*, Buenos Aires, Actas, **1**, pp. 125–130.

NELSON, C. S. 1978. Stratigraphy and paleontology of the Oligocene Te Kuiti Group, Waitomo County, South Auckland, New Zealand. *New Zealand Journal of Geology and Geophysics*, **21**, 553–594.

D'ORBIGNY, A. 1842. *Voyage dans l'Amérique Méridional, 1826–1833. Géologie et Paléontologie*, 551 pp., Paris.

OTTONE, E. G., BARREDA, V. D. & PÉREZ, D. J. 1998. Basin evolution as reflected by Miocene palynomorphs from the Chinches Formation, Frontal Cordillera (32°), San Juan Province, Argentina. *Revista Española de Micropaleontología*, **30**, 35–47.

PALAMARCZUK, S. & BARREDA, V. D. 1998. Bioestratigrafía en base a quistes de dinoflagelados de la Formación Chenque (Mioceno), provincia del Chubut, Argentina. *Ameghiniana*, **35**, 415–426.

PIÑERO, L. 1983. *Litología y Micropaleontología del perfil Puesto Santa Catalina (Terciario), Lago Argentino, Provincia de Santa Cruz, República Argentina*. Unpublished thesis, Universidad Nacional de Buenos Aires, Facultad de Ciencias Exactas y Naturales, 160 pp.

POULSEN, N. E., MANUM, S. B., WILLIAMS, G. L. & ELLEGAARD, M. 1996. Tertiary dinoflagellate biostratigraphy of Sites 907, 908 and 909 in the Norwegian–Greenland Sea. *In*: THIEDE, J., MYHRE, A. M., FIRTH, J. V., JOHNSON, G. L. & RUDDIMAN, W. F. (eds) *Proceedings of the Ocean Drilling Program, Scientific Results*, **151**, 255–287.

RICCARDI, A. C. & ROLLERI, E. O. 1980. Cordillera Patagónica Austral. *Segundo Simposio de Geología Regional Argentina*, **2**, 1173–1306.

THOMPSEN, E. & HEILMANN-CLAUSEN, C. 1985. The Danian–Selandian boundary at Svejstrup with remarks on the biostratigraphy of the boundary in western Denmark. *Bulletin of the Geological Society of Denmark*, **33**, 341–362.

VERSTEEGH, G. J. M & ZONNEVELD, K. A. F. 1994. Determination of (palaeo-)ecological preferences of dinoflagellates by applying detrended and canonical correspondence analysis to Late Pliocene dinoflagellate cyst assemblages of the south Italian Singa Section. *Review of Palaeobotany and Palynology*, **84**, 181–199.

WARNY, S. A. & WRENN, J. H. 1997. New species of dinoflagellate cysts from the Bou Regreg Core: a Miocene–Pliocene boundary section on the Atlantic coast of Morocco. *Review of Palaeobotany and Palynology*, **96**, 281–304.

WILLIAMS, G. L., LENTIN, J. & FENSOME, R. A. 1998. The Lentin and Williams Index of fossil dinoflagellates 1998 edition. *American Association of Stratigraphic Palynologists, Contributions Series*, **34**, 1–817.

WRENN, J. H. 1988. Differentiating species of the dinoflagellate cyst genus *Nematosphaeropsis* Deflandre & Cookson 1955. *Palynology*, **12**, 129–150.

Index

Numbers in *italic* indicate figures, numbers in **bold** indicate tables

abiotic environment change 43
Acanthocythereis meslei meslei 298, 304, 305
Achilleodinium 263
Achmosphaera 263
Achmosphaera alcicornu 312, 319
Acodus delicatus 50
acritarch extinction 28, 29
Actinoptychus 282, 286, 287
Actinoptychus senarius 280, 283, *284*, 287
adaptation, evolutionary 35
Adnatosphaeridium 312, *314*, 321
  buccinum 261, *264*
Aequitriradites spinulosus 180, *182*
Aeronian
  conodont evolutionary cycles 93–96
  sea-level change 98–100
age dating, independent 237
age-dependency, Cenozoic foraminifera 38–39,
  41–44
Ailly *see* Cap d'Ailly
Alaska, Pliensbachian–Toarcian boundary,
  stratigraphy 155–157
Alatisporites hoffmeisterii 127, 128, *129*
Albiconus postcostatus 54
Aleqatsia Fjord Formation, Greenland 92
Alterbidinium 262
Ammobaculites lobus 147, 149, 153, 155, 157
Ammobaculites praefoliaceus 153
Ammodiscus 164, 235
  glumaceus 147, 149, 153, 157
  siliceus 139, 151, 153, 155
Ammoglobigerina canningensis 149, 157
ammonite zones
  Jurassic–Cretaceous boundary 175, 176, 178,
    180
  Pliensbachian–Toarcian boundary 139–157,
    140–143
Amphigymnium 261, *265*
Amphorula monteilii 178, *182*
Anafoveosporites avcinii 127, 128, *129*
anagenesis 40
Anaticinella multiloculata 220
Andalusiella polymorpha 263
angiosperms, K–T boundary, Pyrenees 251, 252
Anglo-Paris Basin, mid-Cenomanian succession
  200–203
Anmarginulina 164
  gerkei 139, 153, 155
Anomalinoides talaria 219
anoxia, marine **16**, **19**, 20–21, **20**, 22, 23–24

Anticosti Island, Québec
  conodont fauna 73–100
  geology *74*
Anticostiodus species 93, 99
Aphelognathus grandis 79, 83–84
Apiculatasporites variocorneus 127, *128*
Apiculatisporites verbitskayae 178, *182*
Apsidognathus tuberculatus 96
Apteodinium 263
Araucariacites 252
Archaeoglobigerina blowi 220, 231, 232
Archaeoglobigerina cretacea 221
Arctic Basin
  Pliensbachian–Toarcian boundary 137–171, *138*
    palaeobiogeography 162, *165*, 164, *166*, 170
    palaeoclimate 158–160
Aren Formation, Pyrenees 244, *245*
Arenobulimina 221, 235
Areoligera 321
  coronata 264
  medusettiformis 264, 263, 259
Areosphaeridium diktyoplokum 315, 317, 319
Areosphaeridium michoudii 314, 317
Argentina, Oligocene–Miocene palynomorphs
  325–341
Ashgillian
  conodont evolutionary cycles 88–91
  extinction *24*
assemblage change 4
Astacolus 157, 170
  praefoliaceus 149, 153, 157
Astropentagnathus irregularis 96
Atavograptus atavus 93, 99
Aulacodiscus 282, 283, *285*, 287, 289
Aulacognathus bullatus 96, 100
Aulacoseira 287
Austral Basin, Argentina 325, *327*, 331

Baculites cf. *yokoyamai* 229–230
Bairdia 298, *301*, 302
Barbatacysta pelionensis 177
Barents Sea, Pliensbachian–Toarcian boundary,
  stratigraphy 153
Baumannipollis chubutensis 330
Baumannipollis variaperturatus 330, 331, *340*
Becsie Formation 88, 91, 98
Beer Head Limestone Formation 200–202, *200*
Berriasian 175–184
Biddulphia 280, 283, *284*, 287
Bifidalithus geminicatillus 223, *227*

bio-events
   Ordovician–Silurian 76–78, *89*
      speciation 97–100
   Palaeogene 276
   Toarcian 137, 157
biostratigraphy
   macrofossil 208–209, *210*
   microfossil 208–209
Biretisporites potoniei 248, 251
Blue Hill Shale Member, Wagon Mound 213, 216,
   233
body stratotypes 1
bolide impact 11, 12, **16**, **19**, 20, **20**, 22, 26–28, 257
bootstrapping 13, 17
Boreal affinity 223, 225, 233, 235, 236
Boreal province 175, *176*
Botryococcus 127
boundary
   definitions 1
   ecological 3
   environmental 2–3
   geological 3
      biostratigraphic 4
      chronostratigraphic 4
      lithostratigraphic 4
      use of palynology 5
   identification, techniques 4
   investigative 2
   spatial 2–3
   survivorship patterns 36–44
   tangible 2
Braarudosphaera regularis 227
brachiopods, stricklandiid 99
Brassfield Formation, Ohio 92
Bulbobaculites 168
   strigosus 149, 155, 157
Bythocypris 298

'c-line' 192, 194, *195*, 203
C–T boundary extinction 38
   age-dependent survivorship 38, *39*, 40, 43
calcispheres 235, 236
Calculites 223
Cambrian–Ordovician boundary, conodont
   communities 47–70
Cambrooistodus 54
Campanian, southern Pyrenees 244, 248
Campo section, Pyrenees
   K–T boundary 244, *245*
   palynology *247*, **248**, **249**, *250*, 251–253
Camptocythere 168
   mandelstami 149, 153, 157, 159
   occalata 151, 157
Camptotriletes superbus 126–128
Canada, arctic, Pliensbachian–Toarcian boundary,
   stratigraphy 153–155
Cannosphaeropsis 337, *338*
   quattrocchiae 330

   utinensis 259, *262*
Cantulodinium arthuriae 182
Cap d'Ailly sections, Dieppe–Hampshire Basin 277,
   278, 279
   pyritized diatom distribution **282**
Cap d'Antifer cliffs, Cenomanian succession *201*,
   203
Cape Phillips Formation 88
Carbon Isotope Excursion 277, 287
carbonate compensation depth (CCD) 257, 258, 309
Carboniferous, Upper
   Langsettian–Duckmantian Stage boundary 123–133
Carlile Formation, Wagon Mound 212–214, 216–218,
   221, 223, 233
Carniodus 85, 96
Carpatella cornuta 261, 263, *264*
Carpathians
   Flysch 257, *258*
      Eocene–Oligocene boundary 309–322
      geology 309, *310*
Caudammina ovulum 235
Cenomanian, mid, non-sequence 192–204
Cenomanian–Turonian boundary *see* C–T boundary
Cenozoic, foraminifera 36, 37
censoring 37–38
Centinela Formation, Argentina
   Oligocene–Miocene boundary 325–341
   palynomorphs *328*
   stratigraphy 326, *327*
Cerodinium albertii 262, 265
Cerodinium diebelii 259, *262, 265*
CFBP *see* eruption, CFBP
Chalk, Lower 187–189
   Dorset 192, *197*
   Dover *193, 198*
Changhsingian Stage 105–120
Changxing Limestone 105–109, *107*
Channel Tunnel 187
   lithology *191*
   site investigation 187–192
   use of foraminifera in correlation 187–192
Charlesdowniea 316
Chatangiella 225, 236, 259
   campbellensis 263, 265
Chenque Formation, Argentina, Oligocene–Miocene
   boundary 325, 330
Chicotte Formation 96, 100
Chicxulub impact 22, 28
Cicatricosisporites 248
circulation, thermohaline 43
Cirrusphaera dissimilis 178, 181
Citharina 164
   fallax 145, 155
   gradata 149
   hofkeri 157
cladistic analysis 75, 78–87
cladogenesis 40
Clarkina 105–120

characteristics 109–116, *110*
longcuspidata 109, *111, 112, 113,* 117–118
orientalis 111
subcarinata 109, *115,* 118
systematics 117–120
taxonomy 116–117
wangi 109, *114,* 119–120
Clavohamulus elongatus 54, 56, 65, 69
Clavohamulus hintzei 54, 56, 65
Clavohamulus neoelongatus 53
Climacograptus rectangularis 98
climate change **16,** 22, 28, 75
Clorinda 99
cluster analysis 50–51, 52–53
Jaccard 164, 295–297
Codoniella campanulata 263, *265*
Colorado Basin, Argentina 325, *327*
Coniacian *see* Turonian–Coniacian boundary
conodonts
Cambrian–Ordovician boundary 47–70
communities 48–50, *51, 57, 68*
statistical analysis 50–53, *53, 54, 56*
effect of sea-level change 67–68
nektobenthic *51,* 64–67
pelagic *51,* 53–61
Ordovician–Silurian boundary 73–100, *77*
database 75–76
diversity 75
effect of sea-level change 97–100
evolutionary cycles 88–97
evolutionary trees 78–88
Permian–Triassic boundary 105–120
Conorboides 164
buliminoides 145, 151, 157
Cope's Rule 40
Cordosphaeridium 263
Cordylodus 50, 53, *54, 56,* **63,** 68
andresi 52, *54, 56,* **63,** 65, 66, 67
angulatus 50, *51, 53, 54, 56,* **63,** 65, 68, 69, 70
caboti 50, *54, 56,* 58, 61, 62, **63,** 64, 66, *68*
deflexus 54, 56, 62, **63,** 64, 65, 66, 68
hastatus 52, *53, 54, 56,* 60, 61, **63,** *68,* 70
intermedius 50, *53, 54, 56,* **63,** 64, 66, *68*
lindstromi 50, *53, 54, 56,* 61, 62, **63,** 66, 68, 70
primitivus 52, *53, 54, 56,* 59, 61, **63,** 66
prion 61
proavus 50, *53, 54, 56,* 60, 61, 62, **63,** 65, 66, *68,* 70
tortus 53, 54, 56, **63,** 66
Coronifera oceanica 259, *263*
Corrected Survivorship Score 37
correlation, graphical 189–192
correspondence analysis 297, 302
Corrudinium incompositum 312, *314,* 318, 319
Coscinodiscus 276, *280, 282*
morsianus var. *moelleri* 276, 283, *285,* 287, 288–289
Côte Ste Catherine, Cenomanian succession *202,* 203
Cox proportional hazards model 38

Craie de Théligny 203
Craspedodiscus moelleri 287
Craspedodiscus oblongus 282, 283, 287, 289
craters, impact 20, 22, 26
Cremnoceramus deformis erectus 208, *209,* 221, 228, 230, 231, 232, 236
Cremnoceramus rotundatus 208, 228
Cretaceous
mid, foraminifera 187–194, *190*
see also Jurassic–Cretaceous boundary
Cretaceous Stage Boundaries, Second International
Symposium 207–208, 227–228
Cretaceous–Tertiary boundary *see* K–T boundary
Cribroperidinium 262
Cristaeleberis reticulata 298, 301, 303, 304
assemblage zone 302, 304, 305
cryptic speciation 37
Cyathidites 248, 251, 253
Cyclogyra liasina 149
Cyperaceaepollis neogenicus 329, 330, *340*
Cystograptus vesiculosus Zone 92
Cythereis mesa mesa 298, 301
assemblage zone 299–300, 304, 305
Cythereis mesa ventroreticulata 298, 303, 304
Cytherella 298
Cytherelloidea attiyaensis 298, 301, 304, 305
assemblage zone 299, 304, *305*

Dactylioceras 157
Damassadinium californicum 261
Danian
southern Pyrenees 246, 251, 252
see also Maastrichtian–Danian
Dapsilidinium laminaspinosum 227
Dapsilodus obliquicostatus 95, 96, 98, 100
dating, independent 237
Deccan Traps 22, 27
Decoriconus fragilis 95
Deflandrea 312, 313, *316,* 318
Dentalina communis 157
Dentalina gloria 139
Dentalina kiterbutica 149
Devon, mid-Cretaceous succession *199, 200*
Devonian, Late 28–29
Diaphanodus cambricus 54, 56
Diaphanodus latus 53, 54, 56
diatoms
Palaeocene–Eocene boundary
assemblage zones 281, 283–286
biostratigraphy 276, 287–288
Dieppe–Hampshire Basin 275–289, *288*
pyritization 276
Dicarinella 221, 234, 235
concavata 222, 231, 232
hagni 231, 232
primitiva 222, 231, 232
Dichadogonyaulax bensonii 178
Dichadogonyaulax culmula 178, *180*

Dicoelosia 100
Dictyotriletes bireticulatus 124
Dieppe–Hampshire Basin
 diatoms, Palaeocene–Eocene boundary 275–289, 277
 geology 277–278, *278*
dinocysts *see* dinoflagellate cysts
dinoflagellate cysts 225, 257
 biostratigraphy
  Portland Stone Formation 177–180
  Purbeck Formation 177–183
 Eocene–Oligocene boundary, 309–322
 K–T boundary 257–271
 Oligocene–Miocene boundary, 329–341
Dinogymnium 261
 acuminatum 261, *262*, 265
 albertii 225, 230
Disphaerogena carposphaeropsis 261, *262*, *264*
Distomodus 78, 89, 92, 93
 kentuckyensis 76, 90, 91, 92
 staurognathoides 93, 94, 95, 97, 99
Dorothia smokyensis 231
Dorset
 geology *196*
 Lower Chalk succession 192, 194, *197*, 198
Dover
 Lower Chalk succession *193*
Drepanodus suberectus 76
Drepanoistodus nowlani 50
Drepanoistodus pervetus 53,
Duckmantian Stage boundary *see* Langsettian–
 Duckmantian Stage boundary
Duckmanton, stratotype section 123, 125, *126*

E–O boundary *39*, 40, 43
 dinoflagellate cysts, Flysch Carpathians 309–322
 extinction *39*, 40, 43
Echinatisporis 248
Eggerellina mariae 219
Egmontodinium polyphlacorum 178
Eiffellithus 223, 225
 eximius 227, 230
Ektyphocythere cf. *debilis* 157
Elaterites triferens 127, *129*
Ellis Bay Formation, Anticosti Island 88
emigration 94
Endoscrinium 181, 227
Endosporites globiformis 124, *126–129*
Endosporites zonalis *126–129*
Eocene, *see* Palaeocene–Eocene boundary
Eocene–Oligocene boundary *see* E–O boundary
Eoconodontus alisonae 54, 59–61, *68*, 70
Eoconodontus notchpeakensis 50, 51, *53*, *54*, 55, *56*, 58, 59, 60, 61, *68*, 70
Eoguttulina? 155
Eouvigerina gracilis 231, 232
Equisetosporites claricristatus 340
eruption

CFBP (continental flood-basalt province) **16**, **19**, **20**, 22–23, *23*, 26–30
Esna Formation, Sinai 294, 295
Eunotogramma weissei *282*, 287
event-correlation 180
Evolutinella taimyrensis 149, 157
evolutionary trees, Llandovery conodonts 78–88
extinction
 age-dependency 39–44
 background 13, 14, 17, 28
 biotic recovery 35–36, 40
 causal mechanisms **16**, 18, **19**, 20–21
 conodont species 94, 95, 97, 98
 controls 12, 15
 effect of sea-level change 97–100
 Law of Constant Extinction 36
 mass 5, 13, 36, 40
  Cretaceous–Tertiary (K–T) 11, 12, 25, 257
  Hettangian–Pliocene 13–14
  Norian 18–19, 22, 25
  Ordovician–Silurian 73, 75
  Pliensbachian–Toarcian 137, 157
  Sandvika 94
  survivor species 35
  Tatarian 25
 mass *v.* background 40
 Phanerozoic 5, 11–30, 73, 75
  data 13–14
 statistical hypothesis testing 12, *18*
 time-dependency *v.* age-dependency 37–44
extinction events 5, **16**
extinction-intensity gradient 17, 23–25, *24*, *25*
extinction-intensity peaks 13, 14–17, *14*, *15*, **19**, 20, 21, *23*, 26–30, *26*

failure time analysis 37
Falsotruncana douglasi *222*, 231
fauna, marine, benthic 21
Favusella washitensis, extinction 192
Fenestrella antiqua 276, *280*, *282*, 283, 287, 289
Fenestrirostra pyrrba 98
fern spike, K–T boundary 243, 251, 252, 253
Fibrocysta vectensis 262
Flabellammina 155
Florentinia 262
 clavigera 225
Florinites junior 124
flysch sediments, Soláň Formation, dinoflagellate cysts 257, 261, 309
Fontllonga section
 Pyrenees
  K–T boundary 244
  palynology 246–253
foraminifera
 distribution model *204*
 mid-Cretaceous 187–194, *190*
  P:B ratio 190–194, *193*, *200*, *201*, 202–203, *202*
 Palaeocene–Eocene boundary, Sinai 294–295

planktonic, Cenozoic 36–44
Pliensbachian–Toarcian boundary 137, *161, 170*
  Alaska 155–157, *156, 157, 158*
  Barents Sea 153, *154*
  Canada 153–155, *154*
  Siberia 139, *141, 142, 143,* 145, *146,* 147, *148,* 149,
    151–153, *151, 152, 163*
  Turonian–Coniacian boundary 216–223
Fort Hays Member, Wagon Mound 214–215, *214, 216,*
  234
Fragilipollenites radiatus 127
Frasnian extinction *24*
Frondiculinita dubiella 139
Frondiculinita lobata 145, 153
Fryxellodontus lineatus 54
Fur Formation, Denmark 287
Furnishina asymmetrica 54, 56
Furnishina furnishi 54, 56
Furnishina primitiva 53, 54, 56

Gamachignathus 92
Gartnerago obliquum 223, 225
Gaudryina 153
Gault Clay Formation 189
Gavelinella 202, 221, 235
  daini 226
  menneri 226
petita 224, 230, 233, 238–239
Gavelinellopsis tourainensis 226, 232
Geinitzinita 159, 164
  tenera 157
Gelatia inflata 315, 319
geochemical cycles, global 28
glaciation, Ordovician 73, 75, 97–100
Glaphyrocysta 262, 321
glass spherules 12
Glencopollis ornatus 330
Global Stratotype Sections and Points (GSSP) 1–2
  Cambrian–Ordovician 47
  Ordovician–Silurian 73
  Permian–Triassic 105, *107*
Globigerinida, Cenozoic 36–37
Globorotalites micheliana 219
Globorotalites subconica 232
Globulina sibirica 147, 149, 153, 155
Glomospira 139, 153, 164, 235
Glyptodontus expansus 53
Glyptograptus persculptus Zone 88
Gochteodinia villosa 181
Gondisporites bulboides 127, 129, 131, *132*
gondolellids, Permian 116–117
graptolites, Ordovician–Silurian boundary 73, *76,* 89,
  96, 99–100
Grauweisse Wechselfolge Formation, Salzgitter-Salder
  215–216
Green Point, western Newfoundland 47
Grigelis 160
  apheilolcula 145

Gun River Formation 93, 98
gymnosperms, K–T boundary, Pyrenees 251, 252
Gyroidinoides 235

Hantkenina 317
Haplophragmium 155
Haplophragmoides gilberti 219
hardground 201, 203
Hastigerinoides subdigitata 220, 231, 232
Hedbergella 233, 234
  implicata 230
  lata 230
Hemiaulus 276, *280, 282,* 283
Hertzina 53, 54
Heteraulacacysta campanula 262
heterococcoliths, Turonian–Coniacian 223
Heterohelix globulosa 230, 233, 234
Heterosphaeridium 259, 262, 264, 312, *316*
Heterostomella austinana 232
Hettangian–Pliocene extinction data 13–14
Hindeodus 106
Hirsutodontus 65, 66
  hirsutus 53, 54, 56
  simplex 53, 54, 56
holococcoliths, Turonian–Coniacian 223
Homotryblium 315, 321
Hymenospora murdochensis 126–129, 132, 133
Hymenospora palliolata 131
Hyperammina odiosa 139, 151, 157
Hystrichokolpoma bulbosum 262, 264
Hystrichosphaeridium tubiferum 259, 262
Hystrichosphaeropsis 315
  nuda 262, 264
  obscura 330
Hystrichostrogylon coninckii 262, 264, 336, 341
Hystrichostrogylon membraniphorum 262, 330, 332,
  335
Hystrichostrogylon sulcatum 329, 332, *333, 334, 335,*
  336

Iapetognathus fluctivagus 47, *50, 52,* 66, 67, *68*
Iapetognathus preaengensis 52, *54, 56,* 66, 67, *68*
Ichthyolaria 159, 164
  lustrata 139, 155, 157
  sulcata 145
  terquemi 145
Icriodella 78, 88, 91, 96, 99
  deflecta 88, 91, 94
  dicrana 88, 91
  discreta 88, 91
  superba 91
Illinites unicus 127, 129
immigration, conodont, Anticosti Island 94, 96, 98,
  99
Impagidinium 263, 263, 312, *314,* 318, 319, 321
Impletosphaeridium tribuliferum 178
Inaperturopollenites 252
indicator taxa 4

invertebrates, benthic 21
Involutina 159
  liassica sibirica 145
Iranognathus tarazi 106
Ireviken Event 97
iridium abundance anomalies 12, 243, 246, 258
Isabelidinium 262
  cooksoniae 230
  pellucidum 329
Isthmia 276
Isthmolithus recurvus 317

jack-knifing 13
Jaculella jacutica 151
Johnognathus 96
Juana Lopez Calcarenite Member, Wagon Mound
  213, *214, 215,* 216–217, 233, *234*
Jupiter Formation 91, 92, 94, 95, 96, 99, 100
Jurassic, Pliensbachian–Toarcian boundary 137,
  140
Jurassic–Cretaceous boundary 175–184

K–T boundary
  dinocysts, Uzgruň 257–271
  south central Pyrenees 243–253
    palynology 246–253
K–T boundary event, causes and effects 257
K–T boundary extinction 11, 12, 25, 36, 243, 257
  age-dependent survivorship 38, *39,* 40, 43
Kalamopsis grzybowskii 235
Kallosphaeridium? inornatum 262
Kamptnerius magnificus 227
kill mechanisms 27, 29
King's Hole Hardground 202–203
Kinkelinella sermoisensis 147, 149, 157
Kleithriasphaeridium 178
Kockelella? manitoulinensis 90, 94
Kockelella? ranuliformis 96
Krithe echolsae 298, *301,* 304
  assemblage zone 300, 302, 304
krummholz zone 3
Kutsevella barrowensis 145, 153, 155, 164

Laevigatosporites 253
Laffiteina bibensis 246, 251
Lagenammina jurassica 149
Langsettian–Duckmantian Stage boundary 123–133,
  124
  microflora 124
  miospore species 124, *126, 128*
  palaeoenvironments 129–130
  palynomorphs 125, *127, 129*
  palynostratigraphy 125–133, *126*
  stratotype sections 125
Law of Constant Extinction 36
Lazarus taxa 94, 99–100
Leiotriletes 248
Lejeunecysta cf. *fallax 335*

Leluchów, Flysch Carpathians
  Eocene–Oligocene boundary succession 309–322
  palaeoenvironmental changes 318–319, *320*
Leluchów Marl Member 309, *311*
  dinocyst distribution 312–313
Lenodus variabilis 50
Lenticulina 164
  gottingensis 153, 155, 157
  margarita 145, 147
  multa 149, 157
  toarcense 157
Lentinia serrata 316
Leptolepidites psarosus 178
Ligonodina 92
Lilliasterites angularis 230
Limitisporites 127, 129
Lingulodinium hemicystum 330
Lingulodinium machaerophorum 329, 330, *335*
Lingulogavelinella cf. *vombensis 224,* 232
Lithastrinus moratus 230, 232
Lithraphidites carniolensis 223, 225
Litosphaeridium 329
Llandovery, Anticosti Island
  conodont diversity 75
  conodont evolutionary cycles 88–97
  conodont evolutionary trees 78–88
  sea-level change 97–100
Lonchodina walliseri 92
Longtan Formation 106–108
Lopingian Series 105, *107*
Loxodentatus bipinnatus 53
Loxognathodus phyllodus 53
Lycopodiumsporites 248, 251

Maastrichtian, southern Pyrenees 248, 253
Maastrichtian extinction 22, *24,* 25
Maastrichtian–Danian, dinoflagellate cysts 257–271
Macerodus crassatus 53
Macerodus dianae 50
Macerodus? wattsbightensis 53
macroevolution 41
macrofossils, biostratigraphy 208–209, *210,* 228
Magura Nappe 257
  Eocene–Oligocene boundary 309
  geology 258
'*Mandelstamia*' *linearis* 139
'*Mandelstamia*' *lubrica* 145
Manicouagan impact 18–19, 22
Manumiella 329
  seelandica 259, *262, 264,* 266
Marginotruncana 221, 235
  marianosi 231, 232
  paraconcavata 222
  paraventricosa 222, 231, 232
Marginulina 164
  amica 157
  prima 151
  spinata interrupta 145, 147

spinata orbicularis 139
Marginulinopsis hatangensis 153, 155
Marginulinopsis quadricostata 155
Marginulinopsis schleiferi 153
Marginulinopsis ventrosa 145
Margocolporites tenuireticulatus 330
marine transgression, Oligocene–Miocene boundary 325
Marthasterites furcatus 227, 230, 231, 232
Martinicythere bassiounii 298, *301*
Matonisporites elegans 178, *182*
Matthesisporites plurituberosus Döring 248, 251
Mauritsina coronata 298, 304
Mauritsina jordanica nodoreticulata 298, 304
Mauritsina martinii 298, *301*, 306
Megommatocythere denticulata 298, *301*, 306
   assemblage zone 302, 304
Melosira clavigera 280
Membranilarnacia? tenella 261
Membranophoridium 321
Mendicodinium groenlandicum 177
Merrimack Formation 98
microevolution 41
microfossils 208–209, 228
micropalaeontology, in boundary identification 5
Microreticulatisporites nobilis 124, *126*, *128*
mid-Cenomanian non-sequence (MCNS) *see* Cenomanian, mid, non-sequence
Miocene
   palynomorphs, Argentina 330–331
   see also Oligocene–Miocene boundary
miospore biostratigraphy, Jurassic–Cretaceous boundary 178–180
miospores, Langsettian–Duckmantian Stage boundary 124, *126*, *128*
Miravetesina ficula 227, 232
Monoclimacis crenulata Zone 97
Monocostodus sevierensis 54, *56*, 65, 67, *68*
Monograptus Zones 93, 97, 98, 99
Monte Carlo simulation 13, 16–17, *17*, 21, 22
Montezuma Valley Shale Member, Wagon Mound 213–214, *216*, 218, 221, 233
Muderongia simplex 178
Murdoch Gas Field, North Sea 125, *126*, *128*
Mutisiapollis patersonii 329
Mutisiapollis viteauensis 330, 331, *340*

Nanacythere 160
   costata 139, 145, 157
nannofossils, calcareous, Turonian–Coniacian 223, 225, *227*, *228*
Nelsoniella aceras 329
Nelsoniella tuberculata 263, *264*
Nematosphaeropsis 262, *314*, 318, *338*
   rigida 329, 330, 331, 336, 337, *338*
Neobulimina 139, 160
Neoflabellina suturalis 231
Neoprioniodus planus 91

Newfoundland, western *49*
   Cambrian–Ordovician conodonts 47–70
      mode of life *51*
   stratigraphy *50*
Niobrara Formation, Wagon Mound 214–215, 223, 234
Nodosaria 164
   claviformis 147
   pulchra 149, 157
   regularis 147
   turgida 139
non-sequence
   definition 189
   Mid-Cenomanian 187–204
Norian extinction 19, 22, *24*
Normalograptus 73
Normapolles, K–T boundary, Pyrenees 251, 252, 253
North Sea Basin, diatoms 276, 287–288
North Sea Plankton zonation 276, 277
Nothofagidites dorotensis 340
numerical methods 4–5

OAE *see* ocean anoxic event
ocean anoxic event (OAE) 43
Odontella 280, 282, 283, *285*
Odontochitina 263, 329
Oepikodus communis 50
Oepikodus evae 50
Oertliella posterotriangulata 298, *301*
   assemblage zone 302, 304, 306
Ogmochoncha 164
   longula 139, 147, 153
   nordvikensis 139
Ogmoconchella conversa 147
Ogmoconchella olenekensis 139
Ogmoconchella ornata 145, 157
Oligocene *see* E–O boundary
Oligocene–Miocene boundary
   Centinela Formation, Argentina 325–341
   marine transgression 325, *327*
Oligosphaeridium totum totum 225, 230, 232
Operculodinium 314
   israelianum 329, *335*
Orbirhynchia mantelliana Band 192, 194
Ordoniya 298
   burmaensis 298, 304, 306
Ordovician, *see also* Cambrian–Ordovician boundary
Ordovician–Silurian boundary 73–100
Osangularia whitei 232
ostracodes
   Palaeocene–Eocene
      Sinai 293–306
         cluster analysis 295–297
         correspondence analysis 302–306
         distribution 297–298
         palaeobiotopes 298–302
      Pliensbachian–Toarcian boundary 137, *159*, *170*

Alaska 156, 157, *160*
Barents Sea 153
Siberia 139, *143*, *146*, 147, 151–153, *163*
Oulodus 76, 78, 90, 91–92, 94, 96, 98
 evolutionary trees 82–84, *85*
 expansus 76, 82–84, 93, 98
 fluegeli 76, 82–84
 jeanne 82–84, 93
 panuarensis 76, 82–84, 91–92, 93, 94, 99
 rohneri 83
 sigmoideus 76, 82–84, 91, 92, 95
 ulrichi 83, 84
Ozarkodina 75–76, 78, 88–97
 aldridgei 79–81, 95, 96, 100
 alpina 79–82
 clavula 79–82, 93, 94, 99
 evolutionary trees 79–82, *82*, 84–88
 gulletensis 79–82, 96, 100
 hassi 79–82, 85, *87*, 88, 90, 91, 94, 99
 oldhamensis 79–82, 84, *87*, 88, 90, 94, 95, 98
 pirata 79–82, 91, 95, 99
 polinclinata 79–82, 96
 sesquipedalis 79–82
 strena 76, 79–82, 91, 94

P:B ratio *see* planktonic:benthic ratio
palaeobiotopes, ostracodes, Palaeocene–Eocene
  298–302
Palaeocene–Eocene, ostracodes, Sinai 293–306
Palaeocene–Eocene boundary
 diatoms, Dieppe–Hampshire Basin 275–289
 Esna Shale 295
palaeoenvironment
 correspondence analysis 297, 302–304
 Eocene–Oligocene boundary 318–319, *320*
 K–T boundary, Uzgrun 261, 263, 266
 Palaeocene–Eocene, Sinai 302–306
 Palaeogene 286
 Turonian–Coniacian
  Salzgitter–Salder 235–236
  Wagon Mound 233–234
Palaeogene, deposits, Dieppe–Hampshire Basin
  279
Palaeohystrichophora infusorioides 225, 235, *262*
Palaeotetradinium silicorum 259, *262*
Palaeozoic, Late, phytoplankton extinction 29
Palmula deslongchampsi 149
Palmula pilulata 231
Palynodinium grallator 261, *262*, *264*
palynology, in boundary identification 5
palynomorphs
 K–T boundary, Pyrenees 248–253
 marine, Turonian–Coniacian boundary 225
 Oligocene–Miocene boundary 329–341
palynostratigraphy, Langsettian–Duckmantian Stage
  boundary 123–133
Panderodus 88
 gibber 76

gracilis 76
recurvatus 91, 94
unicostatus 76, 95
Pangaea 29
Paracordylodus gracilis 50
Paracosta parakefensis 298, *304*
Paracosta pervinquieri 298
Paracypris 157
Parakidograptus acuminatus 73
Parakrithe crolifa 297, 298, *304*
 assemblage zone 302, 304, 305
Paralia ornata 282
Paralia siberica 280, 283, *284*, 286
Parutahconus nodosus 54, 56, 64, 65, 68
passport characteristics 35, 40, 41
Patagonian transgression 325, *327*, 329
Patagoniano sediments 325
Patellasporites 248
Pentadinium 315
Pentamerus 99
Permian–Triassic boundary
 conodont population 105–120
 extinction 28, 29
perturbation, step *v.* spike 43
Pervosphaeridium truncigerum 225, 232
Phacorhabdotus inaequicostatus 298, *301*
Phakelodus tenuis 53–60, 67, *68*, 70
Phanerozoic extinction 11–30
 data 13–14
Phanerozoic sea-level fluctuation 21, 22
Pharus 228
Phelodinium 262
Phthanoperidinium chalossense 316
Phthanoperidinium comatum 329
phytoplankton, Late Permian 29
plankton, zonation 276, *277*
planktonic:benthic ratio, foraminifera 190–194
Planularia 164
Planulina kansasensis 224, 230, 234
Planulina texana 224, 230, 233, 239
Plectina cenomana 188
'*Plectodina*' 79
Plectospathodus flexuosus 91
Pliensbachian–Toarcian boundary
 Arctic Basin 137–171
 stratigraphy 139–157
  Alaska 155–157
  Barents Sea 153
  Canada 153–155
  Siberia 139, 145, 147, 149, 151
pollen, K–T boundary, Pyrenees 246–253
polycolpites 251, 252
Polycostatus falsioneotensis 53
Polypodiaceoisporites 248, 251
Polyporopollenites 251
Pontocyprella recurva 298
Portland Stone Formation 175, 177–183
 dinocyst biostratigraphy 177–180

miospore biostratigraphy 178–180
Portland–Wight Basin 175, 176
Praebulimina reussi 232
Praeglobotruncana 194, 202
Prediscosphaera cretacea 223, 225
Prioniodus elegans 50
Prionocyclus germari 228, 230
Prionocyclus novomexicanus 229
Problematoconites perforata 54, 56
processing techniques
    diatoms 281
    dinocysts 177, 259, 311, 326, 329
    foraminifera 200, 212
    nannofossils 212
    palynomorphs 259, 311, 326, 329
Proconodontus 58, 59, 60
    muelleri 53, 54, 58
    posterocostatus 54, 58
    serratus 54, 58
    tenuiserratus 54,
Prooneotodus rotundatus 53, 54, 56, 58
proportional hazards model 38
Prosagittodontus dahlmani 54, 56
Prosagittodontus eureka 54, 56
Protohaploxypinus 127, 129
Protoprioniodus simplicissimus 50
provincialism 178–180
pseudoextinction 37
Pseudonodosaria 164
    pseudovulgata 145, 153, 155
Pseudooneotodus 95, 96
    dea 151
Pseudoparella? ripleyensis 219
pseudospeciation 37
Pteracontiodus cryptodens 50
Pterodinium 263
    cingulatum 259, 262
Pterospathodus 78, 93, 94, 95, 96, 99
    amorphognathoides 84–87, 87–88, 93, 96,
        97, 100
    celloni 85–87, 87–88, 93
    evolutionary trees 84–87, 87–88
    originalis 87–88, 91, 92
    pennatus 84–87, 87–88, 93
    posteritenuis 84–87, 87–88, 93
    siluricus 84–87, 87–88, 93
Pterotheca 280
Purbeck Formation 175, 177–183
    dinocyst biostratigraphy 177–183
    miospore biostratigraphy 178–180
Pyrenean Basin, K–T boundary 243
Pyrenees, south central
    geology 244, 245
    K–T boundary 244, 246
pyritization 276
Pyrulinoides 160, 164
    anabarensis 145, 155

Quadrum intermedium 228
quartz, shocked 12

Radiizonates aligerens 124, 126
Radiizonates faunus 126–129
Radiizonates striatus 126–129, 130
Radiizonates tenuis 124, 126–129
Rastrites maximus Zone 96
Recurvoides taimyrensis 145, 147, 153, 156, 164
Red Queen Hypothesis 36, 42–44
Reduviasporonites stoschianus 127
regression
    Aeronian 99
    eustatic **16**, **19**, **20**, 28, *see also* sea-level change
    Maastrichtian 21
    Pliensbachian 157
    Telychian 100
Reinholdella pachyderma 147
Reophax metensis 153
Retecapsa 223, 225
Reticulatosphaera actinocoronata 329, 330, *335*
Reticulina proteros 302, 303, 306
Reticulina sangalkamensis 297, *298*, 302, 303, 306
Rexroadus 78, 90, 98
    evolutionary trees 78, 82–85, *85*
    kentuckyensis 82, 88, 94
    nathani 82, 88, 90, 94
Rhizosolenia 280, *282*
Rhuddanian
    conodont evolutionary cycles 88–93
    sea-level change 98–99
Riculacysta? pala 264
Rossodus 56
Rotalipora cushmani 188, 189, *190*, 192, 194, *197*, 202
Rotalipora greenhornensis 202
Rotalipora montsalvensis 192
Rotalipora reicheli 188, *190*
Rottnestia borussica 259, *262*, *315*, 319
Rugulitriporites 251
Russia, arctic *see* Siberia

Saccammina 149, 151, 153, 156, 164
Saepiovirgata biferula 223, *228*
Sahnites 127, 129
Saint Josse borehole
    Dieppe–Hampshire Basin 277, *278*, *279*
        diatom assemblage zones 283, 287
    pyritized diatom distribution **280**
Salzgitter-Salder outcrop 208–209, *209*, *218*, 236–238
    calcareous nannofossils 225, 232
    chronostratigraphy 227–228, 231–233
    foraminifera 221, 223, 231
    lithostratigraphy *211*, *212*, 215–216
    marine palynomorphs 225, 232
    palaeoenvironment 235–236
Samlandia chlamydophora 315
sampling factors 4
San Jorge Basin, Argentina 325, *327*, *331*

Sandvika event 94
Saracenaria 160
  sublaevis 145, 155
Scaphites whitfieldi 229
Schulzospora rara 124, *126–129*, 130
  sea-level change
    eustatic 20–23, **20**, *23*, 26, 28
      Cambrian–Ordovician, effect on conodont
        communities 67–68, 69
      mid-Cenomanian non-sequence 192, 203
      Ordovician–Silurian, effect on conodont
        speciation 97–100
      Turonian 233
      Upper Carboniferous, effect on microflora
        129–130
    see also regression, transgression
sedimentation
  allochthonous 235
  flysch 261, 263
Semiacontiodus nogamii 53–56, 62, 64, 65, *68*, 69
Senegalinium 259, *262*, 263, 266
Senoniasphaera inornata 261
Senoniasphaera jurassica 178
shale, black bituminous, Toarcian 137, 147
Siberia, Pliensbachian–Toarcian boundary,
    stratigraphy 139, *141–144*, 145, 147, 149, 151
Siberian Traps 22, 27, 29
Silurian
  conodont fauna 75, 88
  ocean-climate change 75, *76*
  see also Ordovician–Silurian boundary
Sinai
  Palaeocene–Eocene
    ostracodes 293–306
    stratigraphy 294–295, *294*, *296*
Sinuspores sinuatus 124, *126–128*, 130–131, *132*
Smereczek Shale Member 309, *311*
  dinocyst distribution 313, 317
Smoky Hill Member, Wagon Mound 215, *217*, 234
Soláň Formation, Uzgruň 257–271
  geology 257–258
Sparnacian facies, Palaeogene 286, 287, 289
speciation 36
  conodont 88–97
    effect of sea–level change 97–100
  cryptic 37
species senescence 40
Spelaeotrilites pretiosus windsorensis 126–129
Spilsby Shelf 176
Spinidinium 259, *263*, 265
  densispinatum 270
Spiniferites 263, 263, 312, 313, 336
  mirabilis 335
  ramosus 259, *262*, 329
Spiroplectammina 149, 155
spore:pollen ratio, K–T boundary, Pyrenees
    246–253
sporomorphs, Oligocene–Miocene boundary *328*, 329

Stellarima microtrias 280
Stensioina granulata kelleri 226, 232
Stensioina granulata levis 226, 232
Stephanogonia danica 280, *282*
Stephanopyxis turris 282, 287
Stoveracysta 312, *315*
Stoverius achylosus 228, 230
subtriporopollenites 251, 252
super-impact scenario 27
survivor species 35, 36
  large-body *v.* small-body 40–41
survivorship analysis 37–38, 43
Svalbardella 316, 319
Sweetina 106

Tatarian extinction 22, *24*, 25, 29
Telychian
  conodont evolutionary cycles 96–97
  sea-level change 100
Teridontus nakamurai 53–60, 62, 65, 67, 70
Tertiary *see* K–T boundary
Tethyan province 175, *176*
Textularia 153, 156
Thalassiphora 262, *263*, *315*
Thebes Formation, Sinai 294, 295
timberline 3
Tithonian 175
Toarcian
  mass extinction 137, 157, 162
    see also Pliensbachian–Toarcian boundary
  palaeoenvironments 149
Tortolithus caistorensi 239
Tortolithus carteri 228, 239–240
Total Life Method, survivorship analysis 37
Trachycythere verrucosa 149
Tranolithus 223, 225
transgression **16**, **19**, **20**, *see also* sea-level change
  Aeronian 98, 99
  Cenomanian 21
  Oligocene–Miocene (Patagonian) 325, *327*, 329
  Pliensbachian 157
treeline 3
Tremadocian, conodont fauna 48, 69
Tremp Formation, Pyrenees, K–T boundary
    243–244, *245*
Triatriopollenites 251, 252
Triceratium 276, *280*, *282*, 283, 287
Trichonodella symmetrica 91
Tricolpites trioblatus 330, *340*
Tricolpopollenites 251
Trigonium 282, 283, 289
Trilites tuberculiformis 248
Trinacria 276, *280*, *282*, 283, *285*, 289
Triplasia 170
  kingakensis 147, 149, 156, 157
Tripodus laevis 50
Triporopollenites 251
Trithyrodinium 259, *263*, *265*, 270

Trochammina 170
  inusitata 139, 151, 153, 155
  kisselmani 147, 149, 151, 153, 155, 157
  lapidosa 139, 145, 147, 151–153, 155, 157
Tubulifloridites antipodica 330
Turbiosphaera symmetrica 314
Turonian, Chalk succession 198
  see also C–T boundary
Turonian–Coniacian boundary 207
  choice of stratotype section 236–238
  chronostratigraphy 227–233
  definition 208
  palaeoenvironment 233–236
  palaeontology 216–227
  Salzgitter-Salder *212*, 215, 232
  Wagon Mound outcrop 213, 230, 231
Turritellella volubilis 151, 155

Ufimian–Kazanian extinction *24*
Utahconus utahensis 53, 54, 56, 65, 69
Uzgruň, K–T boundary, dinocysts 257–271

Valvulineria infrequens 219, 231
Vanderbeckei Marine Band 123–130
Vectidinium 316
Verneuilinoides pudica 151, 157
Vestispora pseudoreticulata 124, *126–129*
Virgiana 98

wackestone, calcisphere 235, 236
Wagon Mound outcrop, New Mexico 207–209, *208,
  210*, 236–238

calcareous nannofossils 223, 230
chronostratigraphy 227–231
foraminifera 216–221, 230
lithostratigraphy 212–215, *213, 214, 215, 229*
marine palynomorphs 225, 230
palaeoenvironment 233–234
Turonian–Coniacian boundary level 230, 231
Walliserodus 88
  curvatus 94, 95, 98
  sancticlairi 76
Warrenia californica 178, *181*
Watznaueria barnesae 223, 225
Watznaueria virginica 239
Westergaardodina bicuspidata 53, 56
Westergaardodina fossa 54, 56
Westergaardodina moessebergensis 54, 56
Western Interior sea-way 233
Westphalian Series 123, *124*
Wetzeliella 313, *316*, 318
  gochtii 316, 317
Whiteinella 221, 230
  aprica 220, 235
  paradubia 220, 235

Xiphophoridium 225

Yaoxianognathus 79
Ypresian facies 287

Zeugrhabdotus 223
  biperforatus 228
zonation, planktonic 276, *277*